# The Study of Time III



*Proceedings of the Third Conference of the International Society for the Study of Time Alpbach—Austria*

*Edited by*
J.T. Fraser
N. Lawrence
D. Park

*With 34 Figures*

Springer-Verlag
New York Heidelberg Berlin

Library of Congress Cataloging in Publication Data (Revised)

International Society for the Study of Time.
The study of time; proceedings of the first [third] conference of the International Society for the Study of Time.

English or German.
Vol. 2 edited by J. T. Fraser and N. Lawrence; v. 3. by J. T. Fraser, N. Lawrence, D. Park.
First conference held in 1969 at Oberwolfach, Germany; 2d held in 1973 near Lake Yamanaka, Japan; 3d held in 1976 at Alpbach, Austria.
Includes bibliographies.
1. Time — Congresses. I. Fraser, Julius Thomas, 1923— ed. II. Haber, Francis C., ed. III. Müller, Gert Heinz, 1923— ed. IV. Lawrence, Nathaniel Morris, 1917— ed. V. Title.
QB209.155 1972 529 72-80472
ISBN 0-387-05824-9 (v. 1)



9 8 7 6 5 4 3 2 1

Printed in the United States of America.

ISBN 0-387-90311-9 Springer – Verlag New York

ISBN 3-540-90311-9 Springer – Verlag Berlin Heidelberg

# Foreword

The papers in this volume were delivered and responded to at the Third Conference of the International Society for the Study of Time. The meeting took place during sunny days, punctuated by an occasional brief storm, in the conference facilities of the Österreichisches College in Alpbach, Austria, from July 1 to July 10, 1976. In the middle of it came July 4, the 200th anniversary of the Declaration of Independence, and in honor of participants from the United States there was a special session of papers on the subject of Freedom and Time. [See Fraser, Park in this volume.]

The effect of the papers was kaleidoscopic; reading the table of contents one can surmise the experience of those enthusiasts, and there were several, who heard them all. I think that most people who have been puzzled about time will agree that it is not clear what the puzzle is or from what direction the insights will come that will enable us to understand the situation a little more clearly. As one of the participants wrote afterwards, "After all, we do not know *a priori* whether there exists a real unity in studies about time, but if one exists it must reveal itself progressively in the course of successive experiences such as these lectures. If it were easy to find, it would have been found already without the Society's help."

Nevertheless, the Society intends that its future meetings will be less kaleidoscopic. The next one, scheduled for the summer of 1979, will have as its single though many-headed theme ideas of beginnings and endings: in cosmology, in literature, in the shape of human life, and some other manifestations. If the present volume reads like a collection of short stories, by different hands and concerned with different matters, it is our hope that the next one will read more like a novel. Anyone can see what the difficulty is in organizing a meeting and presenting its proceedings as is done here: it is easier to be multidisciplinary than to be interdisciplinary, and though a multidisciplinary meeting may shower us with ideas, one that is truly interdisciplinary may perhaps lead us from where we are towards a deeper understanding.

I would like to thank the participants in the conference — lecturers and discussants — for coming, for working hard on their papers before delivery, and for maintaining composure in the face of the editors' objections and demands. And also for staying through the whole meeting and contributing to the lively and learned, if occasionally mysterious, conversations of this many-headed group. There are also several referees who have generously assisted the editors on difficult points.

I must thank Dr. Gisela Trommsdorff, of the University of Mannheim, for her unselfish assistance in preparing the facilities. Dr. Helen Green, of Middlesex College, retiring as Treasurer, deserves special recognition for the many hours and much ink (not all of it black) that she has expended in the Society's service.

Dr. J. T. Fraser, founder of the Society and Secretary since its inception, does most of the work and carries it along from meeting to meeting. His knowledge, enthusiasm, and labor brought this meeting to pass as they have all others.

At the close of the meeting Gert Müller, Professor of Mathematical Logic in the University of Heidelberg, was elected the Society's President and Professor Lewis Rowell of the University of Hawaii its Treasurer. As these lines are written plans for the next meeting are taking shape, and I have every expectation that it will be as enjoyable as the one reported in this volume.

I cannot end this note without some reference to the Alpine landscape in which the meetings took place, framed in the great windows of the Schrödingersaal or surrounding us as we walked and talked between the sessions. On the Gratlspitz, which stands over Alpbach, there is a cross and a visitors' book containing a haiku by Frederick Turner, one of the early arrivals:

Alps are a garden:
harebell, mosses, edelweiss.
But cliffs in Eden ...?

*David Park*
*Third President*
*International Society for the Study of Time*

## Membership List

*International Society for the Study of Time*
*Third World Conference*

Stuart Albert, University of Pennsylvania, Philadelphia, Pennsylvania, U.S.A.

Piero E. Ariotti, Delmar, California, U.S.A.

Seth G. Atwood, The Time Museum, Rockford, Illinois, U.S.A.

Silvio A. Bedini, Smithsonian Institution, The National Museum of History and Technology, Washington, D.C., U.S.A.

Robert S. Brumbaugh, Yale University, New Haven, Connecticut, U.S.A.

Thomas J. Bruneau, University of Guam, Agana, Guam, U.S.A.

Eva Cassirer, Technical University, Berlin, West Germany.

Ferrell Christensen, University of Alberta, Edmonton, Alberta, Canada.

Margaret Church, Purdue University, West Lafayette, Indiana, U.S.A.

Peter A. Clark, Queens University, Kingston, Ontario, Canada.

J.L. Cloudsley-Thompson, University of London, London, England.

Denis J. Corish, Bowdoin College, Brunswick, Maine, U.S.A.

Olivier Costa de Beauregard, Institut Henri Poincaré, Paris, France.

Dorothea Watanabe Dauer, University of Hawaii, Honolulu, Hawaii, U.S.A.

K.G. Denbigh, F.R.S., Council for Science and Society, London, England.

Robert Efron, Veterans Administration Hospital, Martinez, California, U.S.A.
David Epstein, Massachusetts Institute of Technology, Cambridge, Massachusetts, U.S.A.
David Finkelstein, Yeshiva University, New York City, New York, U.S.A.
George H. Ford, University of Rochester, Rochester, New York, U.S.A.
Marie-Louise von Franz, Carl Jung Institut, Küsnacht, Switzerland.
J. T. Fraser, International Society for the Study of Time, Westport, Connecticut, U.S.A.
William Gooddy, National Hospital, London, England.
Brian C. Goodwin, University of Sussex, Sussex, England.
Helen B. Green, Middlesex College, Middletown, Connecticut, U.S.A.
John G. Gunnell, State University of New York, Albany, New York, U.S.A.
Francis C. Haber, University of Maryland, College Park, Maryland, U.S.A.
José Huertas-Jourda, Wilfred Laurier University, Waterloo, Ontario, Canada.
Shiro Imai, Hokkaido University, Sapporo, Japan.
Hans Kalmus, University College, London, England.
Susumu Kamefuchi, University of Tsukuba, Ibaraki, Japan.
Robert Kastenbaum, University of Massachusetts, Boston, Massachusetts, U.S.A.
P. T. Landsberg, University of Southampton, Southampton, England.
Nathaniel Lawrence, Williams College, Williamstown, Massachusetts, U.S.A.
Sverre Lyngstad, New Jersey Institute of Technology, Newark, New Jersey, U.S.A.
Samuel L. Macey, University of Victoria, Victoria, British Columbia, Canada.
Masao Matsumoto, Keio University, Tokyo, Japan.
Wolfe Mays, University of Manchester, Manchester, England.
Murray Melbin, Boston University, Boston, Massachusetts, U.S.A.
A. A. Mendilow, The Hebrew University, Jerusalem, Israel.
Jacques Merleau-Ponty, University of Paris, Paris, France.
John A. Michon, University of Groningen, Haren-Groningen, Netherlands.
Otoya Miyagi, Tokyo Institute of Technology, Tokyo, Japan.
Gert H. Müller, Universität Heidelberg, Heidelberg, Germany.
William Newton-Smith, Balliol College, Oxford, England.
J. D. North, Oxford, England.
Helga Nowotny, University of Vienna, Vienna, Austria.
Hideo Ogawa, Keio University, Tokyo, Japan.
Ken-ichi Ono, University of Tokyo, Tokyo, Japan.
Raimundo Panikkar, University of California, Santa Barbara, California, U.S.A.
David A. Park, Williams College, Williamstown, Massachusetts, U.S.A.
Ernst Pöppel, Max-Planck-Institut für Psychiatrie, München, Germany.
Ricardo J. Quinones, Claremont Men's College, Claremont, California, U.S.A.

Albert I. Rabin, Michigan State University, East Lansing, Michigan, U.S.A.
Curt Paul Richter, The Johns Hopkins University, Baltimore, Maryland, U.S.A.
George Rochberg, University of Pennsylvania, Philadelphia, Pennsylvania, U.S.A.
Lewis Rowell, University of Hawaii, Honolulu, Hawaii, U.S.A.
Georges Schaltenbrand, Luitpold Hospital, Würzburg, Germany.
Manfred E.A. Schmutzer, University of Vienna, Vienna, Austria.
Gregor Sebba, Emory University, Atlanta, Georgia, U.S.A.
Charles M. Sherover, Hunter College, New York City, New York, U.S.A.
Masanao Toda, Hokkaido University, Sapporo, Japan.
Gisela Trommsdorff, Universität Mannheim, Mannheim, Germany.
Frederick Turner, Kenyon College, Gambier, Ohio, U.S.A.
Synnøve Vinsrygg, Archeological Museum, Stavanger, Norway.
Eric Voegelin, Stanford University, Stanford, California, U.S.A.
Waldemar Voisé, Academy of Sciences, Warsaw, Poland.
Michael S. Watanabe, University of Hawaii, Honolulu, Hawaii, U.S.A.
Mogens Wegener, University of Aarhus, Aarhus, Denmark.
Eugene Weiner, Haifa University, Haifa, Israel.
Lee F. Werth, Cleveland State University, Cleveland, Ohio, U.S.A.
G.J. Whitrow, University of London, London, England.
Makoto Yamamoto, University of Tokyo, Tokyo, Japan.
Michael Yanase, S.J., Sophia University, Tokyo, Japan.
Jiri Zeman, Academy of Sciences, Prague, Czechoslovakia.

# Contents

## VI. SOCIETY



## VII. LITERATURE AND THE ARTS



## VIII. CHRISTIANITY, HINDUISM, MITHRAISM

# I. PROLEGOMENA

## Metaphysical Presuppositions and the Study of Time

R.S. Brumbaugh

*ABSTRACT*

*It has been assumed in past discussions of Time that the subject of inquiry is enough like a field or a substance so that the law of contradiction must apply to it in the same way. It would then follow that if in some context time necessarily has the property* P, *there is no context in which it can have the property* Not-P. *This is a very strong metaphysical assumption. In fact, in different contexts, time is observed and defined as having essential properties that* are *mutually contradictory. In the past, this has been assumed to be the result of someone's errors in observation in one or another of the cases. In fact, however, four alternative accounts are equally persuasive on the level of* logical coherence, *that of* pragmatic effectiveness, *and that of* aesthetic intuitive evidence. *My thesis in the present paper is that there is no error in observation or formulation, but that there has been an error in allowing the assumption of homogeneity with respect to the law of contradiction to pass unnoticed. The paper's main emphasis is on a demonstration that four alternative and contradictory accounts of time are all coherent logically, applicable technologically, and persuasive intuitively. Given that demonstration, it follows that time is either a radically equivocal term - which I do not believe - or that it is less like a substance, or a field, or a dimension, or as series of elements, than philosophers and scientists have supposed.*

Let me begin by telling a fable. Suppose that there is a planet near Tau Ceti with people on it. But it has a homogeneous surface, and its inhabitants are very much alike genetically and culturally. For centuries, scientists there have been trying to decide what the nature of our earth is, on the basis of reports from rocket probes sent to different latitudes and longitudes. Each laboratory gets an interpretable result, but different from the others. For example, the scientists at A find the reports suggest an earth which is fluid, with a surface temperature above freezing; but the data recorded at B suggest an earth of solid rock, so cold that it must be covered with ice. Over the years, each laboratory has repeated its observations; re-calibrated its instruments; and accused the other group of errors in observation. Finally, a Conference is held, and three suggestions are offered. The first suggestion is that the differences are simply a matter of language: it is a question about the way we should use the phrase "surface of the earth." The meaning will be established once we all know how the phrase is used. A second suggestion is that the problem is not simply linguistic, but psychological. We are constructing alternative models to match our observations: the data themselves are ambiguous enough to fit any of the competing conceptual schemes, and no observation will be able to confirm or disconfirm them.

The third suggestion - and in this imagined case the correct one - is that the difficulty is in a sense metaphysical. The homogeneity of their planet's surface has led them to *presuppose* that every world must have a single quality. Consequently, if evidence shows that some part of the earth is hot, this assumption suggests that then *no part* can be cold; and for moist or dry, or other opposites, the same. Once this presupposition is recognized, we can correct it. But until it is, we are misled by seemingly exclusive possibilities which will not match the data of observation.

My thesis is that our situation in respect to time is exactly that of the observers in my fable with respect to the earth's surface.

In our discussions of time, whether everyday or technical, there is one metaphysical presupposition hidden which is plausible but mistaken. This is the assumption that time is enough like an abstract class or like a concrete physical object so that the law of identity will apply to it in the same way it does to substances and abstractions. If this is so, then it follows that as between contradictory aspects, time can have only one of the pair, to the exclusion of the other. For example, if inspection and experiment indicate that time is continuous, we jump to the consequences that time cannot be discrete, since if continuity is represented by P, discreteness is non-P.

Historically, when there have been alternative exclusive accounts of time, we have inspected them with a view to selecting the right one, and rejecting the rest. This is perhaps clearest on a naive pragmatic level, where both machinist and artist tend to take the relevant aspects of time with which they work, and to generalize these into a proposed account of the sole real nature of temporality. The two generalizations are radically different in respect of time's continuity or discreteness, its causal single-line determinism or branching option trees, its reversibility, the kind of logic that best applies to it, and so on. If time is a kind of thing that only one such definition can apply to, the study of time reveals a situation that is contradictory.

I propose to show that there have in fact been four alternative accounts of time's reality on each of three levels of formality. Each of the four, on each level, is plausible and coherent; no two, on any level, are mutually consistent if consistency entails a strict law of identity. My three levels could be described as time considered purely qualitatively, as it is in myth and literature, on the most concrete step. Next, a second level considers time relationally, as it appears in a pragmatic world of substances, causes, and techniques. Third, we move to the more abstract consideration of time from the aspect of quantity: the mathematical and logical structures that offer formal models for time. Kantians will note that I have not mentioned modality; it is possible that the antinomies of my three levels can be resolved if we find a way to apply that fourth category. But my own generation of these levels is Platonic: I take these levels to match the three lowest segments of Plato's "Divided Line" in *Republic* vi-vii.[1]

Let me begin with the level of abstract systems: of logics, philosophies, and mathematical models. Here, historically, there have been four families of philosophic systems in the West, all internally consistent and useful, but differing in what each presupposes to be the correct *direction* and the correct *method* of philosophic explanation. I will not argue just now that there must be only these four; but I will say that the fourfold classification has a surprisingly wide currency, and that no fifth system family has ever made a place for itself in the competition.

A formal system, as I have said, will be defined in terms of what it assumes to be correct philosophic explanation. As to explanatory *direction*, one may postulate either a move toward the formal or toward the physical. We may, that is, look for the realities of things by seeking abstract types, structures, species, natures; or by seeking physical elements, natural processes, media, causal linkages. The formalist will emphasize logical causality, the physicalist physical causes. Both Platonism and Aristotelianism are classical philosophies with commitments of a formalist type; atomism and modern process philosophy both fall into the class of systems using a physical explanatory direction. For *method* of explanation, there are also two possible preferences, analytic and synthetic. An analytic explanatory method tries to underscore the differences between things, to move toward separate elements, or particles, or species, or specimens. The synthetic method, on the other hand, stresses continuities and similarities: it seeks description in terms of continuous, total fields - of logical space, or physical, or aesthetic, or whatever. The four combinations of preferred direction and method define the four families of Western philosophic systems.[2]

Perhaps the way in which a system is defined by its assumed notion of explanation is seen most clearly in the case of the atomic theories. These are systems that combine physical direction with analytic method. The result is that an atomist seeks indivisible, distinct elementary parts in his search for reality. (Those parts may, of course, be material or psychological or linguistic "atoms.") "Explanation" combines the analysis into elements with a construction of complexes and causal chains by contact and transfer of momentum. (Which we must take metaphorically in the psychological and linguistic dimensions.) Democritus, Epicurus, Hume, and the young Bertrand Russell, all fall into this family.

Opposed to atomism both in direction and method is the family of Platonism. Platonic systems are committed to a formal direction and a synthetic method of explanation. The attempt is to grasp a timeless form - a determinate defining pattern in an abstract field of logical space. But in that field, each form is defined by its relation to the other structural parts and to the whole. The general pattern is one of formal hierarchy. Explanation then must order formal parts hierarchically, indicate a relevant vertex, and study the participation by which structures ingress into and determine history and fantasy.

Aristotelianism represents a third system type, designed by Aristotle to mediate between Platonism and atomism, and sharing something with each. The Aristotelian systems have a formal explanatory direction, but an analytic method of explanation. Thus where a Platonist has logical hierarchies in a continuous field, an Aristotelian has rather a cabinet of natural kinds, species, types, in separate compartments. But science remains a study of species, for knowledge is of the universal. However, Aristotle's forms come in discrete units here, just as the atoms do in the atomic theory. Causality can be read either as teleological or blindly mechanical or both. It is probably correct to say, as is often done, that the Aristotelian world-view is the one that would occur naturally to a biologist or a doctor, who studies not just health and humanity, but health, normalcy, and humanity in individual patients or specimens, each running more or less "true to type."

The fourth pair of commitments, to physical direction and synthetic method, is characteristic of twentieth century process philosophy. It had its classical ancestors - Heraclitus and Anaxagoras come to mind - but it has become a "coordinate force" with the other three families only in our century. (By this I mean, that it has become a coordinate force as a system of philosophy; poets and mystics have held this metaphysical position continuously, but the tendency has been to treat it as alternative to any "properly philosophical" view until recently.) Process philosophy sees the world as a continuous, dynamic field, with new entities and values emerging with the advance of time. Forms or species are abstractions; explanation depends rather on intuition, on an appreciation of concrete individuals. Where the elements of an atomic theory are separate and static, the single field of a process philosophy is continuous and dynamic. Some students of systems call this fourth family "Bergsonian," some "Whiteheadian," and both names are appropriate.

The final tetradic set, then, can be written as a cross, with the vertical axis representing direction, the horizontal, method. This gives:

```
                              FORMAL

      Platonic     I            :            II Aristotelian
                                :
    SYNTHETIC -----------------:-------------------- ANALYTIC
                                :
      Process     III           :            IV Atomic
      Philosophy                :
                                :
                            EMPIRICAL
```

Here, I is Platonic, II is Aristotelian, III is the quadrant of process philosophy, IV is the quadrant of various forms of atomism.

Just in passing, to make this schema more persuasive, we can compare the sort of structure each of these systems expects to find in the world with one standard of scoring responses on a Rohrschach test. The scoring I have in mind recognizes four types of response: static versus dynamic, wholistic versus part-by-part. These four form a tetrad:

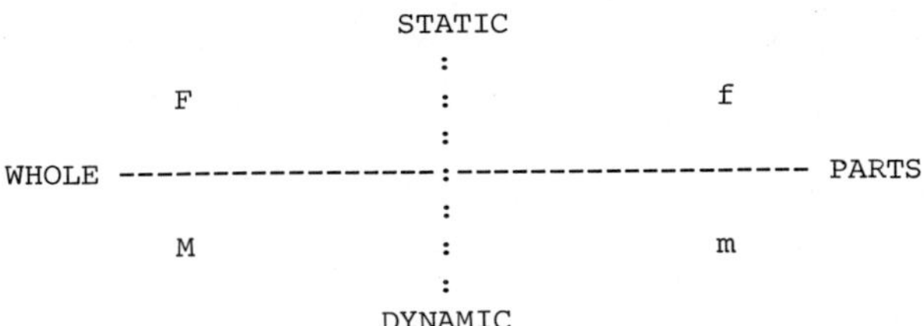


The four correlate beautifully with the systematic presuppositions of the Platonists (F), Aristotelian (f - or better fff), the Bergsonian (M), and the atomist (m - or, better, mmmm). (I have suggested, but so far without persuading anyone, that psychologists could design a test similar to the Rohrschach for projected *temporal structure*.)

With very modest modification and translation, my set of systems resembles that of Richard McKeon (e.g., in *Freedom and History*), Paul Weiss (e.g., in *Modes of Being*), Stephen Pepper (his "root metaphors"), Plato (who sets up four "philosophic systems" of these types in the *Sophist*), and Newton Stallknecht (e.g., in Stallknecht and Brombaugh, *The Compass of Philosophy*).[3]

Each of these formal systems brings with it a different notion of the structure of time, and a different notion of the kind of formal logic most appropriate to reality. This latter point has been developed by Stephan Körner, who points out that one can be "logical" with alternative logics.[4] He distinguishes four types, using two contraries. "L" logics ("logistical") are definite and linear; they offer unique causal lines and unique logical entailments; our standard deductive logics are of this type. "I" ("intuitionist") logics, on the other hand, give a formal picture of branching sequences leading into a future of different, forking, "options." Where *L* logics match a deterministic world, *I* logics match one with an openness in every future. Both *L* and *I* logics come in two varieties, "common sense" and "technical." The *technical* versions (which Körner abbreviates as *L* and *I*), use sharp analytic definitions to exclude borderline cases. The "common sense" logics (which he abbreviates *L** and *I**), assume a world of *continuity*, in which distinctions tend to blur. Clearly, these four "logics" neatly match my four system families, as a diagram will show.

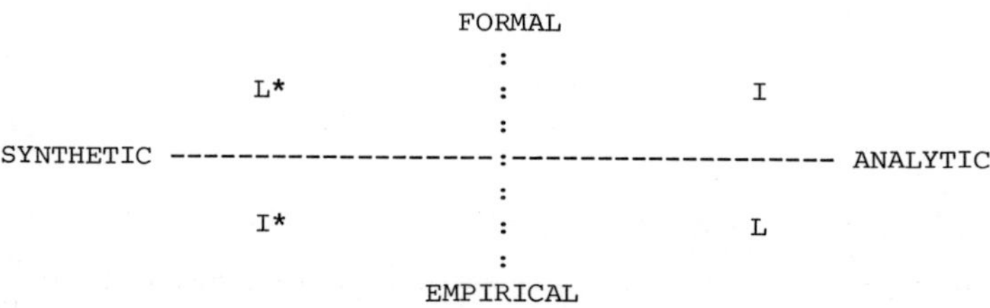


Moving from logic to action, we descend from the level of *dianoia* on Plato's Line to the pragmatic level of *pistis* - the level of knowledge as technique, action, and pragmatic application. Now, it immediately occurs to any student of the history of philosophy, that since these systems claim to explain the world of our experience, it ought to be possible to test them empirically. Why haven't experiments, over more than two millennia of debate, *confirmed* one or more schemes, and *disconfirmed* the others? Clearly, any such elimination would be a gain for metaphysics. But the awkward historical fact - with consequences for the study of time that I will come to in a moment - is that *all four* have been repeatedly confirmed in the pragmatic world of craft and application. The confirmations, however, take place in different theaters of action for the different systems! Thus, a description of reality as an open field of process exactly matches the view of a creative artist, but the notion of determinate causal chains of elements exactly fits the world of a machinist or applied natural scientist. A mathematician's experience confirms the Platonic, a doctor's or politician's the Aristotelian, way. It is just here that our basic metaphysical assumption of the applicability of the law of contradiction to time begins to become a liability; for that assumption, plus the facts about systems we have just presented, leads to the conclusion either that three-fourths of our experience is illusion or is reducible to the fourth; or that our choices of descriptive frame are equally valid but all alike wholly arbitrary; or that we must give up the law of contradiction totally (and with it, all claims to rationality).

Some interesting light is shed on the tetrads we have discussed by Newton Stallknecht's definition of the "four tenses" which he associates with the meanings of "is" in his definition of "ontology."[5] These are a past (perfective) tense, a future (inceptive), and *two* "presents," a present eternal (non-temporal), and a present progressive (dividing past from future). Each "tense" exactly fits the theoretic conceptual structure *and* the practical interest of one of my four types of system, logic, and action.

| PRESENT ETERNAL | PRESENT PROGRESSIVE |
|---|---|
| FUTURE (INCEPTIVE) | PAST (PERFECTIVE) |

The matrix for *practice* is:

| MATHEMATICS AND LOGIC | MEDICINE AND POLITICS |
|---|---|
| FINE ART AND CREATIVITY | TECHNOLOGY AND NATURAL SCIENCE |

It seems no coincidence that each conceptual system finds its use and confirmation in relation to a *different* aspect of action in time. [ In fact, we might correlate the four quadrants, respectively, with COSMOLOGICAL TIME, BIOLOGICAL TIME, AESTHETIC TIME, and TECHNOLOGICAL TIME.]

It might be well to notice here that Professor Stallknecht is a Whiteheadian, and that I was trained as a literary critic as well as a philosopher. Neither of us would be easily persuaded by an abstract description which failed to match our qualitative intuition. But two decades ago, when I undertook a survey of the *concrete quality* of time as I found it amplified in literature, I found the same fourfold heterogeneity that I have been discussing in the fields of practice and of theory.[6]

For my present purpose, I have selected four works in each of which one set of temporal qualities has been enlarged and presented directly. My four case-studies are Kafka's *Castle,* Proust's *Remembrance,* Mann's *Magic Mountain* (the middle section), and Sophocles' *Oedipus Rex*. These catch the qualities, respectively, of a Platonic, an atomic, a process, and an Aristotelian sense of "time"; and do so by generalizing the properties of one of Stallknecht's aspects or tenses so that it becomes the entire temporal universe of each myth. A diagram illustrates the correlation:

| KAFKA<br>(THE CASTLE) | : | SOPHOCLES<br>(OEDIPUS REX) |
|---|---|---|
| MANN<br>(THE MAGIC MOUNTAIN) | : | PROUST<br>(SWANN'S WAY) |

Kafka's *Castle* exists, elusive, at the edge of the world of the Surveyor, K. It is rarefied, almost as though the author had managed to apply a vacuum pump to the temporality of his story. Not only is the time somehow uneventful, and unmoving, but its direction is largely arbitrary. If we were to alter the sequence of episodes, the new ordered mosaics would still illustrate the same fable. In fact, this notion of a Byzantine mosaic offering two-dimensional pictures of some allegory may be a comparison that brings out what I feel to be the distinctive quality of Kafka's time. Even when a character is in a small waiting-room, watching the pointless bustle of ledger-bearing angels, we don't know where the Castle is, who the angels are, or what if anything is changed by the adventure. The episodes are not simply reversible, but have a kind of interchangeability, illustrating J. T. Fraser's notion of "prototemporality."[7]

Consider now the following quotes, given at some length, from *The Castle*. They are from a translation by E. and W. Muir, (New York: Alfred A. Knopf, 1930).

> ...And when now, after finishing his work in the shed, the coachman went across the courtyard in his slow, rolling walk, closed the huge gate and then returned, all very slowly, while he literally looked at nothing but his own footprints in the snow - and finally shut himself into the shed; and now as all the electric lights went out too - for whom should they remain on? - and only up above the slit in the wooden gallery still remained bright, holding

> one's wandering gaze for a little, it seemed to K. as if at last those people had broken off all relations with him, and as if now in reality he were freer than he had ever been...but - this conviction was at least equally strong - as if at the same time there was nothing more senseless, nothing more helpless, than this freedom, this waiting, this inviolability. (p. 140).

> ...Much more important seems to me the way in which Klamm received Barnabas. Barnabas has often described it to me, and even sketched the room....It's a room divided into two by a single reading-desk stretching all its length from wall to wall; one side is so narrow that two people can hardly squeeze past each other, and that's reserved for the officials, the other side is spacious, and that's where clients wait, spectators, servants, messengers. On the desk there are great books lying open, side by side, and officials stand by most of them reading. They don't always stick to the same book yet it isn't the books that they change but their places, and it always astounds Barnabas to see how they have to squeeze past each other when they change places, because there's so little room. In front of the desk and close to it there are small low tables at which clerks sit ready to write from dictation, whenever the officials wish it. And the way that is done always amazes Barnabas. (p. 230).

> "...It's not likely to occur to them to look out of the carriage windows in search of petitioners, for the carriages are crammed with papers which they study on the way."
>
> "But," said K., "I've seen the inside of an official sledge in which there weren't any papers." Olga's story was opening for him such a great and almost incredible world that he could not help trying to put his own small experiences in relation to it, as much to convince himself of its reality as of his own existence.
>
> "That's possible," said Olga, "but in that case it's even worse, for that means that the official's business is so important that the papers are too precious or too numerous to be taken with him, and those officials go at a gallop. In any case, none of them can spare time for father." (p. 227).

The following is from a Postscript by Max Brod, in the same volume:

> ...This is one of the mysteries and part of the absolute uniqueness of Kafka's art, that for the chosen reader of those great unfinished novels the conclusion loses in importance from the point at which the main assumptions are more or less completely given...

This time has continuity; settings and episodes flow and transform into one another. It has "interchangeability": as I remarked, an Aristotelian critic would be ill at ease looking for the plot, character, setting; and would probably go away insisting that this is an *allegory*, not an *epic*. But there is one more thing about this peculiar time, caught beneath the author's magnifying lens, and this, it seems to me, is its weakness of modality. Between waking and dream, actual and possible, there is very little shift of intensity, of color, or of causal coherence.

These three properties capture the quality of the kind of time which I have associated with the metaphysical system of Platonism. And they match the *structural* notion of time as a "dimension", continuous, and isotropic. In practice, this is the time pattern that a mathematician, or a physicist or a cosmologist finds most pragmatically satisfying.

In looking at Plato's astronomy, I found references to four pieces of mechanism, each a model of one level or kind of cosmological "time." The most "realistic" of the four was a static, metal-band model translating pure arithmetical ratios into static geometric circles and radii. By a Platonic law of identity, what stays identical is form, not flow; essence, not existence; structure, not texture. As a result, since forms have a single, present-eternal, modality; an abstract, typical composition; and a causal power that acts from being to becoming; time, as any thing dynamic, discontinuous, modally divided, is "unreal." In Plato's myths, the effect is to reduce story to allegorical fable, where in fact we get qualitative vividness, but only for so long as we stare at the television screen in the Cave.

The most interesting literary discovery I made when I tried to sort out distinctive intensive time-qualities in literature was that his special treatment of time is responsible for much of the dramatic impact of Sophocles' tragedies. If we think of time as a "now," a present balanced between fixed past and open future, a locus of forced choice, we get a sort of metaphysical counterpart of Sophoclean time. Repeatedly, the drama calls for decision; for fateful decision. In *Oedipus Rex,* this is particularly clear because the discovery and reversal come about from repeated relatively brief crises. The hour has struck; the Messenger been sent for; Tiresias threatened; Apollo's word doubted! Each crisis is irreversible; each offers Oedipus an alternative to his hot-tempered persistence; yet at each point, his character and thought dictate a choice leading to consequences the audience can see.

The knife-edged time of Sophocles comes out most sharply in the entrances and exits, the summons and waiting. Thus, consider the following examples from *Oedipus The King,* ed. with a verse translation by F. Storr (London and New York: William Heinemann, Ltd., 1934).

> OEDIPUS: I have sent.../Creon, my consort's brother, to inquire/ of Pythian Phoebus at his Delphic Shrine/ How I might save the state by act or word./ And now I reckon up the tale of days/ Since he set forth and marvel how he fares./ 'Tis strange, this endless tarrying, passing strange./ But when he comes, then I were base indeed/ If I perform not all the god declares./ CHORUS: Thy words are well-timed; even as thou speakest/ That shouting tells me Creon is at hand.
>
> (Lines 70 ff.)
>
> OEDIPUS: Well, I will start afresh and once again/ Make dark things clearer.../ Up, children, haste ye, quit these altar stairs,/ Take hence your suppliant wands, go summon hither/ The Theban commons...
>
> (Lines 132 ff.)
>
> CHORUS: I know not; to my sovereign's acts I'm blind/ But lo, he comes to answer for himself./
> OEDIPUS (To CREON): Sirrah, what mak'st thou here? Dost thou presume/ To approach my doors, thou brazen faced rogue,/ My murderer and the filcher of my crown?/
>
> (Lines 530 ff.)

The same tension carries forward until the final exit ends the play.

Now, this was Aristotle's favorite play, the one he used in his *Poetics* as a prize example. And one reason, I think, is that it exactly matches the analysis of time in practical science which goes with an Aristotelian philosophy. For an Aristotelian can make distinctions, between kinds of time, kinds of change, and kinds of number. The bleak abstract formula of "a number of motion in respect to before and after" hides the concrete diversity of Aristotle's species of time. In theology and astronomy, it is true, time is static: the Prime Mover sees only atemporal reality, the periods of the stars repeat identically, so that the same position becomes before and after. But in his analysis of linear time, Aristotle defines a "now" which divides a fixed past and a modally open future. When this division fails to square with Aristotelian deductive logic, Aristotle changes the logic, to accommodate the sea fight tomorrow. Whenever he works with art, ethics, politics, or history, it is the time of decision that seems to me to be invoked. (At the end of the *Constitution of Athens*, for example, Aristotle sees his story as the account of eleven constitutions and ten revolutions; most of us would have read his data in another way.) Thus Aristotle's enthusiasm for Sophocles reflects, in part, a metaphysical presupposition the two share; one expressing it in the category of quantity, one of quality, but both keenly aware of temporal discontinuity and modality. (Incidentally, this sort of branching sequence matches biological, growth time very well.)

A third quality of time, radically continuous but also radically irreversible, is illustrated by Thomas Mann's *Magic Mountain*. Supposedly, on the top of an enchanted mountain, time would stand still; and Mann's interpolated reflections within the book suggest that he was consciously committed to this sort of enchantment. But the plot itself, as it unfolds, takes on a momentum of its own. From the time that Castorp, entering the sanatorium, notices the clock, calendar, and bell at the reception desk, until the end, when he plunges into a war-torn world in flames, there is a continuous accelerating erosion of structure. As distinctions vanish, one temporal phase blurs into another, and one modality; finally, even the boundary between life and death becomes indistinct. Meanwile, the protagonist - and the reader - have lost track of days, then of seasons, finally of years: but *not* in Kafka's world of suspended animation. The time in this story has continuity, as radical a continuity as Bergson's *durée*.[8] It also has radical irreversibility: we could define this, if we were minded to draw analogies between science and story, as constantly increasing entropy. But in fact, for our present purposes, at least, it serves better to describe what happens as an increasingly intense capture of the quality of time as directed flow. The reason for my choosing this novel, rather than many others, is the single-mindedness with which this one aspect of time dominates and intensifies. If Sophocles captures the progressive present of crisis, Kafka the present eternal of allegory, Mann in this novel has an inceptive dynamic duration, a captured future. (If one were to try to illustrate this temporal quality by selected *parts* of artistic works, the forward-looking frenetic projects of Alexis Zorba would qualify; so would some sections of Faulkner; and surely many other characters and passages which step into the metaphysics of flow, the "Time" of Heraclitus and Bergson.) This is a time with very interesting scientific implications. On the one hand, it exactly matches the structure needed to explain the biological theory of evolution; on the other, its unpredictable branching and shifting, which escape from our equations, make it a time structure which scientists accept very reluctantly.

Just as the time sense of Sophocles is built into his dramatic structure, Mann's rush of time into disorder is not the thing his characters think about on their enchanted mountain, but is built into what they experience. Consider the progression from beginning to end represented by the following three passages, from *The Magic Mountain,* trans. H. T. Lowe-Porter (New York: Alfred A. Knopf, 1939).

The arrival at the sanatorium is factual enough:

> On their right, as they entered, between the main door and the inner one, was the porter's lodge. An official of the French type, in the grey livery of the man at the station, was sitting at the telephone, reading the newspaper. He came out and led them through the well-lighted halls, on the left of which lay the reception rooms.
>
> (p. 11)

With consistent continuity, a loss of order proceeds. Hans Castorp has a love affair, begun on Walpurgisnacht; he becomes disoriented in his thinking about time; he gets lost in the snow. Finally, a seance breaks the barrier between life and death, as the spirit of his dead Cousin, Joachim, returns.

> The records had run off, with a last accord of horns. But no one stopped the machine. The needle went on scratching in the silence, as the disk whirred around. Then Hans Castorp raised his head, and his eyes went, without searching, the right way.
>
> There was one more person in the room than before. There in the background, where the red rays lost themselves in gloom, so that the eye scarcely reached thither...Joachim sat. It was the Joachim of the last days, with hollow, shadowy cheeks, warrior's beard, and full, curling lips. He sat leaning back, one leg crossed over the other.... But that was no proper uniform he wore. No colour, no decorations; it was a collar like a *litewka* jacket, and sidepockets.... And what was it, this headgear? It seemed as though Joachim had turned an army cookpot upside-down on his head, and fastened it under his chin with a band. Yet it looked quite properly warlike, like an old-fashioned foot-soldier, perhaps.
>
> (pp. 855-856.)

And the loss of order is complete at the end.

> What is it? Where are we? Whither has the dream snatched us? Twilight, rain, filth. Fiery glow of overcast sky, ceaseless booming of heavy thunder; the moist air rent by a sharp singing whine, a raging, swelling howl as of some hound in hell, that ends its course in a splitting, a splintering and crackling, a coruscation; by groans and shrieks, by trumpets blowing fit to burst, by the beat of a drum coming faster, faster - There is a wood, discharging drab hordes, that come on, fall, spring up again, come on. ...There is our friend, there is Hans Castorp! We recognize him at a distance, by the little beard he assumed while sitting at the "bad" Russian table.... Look! He treads on the hand of a fallen comrade.
>
> (pp. 895-896; 898)

For the time quality that matches an atomic theory, where a succession of units or states follow, but each intact and insulated from the rest, we turn to Proust. This peculiar quality of Proust's time sense, with its total recall of unchanged past moments and its total bewilderment at passage is exactly the feeling one would attribute to Zeno's "arrow."[9] "If I am at every moment at rest in a space equal to my own length," we can imagine the missile asking itself, "when do I move?" Yet the Arrow does collide with the target. Proust has in his memory file an enormous sequence of colored lantern-slides (an image he himself is fond of). They picture things that have changed - yet there is no static slide that pictures change itself. Proust's "atomic" time sense has been repeatedly studied, for example by George Poulet.[10] Its association with a metaphysics of separate elements in reversible, discontinuous series, and with a scientific structure of separate sequential moments, is particularly clear. So is the *retrospective* direction in which an author looks when this time quality dominates his work. Only *after the event,* when the immediate impression is recalled as a Humean idea, do we know "what happened." Contrast Marcel to Zorba or to Castorp in this regard; we have the perfective aspect of time confronting the inceptive.

In Proust, we encounter an author whose time sense is dominated by absolute recall. The scenes, flavors, sounds of the past are remembered vividly, unchanging, like magic-lantern slides. What makes *us* change when our world and its time are these atomic essences, snapshots, is a mystery lying outside of the novel, but giving it a plot and direction as the author searches for an answer.

The point is illustrated in the following passages from Proust's *Remembrance of Things Past: Swann's Way*, trans. C. Scott Moncreiff (New York: Random House, 1928).

> Certainly I was now well awake; my body had turned about for the last time.... But it was no good my knowing that I was not in any of those houses of which, in the stupid moment of waking, if I had not caught sight exactly, I could still believe in their possible presence; for memory was now set in motion; as a rule I did not attempt to go to sleep again at once, but used to spend the greater part of the night recalling our life in the old days at Combray with my great-aunt, at Balbec, Paris, Doncieres, Venice, and the rest; remembering again all the places and people that I had known, what I had actually seen of them, and what others had told me.
>
> (p. 7)

Later, Marcel remembers Combray.

> And so it was that, for a long time afterward, when I lay awake at night and revived old memories of Combray, I saw no more of it than this sort of luminous panel, sharply defined against a vague and shadowy background, like the panels which a Bengal fire or some electric sign will illuminate and dissect from the front of a building the other parts of which remain plunged in darkness: broad enough at its base, the little parlor, the dining-room, the alluring shadows of the path along which would come M. Swann, the unconscious author of my sufferings, the hall through which I would journey to the first step of that staircase, so hard to climb, which constituted, all by itself, the tapering "elevation" of an irregular pyramid; and, at the summit, my bedroom, with the little passage through whose glazed door Mama would enter; in a word, seen always at the same evening hour, isolated from all its possible surroundings, detached and solitary against its shadowy background, the bare minimum of scenery necessary (like the setting one sees printed at the head of an old play, for its performance in the provinces) to the drama of my undressing, as though all Combray had consisted of but two floors joined by a slender staircase, and as though there had been no time there but seven o'clock at night. I must own that I could have assured any questioner that Combray did include other scenes and did exist at other hours than these.
>
> (p. 33)

Pragmatically, the atomic approach to action matches the tools and needs of everyday technology. Arts and crafts are funded human experience, retrospective; mechanisms are series of separate parts, sequential and reversible. But simple and useful as this model is, it cannot account for continuity, modality, irreversibility, mathematics, metaphysics, fine art, or prudence. It competes with, but by no means dominates, the worlds of abstract explanation, of pragmatic action, of intuition and qualitative appreciation.

With this contrast of four immediate qualitative experiences of time, my program of exhibiting tetrads is concluded. Metaphysical presuppositions may be thought of in either of two ways. On the one hand, we may think of schemes of concepts - for example, my schemata of "explanation" - as paradigms which dictate what can be observed. For, if our concepts set limits to what is possible, those limits apply to what is observable as well. On the other hand, we may think of metaphysical orientations as generalizations of familiar modes of action and qualitative perception, extended to cover *all* experience and phenomena though they originate in one part or another of the total field. But, either way, we find alternative presuppositions directing and limiting the study of time.

We can now return to the very basic metaphysical presupposition that makes us unable to feel at ease with my tetrads. This is, we recall, the assumption that "time" must be some single, homogeneous thing; that the law of identity will apply to it as it would to a physical substance or to a formal structure. Clearly, if that assumption is right, only one of Richard McKeon's philosophic schemes, of Stephan Körner's logics, of Newton Stallknecht's four temporal qualities, of my tetrads of time and practice, can be "right" or "real." Yet I have just shown that there is no test which will show one of these alternatives to be real or right that cannot be used - in a different domain, to be sure - to support the claims of the other contenders.

But it would be a serious error to draw the conclusion from the lack of homogeneity that time is a radically equivocal term. If we decided that each specialist, theoretic, practical, or poetic, had his own time which had nothing in common with the others, the result would be like the total chaos that ends Mann's *Magic Mountain*. Some of us would live in a world where we backed into a future unawares, contemplating only a fixed past; others would float in a logical space, like subjects in a sensory-deprivation tank; and so on.[11] The fact is that "time" is a complex causal nexus, with different modalities interacting and intersecting. This was the theme of Paul Weiss's *Modes of Being*, and though my analysis is not identical with his, I remain convinced that in this central theme he was right.[12]

What we find is that "time" involves *four* entities, not one.

What we also find is that there are a dozen metaphysical confusions that can interfere with our sense of time, and can play havoc with a Conference such as our present one. These confusions take the form of substituting one time concept for another, where the substitution is inappropriate, and takes in too much territory. Thus, we might project the closed, deterministic pattern of the eternal present onto the future, and picture ourselves as four-dimensional worms advancing to meet "future facts" already waiting. Or we might project the plasticity of the future onto a past which has set up causal limits for our present options. Wishing the past were corrigible, we might assume it to be; but only a mismatch of expectation and outcome can follow that assumption.

Plato, in his dialogue the *Parmenides*, proves first that time is nothing, then that it is everything. Both proofs are hypothetical, and neither is right. But the issues they establish are ontological and their dialectic attempts to work through the equations of physics, the canonical forms of logic, the rules of practice, the myths of passage, to capture a vision of the complex reality of time. Once captured, Plato proceeds to dissolve time in a universal solvent of eternity. I hope our present interdisciplinary study of time will be less austere, though unavoidably equally metaphysical. For that result, we need to be aware of, and willing to correct, the metaphysical presuppositions we fall into uncritically.

NOTES

1. The "Divided Line" is a diagram introduced by Plato in *Republic VI* to indicate different kinds and degrees of accuracy of "knowing". Its four levels run from myth and sheer conjecture (*eikasia*) on the lowest level, through a kind of "know-how" stage of arts and techniques (*pistis*), then through a stage of general hypothetical-deductive explanations (*dianoia*), to a final grasp of complete systems (*noesis*). These four types of knowing also represent successive stages of learning. See, on this point, R. S. Brumbaugh, "The Divided Line and the Direction of Inquiry," *Philosophical Forum*, 2 (1970-71), 172-199; "A New Interpretation of Plato's Republic", *Journal of Philosophy*, 54 (1967), 661-670.

2. See R. S. Brumbaugh, "Preface to Cosmography," *Review of Metaphysics*, 7 (1952), pp. 529-534; "Cosmography", *Review of Metaphysics*, 25 (1971), 140-148; "Cosmography: The Problem of Modern Systems", *Review of Metaphysics*, 26 (1973), 511-521.

3. Richard P. McKeon, *Freedom and History*. New York: The Noonday Press, 1952; Paul Weiss, *Modes of Being*. Carbondale, Ill.: Southern Illinois University Press, 1958; Plato, *Sophist* 246-251; Newton P. Stallknecht and R. S. Brumbaugh, *The Compass of Philosophy*. New York: Longmans, Green, 1950.

4. Stephan Körner, *Categorial Frameworks*. London: Blackwell's, 1970.

5. Newton P. Stallknecht and R. S. Brumbaugh, *The Spirit of Western Philosophy*. New York: Longmans, Green, 1950. pp. xi-xvi.

6. R. S. Brumbaugh, "Kinds of Time: An Excursion in Metaphysics," In *Experience, Existence, and the Good: Essays in Honor of Paul Weiss*, Edited by Irwin C. Lieb. Carbondale, Ill.: Southern Illinois University Press, 1961. pp. 119-125.

7. J. T. Fraser, *Time as Conflict*. Brookfield, Vt.: Renouf USA and Basel: Birkhäuser, 1978. pp. 22-26.

8. Henri Bergson, *Time and Free Will*. Trans. by F. M. Pogson. London: George Allen & Unwin, 1910.

9. For the "Arrow", cf. H. D. P. Lee, *Zeno of Elea,* text with translation and notes. Cambridge: Cambridge University Press, 1936; also Richard Gale, Editor, *The Philosophy of Time*. New York: Doubleday and Co., 1967. "Zeno's Paradoxes of Motion", pp. 387-494.

10. Georges Poulet, *Studies in Human Time*. Translated by Elliott Coleman. Baltimore: The Johns Hopkins Press, 1956.

11. R. S. Brumbaugh, "Applied Metaphysics: Truth and Passing Time," *Review of Metaphysics,* 19 (1965), 647-666.

12. Paul Weiss, *op. cit.*

# Levels of Language in Discourse about Time

N. Lawrence

*The paper is intended to show major ways in which our understanding of time is linguistically reflected: (1) In the words through which time is semantically identified, described, or defined, (2) in the syntax employed in exhibiting temporal processes in the world, and (3) in the presentation of the temporal life of consciousness itself.*

*Newton's non-definition of time is taken as an example of the first kind, the semantic level. Newton struggled to cast the idea of time within the limits of subject-predicate syntax prejudiced toward nouns. All three levels are given in Kant. The latter two are expressly identified in a syntax of process, and are thus reflective upon the nature of language. It was Kant's particular genius to look for our different ways of thinking about time in the forms of language in which we talk about it.*

*The uses to which this analysis is put are largely therapeutic, or preventive. They may be summarized as warnings that time, being multi-perspectival, reveals various aspects of itself to various purposes, and that, as a result, no one abstraction can be allowed to obscure, or preempt, the authority of the rest. Further, since time seems to have a sui generis status, no standard tactic of definition is likely to be both general and reliable. In this respect, the approach of this paper may be said to be phenomenonological.*

## I. PRELIMINARY CONSIDERATIONS

This essay is concerned with the ways in which language embodies our understanding of time. It is written with several calculated prejudices or presuppositions in mind: (1) That consciousness is profoundly implicated in the world that it apprehends--thus, to speak of "the world as we know it" is somewhat pleonastic; (2) That the relation between thought and language is so intimate that it is at best misleading to ask whether thought creates language or language creates thought; (3) Finally, that *time, in its fullness, is like nothing else at all.*

Let me comment on each of these briefly. (1) The notion that consciousness is as constructive of the world as it is receptive to it should not be taken to mean that consciousness is confined to human beings. Animal behaviorists, for example, want to know to what extent the worlds of dog and man overlap. I can see straight and far, as the dog cannot; but she can smell around a corner and with great finesse. She knows of high frequency sounds which I can only infer; but my musical subtlety outruns hers. Yet my fingers live in her bowl of food and her fur extends to the allergy in my arm. Nonetheless, we shall, in this essay, concentrate on human consciousness. That it is implicated in the world would hardly be resisted by Plato, who believed in living man, within a living city, in a universe alive. During a brief period in the history of the physical sciences, it's true, we dreamed of a concrete world given to scientific knowledge, yet completely unaffected by the knowledge. But then it turned out that the coordinates of our measuring bodies must be read into relativity calculations, and that the electromagnetic extensions of our senses must be reckoned within quantum computation. One can imagine a whole heavenly Greek cheering section, led by Aristotle of course, nervously watching our intellectual progress, spontaneously breaking into applause as we recovered our wits. A close call, around the turn of the century.

(2) The second presupposition might be called the reflexivity or mutuality of language and thought. It needs little laboring here, I think. One often does not know exactly what he thinks until he has said it, and we sometimes lose our felt inspirations for want of writing them down. But conversely, think how the categories of our language have had to be thrown off like weighted chains, in order to release novel thought. Currently

it is popular and useful to treat of these categories in terms of paradigms, and we often find it difficult to get beyond them. The paradigms seem to have something of a life of their own. Nonetheless the question remains: Does language serve us or do we serve it? The answer is not simple. Much of the *attitude* of approach in the present paper is influenced by these considerations.

(3) Finally, there is the presupposition of the uniqueness of time, namely that in its fullness it stands alone, not definable by any of the familiar genus and species tactics, nor compassable by some procedure of protocol or postulation. Human purposes, concentrated on fatality, generation, fixity, creativity, extension, movement, measurability, etc., can extract from the richness of time, aspects of it appropriate to this or that selected intention. But the language employed in each of these selective approaches will not accommodate all aspects of time, nor can we find an extendable metaphor that will do the whole job. If we are to avoid the difficulties of the blind men, each of whom put his hands on a different part of the elephant, we must be prepared to look at the different aspects of time collectively and apart from sectarian and professional biases.

These presuppositions taken together create a kind of starting point for all that follows: a conviction that *individual* human thought, requiring as it may a groundwork of individual brain activity, is particular, spontaneous, and puny. But language is the ground state of consciousness *in general*, indeed the bearer of its evolution. If we eliminate language, the individual consciousness has to begin at the birth of man, all over again. In this impersonality of consciousness as embodied in language there is a vital kind of objectivity which has little to do with the strange fiction of a world apart from all mentality whatsoever. Even if we accept the existence of a wholly non-human world, whatever that may mean, I know of no warranty assuring us that the time discerned in such a world should somehow have a monopoly on reality, or on "objectivity." It is common to say, "Oh, of course there is subjective time, or human time, but we are talking about genuine, physical, objective time." It is exactly this distinction for which I can't find justification. *Every* concept of time arises in the context of some (no doubt useful) human purpose and bears, inevitably and essentially, the stamp of that human intent.[1]

Turning now to the three levels of language I wish to discuss, they represent aspects of language which I have tried to free from provincialities, not only of English but of Indo-European languages generally. Success in the latter effort may well be limited. I call the three levels the *semantic*, the *syntactic*, and the *presentive*.

(a) The *semantic* level is that of words taken more or less in isolation, without primary regard to their syntactical implications. Our efforts to *describe* time, as in Newton, generally are concerned with this level. (b) The *syntactical* level embodies our sense of time in the structure of a sentence, or, if it is defined, it will be so with at least implicit reference to linguistic form.[2] (c) The third is, almost in the nature of the case, difficult to talk about, because it is so pervasive. I have called it the *presentive* level, because it is that aspect of time in which language, regardless of the semantics of words or the syntax of grammar, is a presentation of consciousness and often self-consciousness. It rests in the mere fact that language--any language--is from, of, by, for consciousness. At the risk of joining those who use oriental insight for cheap effects, let me quote a haiku of Bashō: "My little horse clip-clops over the fields; aha, I am in the picture." That's the point: *I* am in the picture, always. The picture I present when I use language presents me also, and does so in a time-wise fashion. This is a quite different aspect of time and language. Again, at the risk of cheapening an already cheapened subject, body language--so called--does the same thing; it reveals consciousness, not merely attitude but *signal*--here, now. To summarize, then, time given through language may rest in the definitions of words, in the choice of syntax, and in the revealing of consciousness. These obviously overlap; they are interknit functions.

We shall look at Newton for a fine example of a purely semantic description, and at Kant for a model of all three levels. Kant is tough, even for professionals, but it is his brilliant realization of how consciousness structures the apparent world, and our conceptions about it, that is the most evident driving force in contemporary structuralism, whether it be in the sociology of knowledge, the child's cognitive development, or the mathematical structuralism of Nicolas Bourbaki.[3] I shall undertake to present Kant in as popular language as I can, with some technical discussion, confined to footnotes, for the sake of my professional colleagues; but first, let us examine Newton's semantic approach.

## II. THE SEMANTIC DESCRIPTION OF TIME, IN NEWTON

Genius frequently has to invent new words for the eliciting of new thought. Newton did not have this problem. By the time he wrote, the English word "time" had already attained a level of generality, as a noun, greater, I believe, than anything found in other Indo-European languages.[4] As a transitive verb, "time" also had an extraordinary range; one could duratively "time a footrace," punctually "time the arrival of guests," and calculatingly "time a remark," in the English that preceded Newton's writings.[5] In English it's all one big "time." The fusion of noun and verb meanings is almost a semantic disaster, however, if precision is your aim.[6] Precision was Newton's aim; so his task was to provide the many "vulgar" ideas with a backdrop: one "absolute, true, and mathematical time." Such time, he says, "of itself, and from its own nature, flows equably without relation to anything external."[7] Let us pause a moment and make a few observations.

(1) Newton's description is a purely semantic transformation: "time...flows." The noun is dissolved into a verb.

(2) The formula is *not* a definition. It is a description, a formulation. The apparently unerasable tendency to call it a definition has led commentators to say that it is devoid of meaning, leads to no deduction, and is of no practical use.[8] Newton *does* define certain basic ideas: mass, inertia, centripetal force, etc., but he says of other general notions, like time, that they don't need definition, but rather refinement.

(3) Newton's *Principia* and the *Opticks* could have been written in German or Italian or French. In point of fact they were written in Latin and English respectively. It makes no difference. My discussion concerns his native tongue, the language which undergirds any man's intellectual development.

(4) Newton probably took the existence of time for granted, as his predecessor Issac Barrow, from whom he derived some of his inspiration, did not.[9] Newton was a working physicist, equally committed to thought and observation. As he says in the opening lines of the *Opticks*, he isn't trying to explain things by hypotheses, but to "propose and prove them by Reason and Experiments."[10] He packed into the description of mathematical time a uniform, ordinal, and independent sequentiality on which to map the cardinal punctuation and stretches of apparent time.

(5) Newton's time is a hybrid between the static of mathematics and the dynamic of physics. Mathematics can settle for an immobile graph of a block universe (à la Minkowski, for example), but physics requires a dynamic of occurrences which submit to ordinal partitioning--what is normally called a chain of events. After all, it is from these serial occurrences that Newton derived his data. Observation, validation, measurement, all require time in order to be performed. The natural philosopher is not just a time-watcher; he is also a time-user.[11] As a time-user, no natural philosopher would fall into the booby-trap, so commonplace nowadays, of supposing that because the equations of Newtonian mechanics are reversible, time in Newton is reversible. One might as well hold, by the same sort of mathematical overkill, that a square figure of 25 meters square may have a side of -5 meters. It's just that troublesome world of experiments or experience that stops us. It doesn't have anything in it -5 meters long.

Newton's mathematical time has, then, many uses. (a) It binds the ideal of unchanging reason to a changing world. Plato bridged roughly the same gap with the well-known description, "Time is the moving image of eternity." Newton's concession to the ideal of changelessness is to postulate an absolutely invariant flow, change, motion, what-have-you. (b) It provides implicitly the idea of a uniform direction for time, governing what are otherwise ambiguous equations. (c) It not only draws the world of Reason and Fact into one creation, but permits the logical foundations of mathematical thought and the confirmations of experimental fact to share the same universe and its temporality. And in these latter uses, of course, lie the meanings of his formula as well.

Newton's description is semantic. The operative word is "flows"; genuine time flows, whether or not anything else is doing anything. Newton will develop his mechanics well within the standard Indo-European syntax, which tends to give primary reality to nouns. Verbs commonly indicate a kind of derivative reality. They introduce the status, the characteristics, or the adventures of things designated by subjects of sentences or the objects of their verbs. Newton's least particles, extended, hard, impenetrable, mobile, and characterized by inertia, are splendid examples of a subject-predicate grammar that goes with a substance-quality metaphysics. But like all great thinkers, Newton also passes beyond the suppositions of his own era. By way of their mobility, these particles introduce a non-substantial entity, time flowing. Here the verb is no secondary reality. Time is what it does. Newton's "particles" are what they are, regardless of what they do, but not so his "time": time flows or it would not be time. Here the verb is of the essence, denoting a coordinate reality with that of substances, particles. Newton comes close to saying there is an absolute flowing which is just itself, i.e. "without relation to anything external," not the flowing of any thing.

Twenty-two centuries before Newton's description of mathematical time, the Buddha made a similar assault on the idea of a substantial self. "There is," says the Buddha, "a path to walk on, there is walking being done, but there is no traveler. There are deeds being done, but there is no doer." And then, strikingly, he adds, "There is a blowing of the air, but there is no wind that does the blowing."[12] Kant, too, as we shall see, carries his analysis of time up to the level of the non-substantiality of the thinking self.

Newton's successors owe him much more, therefore, than the courtesy of understanding his mechanics beyond the shallow kind of criticism we have been rebutting. They ought to acknowledge his contribution to the scientific rejection of the primacy of substance. His successors will learn to speak of waves which are simply themselves, not the waves of something else, such as water. And other successors will come to speak of a vibratory energy that is not a condition *of* matter, but *is* matter. In short, Newton begins the assault on a substance metaphysics for the physical world, rooted in an Indo-European syntax, in spite of his atomism.

Newton hardly left the notion of time clear beyond question, however. He cleaned house for his own mechanics, but left behind many problems.[13] Perhaps this was the result of his having brought under one name more than a single word can comfortably accommodate. Kant, faced with analogous problems in the purely semantic approach, turns to other modes of analysis, as we shall see.

## III. LEVELS OF LANGUAGE IN KANT'S ANALYSIS OF TIME

The hundred years between Newton's *Principia* and Immanuel Kant's *Critique of Pure Reason* was a period of triumphant advance in physical science.[14] During this same period an army of philosophers sturdily but embarrassingly marched into a swamp. Newton's great contemporary, John Locke, launched the campaign. He pointed out that from the very sensory data which lie at the bottom of what Newton called "experiments" to the abstract concepts of space and time, all of our knowledge is subject to a remarkably human relativity. Our sensations are functions of the nature and conditions of our senses. Yet everything we know of the "outside" world is given in the form of these sensations. As to the real *things* which sensations are supposed to present or represent, what philosophy called "substances," heaven only knows what they are. Substance, says Locke, designates an x, "I know not what."[15] Things of the world are given in terms of our sensations, and the nature of these is relative to ourselves. The same holds true for some very high order abstractions, including space and time. There really are no such things, says Locke, as independent entities. They are abstract ideas distilled from our experience of spatially and temporally extended and bounded sensations. They are nothing in themselves. Thus, where Newton wrote "experiments," Locke wrote "experience."

While Britain coasted toward a skepticism which regarded theory as justified no further than practical applications warranted, the other aspect of science, as Newton saw it, namely Reason, became the cornerstone of Continental philosophy. Sensory data from the Rationalist point of view, being notoriously unreliable, had to be regarded as a confused representation of reality. Since they are a source of error, we ought to get past them and logically investigate what a universe must have and can be, to be a universe. If we want timeless laws, we must not take timewise appearances too seriously.

Kant was at once a physicist and a philosopher. He is a major figure in the development of the nebular hypothesis about the origin of our solar system and of galaxies as well. He is also the first great synthesizer of opposing philosophical systems since St. Thomas Aquinas. His attention was riveted on the success of the Newtonian mechanics. Admitting the relativity of our knowledge to our own nature, the question remains, "How come science succeeds?" Kant puts it more elegantly, "How is science possible?" Faced with the question of whether the deliveries of sense or the demands of reason are the basis of our knowledge of the world, he answered flatly, "*Both*." And by "both" he means "neither of them taken by itself." This is the way he puts it: "The understanding can intuit nothing, the senses can think nothing" (B75). Two things should be noticed here. "Intuit" means "apprehend through the senses"; thus "intuition," in Kant, means "sense presentation." Secondly, "think" is used transitively, so that the active character of thought in the perceptual process is clearly indicated. We do not merely think (as in Descartes' "proof" for his own existence on the ground that he was a thinking being) or even merely think *that*, for instance that it is noontime; we *think* our experience. Our experience is impregnated with thought, structured by it.

What Kant had to do, then, was to analyze experience more subtly than anyone before him. The result of this frontier exercise is a turgid, difficult, and even bewildering theory. It is troubled by eddies of contradiction, and novel vocabulary. To change the metaphor, patches of thought woven over seventeen years of creative work were rather hastily stitched together, with the seams showing. Kant's three approaches to time are deeply intertwined in the theory. He never tries to bring them into accord. In order to extract the theories I shall give a simplified exposition of what seems to me to be the core of his analysis, avoiding most of the controversial issues dear to the hearts of scholars.

For Kant our experience of the world is the interfusion of two elements, consciousness and sensation, but neither, as we have seen, can exist without the other. Let us start with the brute given, sensory appearance. "What is first given," says Kant, "is appearance. When combined with consciousness it is called perception" (A119-120).[16] Again, "Experience is knowledge by means of connected perceptions" (B161). Science succeeds, is "possible," because it rests on both sensory appearance and thinking consciousness. But let us look more closely at the connection.

The utter base of all experience is sheer sensation, which is *qualitative* in itself, but is always given a *quantitative* format, namely, as extended in space and time. This is where we find our first level of time, expressed, as in Newton, semantically. Locke had argued that our ideas of space and time are abstractions from the spatialities and temporalities of things. Kant doesn't deny it. But he does deny that the ideas of space and time are identical with space and time themselves. There are two reasons: (1) Space and time are the prerequisites for having sensations. They are thus prior to sensation, not posterior to it. Far from being generalizations from sense experience, they make it possible. Sensation never appears *simpliciter*, but always spatially or temporally extended, bounded, positioned, and so on, however imperfectly. (2) There are rigorous logical properties of space, taken as pure. Geometry embodies these properties. The same goes for time. Newton's *Principia* is, after all, the *Mathematical Principles of Natural Philosophy*. What Euclid did for space, Newton did for time. The corresponding discipline is simple arithmetic, which underlies mathematical dynamics.[17] Such logical properties could never be verified by mere generalization from experience. Merely because we learn arithmetic from experience, more experience could not upset mathematical truths. And arithmetic expresses the formal properties of numbers, whose meaning refers to the temporal act of counting, ultimately.

Thus, for Kant, the strong hand of rational order stretches down into the most fundamental level of our knowledge of the world. There is indeed a brute surd element in experience, pure sensation, but it is always given in a spatial and temporal structure which is logically analyzable. Hence space and time are neither something in themselves, as Newton had treated them, nor are they mere abstractions from the contingent flow of experience, as Locke had said. They are, says Kant, "forms of intuition," that is, the preconditions for our having sensation. Perhaps my sensations are subjectively mine alone, but they are given through a space and time shared by all consciousness and hence are objectively the same for such consciousness. Science succeeds, in part, by making claims which anyone can verify.

So much for the formal and logical side of space and time. So much, that is, for Reason. What of experience? In regard to experience, space and time are "forms of intuition" (*Anschauung*). Space is the condition of outer appearances, and time is the condition of all appearances whatsoever, both inner and outer--that is to say of the self and the world, both (B 50-51 and context). Sensation is how the outer world appears to us, in its most direct form. What we know through space is our relation to the outer. If there were such things as "things in themselves" we should not know them, by definition.[18] Finally, what we know through time is not only the outer world, but our own inner consciousness as well.

The above is an analysis of what might be called "minimal experience": simple sensations given spatially and temporally. Kant repeatedly says that the forms of intuition comprise a sheer "receptivity." Consciousness need be no more than awareness, and Reason is present only in the rational structure of space and time as exhibited in mathematics. Experience so simple is perhaps found only in the margins of sleep or coma. Normally consciousness is not so supine, as Kant will insist. Here, however, time is exhibited in simple descriptive terms. "Time itself does not alter," says Kant, "but only something which is in time" (B58). In this passage Kant's time lacks even the dynamic of Newton's flow.

Normally there is more to experience than the kaleidoscope of sense, given, for consciousness, by means of a mathematically understandable space and time. Consciousness survives what we ordinarily call the passage of time, and in doing so generates not just a time-structured world of sensation, but one of common experience. Experience is neither momentary nor wholly private. I have experience of my home through a series of images, strung out through time and assembled into the one object, my home. Kant calls this assembly a synthesis. It is the work of what he calls "understanding." The understanding gives unified meaning to temporally discrete sensory appearances. The understanding can thus be regarded as reason restricted to its employment in the domain of possible and actual sensory experience. But understanding has no content to offer to experience, only form, structure, and rules. We recall that Kant says of it that it "can intuit nothing, the senses can think nothing" (B75). It is the latter that supply the non-formal content of experience.

We have, of course, many empirical categories of the understanding; these are sheer generalizations from our experience, things we can easily imagine a world without, such as "fish," "tree," "motorcycle." But behind them there are master categories, necessary to understanding, regardless of what sensation supplies, categories such as thinghood-in-general; Kant uses the conventional term "substance" for this category. Motorcycles there might not be, but a world without entities of some sort is not a world. So also, any particular pattern of causation has to be found by experience, and may have to suffer correction, say, with scientific advance. But a world in which there are no causes at all is inconceivable. The category of cause is just as indispensable as that of substance. Reviving Kant's *leitmotif,* we may say "How is science possible?" By reason of the fact that though we may be wrong about the necessity for any particular cause, as Hume had shown, causality in general is indispensable to science. More briefly, it always makes sense to ask why (provided you are looking for an answer that lies within the domain of a possible experience.)

We have just dealt with two of the twelve basic categories of the understanding, substance-quality and cause-and effect. We will hold to them as examples and see where they derive such final authority from, and how they are applied. Each of these categories is rooted in pure reason, in a timeless syntax of logical form which is valid beyond our sensory experience. The logical structure of the idea of substance (as opposed to that of quality) is given syntactically by Kant as "that which can be thought of only as a subject, without being the predicate of something else" (B 186). Moreover, the logical structure of cause is also given syntactically. The syntax is that of a hypothetical proposition, "If A is true, then B is true." However, when we ask not "What is the logical form underlying these categories?" but "What is their standing in experience?" they lose their timelessness and become temporal rules. The result is a change in the syntax by which they are identified. Thus, "substance," which logically is that which is always the subject and not the predicate of something else, becomes "the permanence of the real in time." So also with the category of cause; its logical form is to be false without recourse to sensory experience. But the sentence, "If the rain falls, then the ground gets wet," arises from experience and is testable only through experience; thus it involves a temporal translation of the otherwise merely logical "If A then B." This *schema*, as Kant calls it, is a rule that a cause, temporally speaking, is something "from which, when posited, something else follows" (B 183). Logical following is one thing, temporal following is another.

*The schematism of Kant is thus the way in which timeless logical categories become temporally significant*. Furthermore, it is displayed, not in a semantic definition, but in the choice of syntactical construction. Here we see time not just as the passive prerequisite for the appearance of sense data. In the *schematism* time is an active ingredient in the integration of sensation into intelligible perceptual experience. The individual times of sensations are thereby synthesized into one continuously unified time (A 110). Human understanding is not a mere open sack into which sensation pours the organized reports from an outside world. Sense, indeed, gives us nothing but sensation. The *understanding* works it up into experience, according to a set of logical rules specified in a time-determinate way. This synthetic process is immediate, much of it automatic, and is not itself usually the object of a thought. It is automatic in that the pure time order, though an aspect of our consciousness, is not subject to our volition, though the contents may be. I can put my home together, so to speak, beginning and ending where I like. However, I am not free to synthesize in the order I please with the position of a boat upstream, followed by that of the boat downstream. Nevertheless, the latter synthesis *is* a process; and, though it is one which weaves sensations upon the warp of space and time, it has itself no sensory counterpart. It is a process *through* which experience is given and it must be distinguished from processes *within* that experience. Kant fails us by not noticing that this is so.

Here we have, then, two levels of time. One is time as the passive condition of sensation; the other is time as the dynamic element in the synthesis of experience. In this process purely logical categories come to have experiential meaning. At the first level, time can be semantically identified as the condition of sensory reception. At the second level we find it as a translator of timeless syntax into the syntax of process. There is a difficulty, however, with having processes within sensory experience and an extra-curricular process which generates that experience. The difficulty is this: Kant tells us that time is "empirically real"--i.e. is objectively valid for sensory experience, but that it is "transcendentally ideal," that is, exists only as idea beyond such sensory experience. Yet it would be very strange if the process that creates articulate experience were somehow less real than the ordinary processes which lie wholly within the compass of experience. Even within that experience, time comes increasingly to dominate the scene in a way that threatens to replace the substance metaphysics with a process view of reality. For example, Kant elsewhere says of substance that it doesn't really need the idea of permanence (B 250-251), but that substances are identified "better and more easily through action" (B 249).

Finally, there is still a third level of time in Kant identified by a third kind of synthesis, involving an even less substantial entity, and indeed going to the roots of the relation between time and language. I call this level *the presentive level*.

There is an overriding phase of the synthesis we have been considering. It deserves separate treatment. Not only is the diversity of sense gathered together in a meaningful fabric of *experience* at the second level, but there is also produced a kind of functional unity of self-consciousness. This unity is not a substance. It has no sensory data in its make-up. It is not a "thing" in the static sense. There is, of course, an empirical self or ego, a kind of segmented historical self, known to myself and others: the child of three who owned and loved a pet lamb in Wyoming, the refractory youth of sixteen nearly expelled from high school, the barely twenty-two-year-old who got married, and so on. This empirical self is an object, an incomplete object for the self-conscious self whose fragile existence needs a body of experience to unify. "I have," says Kant, "no knowledge of myself as I am, but only as I appear to myself. The consciousness of self is thus very far from being a knowledge of self..." (B 159).[19] Here I am aware of myself merely as the subject of thought, the thinker, not the thought about (B 158). I am aware of myself as a certain "spontaneity" or "self-activity" (B 157, B 278). This is again the language of process, but it is a process which reaches down to the bottom line of our experience. For, from the beginning, even brute sensation is not just there; it is there for some *consciousness*. Kant gives this consciousness a linguistic label and thereby exhibits what I have called the third level of discourse. When we raise the self-consciousness out of its subliminal depths and ask what its linguistic status is, it is a kind of "I think," which is only infrequently expressed in judgments, but is always present, sublinguistically. "It must be possible," says Kant, "for the 'I think' to accompany all my representations." The "I think" refers, he says, to a "transcendental unity of self consciousness" (B 131-132.) The "transcendental" here simply means "above the domain of sensory inputs." But the term is significant because Kant denies the transcendental reality of time. It has only empirical reality, we have observed (B 44). But, we may ask, how can we have a process called a "spontaneity" and a "self-activity" without a time proper to and present through that process?

Let us summarize the view of Kant that we have gained. His structural analysis is superb. It is often so turgid that it repels belief by its style. This is a contagious disease which you may feel has crept into the present paper. But the situation he describes is eminently believable, especially this last point about the world and the ego. It is, in its gross outline, exactly what occurs in the development of the ego, *chez* Piaget. Piaget repeatedly points out that for the young child, the more clearly the outer world of objects is discerned, the more acutely the existence of the inward ego is delineated. In an almost photographic replica of Kant's vocabulary, he speaks of the *construction* of the object, but the *awareness* of the self.[20] Kant's insights in his analysis of experience are frontier breaking. The last point alone stretches not just to Piaget, but into the work of Hegel, Kierkegaard, Bergson, Sartre, Coleridge, and Proust as well. But Kant has burst the shell of his original intention, to keep time at the level of the observed world. Two extra-curricular processes, one for the processive synthesis of experience, the other for the processive synthesis of a non-substantial self, have emerged. These processes clearly make little sense if they be non-temporal, or if their temporality be not real. If time is an abstraction, it makes a great deal of difference what it is an abstraction from. As Kant probes these higher levels, he moves from a semantic approach to time to a syntactic one, as we have seen, and then to a kind of hypersyntactic level which I have called *presentive*. It is hypersyntactic in that it rises above this or that syntax, emerging wherever the temporal fluidity of thought is frozen or slowed down or imprisoned, but presented by language. However, these metaphors are prejudicial. It is equally correct to say that the thought matures in or is brought to fruition by language, which must hold the thing thought about more quiet than the thinking that gave birth to it.[21] Thought we may say, is truth declared; thinking is truth postponed.

Let me dwell a bit longer on this term "presentive." I might use it for any presentation of time. There are, then, semantic presentations of time and syntactic ones. Both tend to be systematic, embedded in some articulated scheme. But there are poetic presentations also, having little commitment to system. Indeed, a limited number of artists have undertaken *pictorial* presentations of time; so the presentive level is not even confined to language. Thus to call it the presentive *level* is somewhat misleading, since any use of language, of whatever sort, in order to embody time, presents it. The syntactic level presents time grammatically. I have intimated that this is a somewhat richer mode, but both could fall under the general heading of "presentive." The usually repressed "I think," when admitted--or insisted upon, as in Kant--means that some aspect or aspects of time are presented at the expense of the rest. Language, of course, is always partial; it abbreviates its topics. This is not a problem of vocabulary and grammar; it dwells in language itself. When I think, I think *something*. Pure consciousness, without an object, is an abstraction. In the case of thinking "time," my thought is likely to employ language which illuminates some aspects of time at the expense of others. Even using "flow" or "passage" to show the felt kinesis of time is a misleading limitation, because now I am faced with the common conviction about "the past," that it is fixed, unalterable. The past is unchanging, but flowing? Perhaps then, I should say that the present grows out of and onto the past, like a tree, or a spiral shell. It is a strange river that flows only before my eyes. At what point does the kinetic factor vanish? This is the beginning of what we might call McTaggart's Scottish stew, but that recipe cannot be discussed here. To repeat, presentation is adumbration. The "I think" makes us aware of the adumbrator.

## IV. SUMMARY CONCLUSION AND SOME REMARKS

I believe that the main structure of Kant's analysis is sound. He exposes three perspectives on time. Each of these perspectives has an aspect of language corresponding to it. In the first level, time may be described semantically, almost as an item in a word list. What is time? The first answer is that it is the condition under which both outer and inner sense function, the former yielding the sensory world, the latter the world of self-awareness as well. At the second level, speaking simply, time is the way the world comes together for human understanding and the way a sentence comes together in language, and these closely mirror one another. Time as the condition of sense is rather "static" in nature, but as the ground for bringing logical form to sensory fact it is more "dynamic." Finally, at the third level, a complete judgment of experience exposes an implicit personal component. There is an "I think" in all such judgments, statable in language but generally merely assumed. Experience is not anonymous, and the common objective world we live in has subjective roots. Much of physical science rightly seeks to eliminate or neutralize this subjective component. But it is present, and the continuity of the life of the self is a process which presupposes time also, not in the form of experience as sensory, nor in the form of experience as the result of a synthesis of sensation and logical intelligibility, but as the precondition for a self-synthesizing consciousness, a quite non-substantial, non-thinglike, but temporally structured self.

What we gain from Kant--and I am suppressing all criticism here--is the extreme intimacy of time, thought and self. If the "I think," which embraces the latter two of this trio, turns in upon itself, taking itself as the object of thought, it draws the topic of time with it, and an extraordinary thing happens: the whole experiential realm is afflicted with diplopia.

First, the "I" comes out double. The Wyoming child with the pet lamb, the high school youth in a looming crisis, and the young man with the new wife and the foggy future don't exhibit much objective identity with one another. As time-ignoring snapshots, they have little in common. They are disparate time-slices of Kant's "empirical ego." But then there is the other ego, transcending, objectifying these segments of a life and placing them in temporal perspective, surely functionally distinct from them all, yet hopelessly identified with them, different as they are. All this is hardly unfamiliar, but it *is* singular. I can think of no other phenomenon that is like it, and such singularity warns one that the phenomenon must not be treated by thoughtless analogy with something else. (The same is true of time, as I remarked at the outset of this essay, and so also, for thought.) The phenomenon of self must be uniquely examined, in its own way. The examination is intensely practical. For instance, since I can show my identity--whatever that is--with the Wyoming child, the law would need nothing further to give me an inheritance from the great uncle who disappeared at the Little Bighorn. But the law recognizes both identity and difference. Because it recognizes difference, too, I might as well confess that I threw three bars of sodium into the high school swimming pool. Surely, by now I am immune from prosecution on legal grounds. Some crimes die faster than those who commit them.

Secondly, not only does the self come out double; so does the thinking, for the thinking always outruns what it objectifies. The narcissistic example I have repeatedly given is a case in point. I think I understand those three snapshots better now, and by having identified with them all, I have got beyond them, like Proust, and so has my thought.

Thirdly, there is the double view of time. There is time as the precondition of thinking, and there is time captured, i.e. time thought about, expressed in language. Language transforms everything it touches, expresses, or conveys, and thereby saves it and preserves it. This salvage of the idea of time from time's own ravages is one of our little linguistic formulations. They are numerous and diverse, but vital to our comprehension. But every so often a St. Augustine looks freshly on time and discovers that he knows well enough what time is, until someone asks him to formulate this intuition in language. Then he is appalled at what a finite and partial formulation he must settle for, in order to say anything at all. It is as if one had to shoot and stuff a bird before he could describe it. What then becomes of its flight?

That there are many partial formulations embodies an important fact. Language is a human instrument, and it bears the mark of human purposes. Some of these purposes are thrust upon us; for example, we require a language that facilitates our sharing of the world of sensation, a so-called physicalistic language. But human purposes in general are variable, modifiable, or replaceable. In one of the many meanings of "subjective," language never loses its subjectivity, since the use of language embodies an act of preference, however familiar or automatic. That is the lesson of "I think." We all remember Humpty Dumpty, "When I use a word, it means what I want it to mean." His freedom is not total, as I have suggested. He must communicate. But he has much more latitude than the peddlers of the myth of a purely "objective" language admit. If we have learned anything from the current talk of paradigms, it is this: when an aggressive mind or a highly uniform group of minds becomes single in its purpose, then the language of its interests takes on the semblance of objectivity. I have tried to suggest that Newton performed this service for his discipline and his followers. Two centuries or so later, sharp questions about mathematical continua were being asked, and new astronomical data began to raise fundamental questions about temporal measurement. The old "objectivity" was replaced by a subtler model, interestingly enough one that faintly acknowledged the subjective element, insofar as the observer has a physical standpoint in a human body.

Kant plunged into time more deeply and variously than most, and without containment by a single model for time. I have imposed some order upon his conclusions by following his unwitting hints that the different ways of *thinking* about time are overtly discoverable in our ways of *talking* about it. He thought his revelations were of a unity. I have emphasized the diversity, linguistically reflected.

Any general theory of time must recognize the diversity of purposes which underlie our many insights into the nature of time. Such a theory is primarily concerned with standards of value, in which competing purposes are evaluated and adjusted. If there is any *constructive* use in what I have been saying, it lies in the warning of a need for a critique of the purposes that guide our many insights about time. Failing such a critique, we have no ground for a synoptic understanding of time. We must then preserve a sceptical view of any theory of time that relies on the data of a special discipline.

The three levels of language co-function, but they must remain distinguishable. As a result, some major "don'ts" emerge. (1) Don't put differing descriptions of time into competition with one another without assessing the ends they serve. (2) Don't mix up your metaphysics and wonder why trouble arises. There is no place here to spell out these warnings. Nonetheless, I believe Zeno's paradoxes violate the first rule in a special way; he joins the continuity of *perceived* temporal movement with the continuity of a *conceived* linear metaphor for time. The purposes of perception and those of mathematics often coincide, but not in every element or aspect. A splendid example of mixed metaphysics is to be found in the McTaggart paradox, which incorporates some commonsense aspects of a substance metaphysics with some very appealing features of an event metaphysics. (3) Don't try to create specificity where none exists. In particular, don't treat "now" (or any index word, for that matter) as fully definable out of context. The chronic disturbance about "now," troublesome to philosophers, scientists, and psychologists, among others, is magnified by questions of "objective" and "subjective."[22] There is the "now" of the scintillation in a cloud chamber. There is the "now" of this century. Does one of them have a firmer hold in a so-called "objective" reality than the other? Does it follow, if indeed a "now" can be explicated only relationally, that at least one immediate relatum must be "subjective" and, further, that it has no "objective" status therefore? "Subjective" and "objective" have many diverse meanings. If you must use these terms, be wary of "purely subjective" or "purely objective." Everything you want to talk about lies between these abstract ideas. If anything were purely subjective, you would not, could not, hear about it. If it were purely objective, there would be no need to discuss it.

NOTES

1. A similar point is made by Professor Denbigh in the final part of his paper in this volume. He should not be charged with supporting the present argument, however.

2. A better term, if we were trying to get beyond Indo-European languages, might be the "molecular" level, since super-semantic connections in severely agglutinative languages have "syntaces" that are radically different from European syntax. Furthermore, our tensing largely rests with our verb, but in Japanese it can be carried by an "adjectival" which also inflects for temporal meaning.

3. My knowledge of the work of this *société anonyme* is very limited, but I may refer the reader to the popularization by Jean Piaget in *Structuralism*, trans. and edited by Chaninah Maschler, New York: Basic Books, 1970.

4. *Temps* and *Zeit* have many uses, but you cannot freely substitute *temps* for *fois, heure, siècle,* or *mésure* -- or *Zeit* for *Mal, Uhr, Jahrhundert,* or *Takt*. One does not say that this is *die dritte Zeit* he has visited Austria or ask *quel temps* it is for the time of day. The same is true for other languages. Compare the Italian *volta* and the modern Greek φορά.

5. See "time," *Webster's Revised Unabridged Dictionary*, Springfield,Mass.: G. and C. Merriam, 1913.

6. My colleague, Professor Lászlo Versényi, has given me the following rich array

from Hungarian, a non-Indo-European language: *idő* , time; *idén*, this year; *idényi*, seasonal; *idéz*, to summon, to quote (to make present?); *határidő*, term, deadline; *időleges*, fleeting, temporary; *időz*, to abide; *időköz*, interval. This is strong generality. Apparently, over all, the verb forms have not the scope of English and are inflectionally distinguishable. A friend of the author had the following further comments. About *idő* one may ask quantitative and qualitative questions. *Mennyi az idő?* "how much (is) the time?" means "What time is it?" *Hogy az idő* ? "how (is) the time?" means "how is the weather?"

7. *Mathematical Principles of Natural Philosophy,* trans. by Andrew Motte and revised by Florian Cajori, Berkeley and Los Angeles: University of California Press, 1962, Definition VIII, Scholium. This formula is the ultimate generalization, over and above the diversity of temporal instances from which it arises. The guardian of that diversity on the Continent was Leibniz, writing often in tongues where, for instance, *fois* was conceptually cognate with *temps*, but not etymologically so. So also for *Mal* (*-mal*) and *Zeit*. These linguistic facts are not coercive, but it is arresting that Leibniz, co-founder of the differential calculus, installs time relationally in discrete things -- monads -- and treats of continuous time as an ideal arrived at by abstraction. See Bertrand Russell, *The Philosophy of Leibniz*, London: Allen and Unwin, 1900, p. 111, for references and penetrating exposition.

8. *E.g.*, G. J. Whitrow in his pioneering work, *The Natural Philosophy of Time,* London: Nelson, 1961. Whitrow says that Newton's definition "has no practical use"; that "if time were something that flowed, then it would itself consist of a series of events in time, and this would be meaningless." Shortly, he says that the Newtonian theory of time assumes that "there exists a unique series of moments and that events are distinct from them" (pp. 33-34). The last criticism is inconsistent with the preceding one.

One of the clear uses of this description of time probably would only interest woolly metaphysicians. One understands mechanical systems in terms of laws. These laws identify the dynamic regularities, and they require counting. If the things counted are enduring and spatially distinguishable -- like chunks of matter, atoms, or granite blocks --, there is no problem. But the counting of events, occurrences, which dynamics requires, deals with temporally unique instances. Before I can have a dynamic law of events, I must have distinguishable events. Part of the way of distinguishing, and hence counting, events is by observing them at uniquely different times. A mechanical law should be timelessly true, that is, true at all times, uniformly. But this uniformity of law requires *different* and distinct temporalities, both for its meaning and for its confirmation. Speaking somewhat crudely, all the novelty that the system of uniform laws can tolerate -- but which it must have -- is relegated to a smoothly flowing independent time in which any patch of time is different from its neighbors, in terms of position, but like them as to its properties.

9. Barrow says that we "evidently must regard Time as passing with a steady flow"; that it "can be looked upon as constituted from a simple addition of successive instants or as a continuous flow of one instant." "It denotes not," he says, "an actual existence but a certain capacity or possibility for a continuity of existence" (*Lectiones Geometricae,* trans. by B. Stone, London, 1735, Lecture I). Newton was no mere disciple of Barrow, but if continuous flow and simple addition of instants were feasible alternative hypotheses for Barrow, then they likely were for Newton also. The difference is Newton's famous declaration, *"Hypotheses non fingo"*; Newton declared for continuous flow, not mentioning, in his definition, instants, moments, or parts of time. Perhaps he asked himself the famous question: if instants are unextended, how does a set of them sum up to something extended? In any case, Barrow denied real existence to time. Newton likely took its existence for granted or else found the issue mathematically and physically unimportant.

10. See E. N. DaC. Andrade, "Isaac Newton," in *The World of Mathematics*, ed. by J. R. Newman, 4 vols., New York: Simon and Schuster, 1956, I, 266.

11. Newton rejects vulgar time -- roughly, the relational time that Leibniz sought to explicate philosophically. But his good British commonsense did not therefore desert him; vulgarity is to be avoided, but not practicality. Newton's time is the time that brings the Reason of Mathematics together with the Experiments of Physics. The natural philosopher is a human being in nature doing temporal things about time, and his description and any analysis of time had better reflect that fact and reflect it fully.

12. *The Gospel of Buddha,* comp. by Paul Carus, Chicago: Open Court, 1915, p.115. Carus is citing from Henry Clark Warren, *Buddhism in Translation*. See also in Carus, chap. LIII, verse 9, on p. 153.

13. He says of mathematical time that it is also called "duration" (*Mathematical Prin.*, Definition IV, Scholium). He speaks of the order of the parts of time as analogous to that of the parts of space and remarks that these cannot be seen by our senses. We are reminded of Barrow's "simple addition of successive instants." And indeed Newton himself speaks of the indivisible moment[s] of duration" (*Ibid.*, Bk. III, General Scholium). There arises from such talk an unending dispute about continua, unhappily dominated by the assumption that the real number continuum can be placed into a one-to-one correspondence with that of space and time or space-time. There is no place here to discuss these matters in detail.

14. Immanuel Kant, *The Critique of Pure Reason,* trans. by N. K. Smith, London: 1953, Macmillan. All Kant references are to this work, though I have occasionally altered the translation in minor ways. "A" citations are to the first German edition of Kant, and "B" to the second, revised one.

15. *An Essay Concerning Human Understanding,* Book II, Chapter XXIII, 15.

16. The unsteadiness of Kant's terminology is a bane. At times he seems to identify perception and experience; at others, to distinguish them. The distinction is immaterial to our examination. I use the phrase "perceptual experience" to bridge the (here) unimportant technicalities.

17. The analogy is somewhat inexact. Newton's dynamics introduces empirically derived constants -- e.g. the gravitational constant. However, Kant's basic point is that the arithmetic which underlies mechanics presupposes the temporal act of counting.

18. Kant had a hard time sticking to this formulation, since it represented a rather recent phase of his thinking in the *Critique of Pure Reason.* He occasionally slips and tells us that the things in themselves cause our sensation. The main line of the *Critique* is wholly opposed to the extension of the idea of cause beyond possible experience, however, and Kant does better when he merely treats sensations or appearances as the raw material of what is external. A further point, of course, is that we should not even use the plural "things in themselves," since this too borrows from categories designed for empirical employment, namely, those of quantity: unity, plurality, totality.

19. See Sartre's essay, "Conscience de soi et connaissance de soi" translated as "Conscious of Self and Knowledge of Self," in Nathaniel Lawrence and Daniel O'Connor, eds., *Readings in Existential Phenomenology*, Englewood Cliffs, N.J.: Prentice Hall, 1967. This essay, which Sartre gave as a lecture on leading themes of *Being and Nothingness*, says far too little about its indebtedness to Kant.

20. Jean Piaget, *Six Psychological Studies,* trans. by A. Tenzer, New York: Random House (Vintage 462), 1967, pp. 16-17. See also Robert Brumbaugh and Nathaniel Lawrence, *Philosophical Themes in Modern Education,* Boston: Houghton Mifflin, 1973, pp. 230-231.

21. Professor Versényi points out that a double change occurs in the application of the Schemata. He puts it this way: "...while the logical rule loses its timelessness and becomes a temporal rule [as to what it describes], it also becomes intemporal (as a timeless structure of temporal events)." The brackets are mine, the parentheses his. Not only is there a translation, he points out, from timeless syntax to the syntax of process, "but also the reverse: temporal processes are frozen, made timeless (invariant with respect to the passage of time." This is an acute statement of the dilemma. The first statement points to the "intemporal" character of the rule or the "structure of temporal events," the second to the freezing of the "temporal processes." The rule is invariant (if Kant is right), but the process to which it applies (or from which it is drawn) can hardly be said to be frozen, save as thought about, i.e. as fixed *in idea*. Yet how else, one may ask, do they enter our common understanding, save as so presented?

A psychologistic answer might hold that it is the universal (the rule) which requires invariance, and the particular instance (any single, given process) which exhibits the unique, never-to-be-again, passage. What then of the process of applying the rule? It must exhibit both, it would seem.

Beyond this point the dialogue becomes dense, if not tangled. Does our attribution of singularity to the process have any meaning beyond its bearing the stamp of our own singularity, the stamp of the first personal pronoun "I"? But isn't it precisely the universal aspects of the singular that we seek out and join with other singulars to get a law, a rule, a concept, a class? And what is left over when we withdraw these aspects? Anything beyond the singularity of our experience of them? And if this is so, aren't we close to that peculiar idealism that seems to lurk in contemporary phenomenology?

Those who have followed this lengthy footnote this far may be impressed by the allegation -- in the *American Heritage Dictionary* (Boston: Houghton, Mifflin, 1969), p. 1499 -- that in Indo-European "No pronouns for the third person were in use." So it was an "I and thou" world, with names or descriptions for third persons. Contrast this with the Japanese derivation of the second personal pronoun, in a land where individuality of person is not stressed and pronouns are relatively rare, from the third person designation for "that person": *anata* from *ano hito* (see H. J. Weintz, *A Japanese Grammar*, Hossfeld's Series, London: Hirschfeld, 1919, p. 17).

22. See Kenneth Denbigh, "The Objectivity or Otherwise of the Present," in this volume

## DISCUSSION AND COMMENT

Charles Sherover

This is a perceptive paper. Its delineation of levels of time-discourse is important and it offers valuable insights into their use as well as into the ambiguous use of the word "time" built into the English language -- which suggests special caution to discourse about time in English. I find the paper instructive and suggestive. My comments first suggest four dissenting points which should not be taken as detracting from what is here accomplished; they are followed by an additional reflection of my own.

1.a. Lawrence's insight into the implications of Newtonian time are important, but Leibniz's notion of relational time cannot be so lightly dismissed. Time is, indeed, constitutive but it is also presentative and relational; these modes are a key to the levels of Kant's use of time-language. Time is, whatever else, a functioning relat*ing* ("it is what it does") of event to event and perceiver or actor to event. It would be difficult to make sense of much of Kant without this relational view.

1.b. It is tempting to identify Descartes' *cogito* and Kant's *ich denke*, but the former is momentary while I would like to urge that the latter necessitates the continuity of time.

1.c. Time, as trancendentally ideal, is not "somehow less real" than the particula empirical times that are real for us. For each of them, as our experiences of them, presuppose the one time which we cannot experience but into which all particular experiential times must somehow fit.

1.d. I do not really think it fair to say that the "I" comes out double. Kant presents all sorts of aspectival descriptions of the ego. But it is always one "I" and an application of Lawrence's own notion of levels of discourse would solve this problem readily.

2. But are there only three levels? I think there are at least four. Time is, indeed, receptive, structural and rooted in the *ich denke*. But it is also referential to a world, beyond our possible experiences, which *seems* to be structured, at least analogically, in terms of time. For in the end what is really transcendental are the real "I" *and* the real world which is the object of my knowings and the stage of my activities. The time of that real world must bind the structure of all of my relations -- cognitive, affective, moral, prudential -- and the transcendental subject, which I am, to a transcendentally objective world; for the times between them, as Kant sought to show, are temporal ties.

I agree that Kant never clarified his uses of the word "time", but he consistently made it the constantly functioning center of human experiencing. When referring to the objects of empirical cognitions, he refers to it as linear time, the relational sequences of before-and-after; when he discusses the *how* of our thinking, he involves the perspectival relations of present and past and future.

What is implicitly referred to but rarely named outside of the Second Critique, however, is that durational reality of the world as such which is independent of our awarenesses of it. It is, perhaps, because of the intrinsic unknowability of this ultimate durational reality that he is so hesitant in suggesting any direct cognitive statement or contact, aside from the partial view of human perspectives which are always structured in terms of time.

This is, I am aware, a somewhat heretical view; but it would seem that the only way to bind together Kant's many uses of the word "time" and the cognitive and practical aspects of human reasoning is to presume his underlying conviction, which is often suggested in a number of texts, of the reality of a world whose essential character is to be described by us in temporal terms as durational. This, then, is why reason, as it moves from the scientific knowledge of the cognitive understanding to those beliefs or "existential commitments" which the exercise of practical reason is seen as requiring, finds itself necessarily positing a view of the world to be comprehended in terms of metaphorical projections of our concept(s) of time.

It is here that we find Kant's nascent pragmatism and the beginnings of phenomenological intentionality, as well as the Fichtean, and the Piagetian insight Lawrence mentions, which insists that self-insight presumes some, at least metaphorical, insight into the not-I of the world which is beyond my grasp but which presents itself to me in the limited aspects I can handle in the organization of the object with which I deal and in my growing knowledge of them. This all suggests that many alleged time-paradoxes and confusions of time-language are, as Lawrence has suggested, confusions of level of discourse -- levels of structure and presentation, and levels of particular modes of use when the speaking subject claims to refer to some aspects of his world in some particular way for some particular selective purpose.

# II. PHYSICS

## The Third Storm of the Twentieth Century: The Einstein Paradox

O. Costa de Beauregard

*ABSTRACT*

*A paradox, according to dictionaries, is a surprising but perhaps true statement. Copernicus's heliocentrism was once a paradox. The problem with a true paradox is not in reducing it but in expressing it--as Einstein did with his relativity theory expressing the physical content of the Lorentz-Poincaré formulas of electrodynamics. Today again we have good formulas, those of quantum mechanics, but have not yet understood all their meaning. It is the paradox uncovered by Einstein at the 1927 Solvay Conference (and better known as the Einstein-Podolsky-Rosen [E.P.R.] paradox) which forces us to a dramatic revision of traditional ways of thinking about time.*

*The paradox emerges with special clarity from a conceptual experiment in which two spatially separated systems on the quantum scale are made to interact, but the only causal link between them is by way of an event in their common past. The paradox can be expressed in terms of the formal* (de jure) *symmetry between retarded and advanced interactions in physical theory, interactions which affect the future and the past respectively, independently of the* de facto *preponderance in nature of retarded interactions. The possibility that advanced interactions may occur* de facto *in large-scale systems is briefly discussed.*

* Lecture delivered at the Third Conference of the International Society for the Study of Time, Alpbach, July 1-10 (1976).

Suppose we perform an experiment in which an atom located at a point C emits two successive photons which go to two different places, L and T, where there is apparatus to measure their polarizations. Suppose further that the atom is known to have the the same angular momentum after emitting the two photons as it had before: we then know that if we measure, say, the *x*-component of the spin of one photon at L, we can predict that a corresponding measurement on the other photon at T will give the negative of the value found at L. Now it is proved in quantum mechanics that one cannot simultaneously measure, or even assign values to, the different components of the spin of a particle. But one can choose one component to measure at L and predict the value of the corresponding component at T. This led Einstein, Podolsky and Rosen[1] in a classic paper in 1935 to assert that if by making a choice at L we can predict the value of any of the three components at T, it follows that the photon bound for T *has* a property which determines these three components of spin even though experiment may allow us to reveal only one of them. This property is not the polarization itself, for we know that polarization follows the "paradoxical" laws of quantum mechanics, but something belonging to the classical world of physical properties which determines the result of any measurement we may choose to perform. Because we are not supposed to know about this property directly it is called a *local hidden variable:* local because it is carried by each particle separately. This variable is assumed to be distributed statistically but not at random, for in discovering the value of the polarization at L we learn enough to be able to predict that measured at T. Thus the random event happens at C when the two photons start out; after that everything is causally determined. In 1965 J. S. Bell[2] showed that this reasonable explanation is incompatible with the theory of quantum mechanics, and work in recent years has shown it to be incompatible with experiment also: the die is cast not at C, when the values of the local hidden variables controlling the polarization would have to have been determined, but later, when a measurement is made at T or L. In this sense, the correlation between the measurements at L and T is not only a "telediction", but also (paradoxically) a "teleaction". Bell's theorem provides a quantitative severance between classical statistics and the new wavelike statistics, the experimental evidence being in favor of the latter.

Like other fundamental laws of dynamics, the laws of the electromagnetic field allow two sorts of solution symmetric to each other with respect to past and future. Needless to say, the one in which a moving charged particle generates a wave which subsequently spreads out in space, called the retarded wave, is the one we are used to. The one symmetric to it, the advanced wave, has the exactly reversed behavior. Originating in the environment or in the depths of space, it converges on the point where the charge will be at the moment the wave arrives, as if the universe knew in advance what the charged particle was going to do. But if we place the particle and move it about as we choose, the universe cannot know this--perhaps we were not yet born when the wave started out. Thus the only possible physical interpretation for the advanced wave is that of a causality operating in the reversed direction of time: the moving charged particle determines, *here and now,* the events in the distant past which generated the converging wave.

The only logical, mathematical and physical channel for the correlation between the events at L and T consists in the two timelike vectors LC and CT, and implies a *de jure* equality between retarded and advanced waves in the individual stochastic event (called a quantum). The *de facto* preponderance of retarded over advanced waves, and of increasing over decreasing entropy, is a *macroscopic* property of nature as we know it.

However, the *de jure* symmetry displayed by the E.P.R. paradox (and indeed expressed in the very formalism of the theory) raises the possibility of an "anti-(second law) physics" symmetric to the ordinary physics which derives its time sense from the increasing entropy postulated by the second law of thermodynamics, very much as the *de jure* symmetry between positive and negative energies in Dirac's theory led to the explanation of antiparticles as symmetric to particles.

At the 5th Solvay Conference in 1927, Einstein[3] uncovered a paradox which is inherent in the very essence of the new quantum mechanics and which today, having been thoughtfully pondered quite a few times, truly appears as *The Paradox of the New Quantum Mechanics*. It is what the absence of an optical ether wind was to special relativity, or the riddles of heat capacity of radiation and material bodies were to the old quantum theory.

In physics a good, true, paradox always heralds the coming of a new "paradigm." In the dictionary sense, a paradox is "a surprising, but perhaps true statement". Copernicus' heliocentrism was one such. Through paradoxes science is urged, like Nicodemus, to be "born anew". The problem, then, is not in trying to reduce the paradox, but rather in formulating it adequately. This is what Einstein did by unveiling the true sense of the Lorentz-Poincaré formulas, and what Planck did by introducing the quantum discontinuity into electrodynamics. In this way the smoke of the paradox is changed into light--perhaps a dazzling one, but it gives a new view of things.

My contention here is that, very much as in the days of Lorentz and Poincaré, we possess the right formulas--those of the Heisenberg, Schrödinger and Dirac quantum mechanics--but have not understood yet their complete import. This, the paradox uncovered by Einstein in 1928, now forces us to do.

Lord Kelvin,[4] in 1900, said he saw two clouds in the sky of theoretical physics, pointing exactly to where the two storms of quantum mechanics and of special relativity were ready to burst. The Third Storm of the 20th Century, now over our heads, has been rumbling since the very days when the Tables of the Law of the new quantum mechanics were laid down. Some more lighting was needed, however, to clarify the sense of the Scriptures--that is, some more work on the Einstein Paradox.

I will explain the paradox by using a little fable. At midnight G.M.T. two travellers (Figure 1) leave Calcutta, C: one for London, L, and one for Tokyo, T, each carrying

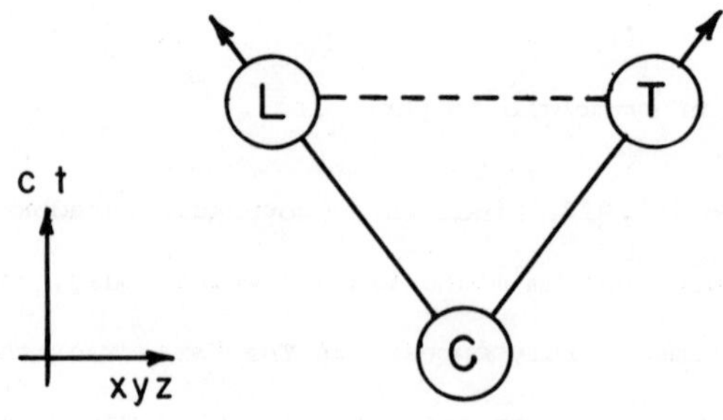


*Figure 1*

a closed box containing, or not, the ball which a third man has previously placed in one of them, behind a veil. At 6 G.M.T., having landed at his destination, each traveller opens his box and immediately learns what the *other* one finds. The point is that the instantaneous inference is a contraction of the explicit reasoning, which does not follow, in space-time, the spacelike vector LT, or TL, but rather the two timelike vectors LC and CT (or TC and CL), once towards the past, once towards the future. For drawing his inference each traveller must remember his flight from Calcutta and what was done there, and imagine the flight of the other one from Calcutta. Not only is the LCT (or TCL) zigzag followed by the reasoning (or the calculation), but also it is the one really traversed by the airplanes. By contrast, the direct, spacelike path, LT, is empty in all three respects. There is still no paradox in this, however, because in this classical information-theory problem it is at C that, so to speak, the die is cast, once and for all. In Bell's[2] words, we are dealing with a local hidden-variable theory, the hidden variable having the value 0 in one box and 1 in the other. We thus have between L and T pure telediction, and not teleaction.

It is at this very point that quantum mechanics upsets our ingrained habits of thought. Far more than a mere wave mechanics, it is a *new wavelike probability calculus*, some rules of which are similar to, but some drastically dissimilar from, those of the classical probability calculus.

The new quantum mechanics has it that in the quantum analogue of the ball and two boxes the die is cast not at C, but later, where and when the measurements are made, that is, at L and/or T. This is the Einstein[3] paradox (better known as the E.P.R. paradox) which in later years he[5] still considered an unacceptable one, as entailing, (said he) either "telepathy" between observers at L and T, or denying "independence as such to things spatially separated." Schrödinger,[6] in the meantime, having independently hit upon the same paradox, said he saw (unacceptable) "magic" in the (accepted) Copenhagen doctrine, which, wrote de Broglie,[7] would "upset our familiar notions concerning space and time". These words, by eminent physicists, should be seriously pondered today in the light of Bell's[2] crucial theoretical severance between quantum mechanics (Q.M.) and local hidden-variable theories (L.H.V.T.), and of the ever-increasing experimental evidence in favor of quantum mechanics.

Why quantum mechanics implies that, in the E.P.R. context, the die is cast not at C [where classical statistical mechanics (C.S.M.) had it], but rather at L and/or T, stems from the very existence of "non-simultaneously measurable magnitudes," and from the open choice that allows an observer to wait until the last moment before deciding what magnitude he will measure. In the present tests of the E.P.R. paradox, what is measured at L and T is, in fact, "position plus polarization" of correlated protons,[8] or photons issuing from a cascade transition[9] or an $e^+e^-$ annihilation at C.[10] A photon either passes, or not, a linear polarizer, thus giving a yes or no answer to the question "is your linear polarization parallel or orthogonal to some direction $\ell$?" By giving his polarization detector an orientation $\ell$ the experimenter at L can determine one, but not more than one component of the photon spin at L, and hence at T. Since the orientation $\ell$ may (in principle) be set while the photon is flying from C to L, it is obvious that quantum mechanics, as it stands, implies that we have between L and T not only telediction, as was the case with classical statistical mechanics, but truly *telediction plus teleaction*--whence the horrified, and extremely specific, words of Einstein,[5] Schrödinger[6] and de Broglie.[7]

It is true that up to now the crucial experiment, where the orientations of the polarizers are changed while the correlated photons are flying from C to L and T, has not been performed. Such an experiment has been designed,[11] however, and the building of the apparatus has begun. In the meantime one is allowed to lay bets. As quantum mechanics is by far the most precise sort of probability theory ever used in physics, my bet is in its favor: that nothing new will be observed. And I will draw some consequences that follow if I am right.

The existing experimental evidence is today considered to be in favor of Q.M. because of Bell's clever theorem, which he later[12] cast in the following didactic form: Denote symbolically by $\mathscr{L}$ and $\mathscr{T}$ the results of the measurements at L and T, $\ell$ and $t$ the corresponding orientations of the polarizers, and $\lambda$ the values of a set of hypothetical hidden variables specifying at the instant (in the laboratory frame) of the two measurements, the states of the measured system and the measuring devices. Under the assumption

$$\mathcal{L} = \mathcal{L}(\lambda, \ell) \qquad \mathcal{T} = \mathcal{T}(\lambda, t)$$

it is *not* possible to reproduce the quantum predictions, but under the assumption

$$\mathcal{L} = \mathcal{L}(\lambda, \ell, t) \qquad \mathcal{T} = \mathcal{T}(\lambda, \ell, t)$$

it *is*. And as this is a *non-locality statement*--the result in London depends on the value of something in Tokyo and vice versa--the hidden-variable remedy is no less paradoxical than the quantal illness it was aimed at curing. As we have said, the experimental evidence up to now is very strongly in favor of Q.M.

So, contrary to the common sense feeling *and* to what Einstein, Podolsky and Rosen[1] stated as an unquestionable assumption, *the measurements at* L *and* T *with a spacelike separation are not independent*. Moreover, as previously said, the only non-empty channel joining L and T consists of the two timelike vectors LC and CT or (TC and CL), so that this connection occurs along the zigzag line LCT, one line towards the past, one towards the future--thus upsetting, in de Broglie's[7] words, "our familiar notions concerning space and time". I[13] have proposed this interpretation quite a few times since 1953, and today Stapp,[14] Bell[15] and Davidon[16] have come to similar conceptions.

At this point it should be obvious that a tight connection exists between the Einstein paradox and the older paradox of lawlike time symmetry in microphysics versus factlike time dissymmetry in macrophysics. Let us recall what the older paradox was, and then examine what new traits are added when a wavelike probability calculus replaces the old one.

The paradox in classical statistical mechanics has received the well-known Loschmidt[17] and Zermelo[18] expressions. The point is, however, that the paradox was already present in the classical theory of probability *per se*, without reference to any specific dynamics. Consider for instance the shuffling of cards. The probabilities that a card will go from rank *r* to rank *s* or from rank *s* to rank *r* are assumed equal, and also the same as that a card has come to rank *s* from rank *r* (there is no reason to believe *a priori* that predictive and retrodictive probabilities are the same.) Then, given any arbitrary configuration of the deck as being "in order", *blind statistical prediction* (in Watanabe's[19] words) will very well describe the effect of shuffling, while blind statistical retrodiction would be contrary to ordinary facts. Nobody will rely on shuffling for putting the deck in order *at will*. This is why classical authors treated retrodictive problems completely differently from predictive ones; they called them problems in the probability of causes, and introduced Bayes's extrinsic probabilities for solving them. These extrinsic probabilities were chosen to describe as well as possible the interaction out of which the system under study had emerged, and the prescription to use them in retrodiction rather than in prediction implied that interactions produce after-effects and not before-effects. It implied causality. To my knowledge van der Waals[20] was the first to recognize that the statistical derivation of the *H*-theorem rests on a temporal application of Bayes's conditional probability statement. In other words, far from being *deduced*, statistical irreversibility is *postulated*. It is expressed in the form: *blind statistical retrodiction is forbidden* or, in other words, as the following boundary condition: any arbitrarily heterogeneous configuration may be chosen as an initial, but not as a final condition, for integrating the statistical evolution equation.

A quite similar statement exists in the classical theory of waves, for integrating the wave equation. Thus it is only natural to ask if perhaps there is not a physical link between the two statements. All sorts of examples support this view, for example: between times $t_1$ and $t_2$, a piston is moved in a cylinder containing a gas in equilibrium. The fact (if not the mathematical truth) is that Maxwell's velocity distribution is perturbed after time $t_2$ and not before time $t_1$. And the fact is also that this interaction is propagated as a retarded pressure wave emitted, and not as an advanced pressure wave absorbed, by the piston.

In the 1905's a bitter controversy[21] opposed Ritz, maintaining that retarded waves are postulated in the derivation of the Second Law, to Einstein, holding conversely that wave retardation should be understood as a statistical effect. Both opponents (somewhat overlooking the factlike rather than lawlike[22] character of their respective assumptions) thought to be contradictory reasonings which in fact were reciprocal to each other. This was because, though Einstein's photons were known by then, de Broglie's matter waves were not. Statistical scattering of particles and of waves were thus not seen to go hand in hand.

The tight connection between the two irreversibility statements is also implied in Planck's[23] thinking, and is made explicit in his expression for the entropy of a light beam, which is increased by scattering.

However, in this field also the Old Covenant has to yield to the New Covenant of quantum theory. Then the lawlike (microphysical) time symmetry versus the factlike (macrophysical) time dissymmetry turns out as even more paradoxical than before.

In quantum mechanics a wave function $\psi$ is postulated to specify *all* the information that can be specified about the physical system it describes. Normally, this information is in the form of statistical statements: the probability that the electron will be inside a certain cubic centimeter of space at 10:30 is such-and-such. But suppose we now observe the cubic centimeter at that moment and find the electron. The structure of probabilistic statements contained in the wave function collapses: the electron actually is there, and statements about probabilities are no longer relevant. This sudden change of the state of our description is known as the collapse of the wave function. Is this event endowed, like the collision of classical statistical mechanics, with an intrinsic time symmetry? Yes, indeed. This intrinsic time symmetry has been written since the beginning in the Tables of the Law, but nobody yet has taken proper notice of it.

Is, then, factlike time asymmetry a purely macrophysical statement, implying ensembles, plus a specific boundary condition? Yes, indeed. And this also was written long ago in formulas, the meaning of which was not fully grasped.

Let us discuss the $\psi$ collapse in the example that fits best the present context: position-plus-spin measurement of a relativistic particle[24] (of possibly zero rest mass[25]). The formula solving the Cauchy problem [24,26]

$$<x|a> = <x|x_0><x_0|a> \tag{3}$$

can be interpreted[24] as expanding the wave function $\psi_a(x) \equiv <x|a>$ at any point-instant $x$ on the complete orthogonal set of Jordan-Pauli propagators $<x|x_0>$ such that

$$<x|x'> = <x|x_0> <x_0|x'> \quad \text{iff } x\text{-}x' \text{ spacelike,} \tag{4}$$

the coefficients of the expansion being the values $<x_0|a>$ of $<x|a>$ on a spacelike surface $\sigma$.

Thus, if the particle is found to cross a given element of $\sigma$ centered at $x_0$, the corresponding eigenfunction is $<x|x_0>$. And as $<x|x_0>$, zero outside the light cone, is non-zero inside *both* future and past, this says that the particle will go inside the future, and has arrived inside the past light cone. This may sound trivial but it is not, because *something is implied which everybody has overlooked:* the $\psi$-collapse occurring at $x_0$ affects the future (of course), and symmetrically the past also.

This is the key I am proposing not for reducing, but for expressing the Einstein paradox--which its discoverer did not believe to be a paradox as we are using the word. There is no other choice, however, than accepting it--either for good or for evil, depending on one's taste.

I need not say that intrinsic time symmetry is explicit in many of the formulas of quantum field theory, and not only confined to the present discussion.

Whence, then, comes probability increase and wave retardation? From statistics on ensembles and a specific boundary condition.

Von Neumann's[27] entropy increase in quantal measurements is derived under the assumption that the collapsed waves of the ensemble are used for (blind statistical) prediction rather than for retrodiction. Thus it is a macrophysical statement, where irreversibility stems again from a time-dissymmetric boundary condition. What is novel is that the new quantum mechanics, being a wavelike probability calculus, produces entropy increase and wave retardation as two facets of one and the same irreversibility statement.[28] Fock[29] *and* Watanabe[19] have both pointed out that in quantum mechanics retarded and advanced waves should be used respectively for blind statistical prediction and retrodiction, which of course has this same implication.

Now I come back to the discussion of the Einstein paradox and the recent experimentation pertaining to it. The correlation between the two position-plus-spin measurements at L and T consists in that both produce the same wave collapse--in their common past. This is implied in the experiments already performed, and is the *truly* paradoxical fact which would be unambiguously established if quantum mechanics turns out as once more vindicated by the experiment[11] in which the polarizers will be turned while the photons are in flight between C and L and T.

That such a conclusion is of general rather than exotic significance is made obvious if we remark that two (or more) observers of *any* quantal measurement are E.P.R. correlated. This is exemplified in Figure 2, picturing the observation of impacts of $\alpha$ particles on a scintillation screen. If one of the observers sees a scintillation on the screen, then the other must see it also.

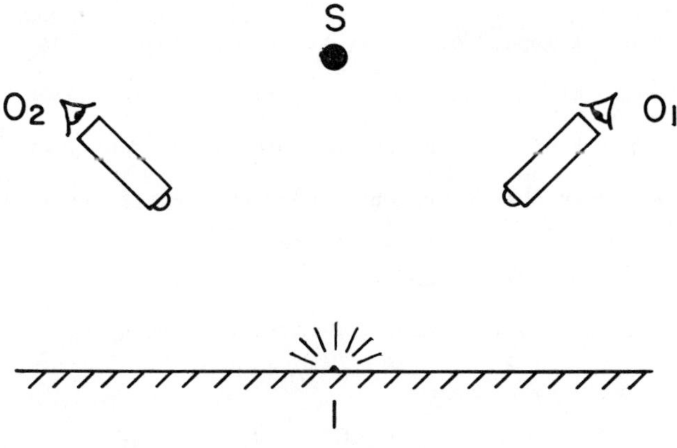


*Figure 2*

Finally, what overall philosophy is implicit in the findings under discussion?

Let me recall that there is, in relativistic quantum mechanics, another striking example of a lawlike symmetry somewhat hidden behind a large factlike dissymmetry--and a case where unravelling the lawlike symmetry has revealed a new world. In Dirac's theory (and even more so in Feynman's presentation of it) the positron is the exact lawlike twin of the electron. In fact, however, it is much rarer. But today we easily find it, because we know well where to look for it and how to produce it. We thus have learned that the world of anti-matter does make some incursions inside our familiar world of matter.

By analogy with anti-paricles let me define (macro) anti-physics as the paradoxical doctrine obeying a "reversed Second Law". As we have already seen, at the elementary level, quantum mechanics does have, symmetrically and essentially, one foot in physics and one foot in anti-physics--just as was the case with positive and negative energies. It is then only natural to inquire if, perhaps, (macro) anti-physics does not make some incursions inside our familiar world of physics. Then the problem is, where should we look for it, and what should we do?

Von Neumann[27] and London and Bauer[30] have it that the $\psi$ collapse is due to "the act of consciousness of the observer when he takes cognizance of the experimental result". I believe this statement to be right on one point and quite wrong on the other.

What is wrong is that, as it stands, the statement is time asymmetric, which it should not be. What is right is that it views the stochastic event as *indissolubly objective and subjective*--which it should certainly be in any theory holding probability as essential. This would bring to an end the everlasting discussion between the objectivistic and the subjectivistic schools in probability theory, by stating that probability is the very hinge around which mind and matter interact.

The same, then, should be said of information, and fits very well what information theory tells us. Consider a telephone conversation. When received, the signal along the wire (with a negentropy assigned to it) is decoded and understood. This is the learning transition, where *information as knowledge* is extracted, according to the symbolic formula

$$N \to I_2 .$$

When emitted, the signal was coded from conceived information, and what we have is information as an organizing potentiality according to the willing transition

$$I_1 \to N .$$

With the advent of cybernetics the notion of information as knowledge has become quite trivial--the man in the street buys a newspaper for a few cents to find "information" in it, while information as organizing power has become a rather esoteric concept, used by those few philosophers interested in will or in finality. Why this accident has occurred is fairly obvious; it is because of the factlike physical irreversibility, according to which

$$I_1 \geqslant N \geqslant I_2 .$$

The learning transition is thus seen to be a slight generalization of the Second Law (part of the decaying negentropy being saved as knowledge), while, isolated from the surroundings, the willing transition would go straight against the Second Law.

We know well, however, from the theory of antiparticles, that the creative approach to physics does not start from merely taking as granted the overall factlike situation, but rather from unravelling almost hidden lawlike symmetries. Just as, according to von Neumann's irreversiblity statement, the learning transition is associated with increasing entropy and retarded waves, so is, symmetrically, the willing transition accociated with decreasing entropy and advanced waves. In other words, the lawlike symmetry between the two facets of information--cognizance and will--is projected, so to speak, in space-time in the form of the lawlike symmetry between retarded and advanced waves. This is precisely what was implied in our previous discussion of the $\psi$-collapse. At the elementary level, the spark, so to speak, of the act of consciousness is indissolubly cognizance *and* will, source of a retarded *and* sink of an advanced wave. Schopenhauer's title, *The World as Will and as Idea*, looks very appropriate when seen in this light.

It has been said humorously that Einstein, in discovering Relativity in 1905, had lost the subject of the verb *to undulate*. When Born rediscovered it in 1926, it was in a form far more "subtle" than that of the lost ether: a probability amplitude, obeying the superposition (or interference) law from which spring almost all quantal extravagances. My contention then, is that the new wavelike probability calculus has much to teach concerning the world we live in, and the way in which mind and matter interact.

Let us consider the Schrödinger[6] cat paradox. Schrödinger imagines a cat in a box with a gun pointed at it, and, attached to the trigger, a counter which can detect radiation from some atomic nucleus. Whether or not the radiation is emitted is a matter of chance: the wave function of the nucleus contains two parts describing the situations in which the radiation has and has not been emitted. And, correspondingly, the poor cat is described by a wave function which is part live-cat and part dead-cat. It continues in this ambiguous condition until someone opens the box and looks in. Only at this moment is the die cast: the wave function collapses and the cat is truly alive or truly dead. What is obviously wrong in Schrödinger's presentation of it is that the cat is as good a wave collapser as anybody else. He has some sort of consciousness, and certainly knows (in its own way) when he is alive, and also, as it seems, if he is being killed. If, then, Schrödinger's observer is looking at the radioactive decay (which triggers or not the lethal weapon) along a channel parallel to the cat's, then both cat and observer are E.P.R. correlated. They are cooperating or competing to produce the same $\psi$-collapse--in their common past.

One guesses that in this, the cat is more motivated than his tormentor, and that a normal cat will favor the issue which leaves him alive. Thus, he will try to call in, from the past, the appropriate advanced wave.

Believe it or not, this very experiment has been performed and published by parapsychologists,[31] with the claim that the results have been significantly conclusive. Not having heard of Schrödinger's cat, they have replaced the life-or-death by a reward-or-punishment dilemma (which allows an easier statistical analysis). Using a random-outcome generator (eventually monitored by radioactivity) which, tested both before and after the experiment, is found perfectly normal, they have observed that when the animal is inside the box the outcome is displaced in the direction of more rewards and fewer punishments. This means that blind statistical prediction is not working in this case and must be replaced by a Bayesian problem in the probability of ends, rather than of causes. This also implies a contribution like that from advanced waves. Thus, parapsychology belongs to "anti-physics".

So where are we now? We are timorously stepping inside that land which both Einstein[5] and Schrödinger[6] said is a forbidden one. Why we can no more avoid doing so is that Bell's crucial test has been enunciated, and that the experimental results definitely favor quantum mechanics. That is, in de Broglie's[7] words, they are definitely "upsetting our familiar notions concerning space and time".

*Note added in proof.* In some of its parts, this paper is an adaptation of my 1976 lecture at Alpbach by my good friend David Park. This may clarify matters for the non-professionals, and I believe that it should be said in fairness towards both David and me. My thinking on the subject has expanded since 1976, and is expressed e. g. in *Nuovo Cim. 42B, 41* (1977) and *Phys. Lett.* (in press).

REFERENCES

1. A. Einstein, B. Podolsky and N. Rosen, *Phys. Rev. 47,* 777 (1935). In this paper the paradox is presented in non-relativistic quantum mechanics.

2. J. S. Bell, *Physics 1*, 195 (1965).

3. A. Einstein in *Rapports et Discussions du 5e Conseil Solvay,* Gauthier Villars, Paris, 1928, p. 253-256.

4. Lord Kelvin, *Phil. Mag. 2,* 1 (1901).

5. A. Einstein in *Einstein, Philosopher Scientist,* P. A. Schilpp, ed. The Library of Living Philosophers, Evanston, Illinois, 1949, p. 85 and p. 683.

6. E. Schrödinger, *Naturwiss. 23,* 807, 823, and 844 (1935).

7. L. deBroglie, *Une Tentative d'Interprétation Causale et Non Linéaire de la Mécanique Ondulatoire,* Gauthier Villars, Paris, 1956, chap. 7.

8. M. Lamehi-Rachti and W. Mittig, *Phys. Rev. D14*, 2543 (1976).

9. S. J. Freedman and J. F. Clauser, *Phys. Rev. Lett. 28,* 939 (1972).
J. F. Clauser, *Phys. Rev. Lett. 36,* 1223 (1976).
E. S. Fry and R. C. Thompson, *Phys. Rev. Lett. 37,* 465 (1976).

10. C. S. Wu and I. Shaknov, *Phys. Rev. 77,* 136 (1950).
G. Bertolini et al. *Nuovo Cim. 2,* 261 (1955).

H. Langhoff, *Zeits. Phys. 160*, 186 (1960).

L. Kasday in *Foundations of Quantum Mechanics*, B. d'Espagnat ed., Academic Press, 1971, p. 195.

11. A. Aspect, *Phys. Lett. 54A*, 177 (1975).

A. Aspect, *Phys. Rev. D14*, 1944 (1976).

12. J. S. Bell, *Epistemological Letters 9*, 11 (1976).

13. O. Costa de Beauregard, *Compt. Rend. Acad. Sci. 236*, 1632 (1953).

O. Costa de Beauregard, *Rev. Intern. Phil. 61-62*, 1 (1962).

O. Costa de Beauregard, *Dialectica 19*, 280 (1965).

O. Costa de Beauregard, in *Proc. Intern. Conf. Thermod.*, P. T. Landsberg, ed., Butterworth's, London, 1970, p. 540.

O. Costa de Beauregard, *Found. Phys. 6*, 539 (1976).

O. Costa de Beauregard, *Synthere 35*, 129 (1977).

14. H. P. Stapp, *Nuovo Cim. 29B*, 270 (1975).

15. J. S. Bell,, *Epistemological Letters 9*, 11 (1976).

16. W. C. Davidon, *Nuovo Cim. 36B*, 34 (1976).

17. J. Loschmidt, *Wiener Ber. 73*, 139 (1876) and *75*, 67 (1877).

18. E. Zermelo, *Ann. Physik 57*, 585 (1896) and *59*, 793 (1896).

19. S. Watanabe, *Rev. Mod. Phys. 27*, 179 (1955).

20. J. D. van der Waals, *Physik. Zeitschr. 12*, 547 (1911).

21. W. Ritz and A. Einstein, *Physik. Zeitschr. 10*, 323 (1909).

22. H. Mehlberg in *Current Issues in the Philosophy of Science*, Feigl and Maxwell eds., Holt, Rinehart, Winston, New York, 1961, p. 105.

23. See in this respect M. J. Klein, *Paul Ehrenfest*, North-Holland Pub. Co., Amsterdam, 1970, vol. 1, pp. 218-235.

24. For a systematically covariant treatment of one-particle quantum mechanics, see O. Costa de Beauregard, *Précis de Mécanique Quantique Relativiste*, Dunod, Paris, 1967.

25. *Particle* and *spin* are of course loose, but convenient, terms if the rest mass is rigorously zero.

26. J. S. Schwinger, *Phys. Rev. 74*, 1439 (1948); see p. 1451.

27. J. von Neumann, *Mathematical Foundations of Quantum Mechanics*, Princeton University Press, Princeton, N.J., 1955.

28. O. Costa de Beauregard, *Cah. de Phys. 12*, 317 (1958).

29. V. Fock, *Dokl. Akad. Nauk SSSR 60*, 1157 (1948).

30. F. London and E. Bauer, *La Théorie de l'Observation en Mécanique Quantique*, Hermann, Paris, 1939.

31. H. Schmidt, *Journ. Appl. Phys. 41*, 462 (1970).
H. Schmidt, *Journ. Paraps. 34*, 175 (1970).

## DISCUSSION AND COMMENT

*by Nathaniel M. Lawrence*

The "third storm" may only be a new low pressure system developing in the second storm, or an outgrowth of that storm.

Heisenberg uncertainty can be understood as an ontological description, namely: particles don't have perfectly precise properties of both momentum and position, and this fact is reflected in our efforts to measure these properties. On the other hand uncertainty may also be understood as an epistemological description, namely: particles may or may not have such precision of properties, but in any case we can not tell, since any instrument of detection of these properties necessarily contributes to them.

I incline to the latter view in this form: All that we can say about the being of a particle is derivative, strictly speaking, not from its behavior, but from how its behavior is known. Knowing seems always to have some relationality about, that is, some kind of contribution which comes from the side of the knower. Efforts to minimize the role of the knower in shaping the nature of the known constitute the purified ideal of scientific description. But neutrality of the observer does not require his disappearance. The most we can have is a set of data coherently accounted for in a theory which is verifiable by any qualified observer. What we want to neutralize is not the observer, therefore, but any eccentricity in him. The observer is presupposed in every scientific judgment that appeals to verifiabliity.

If the CLT data are of such a nature that we can't determine what the conditions at C were until we have the L data or the T data, why must I insist that teleaction as well as telediction has occurred? For example, suppose I awake from a coma. I do not know what day it is. I'm told that "The number of days between today and the nearest Sunday (future or past) is exactly two." This information won't specify what today is. However, tomorrow, the truth or falsity of that statement will tell me what both days are. But I can't know about today until tomorrow comes. The relationship of contiguity and temporal sequence is given for the two days, unequivocally.

Are the days unequivocal? It depends on what is meant by "day," clearly. "Wednesday-Thursday" means something different from "Thursday-Friday", yet the actual days in question pay no attention to some arbitrary designation. So much for the formal side. The nature of entities *in a system* may be definite, but undecidable without temporally contextual reference. Moreover, it is impossible to know about the status of one of these members of the system without knowing about the other. Notice that there is no doubt about the nature of their temporal order, in spite of the fact that the second-day information throws light, "backward in time," on that of the first day. Finally the probability of any rational guess as to what day the first day was was ½. This has "collapsed" to 1 or 0, on the second day. Has anything happened in "objective" nature or only in the thought about it?

On the material side, analogous considerations hold. Does a photon have to be composed of temporal units having homologous properties? If not, in how thin a time slice do I find it, fully represented, so to speak? If a photon is passed through an apparatus with two slits, then a diffraction pattern forms. Close one slit and the diffraction pattern disappears. If at the outset the photon must be regarded as both wave and particle, the usability of middle-sized objects as suitable models for very small things seems unsatisfactory. If the photon is understandable at one phase only as a member of a set and at other times as a single entity, then maybe we would do well, as Bohr seems to think we should, to regard the problem of its description as a mathematical one, rather than one of trying to make a subject-predicate language serve purposes it was never meant for. The photon is what it does. If it remains constant in charge, rest-mass, spin, energy, etc., but refuses to stick to rules of either middle-sized objects or waves that require a medium, perhaps the problem lies in the choice of models.

I sometimes wonder if there is not a very simple assumption in Bell's argument that should be challenged, therefore--that what is determinate for thought--the observation at L or T that lets me determine the state of affairs at T or L, respectively--must be directly correlated and can only be correlated with a determinateness in the state of affairs itself. A little reflection will show that this assumption is not subject to experiment in any direct way, since the experimenter would need to assure himself that he has an independent grasp of the state of affairs as it *really* is and thus could see if the thought did correspond to it. But of course, the same problem arises all over again: we must assume correlation in order to claim independence.

To return to probability, consider a Minkowski Universe--all probability would be subjective here. The likelihood that my friend who was in yesterday's plane crash is dead is 1/15, since 5 of the 75 aboard perished. The likelihood that the die I shall throw in a moment will come up 2 is 1/6, adjusted for those physical discrepancies between an ideal cube of absolute uniform distribution of density and the actual cube in hand. Considered from this point of view the "collapse" of the psi-function is only a special case of collapse from a distribution of possibilities (not actualities, *please*) down to a single member identification.

# Space—Time Singularities in Cosmology and Black Hole Evaporations

P.C.W. Davies

*The concept of cosmic time and the conventional models of cosmic dynamics lead to occurrence of space-time singularities, where physical predictability is destroyed. The implications for space-time structure and for physics in general are profound. The properties of singularities are important for an explanation of cosmological time asymmetry, and in the discussion of quantum black hole evaporation processes.*

## 1. COSMIC TIME

We are used to thinking of living organisms as growing and changing, having a life cycle bounded by birth and death. One of the greatest discoveries of science is that the universe also changes with time and, like living systems, may well have a kind of birth and death also.

Cosmology is the study of the universe as a whole. Implicit in this definition is the assumption that the universe may be treated as a coherent entirety, rather than merely as a large collection of smaller systems. A changing cosmos implies evolution with time, so that a prerequisite for discussing global change is a suitable definition of global time.

Newton's concept of time was well suited to cosmology because it was *universal* and *absolute*. It was also wrong. The theory of relativity reveals that clock rates depend upon the motion and gravitational situation of the observer. In such a scheme, every place in the universe possesses a different natural time scale. Moreover the discrepancies can be very considerable. The Earth and the quasar 3C 196 are apparently in relative motion at an appreciable fraction of the speed of light. The time dilation factor is as great as 0.75.

In the 1920s the astronomer Hubble discovered that the entire universe was in a state of relative expansion. Everywhere we look through large telescopes we see matter in high velocity motion. This is not a promising situation for the construction of a single cosmic time.

However, the expansion of the universe has a remarkable and beautiful feature that we had no right to expect. The pattern of motion of the distant galaxies is not haphazard, but highly systematic. So systematic in fact, that there is no detectable anisotropy. This is consistent with the simplest conceivable model of an evolving cosmos - one which is populated, and expands everywhere, *uniformly*.

The assumption of a uniform universe is central to modern cosmology. It is, of course, only an approximation. At best it applies to the "smeared out" condition of the matter content over distances of the order of clusters of galaxies (several million light years). Nevertheless, it enables the introduction of a cosmic time and, through that, a theory of cosmic dynamics.

The existence of a cosmic time in a uniform universe can be understood by visualising the universe as seen from a fast rocket passing the Earth. Although terrestrial observations show galaxies receding equally fast at equal distances in all directions, the astronaut would see antisotropic expansion, because he would be chasing rapidly towards the galaxies in his forward direction of motion.

At any given place in the universe, there is only *one* reference frame in which the universe expands isotropically. This priveliged reference frame defines a priveliged time scale (the time as told by a clock at rest in that frame). Two separated places have their priveliged reference frames in mutual motion, because of the expansion of the universe. Nevertheless, the time measured by the entire collection of imaginary standard clocks are obviously correlated such that the global condition (e.g. average separation of two galaxies) of the universe appears the *same* at equal times as registered by every priveliged clock (assuming they are all properly synchronised). Happily, the Earth is moving very slowly relative to the local priveliged frame in our vicinity of the universe, so that Earth time is a fairly accurate measure of cosmic time.

## 2. COSMIC DYNAMICS

The universe is globally dynamic, i.e. its internal geometry varies from moment to moment. Cosmologists assume that the geometrical rearrangement obeys the same dynamical laws that apply to any portion of the universe. This is clearly an act of faith. The only force which is appreciable over cosmic dimensions is gravity. The motion of gravitating systems is believed to be described by Einstein's general theory of relativity. The field equations of this theory are easily solved if the uniformity assumption is made.

First note that the field equations relate the *geometric* structure of spacetime to the *material content*. If the matter is always uniform, then the only way in which the spatial geometry can change is by an overall change of scale i.e. a uniform dilation or contraction, the former being just what is observed. Such a geometrical evolution is entirely described by a single function of the cosmic time, $R(t)$, which is a relative scale factor. The ratio $R(t_1)/R(t_2)$ gives the fractional change in the distance between any two average galaxies during the time lapse $t_1$ to $t_2$. At present $\dot{R}(t) \equiv \frac{dR}{dt} > 0$.

In terms of $R(t)$ the field equations reduce to

$$\frac{\ddot{R}}{R} = -\frac{4\pi G}{3}(\rho + 3p) \quad (1)$$

where $G$ in Newton's gravitational constant, and the matter content of the universe, contained on the right-hand-side of (1), is described in terms of a smoothed-out perfect fluid (a good approximation) of pressure $p$ and energy density $\rho$. It is very natural to assume that the quantity $\rho + 3p > 0$. The condition $\rho + 3p < 0$ would require negative energy densities, negative pressures or both. Unless the latter is possible equation (1) reveals that $\ddot{R} < 0$ (as $R > 0$ by definition). It follows that, as $\dot{R} > 0$ now, then $R(t)$ must have approached zero at some finite moment in the past. At $R(t) = 0$ the entire universe disappears at a point. What does this mean?

## 3. SPACETIME SINGULARITIES

The result obtained in the previous section is really just an expression of the well-known fact that gravity always attracts. According to this view the universe cannot ever have been static, because it would have been unstable against gravitational implosion. It must have always been expanding.

In the past, the galaxies must have been closer together, and the average matter density higher. The farther back in time we go, the smaller the value of $R$, the greater the density, and, reasonably enough, the temperature. Moreover, for a realistic fluid, $\dot{R}$ grows without limit as $R \to 0$. According to this model the universe was once enormously shrunken, with a very high temperature and density, and expanding explosively. These conditions have prompted the appelation "big bang" and "fireball" for the past high density phase of the universe. There is exciting observational evidence that the universe really was in a fireball phase about 15 billion years ago. A universal background radiation from space was detected by Penzias and Wilson in 1966. It is believed to be a direct relic of the fireball phase, a fading glow of the primeval heat, cooled now to a mere 3°K.

As we pass back to progressively earlier epochs of the fireball phase, the theory of relativity predicts that, so long as $\rho + 3p > 0$, the compaction rises without limit at an escalating rate. If we extrapolate this prediction to its extreme, we reach a moment when all distances in the universe have shrunk to zero. The density of matter, and the curvature of spacetime, become infinite. At this point the theory of relativity, and indeed the whole of physics, ceases to apply. Such a pathological circumstance is called a *singularity*.

Before discussing the significance of singularities, one or two possible objections should be countered. In a completely uniform universe, geometrical singularities are not really surprising. Loosely speaking, they can be envisaged as all the matter falling into (or in this case, emerging from) the same point. In Newtonian theory such a situation would have been dismissed by appealing to the small departures from exact uniformity which would be present in practice. These slight pertubations would cause the trajectories of different particles of matter to pass very close together, but never precisely intersect. In short, the system should "bounce" out again after a very high density encounter. In general relativity, it is not possible to avoid singularities so easily. A series of powerful general topological theorems[2] due mainly to S. W. Hawking and R. Penrose have shown that, subject only to a relation essentially of the form $\rho + 3p > 0$, then singularities of some sort are unavoidable, though it may happen that most of the material in the universe would "miss" them.

The presence of a singularity in the universe may be regarded as an edge or boundary to spacetime. An initial cosmological singularity therefore forms a past temporal extremity to the universe. We cannot continue physical reasoning, or even the concept of spacetime, through such an extremity. For this reason, most cosmologists think of the initial singularity as the "beginning" of the universe. On this view, the big bang represents the creation event; the creation not only of all the matter and energy in the universe, but also of spacetime itself. Questions such as "What caused the big bang?" or "What preceded it?" are meaningless. Causality and sequence break down altogether at a singularity.

Physics is faced with a great crisis. Either relativity is wrong at regions of high space curvature, or the spacetime concept (and thus, of course, relativity) breaks down. The big bang is not the only situation in which singularities are expected to occur. Another possibility would be at the end-point of the catastrophic collapse (implosion) of a body under the force of its own gravity, which astronomers widely believe occurs to most burnt-out stars of high mass. Relativists are by now so familiar with concept of singularities, that rather than trying to avoid them, they are searching for a means of peaceful coexistence.

The most unpalatable feature of a singularity is its effect on the causual structure of spacetime. Because causality fails at a singularity, no physics is safe in its vicinity. Any influence at all may come out of such a thing - picturesquely speaking. One way of taming singularities is to hide them behind *event horizons*. In this location all causal influences are trapped inside a black hole and cannot invade the outside universe. No information can escape from inside the horizon. To date, so long as quantum effects are excluded, all realistic theoretical models of gravitational collapse give rise to singularities inside event horizons. As we shall see, quantum effects might modify this.

A hypothesis that singularities would always form inside event horizons has been made by Penrose, and is known as the cosmic censorship hypothesis. Even if cosmic censorship is correct, we are still apparently faced with the "naked" big bang singularity (or singularities) in our past. Can we say anything at all about such a thing?

## 4. RANDOMNESS AND SINGULARITIES

The characteristic feature of singularities is the breakdown of predictable spacetime physics. What is required, then, is the application to singularities of non-spacetime laws of physics - laws which will be more fundamental to physics than even the spacetime concept itself. Some relativists are coming round to believe that there are such laws which transcend spacetime considerations; namely, the laws of thermodynamics. Thermodynamics is not framed specifically in spacetime language. In addition, the laws of thermodynamics command an application right across the whole range of topics in physics. No other physical laws can be applied successfully to systems as widely diverse as liquid helium and stellar interiors. Moreover, thermodynamics is tailor-made for situations in which a complete absence of microscopic information precludes a detailed causal description.

In this spirit, the most reasonable assumption to make about the initial naked singularity is that, in view of its total unpredictability (even in principle), then what emerges from such a thing is in some sense completely *random*. One meets this notion often enough in more conventional thermodynamics and statistical mechanics. The assumption of equal a priori probabilities, on which the whole of (non-ergodic) statistical mechanics is founded, is essentially the same. Normally this assumption is accepted without question. But now we can see that it receives a cosmological justification, for in a universe whose past is bounded by an inherently unpredictable singularity, then the a priori situation is indeed overwhelmingly likely to be a "random" one (containing no microscopic correlations).

If the condition of matter emerging from the initial big bang is random and chaotic, then we have an immediate explanation of the time asymmetry observed in the universe. For example, the reason we do not observe advanced electromagnetic radiation is precisely because such radiation would require strong correlations in the remote past between photons emerging from quite different directions. The probability of a random initial state of the electromagnetic field happening to give rise to coherent converging wavefronts of radiation is obviously staggeringly small.

Also, in laboratory systems, it is always necessary to make an assumption about initial randomness to prove that the direction in time of entropy increase is the same in the overwhelming majority of the members of an ensemble. Boltzmann's *Stosszahlansatz* (molecular chaos assumption) is also related to this.

The crucial importance of a priori randomness for understanding "everyday" time asymmetry is nicely illustrated by the model piston and cylinder system depicted in figure 1. In this system a non-relativistic gas resides beneath a piston inside an ideally smooth cylinder. The piston may be raised and lowered by an external energy supply. Consider a single cycle of expansion and compression. If the piston is raised rather rapidly compared to the average molecular velocity of the gas, then the gas will take a short while to expand into the opening vacuum left by the retreating piston. This time lag will be of the order of the *relaxation time* of the gas. Similarly, on the downstroke, the molecules will tend to crowd up in the region immediately beneath the piston. There will be a time lag before they redistribute themselves throughout the container at a higher density. It follows that at no time during the piston motion is the gas in exact equilibrium - it always trails a little *behind* equilibrium conditions. Because the pressure beneath the piston is therefore somewhat greater at a given position on the downstroke than at the corresponding position on the upstroke, there will be a net delivery of work to the gas at the end of one complete cycle. This appears as heat energy - the gas temperature increases, and so does its entropy, as required by the second law of thermodynamics. This entropy increase will continue through cycle after cycle so long as the external energy supply lasts.

At this point we may enquire why it is that in a system whose global constraints are being changed in a cyclic and time-symmetric fashion, the entropy and temperature of the gas always increases. Where have we slipped in the time asymmetry?

The answer is, of course, that the gas molecules were *lagging behind* the piston motion. The time reversal of this situation would be for the molecules to *anticipate* the piston motion; to congregate beneath the piston just before it was raised and to

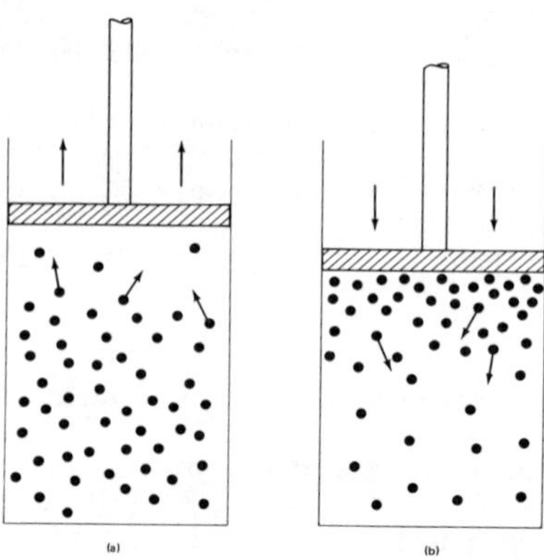


Figure 1. In (a) the piston is rapidly raised. The molecular motions lag somewhat behind equilibrium conditions, thereby reducing the pressure beneath the piston. In (b) the piston is depressed. The lag now causes the molecules to crowd beneath the piston, thereby increasing the pressure there. The piston therefore supplies a net quantity of energy to the gas in one complete cycle. This energy must come from the external source, which drives the piston, and appears as an increase in the entropy of the gas. An analogous situation occurs with the cosmological expansion.

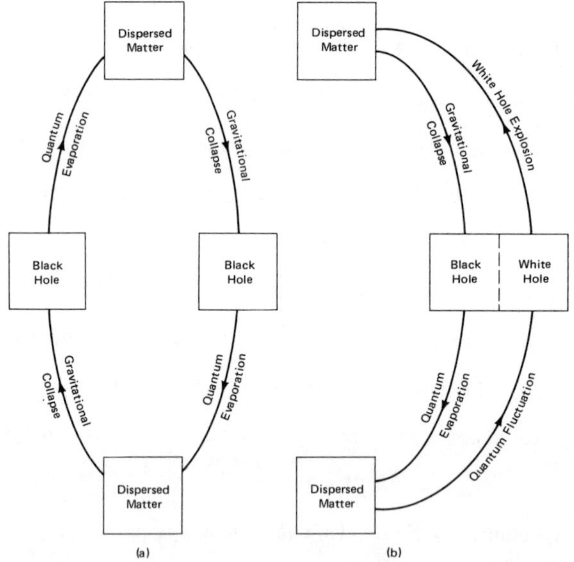


Figure 2. (a) Time- asymmetric black hole behaviour. In this cycle, black hole formation is favoured probablistically over white hole formation, so that the system tends to visit, via random fluctuations, the states shown, in clockwise rotation. (b) Time-symmetric behaviour in which black and white holes occur with equal probability (due to random fluctuations). The clockwise path tends to reverse itself.

In the absence of detailed calculations, it is not known whether quantum black and white holes behave time-symmetrically or not.

retreat, leaving a partial vacuum, just before it was lowered. This situation would indeed occur, as frequently as the more usual one, if the total system, *including the external energy supply*, was allowed to approach equilibrium. The only way that the piston could then perform cycles of expansion and contraction would be through stupendously rare, large statistical fluctuations in the molecules of the total system. These would be just as likely to result in the entropy of the gas increasing as decreasing. However, whilst the piston is driven *independently* of the molecular correlations in the gas, piston etc. then it is overwhelmingly improbable that the gas entropy would decrease by the above-mentioned anticipatory motions.

A convenient way of expressing this fact is to say that, so long as the molecular motions are *initially random*, then it is overwhelmingly probable that the gas entropy will increase. Equivalently we could atribute the randomness to the piston and require that its motion is not correlated with the molecular motions. Clearly, if one was prepared to wait, a moment would eventually arise when a rare statistical fluctuation did indeed produce the remarkable anticipatory behaviour of the molecules. If the piston was raised at this specially selected moment then the gas entropy would decrease. But for a *randomly* moved piston, this is exceedingly improbable.

It is possible to take over this reasoning more or less intact to the cosmological situation. The role of the gas is played by the material contents of the universe, and that of the piston and cylinder by the expanding (and perhaps eventually recontracting) space. The external energy supply is, heuristically, identified with the cosmological gravitational field. The most important entropy-generating processes analogous to the inhomogeneous gas expansion are the production of starlight and the formation of local gravitational condensations (these are often interdependent). As the universe expands, energy is redistributed from non-relativistic matter into the massless particles (photons and neutrinos) by nucleosynthesis in stars. The relaxation time required for the stars to heat up the universe to thermal equilibrium with their surfaces is of the order $10^{23}$ years, compared with an expansion rate of $10^{-10}$ year$^{-1}$. There is evidently an enormous lag behind equilibrium conditions. The resulting disequilibrium is manifest in the darkness of the night sky (Olbers' "paradox") relative to the hot stars. It is, of course, precisely this thermodynamic disequilibrium in the vicinity of the sun that enables the existence of life on Earth.

The time asymmetry inherent in the "starlight" lag may now be attributed to the aforementioned initial "randomness". The microscopic motions of the cosmological particles which emerge from the initial singularity are uncorrelated. Equivalently, one may say that the global dynamics of the universe - the big bang expansion - is not correlated with the microscopic condition of the cosmological fluid.

We seem to have a picture of primordial chaos, with the universe beginning in a randomly selected state, subsequently increasing its entropy, but at the same time producing order and structure. There is no contradiction in this latter phenomenon, because the global constraints on the universe are changing due to the expansion. In this sense, the universe behaves like an open system. There is no maximum entropy. Indeed, mathematical models show that a cyclic expansion and recontraction can bring about a monotonic entropy growth (see the paper by P. T. Landsberg in this volume).

The idea of a cyclic universe of infinite age is popular, but suffers from two drawbacks. One is the arbitrariness of its time asymmetry. There is no initial singularity to produce randomness. The second concerns the very avoidance of singularities, which requires a modification of general relativity, or a very unusual behaviour of the energy-momentum tensor in regions of high density.

If the universe eventually recontracts, and we accept the singularity theorems at face value, we encounter a picture of the cosmos with *two* temporal extremities. In this case we are not free to choose the state of the cosmological material at each extremity independently, because they are causally connected. We cannot select the states at both singularities to be "random". In fact, if the universe started recontracting in its present condition, the final state would be anything but random. To see this, imagine the collapse of the universe viewed in reverse. We should have matter emerging from a singularity and forming very "old" stars, upon which radiation converged in advanced waves etc. Such a situation requires strong correlations among the microscopic constituents of the universe, in direct contradiction to the randomness concept.

In spite of this, there may still be a sense in which such a universe is a "random" one. Any causally connected *pair* of states chosen *together* in a random way from the set of all boundary conditions would be far more likely to possess a large entropy difference between them than to have roughly the same entropy, for the latter situation would require that the aforementioned "lag" of cosmic processes behind equilibrium conditions would have to reverse itself at some stage during the cycle, and become "anticipatory". This unusual behaviour has indeed been postulated by some authors, notably T. Gold.[3] It fits quite naturally into the framework of the recontracting cosmological model: during the expansion phase the usual lag behind equilibrium condition occurs, leading to entropy increase, retarded radiation etc. During the contracting phase, these asymmetric processes reverse, and entropy decreases again. Picturesquely speaking, everything "runs backwards" in the contracting phase, though an observer, whose brain functions are also reversed, would not be able to distinguish one phase from the other. There is complete time symmetry, both globally and locally. Observers would always regard the universe as expanding.

In order to produce such remarkable behaviour it is necessary for the motions of all the particles in the universe to be very carefully chosen. More precisely, among the set of all possible boundary conditions, those which produce an entropy-reversing behaviour form a very small subset. A random selection from this set would therefore be exceedingly unlikely to produce the Gold time-symmetric universe. In other words, the particle motions in the Gold universe are highly correlated (in direct contradiction to the randomness assumption).

If we live in such a universe, we might be expected to notice these strong correlations, in thermodynamic experiments for example (the usual treatment of which assumes equal a priori probabilities, or initial randomness). A direct experiment to detect radiation correlation effects (advanced radiation) has been carried out by R. B. Partridge,[4] with negative results.

## 5. BLACK HOLE EVAPORATION

Besides the big bang, it is probable that spacetime singularities also form at the end point of gravitational collapse of stars. In this case, it is widely believed that the singularity would always be hidden inside an event horizon. Such an object is known as a black hole. The intimate association of event horizons with singularities has an important bearing on the question of randomness.

The essential feature of an event horizon is its role as an information sink. It may be envisaged as a surface surrounding a black, empty region of spacetime (indeed a black hole) into which anything may pass, but from which no information may emerge. No experiment performed outside the black hole can provide any knowledge about objects dropped into its interior except for their total electric charge, mass and angular momentum. In this respect the internal states of a black hole play a role analogous to those of a thermodynamic system, where only a small number of global parameters label the macrostates, but no information is available about the internal microstates.

Modern information theory has provided a connection between information and entropy. This implies that the loss of information down a black hole contributes to its entropy. In classical physics, this information loss is actually infinite - a finite black hole can swallow up an unlimited amount of information in the form of particles of arbitrarily small mass. This is consistent with the fact that the hole is totally black i.e. has a temperature strictly zero. A body with finite energy and zero temperature formally possesses a divergent entropy.[5] However, when quantum effects are taken into account, we have to contend with the uncertainty principle, which limits the smallness of the energy of the particles which a black hole may contain. It was therefore anticipated in 1972 by J. D. Bekenstein[6] that the entropy of a black hole might be finite after all.

In retrospect, one might have also anticipated that the black hole would have a non-zero temperature (so not "black" at all). A quantum field theory treatment of black holes was carried out by Hawking,[7] resulting in the remarkable prediction that the object apparently emits radiation (electromagnetic, neutrino, etc.) with a spectrum which corresponds precisely to that of a black body with temperature $T = \hbar c^3/8\pi GMk$ for a spherical black hole of mass $M$. The corresponding entropy $S = 4\pi GMk^2/hc$. It is seen that as $\hbar \to 0$, $T \to 0$, and $S \to \infty$ , and we recover the classical case. (It is important to note that the radiation does not come from inside the black hole, but is produced in the empty space outside the event horizon.[8])

More detailed density matrix analyses have demonstrated that the radiation is identical to that from a black body, even for the particle expectation numbers in each mode. In particular, there are no correlations between particles emitted in different modes of the radiation field, or between different numbers of particles in the same mode. Each quantum emission is an independent event. Expressed differently, the radiation from a black hole is completely random. The Planck spectrum is simply the most probable spectrum. It follows that there is no way in which the black hole radiation can carry any information about the black hole interior. The black hole is therefore a perfect dissipator. Any structured system dropped into one gets converted into pure random radiation. This is consistent with the total destruction of information as the sacrificed system leaves our region of space-time altogether, eventually hitting the singularity (or passing to another region of space-time).

These new developments change the whole complexion of the time-asymmetry properties of black holes. The classical black hole is a truly irreversible physical system. A dispersed cloud of gravitating matter which undergoes gravitational collapse inside an event horizon cannot re-emerge and disperse itself again. The horizon is a one-way surface. The collapse is completely irreversible. There are no Poincare recurrences in classical gravitating systems; once the system has visited a black hole state, it cannot revisit its initial state.[5]

However, the existence of the Hawking quantum radiation process modifies this picture. If the black hole radiates energy, its mass must decrease. Consequently its event horizon also decreases. The black hole literally shrinks. A non-rotating, uncharged black hole clearly has a *negative* specific heat. The smaller its mass $M$ falls, the greater the temperature $T$. Eventually, it would seem that the black hole must disappear completely in an explosive burst of radiation. This fate should have befallen any black hole formed in the primeval fireball whose initial mass was below about $10^{15}$ *gm*. Just what happens to the matter which went to make up the black hole is not clear. Presumably it simply disappears from the universe at the singularity. The singularity itself, according to the current view, becomes momentarily naked when the horizon shrinks down to zero radius (thus the quantum theory demolishes the cosmic censorship hypothesis). But by this time all the black hole mass has been radiated away, so it is conjectured that even the singularity just disappears!

The black hole evaporation process as it is described above is still clearly time-asymmetric. We start out with highly ordered matter falling inwards, and end up with highly disordered radiation flowing outwards. The exceedingly unlikely reverse process is for the disordered radiation to implode and produce a singularity, out of which emerges ordered matter. Nevertheless, if the system were sealed up in a box, one might expect on the basis of the underlying time symmetry of Einstein's equations, that after an enormous duration, the time asymmetry would disappear, and each fluctuation would occur as often as its reverse. Because the evaporation radiation is random, mostly it will consist of thermal radiation. Occasional fluctuations might produce an overabundance of non-thermal radiation, or protons or electrons, but most of the time the box contents will contain mainly thermal radiation. Fluctuations in this radiation would occur from time to time to produce black holes which would then evaporate away again. Sometimes white holes" (the time reverse of black holes) would form and disperse. The question now arises: do the white holes form as often as the black holes? Or is there still a residual time-asymmetry favouring black hole formation and evaporation, even though the system is now reversible (in the sense that it may eventually revisit similar states of dispersed matter again and again). Two possibilities for recurrences are shown in figure 2. The first path takes a dispersed state to a black hole, which then evaporates to a dispersed state again, finally undergoing a fluctuation to form another black hole, and so on. This path is cyclic but asymmetric - we go around the loop clockwise. The second path returns the system to a dispersed state via a white hole, by simply time-reversing the black hole evaporation process, and going back round the same loop anticlockwise.

Both paths clearly depend on staggeringly rare statistical fluctuations, but are they equally rare? In the first case, only black holes form, by the unlikely process of all the material in the box happening to congregate spontaneously inside its Schwarzchild radius. The second case requires the time-reverse of the evaporation process, in which a few very hot bursts of radiation converge to produce a white hole, which then steadily grows in size as more and more radiation flows in along precisely correlated trajectories. This radiation is then annihilated, and converted into the mass of the white hole, which then spews out particles which have originally emerged from the singularity.

There is no universal agreement on whether these two processes are equally probable. If they are, then black and white holes will form inside the box with equal probability, thereby restoring the overall time symmetry, provided that the material which emerges from the white hole singularity is completely random (just as the black hole evaporation radiation is random). This step is necessary because in the presence of singularities the system is no longer strictly isolated. The assumption of randomness then ensures that no information may enter the system through the singularity. This assumption has been made by Hawking[9] and dignified with the title *principle of ignorance*. It states that

> "What comes out of a singularity is completely random; the singularity emits with equal probability every configuration of particles compatible with the external constraints".

This principle is to be placed alongside Heisenberg's uncertainty principle as a fundamental property of quantum systems. It is a generalisation of the earlier ideas of a priori randomness in cosmology, discussed in section 4, and which is so essential for understanding time asymmetry in the universe.

## 6. CONCLUSION

Time asymmetry of the world requires an assumption of initial randomness. A study of cosmology provides a justification for this if one invokes the inherently unpredictable nature of space-time singularities. The global, topological features of space-time, such as singularities and horizons, plus the use of quantum statistical mechanics and thermodynamics, is leading to a new understanding of the relationships between thermodynamics, quantum theory and gravity.

## ACKNOWLEDGEMENTS

The presentation of the black hole discussion here owes much to the ideas of Professor R. Penrose (particularly figure 2) and Dr. D. W. Sciama, to whom I am indebted.

Davies

# REFERENCES


1. A. A. Penzias and R. W. Wilson, *Astrophys.J 152* , 149 (1968).

2. See for example, S. W. Hawking and G. F. R. Ellis "The Large Scale Structure of Space-Time" (*Cambridge University Press* 1973).

3. T. Gold, *Amer.J.Phys. 30*, 403 (1962).

4. R. B. Partridge, *Natur 244* , 263 (1973).

5. P. C. W. Davies "The Physics of Time Asymmetry" (*University of California Press 1974,1976; University of Surrey Press (Blackie-Intertext) 1974)*.

6. J. D. Bekenstein, PhD thesis, Princeton (1972); *Phys.Rev.D 7,* 2333 (1973).

7. S. W. Hawking, *Comm.Math.Phys. 43*, 199 (1975).

8. P. C. W. Davies "Space and Time in the Modern Universe" (*Cambridge University Press* 1977).

9. S. W. Hawking, *Phys.Rev.D 14,* 2460 (1976).

## DISCUSSION AND COMMENT

S. Kamefuchi

Among the natural sciences cosmology occupies a very particular place. This may be seen from the following argumentation.

In my opinion there exist two different approaches to the physical world, which are to be referred to as the *N*- and *M*-approaches, and most of the researches made so far seem to be based on the former.

In the *N*-approach objects of observation are restricted to those confined in small space-time regions, small as compared with the dimension of the entire universe. And the local behaviour of such objects is studied in relation to the surrounding matter, the role of which is simply to specify the initial and/or boundary conditions. Thanks to the relative smallness of our objects these conditions are regarded as freely adjustable, and the statistical treatment (preparation of many objects of the same kind, many repetitions of the same experiment, etc.) becomes possible. Causality arguments are effective here, thereby leading us to the local physical laws.

In the *M*-approach, on the contrary, we may take as an object of observation any system enclosed in a large space-time region, with the emphasis upon the mutual relations among those subsystems contained in the region concerned. Thus the entire universe could, in principle, be adopted as a possible object. In view of the relative largeness of such objects the statistical treatment is not always possible. Causality arguments become less effective, and should be taken over by the so-called self-consistency arguments. The global aspect of the physical world is thereby revealed. Since what corresponds to "cause" in the *N*-approach is not freely adjustable here, the"cause" must be so fixed as to be consistent with "effect": Cause and effect prescribe each other, so that the description becomes of a teleological nature.

As our object of observation gets larger, the *N*-approach becomes less effective, whereas the *M*-approach becomes more effective. We may therefore say that the two approaches are complementary to each other in the sense of N. Bohr: They clarify the complementary aspects of the physical world. For sciences of the *N*-type one is better than the other if it can explain more. Obviously such a criterion is not applicable to sciences of the *M*-type, because there are not always many things to explain. Thus, any science of the *M*-type can claim to be a good one as long as the description is consistent within its framework: Which one to choose is then a matter of taste or of belief. In this sense the latter resemble humanistic sciences, or even religions.

In summary, sciences of the *N*-type are those of explanation, whereas sciences of the *M*-type are those of description. Cosmology, of course, is one of the latter type, to which Dr. Davies' paper tries to approach from sciences of the former type. Incidentally the symbols *N* and *M* stand for Newtonian and Machian, respectively.

# Beneath Time: Explorations in Quantum Topology

D. Finkelstein

*ABSTRACT*

*Relativistic and quantum theoretic conceptions of time are considered. An extrapolation based on the common features of these conceptions is attempted. It is suggested that at the basic level of the physical world there are no indicators of time, such as the local light cone of relativity, and that not only the distinction between past and future but also the distinction between time and space are emergent characteristics of a higher, more statistical, level.*

## I INTRODUCTION

For the physicist the study of time is the study of the laws underlying the creation and evolution of the universe.

It will not take long for me to present my conception of time. Once six days was allowed for creating a universe. Today, thanks to modular construction and hierarchical organization, genesis goes faster. My proposal for the law of evolution of the universe will not take ten minutes or I would be sure I was wrong again. What shall we do with our spare time? Let us use it for a historical preamble and a science-fiction postscript.

---

*Supported by the *est* Foundation, the National Science Foundation, and the Young Men's Philanthropic League.

## II RESPICE

Truth and time, those ancient absolutes, have evolved remarkably in this century. I find this evolution an important signpost for my own path, and read from it what I believe are the essentials for a unified conception of nature.

Most of the papers I have written are abortions of previous conceptions. These died, each of them, from the clash and contradiction of its structural elements, from a redundancy of structure. The quest for a viable universe leads to models with fewer and simpler independent elements of structure. The universe I will show you is so stark I believe it is the end of that path.

This starkness reflects the drastic economy and simplicity of modern physics.

*Modern* physics! What an uninformative name for a now venerable enterprise dating from the discovery of radioactivity. A better name for the successor to classical physics is *romantic* physics, for it shares with other romantic movements the renunciation of the classical pose of objectivity and absoluteness, of the classical canons of form, of the classical attachments to stasis over process and to deterministic fate over adventurous chance.

Let me indicate its simplicity, treating first quantum theory as a revised theory of truth, and then relativity as a revised theory of time, before attempting the synthesis of truth and time in one concept of process.

### TRUTH

In both relativity and quantum theory our main working symbols stand not for objective entities but for epistemic processes, acts of knowing, linking observer and observed.

The primary symbols of quantum theory stand for processes of control, quantum production and detection processes, like the holding of one polarizer before a light source, or another before one's eye. The essential features of the polarization process are summed up in a directed line or vector giving the orientation of the polarizer; this is the prototype of the most general so-called *state vector* generally represented by a $\psi$ or a bracket symbol $|\rangle$. Bohr emphasized that $\psi$ represents the entire situation, the polarizer as well as the quanta of light or photons on which it acts. The word *situation* has a built-in static element in the stem *situs*, place; I prefer to speak of the *whole process* with due homage to Whitehead.

Quantum theory is simpler than classical in that a quantum physicist can build more with less material than a classical physicist. The quantum physicist has a more powerful way to put processes together; it is called *superposition*. The superposition principle is a more important departure of quantum theory from classical than the more often mentioned indeterminacy of quantum theory, which it implies, and is harder to understand because it transgresses the principles of classical logic applied to microscopic systems.

First I describe superposition as a relation between predicates. The predicates entering into the relation are defined by the control processes already mentioned, are described by stators. These, then, are determinations of maximal precision or information, the kind that classically would be represented on a map by a single precise point; call such predicates therefore *points*.

If *A*, *B*, and *C* are such points, *C* is said to be a *superposition* of *A* and *B* (I will give an example soon) if C evades every detection process that A and B evade.

Thinking of *A*, *B*, and *C* as fixed map regions, and detection processes as other map regions, a little reflection will convince you that if C evades every detection process that *A* and *B* evade then it is logical to infer that *C* is contained in the united regions *A* and *B*. Since classically *C* is a single point included in the union of points *A* and *B, C* must therefore coincide with either A or B.

The *superposition principle,* one of the basic logical postulates of quantum theory, states that any two points A and B have a superposition distinct from themselves. Classically "*A* or *B*" is a dilemma for *C: C* must be one or the other. In quantum logic there is a third alternative for every such dilemma, a superposition. Every dilemma has three horns, and indeed an infinite number. Thus the classical representation of propositions or classes as arbitrary sets of points becomes deceptive. Learning to think in quantum logic is an exercise in non-objective thought.

In the traditions of Plato and Aristotle, a proposition like an idea inhabits a separate but parallel world, completely and forever imaging the real world without disturbance. Call such ideas Logos. In the quantum conception a proposition inhabits the same world we do, and is related to its referent in a part-to-whole way, inevitably incomplete, selective, interactive and reflexive. I call such an idea Mythos. Logos is mystical, mythos practical.

We deal here with a difference between logical laws obeyed by microscopic entities, quanta, and macroscopic ones, especially symbols. We usually think of names as evanescent, immaterial, but the name *electron* in any notation is monstrously gross next to an electron, and responds less sensitively and unpredictably to our reading. Symbols are deader than quanta.

Thus Aristotle made an error -- call it an approximation if you prefer -- with the concept of proposition, significantly similar to the error Euclid made with position: He omitted temporality.

Of course Aristotle understood that propositions may involve time, and that in a principle like "*A* or not -*A*" both *A*'s have to be at the same time. This is not the temporality he repressed.

Rather, the omitted temporality is that expressed in many natural languages by *tense*. If we want to state a proposition (say the ripeness of a certain apple, understanding a fixed time and place such as Philadelphia, July 4, 1776) we must in English choose between past (the apple *was* ripe) present (*is* ripe) or future (*will be* ripe) describing quite distinct personal experiences. Aristotle imagined, instead, a tenseless ripe, ripeness under an eternal aspect. Tense, the Aristotelian might say, adds nothing essential to the fact of the apple's ripeness; tense merely gives the accidental relation of the speaker to the fact; and the tenseless proposition gives nothing but the fact.

This logic of the fact seems to violate quantum experience, repressing the essential difference between those processes of control that give rise to past and future predictions. To discuss these, we must reconstitute our language. Let us call *predicate* only the assertions (of the future tense) expressing preparation processes. Detection processes, I will say, define *copredicates* (past tense) the sharpest of which are *copoints*.[1] We know predicates with our effectors, copredicates with our receptors, in the main.

A phenomenological language has no need for the present tense. The present, according to relativity, is just what we do *not* experience of the rest of the world.

The logic of facts arises from the Aristotelian assumption that every point (predicate) compels exactly one co-point p'; that is, one process *pp'* (first preparation *p*, then detection *p'*) is allowed and all other processes *pq'* involving *p* are forbidden. This uniqueness means: *What is not forbidden is compulsory*. The assumed one-to-one correspondence between past and future makes the aspect of eternity a consistent position.

The actual experience with quantum predicates is startlingly different. Each point *p* allows more co-points than it forbids. *What is not forbidden is allowed*. The one-to-one correspondence of past and future predicates goes, as does the identification of past and future tenses with a timeless one. There is no aspect of eternity.

We choose as symbols physical systems that behave predictably, and so symbols come close to having the aspect of eternity. Logos supposes a perfect match between symbolic processes and physical, like that once supposed between the laws of Newton and the planetary process. The logos is eternal, the process transient, but somehow they match.

In mythos, which is older than logos, process, including our involvement in it, is primary, and symbols are a kind of demonstrative accompaniment, like chants accompanying ancient rites, declaring the rhythm and the values of the process but never defining it.

The historic transition from mythos to logos seems part of a pre-Platonic passage from the oral to the written tradition.[2] Today the tide reverses.

If 17th century science evolves out of 16th century magic to minimize the mythical, romantic, illogical, and arbitrary in the world, then the greatest surprise of science must be that the actual world is to an overwhelming extent illogical, irrational and arbitrary. The illusion of rationality that fostered classical physics turns out to be the law of large numbers, which is not even a law in the sense of logos. Twentieth century psychoanalysis and quantum physics rediscover the enormous unperceived irrational content of the mental and physical process.

The temporality of quantum propositions manifests itself in the ordering of the processes of quantum logic and ultimately in the ordering of factors in quantum algebra, where $p$ times $q$ is unequal to $q$ times $p$.

The situation is bizarre enough to merit demonstration. The standard one is photon polarization. Take two polarizers $A$ and $B$. (If need be, sacrifice a pair of polarizing sunglasses.) Consider them embodiments of production processes, emissions: use them to produce photons by streaming light through them. They define point predicates. $A$ and $B$ are identical but turned $90^\circ$ relative to each other about the direction of

the light (If you look through them both, all the light from *A* is stopped by *B*, practically.) The predicates defined by *A* and *B* are points, in that no more restrictive way of preparing the polarization of photons is known, barring the trivial case of a shutter, which stops all photons. The paradox is that if a detector rejects light from *A* and light from *B* it will also reject light from *C*, a third polarizer at an angle of $45^{\circ}$. As it were, any "set" that contains the two "points" *A* and *B* contains a third point *C* as well, distinct from *A* and *B*. *C* is a superposition of *A* and *B*.

There is another statistical kind of superposition of a classical nature, a probabilistic mix of *A* and *B* with definite weights. The two kinds of superposition, quantum and classical, are also called coherent and incoherent. The incoherent gives nothing new.

More dramatically, use the polarizers as filters to define tests, and subject photons to the tests *A*, *B*, and *C* in sequence. In classical logic, the more tests in sequence, the fewer subjects pass. Since no photons pass *A* and *B* in sequence, none should pass the three tests *A*, *B*, and *C*. Indeed this is the case when *C* is before or after *A* and *B*, but when *C* is between *A* and *B* about 1/8 get through; the black area turns gray.

This is one of many cases in quantum logic where closing a channel increases the flow, closing a window brightens the light. Two-slit interference is another. These effects, the Heisenberg uncertainty relation, the breakdown of the logical principle of distribution, which I do not take up, and Bohr's principle of complementarity are all manifestations of the temporality of quantum logic and the principle of superposition.

Now I want to remind you how strange the mechanics of Newton seemed to followers of Descartes, for that strangeness is an anticipation of quantum superposition. It was said that Descartes understood everything and could compute nothing, Newton the reverse. Newtonian mechanics starts from the concept of time and static concepts such as position, but also specifically dynamical ones such as inertia and momentum, which scandalized many of Newton's contemporaries. The job of physics (let us stipulate for now) is to predict future observations from the present. But the dynamical concepts, unlike the static ones, cannot be measured by present observations along. They require a span of time, as in a collision determination of momentum. They are hidden from observations at any one instant. How does the system remember these non-static quantities? Did Newton attribute purpose to the mechanical system by so supplementing geometry with these hidden variables?

Newton seemed to call down the accusation of vitalism by the very choice of names for these quantities, all taken from psychology. It is amusing to feel the discomfort of the physicist when today a word like energy is used for an attribute of mind, as though a technical tool were being stolen for household use. The thefts are all the reverse.

In classical mechanics, these two sets of concepts, the static and the dynamic, are logically independent. Euclidean geometry in no wise entails the dynamic concept of momentum. Geometry abstracts from protractors and rulers, dynamics from balance and ballistic pendulums, quite separate and logically independent experiences.

In quantum mechanics the static and dynamic quantities are logically inseparable. There each momentum determination process is a superposition of many position determination processes. Any entity with position that obeys quantum logic must have momentum. The units that distinguish the dynamic from the static are supplied by a fundamental constant of nature, Planck's constant. We can measure momentum with a rule, energy with a clock, using superposition and the relations of de Broglie and Planck. We use the rule to make a grating. The balance and the ballistic pendulum are redundant and derivative, now that we can diffract quanta from gratings and crystals. The concepts that seemed vitalististic or purposive in the 17th century are quantum superpositions of the ones then considered basic and geometric. Dynamics is geometry with superposition.

So quantum theorists can build with half the raw materials of classical ones. Change need not be added, it is implicit.

Moreover, thanks to the incompleteness of quantum descriptions of the universe, we have less to build. We leave most decisions to nature. The questions answered by our theory are a negligible part of the totality of possible questions. We may as well say the photon makes up it own mind impromptu whether to go through the polarizer, except for exactly parallel or crossed polarization. The law impels, it does not compel.

The main economy of quantum theory is implicit in what I have already said and struck me forcibly when I first learned from the writing of von Neumann that we are dealing with a modification of logic.[3] Perhaps at the deepest, most microscopic, level the right language for the law of nature is a quantum logical calculus rather than the differential calculus of Newton, qualitative rather than quantitative, and that much closer to ordinary thought.

We have heard much how qualitative changes emerge from quantitative, in processes like boiling and condensation. But I claim quantitative changes of nature themselves emerge in actuality from qualitative. For example, an increase in the electric charge of a pith ball first appears to us as a merely quantitative change in one of its parameters, but a deeper analysis reveals successive additions of individual electrons, each addition a qualitative indivisible change in the composition of the body. I suggest all continuity in physics is just the superficial description of deeper atomicity.

Can we understand temporal processes, duration, the passage of time, in this way?

We do not understand a concept until we can measure it, to be sure. But the measurement is not even the beginning of understanding, it is just the posing of the question, directing our attention to what is to be understood.

We may define quantity of water, say, by some process involving pint bottles, but we do not understand the quantity we measure until we discover the water molecule, if then.

The Pythagorean distinction between measuring and counting seems correct. We understand a concept not when we reduce it to measurement but when we reduce it to pattern and counting.

Can we so understand time and energy? Yes, clocks measure time. But what do they measure? The quantum topology, to which I shall come soon, attempt to answer this ancient question.

TIME

"A point is that which has no parts," Euclid tells us. Look at this dot:

Now observe your own process and consider whether your experience has parts. Not the picayune ones that show under a magnifier, but gross, conspicuous parts. If you do not see these parts at once, continue for a time and you will see them.

These are the parts marked off by your pulse, your breath, or dawns and sunsets, dc pending on how long it takes to become conscious of duration. The error of Euclid I spoke of before was not one of the logical and topological ones fixed up by Hilbert in this century, but the phenomenological one of regarding the enduring point as timeless, omitting duration as irrelevant to distance. -- The Euclidean error is the origin of Newton's error, identifying the timeless point with the instantaneous point of our perception, the reification of absolute space.

A more phenomenologically accurate geometry is, like our logic, tensed, dealing with lines to us from the past and lines from us to the future, representing communication processes, signals.

The time of Newton was linear and deterministic. The time of special relativity is already a ramified structure, with a conception of local causality foreign to Newtonian mechanics. The wheel of fate is an appropriate metaphor for the world system of Newton, but Einstein's is a web of fate. At first, in special relativity, the lines of this web run fixed and straight, but then in general relativity we study how they themselves flex and tangle in the world process. Finally in quantum topology I will erase the lines of time. There is no timelike indicator at the basic level, and time must be laboriously constructed with clocks.

The main working symbol of relativity represents an act of communication, like the passage of light from one signal tower to another, and is called a time space vector and written *dx*. Since communication is the production and detection of symbols, the two disciplines of relativity and quantum theory are but differing abstractions from one, and the quantum topology described here is inteded to be a unification.

We saw how superposition saves quantum physicists half their raw materials. Relativity saves half the balance of more. Consider:

If we once form a sound conception of any dimension of time (which is a plural rather than singular entity in relativity) then the three dimensions of space come *gratis*. Indeed in radar practice all four coordinates of an event are best taken to be times, the times at which various signals leave or reach the radar unit.

So, an understanding of time, or one other suitably chosen concept, leads to an understanding of the rest of physics. The first steps in this conceptual linkage form a square. The horizontal lines represent laws of quantum theory and the vertical, laws of relativity.

The conception of time that prevails in present physics, however, is absurdly inappropriate as a starting point for this construction, both in the idealizations that enter into it and the consequences that flow out of it. Is it too revolutionary to suggest that time is only what clocks read? I mean this in the sense that temperature is only what thermometers read. Today we renounce temperature as a basic concept of physics,

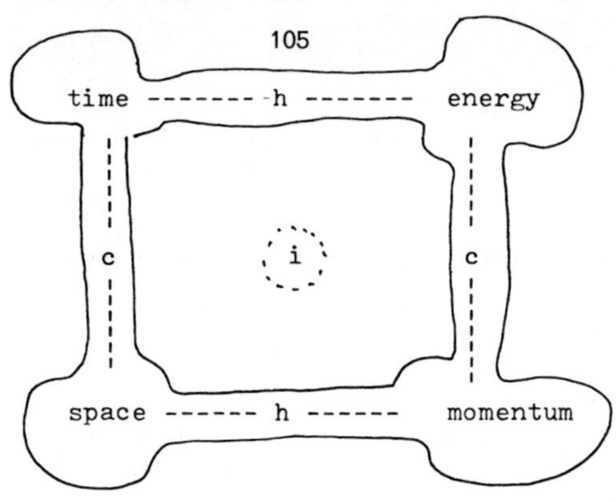


defining thermometers without mentioning temperature, although in the days of the caloric fluid thermal concepts were considered basic. I mean to renounce time, the continuous classical numerical coordinate, in the same sense: defining clocks in more primitive terms, still involving temporality, evidently, but not classical time. Now no clock, digital or analogue, can read a continuous real-number-valued time. The atomic constitution of matter and the quantum nature of dynamics prevent this, and the smaller the clock, the poorer the resemblance to Newtonian time. Perhaps if the particle spectrum were drastically different we could make better and smaller clocks, but it is as it is. And the usual conception of time is compatible with a large variety of particle spectra, only one of which exists. The entire mathematical machinery of Lagrangian and Hamiltonian functions and the like in modern particle physics is, I suggest, compensation for our overidealization of the nature of time, our reification of what is at best a limiting case, our failure to describe what actually goes on. All the concepts in the square are surface structure, instrumental illusion.

The views that time is an illusion and processes are discrete are older than Newton's views of time and process. They are found in the Buddhist logic and ontology of sixth and seventh century India,[4] for example, as well as the following quantum topology.

III ADSPICE

For me a theory, the goal of theorectical physics, consists of three overlapping domains: *syntax, semantics*, and *law*.

The *syntax* is a formal symbolic scheme for generating process descriptions.

The *semantics* is our correspondence between the processes of actual practice and these symbolic descriptions.

The *law* is the formal rule telling which descriptions describe possible processes.

These three parts seems already recognized by Leibniz,[5] whose relational philosophy of time and space is also followed here.

The syntax of my still incomplete theory is pure topology, taken with the superposition process of quantum logic. Topology is the theory of contiguity, which may be either infinitesimal or finite, continuous or atomic. Topology is the theory that ignores the difference between a doughnut and a drinking straw. (Both have one hole.) It is currently believed that some important entities of physics have essential topological elements: black holes, strings, bags, kinks, solitons, etc. I suggest instead that all physics is topology.

For the most complete possible description of a physical process I am trying a finite discrete network of directed flows with crossings. This comes from experience with discrete approximations to general relativity.

Draw any number of continuous open or closed curves on a sheet of paper. Direct them with arrows, one per curve. Mark some of the crossings between two curves with a dot; unmarked intersections do not count. This "plexus" describes a physical process. Each dot has four arcs touching it and represents an event consisting of two annihilations and two creations. Each arc links two such events. Only the discrete topological structure counts, the dots and the sequences of dots lying on lines.

The arrow of the graph is all that survives of the arrow of time. Antiparticles can be imagined as running against this arrow as usual.

I arrive at this primitive language by boiling relativity and quantum mechanics down to a stock of concepts sufficient to reconstitute all the rest, just as we reconstitute energy, momentum and space from time (Figure 1). The topological element of this graphical language is the essence of relativity, the logical element that of quantum mechanics.

For a whole process, including both production and detection, the serpent swallows its tail. Any subject-object cut leaves two pieces with loose ends, and is rather arbitrary.

The most general description is a superposition of such nets (with integer coefficients or, amounting to the same in practice, real number coefficients), a "plexor".

There may be restrictions on the form of the net. I think it is usually near to a chessboard lattice, a configuration important for its simplicity. In such a world, a particle at rest is actually zigzagging at the speed of light. Each line segment of the checkerboard bears an arrow, a binary decision. Each vertex of the checkerboard bears a flow pattern, and there are three possibilities: A line entering a vertex can turn up, go straight through, or turn down. But once the arrow on the lines are fixed only two flow patterns are possible -- another binary decision.

All these binary decisions are interrelated by consistency conditions. The decision at one arc or vertex must be compatible with the decisions at its neighbors. This is supposed to be the origin of all interaction, propagation, and motion.

The law of nature, the rule that tells us from a description of the process whether it is possible or impossible (allowed or forbidden, we say in quantum physics), is simple:

*A whole process is forbidden if and only if its coefficients sum to zero.*

This incorporates the laws of ordinary quantum mechanics.

Notice that there are no fundamental constants in the law in the usual sense. The inputs are all topological in nature: How many lines can meet at a vertex? How many lines may connect nearest neighbots? Next nearest? And so forth. Is the beautiful conjecture of Wheeler and Feynman valid in this theory?: Does the whole net consist of a single multiply self-crossing line, are we all one in the strongest possible sense? I doubt this because it is not a local condition but a global one.

After this topology is specified the meanings of the various nets have to be given before the theory is complete. Until then the theory is pure mathematics.

## IV PROSPICE

What will come out of such a theory if it is right? What is the payoff for this gamble?

Knowledge of all the natural constants, the quantities that do not depend on accidents of initial conditions or choices of units: the masses of the particles in units of the lightest; the strengths of their interactions; the natures of the fields that dominate our classical experience, such as gravity and electromagnetism. All that is not arbitrary in the world.

How much of this can be exhibited yet?

The first step was Feynman's demonstration that such a checkerboard of binary decisions can support a kind of electron theory, the Dirac equation in one space dimension (and one time).[6] Later I showed how to modify the checker game along less classical, more quantum logical lines, and construct the 1+3 dimensional world of special relativity.[7] Graham Frye and Leonard Susskind showed how other kinds of particles and fields, and entire mass spectra, arise from such games, without attention to realism.[8] But the payoff still eludes us.

The problem is semantics. We must build a kind of dictionary that tells which superposition of nets represents a given laboratory process. Thanks to the conceptual linkage discussed above, we may have to express only one suitably chosen concept of classical physics in quantum topological language to be able to build up the rest. Which? A natural first candidate is time, the relativistic invariant duration or proper time. What is the time if that is the right question, between two points *a* and *b* of a checkerboard flow pattern? Here are some possibilities.[9]

1. A first guess is: Time is the least number of moves required to go from *a* to *b*. This violates an important law of relativity, the triangle inequality,

$$\tau_{ab} + \tau_{bc} \leq \tau_{ac}$$

that embodies the twin paradox. (Here $\tau_{ab}$ means the time between events *a* and *b* according to an unaccelerated clock present at both events. The law says: to stay young, travel.) Next, please.

2. One candidate for time in quantum topology depends not on the number of moves from *a* to *b*, but the number *N* of distinct directed paths from *a* to *b* (following the arrows). The relation might be

$$N = 2^{\tau}, \quad \tau = \log_2 N.$$

This obeys the triangle inequality but seems absurd to classical thought: Don't we take just one path? How can our experience of time depend on the paths we did not take? But in quantum physics, Feynman has accustomed us to the fact that most properties of a system are complementary to a specification of its path and require a superposition of many paths.[10] Moreover, for macroscopically separated points, most points lie close together and pass for one.

The paths of time zero, which seem so paradoxical otherwise, are simply unique paths; they connect points that are joined by no other paths. If $N = 1$, $\tau = 0$. Light is supposed to follow such a path, like the bishop in the game of chess. For particles at rest on the checkerboard, zigzagging at the speed of light, the two concepts of time agree. That is why I chose the number 2 as a base.

3. Another quantity $\tau$ might depend on is the number of events on directed paths from $a$ to $b$. This, too, obeys the triangle inequality.

4. Operational thinking suggests another approach to time. Perhaps, time is to be defined by first defining a clock, as a periodic process, a plexus made up of sub-plexus repeated over and over. Then the question is not the time between two vertices, but the time of an entire sub-plexus.

5. The foregoing are optimistic guesses. Possibly one net has no time concept. Perhaps time is complementary to the net, and more complex than any of the above suggestions.

The situation is still confused by too many possibilities. A great deal of theoretical work is required before this conception of a physical process becomes a testable theory and I can be justified in my conviction that this quantum topology is the viable universe I seek. At present, the physicist knows how time is coupled to space by relativity, and how time is linked to energy via quantum theory, but he does not know what time is.

FOOTNOTES

1. A temporal logic of possibilities is advocated for quantum theory by C. F. v. Weizsaecker, *Die Einheit der Natur*, Munich, 1971, p. 201. Predicates and copredicates are also called states and tests.

2. E. A. Havelock, *Prelude to Plato*, Cambridge, Belknap Press, Harvard University Press, 1963.

3. J. v. Neumann, *Mathematical Foundations of Quantum Mechanics*, Princeton, Princeton University Press, 1955. G. Birkhoff and J. v. Neumann, "Logic of Quantum Mechanics,: *Ann. of Math. 37*, 885 (1936).

4. F. Th. Stcherbatski, *Buddhist Logic*, Dover, New York, 1962. I refer to the following resemblances between that cosmology and the present one, despite the fuzziness inherent in comparing ordinary language (translated Sanskrit) with mathematical language:

   1. The rejection of absolute negation.
   2. The description of the world as a pattern of interdependent acts of termination and origination, the extension of *karma* from the moral to the microphysical domain.
   3. The atomicity of time.
   4. The holistic indecomposability of the world.
   5. The incompleteness of every symbolic description of the world. These tenets recur in process philosophies down the centuries.

5. His *ars combinatoris*, *characteristica universalis*, and *calculus ratiocinator*, respectively. See Philip P. Weiner (ed.), *Leibniz Selections*, Chas. Scribner, 1951.

6. See the Nobel Lecture of R. P. Feynman, and R. P. Feynman and Higgs, *Quantum Mechanics Via Path Integrals*, Ch. 2., Wiley, New York.

7. D. Finkelstein, "Space-Time Code", *The Physical Review, 184*, 1261 (1969).

8. D. Finkelstein, G. Frye, and L. Susskind, "Space-Time Code IV" *The Physical Review,* D9, 2231 (1974).

9. D. Finkelstein and G. McCollum "Quantum Topology", *International Journal of Theoretical Physics (*in press).

10. Op. cit. 6, and references there.

## DISCUSSION AND COMMENT

*By David Park*

The Old Masters understood that there are, with respect to time and process, two ways of looking at the world; we may name them after Heraclitus and Parmenides, after Bergson and Minkowski, after Schrödinger and Heisenberg or, using McTaggart's terminology, after A and B. Heraclitus and Bergson taught that the world is to be understood in terms of process, that the world is new and newly perceived in each instant. For Parmenides the truth is seen if the world is contemplated together with its history. Seen in this way the world is a single unit of existence; it is what it is and does not become something else. Though many writers had mentioned that this view of the world can be represented in diagrammatic form, Minkowski was the first to show that such space-time diagrams are nontrivial: they can be drawn so as to exhibit the latitude within which it does not matter how one distinguishes between space and time in describing the interval between two separate events. In the 1920's two forms of quantum mechanics sprouted side by side, one (Heisenberg) based on a timeless description of the state of the world and the other (Schrödinger) emphasizing process. The moment of illumination came when Pauli, Schrödinger, and Epstein independently understood that these do not represent competing mathematical descriptions of the world but rather that they lead to all the same specific predictions of the results of experiment -- the mathematical form of either can be derived from that of the other by mathematical transformations. This is not to say that Parmenides and Heraclitus were, at bottom, saying the same thing; they were not, but each defined an essential component of a complete and harmonious description of our knowledge of the world. Before its final explanation, this had probably been seen more clearly by Bergson than by anybody else.

In modern physics, the necessity of complementary modes of description is simply a fact, forced upon us by the quantal nature of the world. Whether there are other kinds of complementarity with different fundamental explanations is not known, and very likely the question does not belong to physics. My point in making these remarks is that Finkelstein, in his search for a new form of description, has strayed outside the Covenant: he has made process epistemologically prior to existence. He sees a world that is all process, described by an appropriate logic. "A proposition," he has written, "is a kind of process."

Yet his mathematics is finally that of quantum mechanics and whatever may be the results, it seems to be likely that its content will ultimately admit the same dual modes of description as the rest of modern theory. And this is necessary, since the duality is anchored firmly in our own perceptual modes. I therefore believe that, to the extent that Finkelstein produces a coherent physical theory, it will finally be able to give a coherent answer (though perhaps a very novel one), in their own timeless terms, to those who insist on asking "But what *is* the world?"

Professor Finkelstein has given a largely self-contained account of his recent work. The following references, drawn from his recent writings, will help the reader who wishes to go further.

On the view of nature as process: D. Bohm in C. H. Waddington, ed., *Towards a Theoretical Biology, 2,* Aldine, Chicago, 1969.

On the view that properties of space-time follow from a theory of process: C. F. v Weizsäcker in C. Enz and J. Mehra, ed., *Physical Reality and Mathematical Representation,* Reidel, Dordrecht, 1974; R. Penrose in J. Klauder, ed., *Magic Without Magic,* Freeman, San Francisco, 1972, and in D. J. A. Welch, ed., *Combinatorial Mathematics and its Applications,* Academic Press, London, 1971; J. A. Wheeler in J. Mehra, ed., *The Physicist's Conception of Nature,* Reidel, Dordrecht, 1973.

The development of the idea presented here: a series of papers in the *Physical Review* of which the two most recent and most relevant are D. Finkelstein, G. Frye, and L. Susskind, *Phys. Rev.* D9, 2231 (1974) (paper V), and D. Finkelstein, *Phys. Rev.,* submitted (paper VI). See also D. Finkelstein and G. McCollum, "Unified Quantum Theory," in L. Castell, M. Drieschnes and C. F. von Welzsäcker (eds.). Quantum Theory and Structures of Time and Space, Carl Hansen Verlag, Munich, 1975, pp.15-54.

# Thermodynamics, Cosmology, and the Physical Constants

P.T. Landsberg

*ABSTRACT*

*Certain problems arise when cosmology and thermodynamics are combined, and these are explained. Reasons are given why the cosmological arrow of time should not be regarded as more fundamental than other arrows of time. It is shown by analogy how certain restrictions in classical thermodynamics can be lifted if a self-gravitating object is included in one's thermodynamic system of interest, and if general relativity is used. A matter-plus-radiation type of cosmology is discussed which leads to the view that the universe is old, having gone through many cycles. Finally the values of the constants, h, c, G, and H are used, together with the qualitative assumption that G and H depend similarly on time, to give rough estimates of the mass of an elementary particle, the number of particles in the universe, and the ratio of the gravitational to the electrical force between two particles. The same type of argument can be used to show that if electric charges can depend only on h, c, and H, of which only H depends on time, then these charges must be independent of time.*

## 1. INTRODUCTION

Seven years ago I appended to my discussion before the Society[1] 19 views on irreversibility and entropy, and today I should like to supplement these by adding some physicists' views concerning the arrow of time (Appendix). Contradictions are revealed in both cases, and caution should be induced; all the more so if one considers the categorical nature of some of the statements cited. My own views have been reformulated in an inaugural lecture last year[2] and I must therefore forego the temptation to try and paint a comprehensive picture of the physicist's time concept on the present occasion.

Nevertheless some broad viewpoints will be put forward: that certain specific problems arise when cosmology and thermodynamics are combined (§2); that, while cosmology is important, the view that the cosmological arrow dominates all other arrows of time is not established (§3); that the inclusion of gravitation and of general relativity lift certain restrictions imposed by classical thermodynamics (§4); and that there is some evidence that the universe has gone through many cycles already (§5). The delight of a theorectical physicist is to deduce quantitative estimates from qualitative assumptions. This is attempted in Section 6 where the number of particles in the universe and the mass of a typical stable particle are deduced from the numerical values of $h$, $c$, the gravitational constant $G$ and the Hubble parameter $H$, together with the qualitative assumption that $H$ and $G$ have the same time dependence.

## 2. RELATIVISTIC COSMOLOGY + THERMODYNAMICS = SOME DIFFICULTIES

In this section attention will be drawn to two difficulties which arise when one relates thermodynamics to general relativity and cosmology, difficulties which do not seem to have been pointed out before. (a) When a system of interacting particles is considered, the interactions may tend to cancel out in a large system. This occurs in a plasma consisting of positively and negatively charged particles, since a large enough volume tends to be electrically neutral. It then hardly interacts electrically with another large and electrically neutral part of the same system some distance away. However, gravitational interactions do not cancel, and large but distinct parts of a system are generally in gravitational interaction. Under these condition the energy, which in normal thermodynamics is an extensive quantity, loses its extensivity; on doubling the system its energy does not double because of the gravitational interactions which enter as an "extra". The same point applies to the entropy. This means that in relativistic cosmology energy and entropy are not extensive: if one halves a volume element, ones needs a convention which tells one how to associate the gravitational interaction energy with each of the two halves. On the other hand, in theoretical analyses one employs the cosmological principle and simple metrics, which asserts precisely that the energy (or entropy) in any comoving volume element is the same as that in any other of the same size. We thus have the puzzle that whereas simple models in cosmology imply extensivity, gravitational interaction denies extensivity, and hence some convention is called for to harmonize the two views. (b) It is well-known in relativity that when the masses of objects are large enough the objects become unstable and collapse. Hence large masses do not necessarily exist. A well-known example is provided by the Chandrasekhar limit: white dwarf stars cannot be more massive than about 1.4 solar masses. This type of consideration is in flat contradiction with a procedure known as taking the "thermodynamic limit". This procedure secures simplified equations for a thermodynamic system by imagining it to become infinitely massive and infinitely extended, while keeping its mass density at the original value. It is widely used. Thus the existence of limiting masses is incompatible with arguments based on the thermodynamic limit.

The above considerations result ultimately from the fact that systems of particles interacting by long-range forces (such as Coulomb or gravitational forces) ought to be ruled out on p. 1 on any book on thermodynamics, even though they seldom are [I did it on p.9 [3]] . Later on systems can be considered which are subject to externally applied fields. Even Coulomb systems can be considered because of the simplifying feature mentioned above. But self-gravitating systems are more difficult to handle. Their gravitational collapse (to black hole states) does not seem to be reproducible in computer studies which are, however, confined to small system. These studies show that such systems can contract by ejecting a particle of comparatively high kinetic energy. Indeed the absence of an equilibrium state makes it difficult to apply thermodynamics unless some dissipative medium is also included in the considerations.[4,5]

The way around the difficulty (a) in cosmology is to use relativistic equations which include the dynamic effects of the gravitational interactions in some kind of smeared-out universe. When it comes to the equations of state of the cosmological fluid, the gravitational effects are not imposed again: first of all, it is difficult and little of this sort of theory has been attempted. Secondly, this second introduction of gravitation may involve a kind of "double counting," and should be best avoided. The combination of cosmological equations (which take account of gravitation) and of statistical mechanics (in which gravitation is ignored) leads therefore to hybrid theories. Most present theories are of this type.

We shall adopt this approach also in this paper (see Section 5). We shall get around difficulty (b) by simply not using the thermodynamic limit.

## 3. THE COSMOLOGICAL ARROW OF TIME DOES NOT DOMINATE

It has been suggested that thermodynamic irreversibility is due to cosmological expansion. It is said that it causes the darkness of the night sky and the red shift of the spectral lines and it is therefore a real phenomenon which can cause other effects such as irreversibility. In a sense cosmology contains all subjects because it is the story of everything, including biology, psychology, and human history. In that single sense it can be said to contain an explanation also of time's arrow. But this is not what is meant by those who advocate the cosmological explanation of irreversibility.[6] They imply that in some way the time arrow of cosmology imposes its sense on the thermodynamic arrow. I wish to disagree with this view.

The explanation assumes that the universe is expanding. While this is current orthodoxy, there is no certainty about it. The red-shifts might be due to quite different causes. For example, when light passes through expanding clouds of gas it will be red-shifted.[7] A large number of such clouds might one day be invoked to explain these red shifts. It seems an odd procedure to attempt to "explain" everyday occurrences, such as the diffusion of milk into coffee, by means of theories of the universe which are themselves less firmly established than the phenomena to be explained. Most people believe in explaining one set of things in terms of others about which they are more certain, and the explanation of normal irreversible phenomena in terms of the cosmological expansion is not in this category.

As regards the darkness of the night sky, it shows indeed that the universe is a sink for radiation, which it absorbs as a gourmet does his paté. Does this *prove* that there is a cosmological arrow of time and that the universe is expanding? Not at all; a static universe with stars of finite ages could also produce a dark night sky, and there are several other possible explanations.[8]

I am not saying that the universe *is* static, but I *am* saying that the theory of the dominance of the cosmological arrow cannot be established by the above arguments. I regard as the most fundamental arrow that which is furnished by statistical thermodynamics (See Appendix).

Professor Park has suggested to me a wider interpretation of the notion of a cosmological arrow. The term could be used without caring about what precisely the universe is doing, in particular whether it is expanding or not. The universe is then simply a large system with which every small system is in interaction. While this is indeed another way of using the idea of a cosmological arrow, I would prefer this type of consideration to be considered as part of statistical thermodynamics. The reason is that specific properties of the universe are not used, so that it has really the status of a reservoir.

How the continuing increase of entropy can be explained without reference to the evolution of the universe will be illustrated by means of a picturesque example in the next section.

## 4. ENTROPY CAN INCREASE WITHOUT LIMIT IN AN ISOLATED SYSTEM WITH GRAVITATION

A gravitational system reaches on contraction states of more and more negative total energy, since the gravitational potential energy of masses $m_1$, $m_2$ separated by a distance $r$ is $-Gm_1m_2/r$, where $G$ is Newton's gravitational constant, and r can approach the value zero. What effect does this have on the entropy?

Although gravitational thermodynamics is only in its early stages, one can see the effect of such systems by recalling some old friends[9] in a Himalayan hilltop community which was completely isolated except that it provided for fuel and food by paying porters who carried these things up the mountain. To pay for this, without reducing the total happiness of the community, it was always arranged that some money (£$x$) was taken from a rich man, and a smaller sum (£$y$) was given to a poorer man in the community. Although $y$ is smaller than $x$, the poor man's gain in happiness was as great as, or even greater than the rich man's loss in happiness, for two pounds means less to a rich man than one pound means to a poor man. The difference of $x-y$ pounds was available to the porters. Now this community increased in happiness until in the end it was in danger of dying out, since a state was being approached in which all men had the same amount of money and so nothing was available for paying the porters. This model community would have increased in happiness, which was its self-imposed constraint, and then it would have died. This indeed would have corresponded to the heat death of the universe, or indeed to the attainment of equilibrium in any isolated system according to classical thermodynamics. Time's arrow would eventually have died out.

This correspondence to classical thermodynamics is brought about because the entropy of an isolated system never decreases, just as the happiness in our Himalayan community never decreases. Furthermore the final state of a classical physical system is one of uniform temperature (this corresponds to the maximum happiness). Underlying this model is the assumption that money must not be printed in the community, and this corresponds to the conservation of energy according the first law of thermodynamics.

I left this community to linger in its perilous state sixteen years ago. Like the writer of thrillers who cannot afford to let his hero die, I must now relate a marvellous event. One of the porters, Mr. P. say, hearing of the precarious state of the community, offered to join it for good. "But", he said, "I shall be different from all the others, for I shall not mind accumulating any amount of debts." The social scientists in the community of course did not know how to assess the happiness of this immigrant, and their situation illuminates our situation as present-day physicists, in that we have difficulties with the entropy of self-gravitating systems. However, the porter's action enabled new life to pulse through the community. When the porters who had carried food and fuel up wanted to be paid, Mr. P's a account was debited. The village printed extra pound notes and gave a little to some members of the community, while keeping the rest for food and fuel. In this way new inequalities of wealth began to develop in the community and, although Mr. P's debts rose to astronomical proportions, he did not mind, and indeed some transactions became possible again in the community, and this is how it happened.

Every Friday all money was deposited in banks; accounts (all positive) were added up on Saturdays; and the total $W$ (i.e., wealth in terms of readily available cash) of the community was determined. This remained constant for long periods while there was no external trading, since of course money was not being printed or lost. Mr. P's arrival did not change the constancy of the total liquid cash $W$. But it did mean that by assigning a debit balance to his account, the community was able to print money which could be assigned to certain accounts without altering the total $W$. This increased happiness and set up inequalities which then formed a basis for renewed trade inside the community. The total happiness *did not decrease* in this trade and money for food and fuel could again be put aside. When the stage of equal wealth and hence stagnation approached again, Mr. P's account was debited by an additional amount and an equal amount of money was printed. Without changing $W$, trade inside the community was again able to flourish. In this way the community was able to live with increasing total happiness for ever after.

The source of this renewal was Mr. P's account which could go increasingly into the red, just as gravitational potential energy becomes more negative as a body contracts.† This is the first consequence of note, and it is connected with the fact that general relativity does not know a law of energy conservation and that the integrated proper energy of the cosmological fluid does not have to remain constant but can change. The manner of this change arises from the details of the processes involved (this has not been modelled here). Thus the proper energy of an element of the cosmological fluid decreases with time during expansion, increases during contraction, and in both cases its magnitude is affected by the pressure [equation (5.2), below].

As a second consequence note that there is no final limit on the happiness which can be generated, once the money supply can in principle be increased. It illustrates that in relativity a developing model of the universe which has some irreversibility built into it (i.e., happiness is increasing rather than remaining constant) is able to exhibit an ever increasing integrated proper entropy. It does not reach a final state of maximum entropy compatible with the given total energy available at the time, as expected from classical thermodynamics. This is due to the presence of gravitation in a system, consisting of two or more fluids[10, 11].

These ideas should help with the next section.

## 5. HAS THE UNIVERSE ALREADY GONE THROUGH MANY CYCLES?

Considering a homogenous and isotropic Friedmann model with matter and radiation, one knows that if they are independent of each other each develops adiabatically, i.e., according to the law

$$T_i V^{\gamma_i - 1} = A_i' \qquad (i = m \text{ or } r)$$

where $V$ is a standard comoving volume, $T_m$ and $T_r$ are the temperatures of non-relativistic matter and radiation, the $A_i'$ are constants, and

†Quantum effects may provide a lower limit, in which case Mr. P's account can carry only finite debts.

$$\gamma_m = \frac{5}{3} \qquad \gamma_r = \frac{4}{3}$$

Now $V \propto R^3(t)$ where $R$ is the cosmological scale factor which is a function of time. It follows that, if the $A_i$ are other constants,

$$T_m R^2 = A_m \;, \quad T_r R = A_r \;, \quad T_m/T_r = \frac{A_m/A_r}{R} \tag{5.1}$$

Suppose now that the interaction energy rises without limit as $R \to 0$. It is then reasonable to suppose that matter and radiation are in equilibrium, in the sense that $T_m = T_r$, at times near the big bang. As expansion proceeds, and $R$ rises, the interaction weakens and one would expect the matter temperature to drop more rapidly ($T_m \propto R^{-2}$) than the radiation temperature ($T_r \propto R^{-1}$). During the long period including the present there is weak interaction and (5.1) holds. If there is an oscillation, compression will turn non-relativistic matter into relativistic matter which also satisfies $T_m R$ = constant, so that $T_m R$ should drop during this period. During high compression at the end of the cycle the strong interaction will make the matter and the radiation temperature again roughly the same. Indeed, as matter gains heat from the still hotter radiation, one may even find that $T_m/T_r$ can overshoot unity for a while, but there should then follow a return to equilibrium.

Similar arguments should hold for the total energies $U_m$, $U_r$. During the middle part of the cycle one would expect the standard results

$$U_m \propto R^{-3}, \qquad U_r \propto R^{-4}$$

Thus the energy of the radiation would drop more rapidly during the expansion and rise more rapidly during the contraction.

If $E_m$ is the rate of transfer of energy from radiation to matter, the entropy production rate as a function of time can be taken to be

$$\dot{S} = \left[\frac{1}{T_{\mathrm{m}}} - \frac{1}{T_{\mathrm{r}}}\right] E_{\mathrm{m}}$$

This is always non-negative, provided only

$$E_{\mathrm{m}} > 0 \rightarrow T_{\mathrm{r}} > T_{\mathrm{m}} \qquad \text{energy passes to matter}$$

and

$$E_{\mathrm{m}} < 0 \rightarrow T_{\mathrm{r}} < T_{\mathrm{m}} \qquad \text{energy passes from matter}$$

The constraint $\dot{S} > 0$ can be realised, for example, by choosing the radiative interaction

$$E_{\mathrm{m}} = AU_{\mathrm{m}}U_{\mathrm{r}}(T_{\mathrm{r}}^{4} - T_{\mathrm{m}}^{4})/(\text{volume})$$

when entropy is found to increase continuously,[12] and the other statements made above can also be verified.

At high compression the entropy is roughly constant, since there is almost equilibrium. For purposes of machine computation one can cut out the singularity and start the next cycle with the same entropy at the same values of $U_{\mathrm{m}}$ , $U_{\mathrm{r}}$ , and $R$ as occurred at the cutoff, but with an equal and opposite value of $dR/dt$, which turns the contraction into an expansion. This is of course a highly irregular procedure since such singularities as the contraction of the universe to a point follow from the equations of motion if they are taken literally. This singularities have been the subject of much work, some of which is described in this volume by Dr. P. C. W. Davies. Nonetheless there are some (and the present author is one of them) who regard such "point states" of the universe as unphysical. This is not to deny the importance and intrinsic interest of the singularities. It is, however, a justification for the highly irregular procedure to which reference has just been made.

If $U_o$ is a fixed unit of energy and $R_o$ a fixed value of the scale factor, one can use dimensionless variables

$$y_m \equiv U_m/U_o, \quad y_r \equiv U_r/U_o, \quad r \equiv R/R_o$$

At the maximum extent of the computed model one finds the values given in Table 1. The total energy at maximum extent is seen to increase with cycle number while the energy density at maximum extent decreases with cycle number.

Table 1 -- Values at the Point of Maximum Expansion

| | $y_m$ | $y_r$ | $y \equiv y_m + y_r$ | $r$ | $y/r^3$ |
|---|---|---|---|---|---|
| 1st cycle | 1.032 | 0.158 | 1.190 | 2.697 | 0.06066 |
| 2nd cycle | 1.032 | 0.161 | 1.193 | 2.704 | 0.06034 |
| 3rd cycle | 1.032 | 0.164 | 1.196 | 2.711 | 0.06003 |

This may be understood in terms of the basic equations of the model, which are

$$\dot{U} + 4\pi p\, R^2 \dot{R} = 0 \qquad (p = p_m + p_r, \quad U = U_m + U_r) \tag{5.2}$$

$$\tfrac{1}{2}\dot{R}^2 + \frac{G}{c^2}\,\frac{U}{R} = C$$

where $C$ is a negative constant and $p$ is the pressure. If the maximum of $R$ in cycle $j$ is denoted by $R^{(j)}$, it follows that, since $U$ and $R$ have opposite signs, $U$ goes through its minimum when $R$ goes through its maximum. Also at this maximum

$$U^{(j)} \propto R^{(j)}, \quad \text{i.e.} \quad \rho^{(j)} \propto [R^{(j)}]^{-2}$$

where $\rho$ is the total energy density. The model shows that $R^{(j)}$ (i.e., $r^{(j)}$) increases with $j$, hence $\rho^{(j)}$ (i.e., $y^{(j)}/r^{(j)3}$) decreases with $j$. Thus, away from the endpoints, the energy density drops to lower and lower values as the cycles follow each other.

This makes it difficult for someone alive in this model during a "late" cycle to believe that there is an adequate energy density present for another contraction to occur. This seems to be the precise position in which we find ourselves. The model thus suggests an explanation of the fact that cosmologists find it difficult to decide if the universe will contract again, or if it will continue to expand indefinitely.

As the cycles continue the entropy goes on increasing, and the model is then found to make full use of the freedom bestowed on a thermodynamic system which includes gravitation and is relativistic: its entropy can increase without limit (see Section 4).

Our model is somewhat artificial and so we did not pursue its properties to many cycles. Its properties are those already expected on general grounds, but it furnishes a specific example of these general principles and shows how one can calculate through the discontinuity. It furthermore finially disproves the notion that the entropy law excludes a cyclic world process.[13]

The model also suggests the possibility that the cycles may have started off with a minor fluctuation which have become larger and larger as the millennia passed. It is rather like a weight oscillating at the end of a spring which becomes weaker as time passes, thus allowing the oscillations to become larger.

## 6. AN ESTIMATE OF THE MAIN MASSES IN THE UNIVERSE

In this concluding section I should like to tell a different story. It belongs to a meeting on *Time* because the crucial assumption to be made is that Newton's gravitational constant $G$ depends on time, and that it does so in precisely the way in which the Hubble parameter $H$ depends on time. This hypothesis, due to Dirac, is forty years old and the justification is as follows.

The ratio of the electrostatic to the gravitational forces between proton and electron is a huge number

$$\frac{e^2/r}{Gm_p m_e/r} \simeq 10^{40} \qquad \begin{array}{l} \mathrm{e} = \text{electron} \\ \mathrm{p} = \text{proton} \end{array}$$

Let the age of the Universe, or more precisely the time since the last big bang, be $T$. From the reciprocal of the present value $H_0$ of the Hubble parameter it is

$$T \simeq H_0^{-1} \simeq 10^{17}\,\mathrm{sec}$$

One then finds that $T$ expressed in terms of an atomic unit of time such as $e^2/m_e c^3 \simeq 10^{-23}$ sec is also of order $10^{40}$. An empirical relation results of the type (other units of time and other masses could be chosen)

$$G \simeq \frac{2^4}{Tm_e^2 m_p c^3}$$

Now the rough equality of two distinct huge dimensionless numbers is perhaps no accident, but could be fundamental, and therefore valid at *all* times. This "large number hypothesis" implies a time-dependence of $G$ such that if $c$ and the masses of the elementary particles are assumed constant,

$$G(T) \propto H(T)$$

After this preliminary remark we proceed with description of more recent work.

In cosmological theories which involve as the only fundamental quantities $G$, $H$, and the constants $c$ and $h$, all masses must have the form $h^\alpha H^\beta G^\gamma c^\delta$, whence dimensional analysis shows that the unknown constants $\alpha$, $\beta$, $\gamma$, $\delta$, can all be reduced to one unknown constant which will be called $b$. The other constants ($e$, $h$, $c$) will be assumed time-independent, in agreement with current views.[14] One then finds that all masses are reducible to the basic masses

$$m(b) = k(b) \left[\frac{h^3 H}{G^2}\right]^{1/5} \left[\frac{c^5}{hH^2 G}\right]^{b/15}$$

where $k(b)$ are unidentified dimensionless constants. Dimensional analysis depends on the assumption that these constants are of order unity, and this will be assumed.

The point about making the Dirac hypothesis is that $m(b)$ will in general be time-dependent unless the value of $b$ is such that $m(b)$ depends only on the ratio $H/G$. In other words the hypothesis taken together with (6.1) leads to a unique value of $b$ which should furnish time-independent masses, i.e. masses of the stable elementary particles. Now in terms of time dependence

$$m(b) \propto H^{(3-2b)/15} \Big/ G^{(6+b)/15} \propto G^{-(b+1)/5}$$

Hence $b \simeq -1$ for elementary particles. The interactions between particles, and other effects, make this only a rough theory, but Fig. 1 shows that the rest masses of the known particles do cluster around the value $b = -1$. If in fact $G$ decreases with time,

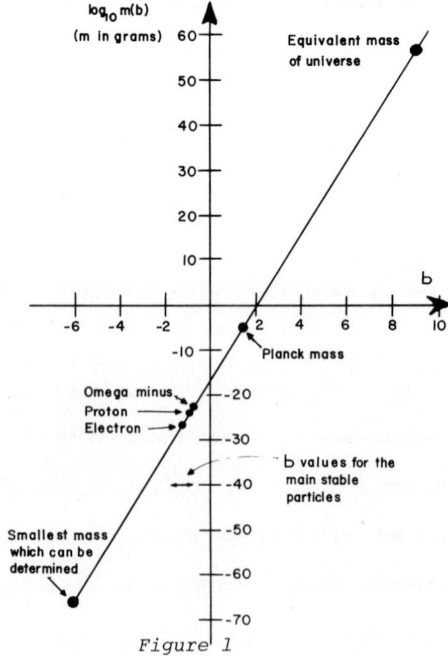


*Figure 1*

then the large masses $m(b)$ increase ($b > -1$), the small masses decrease ($b < -1$), while length standards based on $b = -1$ remain constant in time. A typical example of the latter is the Compton wavelength $h/cm(-1)$.

The smallest mass determinable in the period $T \simeq H^{-1}$ since the last big bang is from the uncertainty relation $h/c^2 T$ which is of the order $m(-5)$, and it should become smaller with lapse of time, while the mass equivalent of the energy of the universe is of order

$$m(9) \simeq c^3/GH \quad (6.2)$$

which increases with time.[15]

In order that this analysis be compatible with an oscillating universe the time periods involved must be confined to the interval between the beginning of the last cycle and the period of maximum extent of that cycle. In this way one can avoid the infinite mass (6.2) at the maximum extent, when $H = 0$. It would appear therefore that Dirac's hypothesis can be valid only within limited periods in each cycle if an oscillating universe is assumed.

If one grants this, one can take several further steps. One of them is to estimate the number of particles in the universe at

$$n \simeq \frac{m(9)}{m(-1)} \simeq \left[\frac{c^5}{hGH^2}\right]^{2/3} \simeq 24 \times 10^{80}$$

As regards the time dependence of n since the last big bang, we have

$$n \propto G^{-2}$$

because $H \propto G$. We may ask: Why is the dimensionless quantity $n$ so large, contrary to the usual properties of dimensionless numbers? The answer could be: Because $G$ has decreased so much since the last big bang; it is large because the universe is old[16], or, more precisely, it has come a long way since the last big bang.

The ratio $\lambda$ of the gravitational to the electric forces between two particles can now be calculated, for a time-independent electronic charge $e$. One has, if the fine structure constant is denoted by $\alpha \equiv e^2/hc \simeq 1/137$,

$$\lambda = \frac{Gm^2/r^2}{e^2/r^2} \simeq \frac{1}{\alpha}\frac{Gm(-1)^2}{hc} = \frac{1}{\alpha}\left[\frac{hH^2G}{c^5}\right]^{1/3} = \frac{1}{\alpha\sqrt{n}} \simeq 10^{-43}$$

The smallness of the ratio $\lambda$ is thus a consequence of the theory outlined, and depends on the length of time since the last big bang. The other cosmological coincidences can be explained in the same way.[15]

There is some evidence for the time-dependence of $G$, which is crucial to the present argument[17,18]: $\dot{G}/G \simeq -8 \times 10^{-11}$ (years)$^{-1}$. Such variations of $G$ can be incorporated in Newtonian[19] and relativistic[20,21] theory.

As an admirer of F. Hund, I want to amend his remark (See Appendix) that past and future are markedly different "because the universe is young." An entropy curve is still steeply rising with time in the early part of a cycle and then flattens out near the maximum. In this region the difference between past and future is liable to be blurred. We now incorporate this view into our philosophy by remarking that the strong difference between past and future is due to the fact *that in the present cycle we are not yet close to the epoch of maximum extent*. There is now no reference to an absolute beginning of the history of the universe, as is implied by Hund's reference to its *youth*. I insist only that the universe is at an early stage of its cycle, even though this may be the hundredth cycle of an old and tired universe. These comments may illustrate the remark, attributed to Bondi,[22] that the universe has a low entropy because "the night sky is very black with very bright points, the stars, in it": the entropy may be relatively low even in an old but oscillating universe.

There has been some discussion in the literature concerning the possibility that the basic electronic charge depends on time, but the consensus is that it does not. One can investigate this point by dimensional analysis. The coupling parameter for the interaction is now $e^2$ instead of $Gm^2$, and we seek to determine its order of magnitude. Suppose it can depend on $h$, $H$, and $c$. Then the possible dependence on time is implied by the possible dependence of $e$ on $H$. Let us put

$$e = kh^{\alpha}H^{\beta}c^{\gamma}$$

where $k$ is a dimensionless constant. Then

$$\left[M^{\frac{1}{2}}L^{3/2}T^{-1}\right] = \left[M^{\alpha}L^{2\alpha+\gamma}T^{-\alpha-\beta-\gamma}\right]$$

and the resulting three equations imply

$$\alpha = \gamma = \tfrac{1}{2}, \qquad \beta = 0$$

so that

$$e = k(hc)^{\frac{1}{2}}$$

Thus $e$ is independent of time and $k^2$ is in fact equal to the famous fine-structure constant $e^2/hc \simeq 1/137$.

REFERENCES


1. P. T. Landsberg, 1970, "Time in statistical physics and in special relativity," *The Study of Time*, Vol. 1, p. 59.

2. P. T. Landsberg, 1975, *A Matter of Time* (Southampton University). An inaugural lecture.

3. P. T. Landsberg, 1961, *Thermodynamics with Quantum Statistical Illustrations* (New York: Wiley).

4. R. H. Miller, 1973, "On the 'thermodynamics' of self-gravitating *N*-body systems," Ap. J. *180*, 759-782.

5. M. J. Haggerty and G. Severne, 1974, "Monotonic evolution of Boltzmann's *H* in weekly coupled gravitational fields," Nature *249*, 537-538.

6. B. Gal-Or, 1972, "The crisis about the origin of irreversibility and time anisotropy," Science *176*, 11-17.

7. P. T. Landsberg, 1971, unpublished.

8. P. T. Landsberg and D. A. Evans, 1972, "What Olbers might have said," in *The Emerging Universe* (Ed. W. C. Saslaw and K. C. Jacobs; Charlottesville: University Press of Virginia) p. 107-130.

9. P. T. Landsberg, 1961, *Entropy and the Unity of Knowledge* (Cardiff: University of Wales Press). An inaugural lecture.

10. R. C. Tolman, 1934, *Relativity, Thermodynamics and Cosmology* (Oxford: University Press).

11. P. C. W. Davies, 1974, *The Physics of Time Asymmetry* (Leighton Buzzard: Surrey University Press; Berkeley: University of California Press).

12. P. T. Landsberg and D. Park, 1975, "Entropy in an oscillating universe," Proc. R. Soc. *A346*, 485-495.

13. E. T. Whittaker, 1942, *The Beginning and End of the World* (Oxford University Press) p. 39. The Riddell Memorial Lectures.

14. A. M. Wolfe, R. L. Brown and M. S. Roberts, Phys. Rev. Letts. *37*, 179 (1976).

15. P. T. Landsberg and N. T. Bishop, 1975, "A Cosmological deduction of the order of magnitude of an elementary particle mass and of the cosmological coincidences," Physics Lett. *53A*, 109-110.

16. S. Weinberg, 1972, *Gravitation and Cosmology* (New York: Wiley), p. 621.

17. T. C. van Flandern, 1975, "A determination of the rate of change of *G*," M. N. Roy. Astr. Soc. *170*, 333-342.

18. D. S. Dearborn and D. N. Schramm, 1974, "Limits on the variation of *G* from clusters of galaxies," Nature *247*, 441.

19. P. T. Landsberg and N. T. Bishop, 1975, "A principle of impotence allowing for Newtonian cosmologies with a time-dependent gravitational constant," M. N. Roy. Astr. Soc. *171*, 279-286.

20. C. Brans and R. H. Dicke, 1961, "Mach's principle and a Relativistic Theory of Gravitation," Phys. Rev. *124*, 925-935.

21. N. T. Bishop, 1976, "Cosmology and a general scalar-tensor theory of gravity," (Unpublished).

22. J. Gribbin, 1975, "Oscillating Universe bounces back," Nature *259*, 15-16.

# APPENDIX

## *Remarks made by physicists on the direction of time*

The selection is somewhat arbitrary and possibly not typical of the cited authors' present views.

1. Statistical thermodynamics furnishes the clue

"Only the second law of thermodynamics indicates clearly a direction of time".

C. F. V. Weizsäcker, 1939.

"It is not at present clear if...it is possible to deduce the law of entropy increase from classical mechanics".

L. D. Landau and E. M. Lifshitz, 1966.

"We thus come to an interesting relation between the effect of the cosmological arrow of time and of the 'microscopic arrow of time' on the thermodynamic evolution of a system: both suppress the anti-kinetic behaviour and lead to an irreversible approach to equilibrium".

A. Aharony, 1971.

"No asymmetry between the two directions of time is to be found in the general laws of nature; it is due to another fact about the world, namely its low entropy. The first appearance of the earlier states of still lower entropy cannot be understood physically..... Past and future are so markedly different because the universe is still very young".

F. Hund, 1972.

"If, however, the choice were between abandoning the Friedmann models and deriving the direction of time from some source other than cosmology (such as thermodynamics) then I think most physicists would chose the latter".

G. J. Suggett, 1975.

"Suppose a system develops without interference from the outside. Then it chooses among its available equilibrium states in proportion to their realisabilities. I shall call this principle *P*. Time has a direction in virtue of principle *P*, but, for more penetrating observers, the direction of time has to be *derived* by averaging".

P. T. Landsberg, 1975.

2. Statistics does not provide the answer

"If all the laws of physics are time-symmetrical, they would not be able to describe a contracting universe".

"Surely it is not by rejecting information about our system that we can make it reveal to us the sense of time which it would not otherwise show".

T. Gold, 1958.

"It is somewhat offensive to our thought to suggest that if we know a system in detail then we cannot tell which way time is going, but if we take a blurred view, a statistical view of it, that is to say throw away some information, then we can..."

H. Bondi, 1962.

"The 'arrow' of time...does not seem to be of a stochastic character".

K. Popper, 1965.

3. Explanations using past and future as unexplained (or primitive) concepts

"But while the distinction of prior and subsequent events may be immaterial with respect to mathematical fictions, it is quite otherwise with respect to the events in the real world. It should not be forgotten...that while the probabilities of subsequent events may often be determined from the probabilities of prior events, it is rarely the case that probabilities of prior events can be determined from those of subsequent events, for we are rarely justified in excluding the consideration of the antecedent probability of the prior events".

J. W. Gibbs, 1902.

"We can now understand the anisotropy of time. The future is, by definition, the direction in which prediction is possible.... A complete mathematical description of the universe must unfold from a description of the initial state. It is not possible to reconstruct the past history of the universe by working backward from a complete macroscopic description of the present state".

D. Layzer, 1967.

"One can *define* a direction of time by stating that the instant of reception is *later* than the instant of emission...this point of view makes it possible to avoid the paradoxes and confusion found in the literature. In fact, the invariance of the mechanical laws for time reversal is not contradictory with the distinction between past and future just introduced".

L. Rosenfeld, 1972.
See also in Caldirola, 1961, page 3 and in Gold 1967, page 193.

"Irreversibility and the generalised second law are derivable from the existence of...two categories of instants: an 'information gathering category' (the past), and a 'prediction category' (the future). The existence of these two categories seems to be a fundamental feature of nature, not explainable in terms of the second law or in terms of any other physical law".

A. Hobson, 1971.

4. Gravitation is responsible

"...a falling apple a kilometer away over an arc of ten centimeters is ample to mix up the trajectory of a mole of normal gas in a time of milliseconds..."

"...the arrow of time then only an illusion? It is the purpose of this note to answer stoutly the arrow is real, that is, not subjective, that it is not essentially cosmological, that it arises from an inescapable feature of all physical theory".

P. Morrison, 1966.

"We have reached a remarkable conclusion. The origin of *all* thermodynamic irreversibility in the real universe depends ultimately on gravitation. *Any* gravitating universe that can exist and contains more than one type of interacting material *must* be asymmetric in time, both globally in its motion, and locally in its thermodynamics".

P. C. W. Davies, 1974.

5. The undiscovered half of the universe is the culprit

"One finds that the physical difference between the two directions of time can be explained only by the circumstance that there are in the world areas which do not satisfy the theories [classical and wave mechanics] which lead to thermodynamics".

M. Bronstein and L. Landau, 1933.

"In a world that was perfectly symmetric with respect to the time axis, matter of opposite time senses would decouple...all observers would be aware of an apparent asymmetry in time...that was merely a measure of their ignorance of the other half of the universe".

F. R. Stannard, 1966.

6. Other contenders: Quantum mechanics, electrodynamics, boundary conditions, and interactions with the surroundings

"The two directions of time are not equivalent in quantum mechanics and it is possible that the law of entropy increase is the 'macroscopic' description of this state of affairs".

L. D. Landau and E. M. Lifshitz, 1966.

"It is sometimes said that electrodynamic theory itself introduces time asymmetry...it is a matter of experience that retarded potentials give the correct answer while advanced do not. Is this a case of time's arrow being contained in each elementary process... ? More careful consideration shows that this is not so".

T. Gold, 1974.

"...the laws of physics are symmetric in regard to time, and so the asymmetry must arise from boundary conditions".

W. H. McCrea, 1975.

"The thermodynamic arrow of time does not come at all from the physical system itself..., it comes from the connection of the system with the outside world".

"We can say that if the physical laws are such that matter is created then time's arrow is explained and understood".

F. Hoyle, 1962.

"It is entirely possible and consistent to speak of the *atypically* behaving branch systems, whose entropy increases are *counter directed* with respect to those of the majority, as *decreasing* their entropies in the positive direction of time...we are able to give the usual temporal description of fluctuation phenomena in this way..."

A. Grünbaum, 1974.

REFERENCES TO THE APPENDIX

Aharony, A., 1971, "Time reversal, symmetry violation and the H-theorem." Physics Letters, *37A*, 45-46.

Bondi, H., 1962, "Physics and Cosmology." Observatory, *82*, 133-143. (Halley Lecture).

Bronstein, M. and Landau, L., 1933, "On the second law of thermodynamics and global connections in the cosmos." Phys. Z.d. Soviet Union, *4*, 114-119. In German.

Caldirola, P. (Ed.), 1961, *Ergodic theories*. (New York: Academic Press.)

Davies, P. C. W., 1974, *The Physics of Time Asymmetry*. (London: Surrey University Press) page 109.

Fraser, J. T., Haber, F. C. and Müller, G. H. (Ed.), 1972, *The Study of Time*. (Berlin: Springer.)

Gal-Or, B. (Ed.), 1974, *Modern Developments in Thermodynamics*. (New York: Wiley.)

Gibbs, J. W., 1902, *Elementary Principles in Statistical Mechanics*. (New Haven: Yale University Press) page 150-151.

Gold, T., 1958, at the 11th International Physics Congress, Solvay. See also Am. J. Phys. *30*, 403-410, (1962) Richtmyer Lecture).

Gold, T. (Ed.), 1967, *The Nature of Time*. (Ithaca: Cornell University Press.)

Gold, T., 1974, "The world map and the apparent flow of time," in Gal-Or (Ed.), 1974, 63-72.

Grünbaum, A., 1974, "Popper's view on the arrow of time," in *The Philosophy of Karl Popper* II (Ed. P. A. Schlipp). (LaSalle, Illinois: Open Court) page 793.

Hobson, A., 1971, *Concepts in Statistical Mechanics*. (New York: Gordon and Breach) page 156.

Hoyle, F., 1965, "The Asymmetry of Time," Third Annual Lecture to the Research Students' Association, Canberra, 1962 (Canberra: Australian National University).

Hoyle, F. and Narlikar, J. V., 1974, *Action at a Distance in Physics and Cosmology*. (San Francisco: Freeman.)

Hund, F., 1972, "Time as physical concept," in: Fraser, J. T., et al. (Eds.) 1972, 39-52. In German.

Landau, L. D. and Lifshitz, E. M., 1966, *Statistische Physik* (Berlin: Akademie Verlag). Translation of the second Russian edition, revised by E. M. Lifshitz.

Landsberg, P. T., 1975, *A Matter of Time*. ( Southampton: University) 18-19. An inaugural lecture.

Layzer, D., 1967, "A unified approach to cosmology," in *Relativity and Astrophysics* (Ed. J. Ehlers), Lectures in Applied Mathematics, Vol. 8, (Providence, R. I.: Am. Math. Soc. Press).

McCrea, W. H., 1975, review of P. C. W. Davies, 1974, in Nature, *253*, 485.

Morrison, P., 1966, "Time's arrow and external perturbations," in *Preludes in Theoretical Physics* (Ed. A. de-Shalit, H. Feshbach, L. van Hove). (Amsterdam: North-Holland) 347-351.

Popper, K., 1965, "Time's arrow and entropy." Nature, *207*, 233-234.

Rosenfeld, L., 1972, "General introduction to irreversibility." In *Irreversibility in the Many-Body Problem* (Ed. J. Biel and J. Rae). (New York: Plenum), page 10.

Stannard, R. F., 1966, "Symmetry of the time axis." Nature, *211*, 693-694.

Suggett, G. J., 1975, review of Hoyle and Narlikar, 1974. Nature, *254*, page 223.

von Weizsäcker, C. F., 1939, "The second law and the distinction between past and future." Ann. d. Phys., *36*, 275-283. In German.

## DISCUSSION AND COMMENT

*by David Park*

Isaac Newton taught us to distinguish between the fact-like and law-like components of our understanding of physics. The law-like components are expressed as general statements, analytical in character, in which physical magnitudes are represented by letters. Thus Newton's theory of planetary motion can be adapted, by substituting suitable numbers for the letters, to the Solar System or any other planetary system; to the moons of Jupiter or of any other planet. The fact-like components of our understanding are the adventitious values of these numbers: there is probably an explanation based on natural law why Jupiter has a mass about 300 times that of the Earth, but it is not an interesting question to contemporary science why the ratio is 317.90. That is just a fact.

Normally one can be sure, regarding a scientific statement from the perspective of its particular epoch, whether the statement is law-like or fact-like, but there is one case in which one would at first think it impossible: that of statements concerning the universe as a whole. The reason we can be sure that Newton's planetary theory is law-like not only in form but in actuality is that we can study more than one system to which it applies. But how can one do this when contemplating the universe? We are tempted to argue by analogy that just as there seems to be no law-like reason why the Solar System contains nine planets, or why its diameter is exactly what it is, so the mass and size of the universe (assuming them finite) need not be assigned any particular value in the equations of cosmology. The implication is that if the universe happened to be of different mass and size, it would nevertheless be governed by the same equations as those we use. Logically this is indefensible. How can we possibly know that the laws which we treat as general are not contingent on those very properties which we regard as fact-like?

With respect to the ultimate laws of cosmology, the question may remain open; it is hard to see any alternative, but with respect to the kinds of generalization we have so far been able to formulate there seem to be two circumstances that facilitate the distinction between fact and law. The first is that the universe seems to be expanding, so that its size and energy content change on the scale of a few parts in $10^{11}$ per year. Thus any generalizations which are actually fact-like but have mistakenly been formulated as laws should, if they depend on these variable quantities, change with time. The second is that we have information relating to the state of things up to about $10^9$ years ago: in terrestrial rocks and corals, and in the light from very distant objects in the universe which has taken that long to reach us. Thus we have some means of detecting changes in the laws of nature; these are usually expressed in terms of changes in the "constants" that occur in them. The evidence at present is rather against any change. The reader may choose between arguments that the Newtonian constant $G$ changes[1] (as Professor Landsberg requires) and that it does not.[2] In the latter case, Landsberg's very attractive theory falls for lack of support. On the other hand, he requires that $e$, $\hbar$, and $c$ remain constant, and this seems to be the case,[3] even more accurately than needed.

The evidence at the moment, encourages us to believe that the separation between fact and law was made correctly by Newton and his successors, and a slight refinement in the evidence on $G$ could deal Professor Landsberg a heavy blow.

NOTES

1. T. C. Van Flandern, *Monthly Notices, Roy. Astron. Soc.* 170, 333 (1975) calculates a change of about 1 part in $10^{10}$ per year.

2. E. Teller in F. Reines, ed., *Cosmology, Fusion, and Other Matters* (Gamow memorial volume), Colorado Assoc. Univ. Press, Boulder, 1972; see also Dirac's paper in the same volume; J. van Diggelen, *Nature*, 262, 675 (1976).

3. See Landsberg's Ref. 14. It is shown that the ratio $e^2/\hbar c$ has changed by less than 8 percent in a time equal to the usual figure for the age of the universe.

# On Two Fundamental Laws of Nature and the Role of Time in Time—Space Manifold

K. Ono

*ABSTRACT*

*Considering time-space as subordinate to the laws of nature, it becomes possible to explain the internal inevitability of Lorentz invariance and the three-dimensionality of physical space.*

*Section 1 explains the importance in physics of the concept of symmetry. The possibility is discussed for symmetry to take the place of the Hamiltonian in describing the properties of a dynamical system.*

*In Sections 2 and 3, two general laws are proposed which are considered to be the most fundamental when we look at physics from the viewpoint of symmetry. One of them is the law describing the relation between symmetry and a conservation law. The other is what I called the law of complexification. In order to state the second law, the concepts of complexification, and its real form describing the relation between linear spaces are generalized, and the complexification and its real form are defined for Lie groups. Then the possibility is shown, using the law of complexification, of deducing Lorentz invariance from rotational invariance in three-dimensional space, and, using the Lorentz transformation, of which the existence is assured by the law of complexification, to build up the freedom of time itself. In other words, the difference is made clear between the role of time and that of space in four-dimensional time-space, or the existence of time is made subordinate to the existence of space.*

*In the last section, a short explanation is given of the three-dimensionality of physical space, based on the fact that there is no action at a distance in nature.*

## 1. INTRODUCTION

There may be a great variety of opinions about what is the fundamental character of the laws of nature. But I think it is most proper to consider each one as a kind of selection rule. If the laws of nature are selection rules, we may say that the concepts of allowed transition, forbidden transition, and other similar ones in quantum mechanics, are concepts very much in conformity with the fundamental character of the laws of nature.

The term "selection rules" used here means the rules for selecting out of kinematically imaginable phenomena those which are dynamically allowed to take place in reality. It is true that the border between kinematics and dynamics is not very clear. Possibly, at some stage in the progress of physics, the border may fade away and they may be united into one. So the above explanation might be too formal. Nevertheless, I dare to use it, as I think it is a good explanation for making prominent the character of the term "selection rules."

Accepting that we consider the laws of nature as selection rules, we may say that in physics the criterion of selection is expressed as some kind of symmetry which a phenomenon must have in order to take place in reality.

To describe the laws of nature, present physics uses the Hamiltonian formalism. Hamiltonian formalism has been conveniently used both in classical mechanics and in quantum mechanics. Even when non-relativistic theories were made relativistic, the change was limited to the shape of the concrete Hamiltonian, while the theoretical form itself remained unaltered. History shows that the Hamiltonian formalism is a theoretical form having very wide applicability. However, though it was so in the past, there is no assurance that the Hamiltonian formalism will always be so useful in the future. In fact, in quantum field theory, if we calculate rigorously in the theory based on the Hamiltonian formalism, we are inevitably led to results where all those quantities diverge to infinity which ought to be finite in the nature of things. It might be better to understand this difficulty not as pointing to a flaw removable by partial modifications within the framework of the Hamiltonian formalism, but as showing the breakdown of the Haniltonian formalism itself.

At the Second Conference of this Society at Lake Yamanaka, I professed a modest doubt about the usefulness of the Hamiltonian formalism in connection with the intrinsic indeterminacy of fundamental laws. This might mean that I have put myself under an obligation to present some ideas about a theoretical form to be used as a substitute for the Hamiltonian formalism. However, this is a very difficult task and cannot be performed in a short time. What I can do here is only to seek orientation towards solving the problem in my own way.

In the Hamiltonian formalism, the characterization of a dynamical system is done by a Hamiltonian function, expressing the system's total energy in terms of coordinates and momenta. When the Hamiltonian is given, there is determined the totality of those transformations which leave that Hamiltonian invariant. This totality of transformations we call the symmetry of a given dynamical system. As is well known, it forms a group. That is the group describing the symmetry of dynamical system.

However, the concept of symmetry does not necessarily need the Hamiltonian formalism as a premise. When a dynamical system has a Hamiltonian, the group describing the symmetry of that system consists of those transformations which leave that Hamiltonian invariant. However, even when a dynamical system has no Hamiltonian, there must exist a transformation group corresponding to that mentioned above. The concept of symmetry is a far more general and fundamental concept than that of a Hamiltonian.

Considering the situation in the future when we may be forced to abandon the Hamiltonian formalism, may we imagine that the group representing the symmetry will come to play the role of the Hamiltonian? Though it is difficult to decide either way, this may be a worthwhile conception to keep in our minds as one of the conceivable possibilities.

One piece of evidence suggesting the possible validity of the above conception is the fact that we can derive the equations of motion from the conservation law of energy plus the equivalence between inertial systems. The conservation law of energy is, considered alone, no more than the intermediate integral of the equation of motion existing as the result of the symmetry of dynamical system with respect to translation in the direction of time. But if it is used together with other symmetries, it exhibits a function equivalent to that of the equation of motion. This fact suggests to me the possibility that the group describing the symmetry, if considered as a whole, can behave as the substitute of the Hamiltonian.

The outline of the way to derive the equation of motion from the conservation law of energy is as follows. For the sake of simplicity, let us consider one-dimensional motion. Let us denote the kinetic energy of a mass point as $K$. $K$ is a function only of the velocity $v$:

$$K = K(v)$$

Suppose a force $F$ acts on the mass point in the direction of its motion. As $F$ carries out work at the rate of $Fv$ per unit time, so long as the conservation law of energy is assumed, the kinetic energy of the mass point must increase at the same rate. That is, the following equation must hold:

$$\frac{dK}{dt} = Fv$$

Yet, as $K$ is a function only of $v$,

$$\frac{dK}{dt} = \frac{dK}{dv}\frac{dv}{dt}$$

Therefore the above equation is reduced to

$$\frac{dK}{dv}\frac{dv}{dt} = Fv \tag{1}$$

Now, let us imagine a system of coordinates moving with a constant velocity $v_0$ relative to the present system. Let us denote the velocity of a mass point referred to the second coordinate system by $v'$. Then

$$v' = v - v_0 \tag{2}$$

While as $v_0$ is constant,

$$\frac{dv'}{dt} = \frac{dv}{dt}$$

Inserting this equation into equation (1) gives

$$\frac{dK}{dv}\frac{dv'}{dt} = Fv$$

Thus we have

$$\frac{dK}{dv}/v = F/\frac{dv'}{dt}$$

The left-hand side of this equation is a function of $v$, while the right-hand side is a function of $v'$. Therefore, in order that this equation holds identically, both sides must be equal to a certain constant m. Thus we have the following two relations:

$$F/\frac{dv'}{dt} = m \tag{3}$$

$$\frac{dK}{dv}/v = m \tag{4}$$

Equation (3) is nothing but the Newtonian equation of motion. From equation (4) we obtain

$$K = \frac{1}{2}mv^2 + \text{const.}$$

This is the equation describing the relation between velocity and kinetic energy. The constant $m$ common to both equations is called the mass of the mass point.

In this case we obtained the Newtonian equation of motion. But, if we had replaced the Galilean transformation with a Lorentz transformation, in the above calculation, we would have obtained the relativistic equation of motion. The procedure is considerably more troublesome. But, in principle it is no more than the repetition of our calculation, so I shall omit the explanation.

In our deduction of the equation of motion we used the conservation of energy as the starting point. So it was also in the history of physics. The discovery of energy conservation was earlier than that of the equation of motion. It was Galileo who established the conservation of work as a prototype of the conservation of energy.[1)] However, as for the recognition of the impossibility of perpetual motion, Leonardo da Vinci had already stated that very clearly.[2)] If we adopt the point of view that considers the laws of nature as selection rules, we may say that the recognition of impossibility is a genuine scientific principle.

In dynamics, on the contrary, we ordinarily deduce the conservation of energy from the equation of motion. The true meaning of doing so, however, is that, using the conservation law of energy as criterion, we are testing the adequateness of the equation of motion. If we fail to obtain the law of the conservation of energy, it does mean not that the law does not hold, but that the equation of motion is inadequate. As mentioned before, the conservation of energy is an intermediate integral of the equation of motion. The reason such an intermediate integral exists is that the equation of motion, or Hamiltonian in other words, is invariant under translation in the direction of time. Such a relation between invariance and the conservation law is very general, and has little dependence on the kind of fundamental theory underlying as the base.

The mathematical form of physics is tightly bound to fundamental physical concepts. Classical mechanics is bound inseparably to the view that the elementary process of natural phenomena is the motion of a mass point in homogeneous and isotropic space. Quantum mechanics is the theoretical form taking the concept of dynamical state and its variation with time as foundation. Therefore, if the concept of symmetry is of basic importance for physics, we may expect that any future theory will properly be of a form in response to this fact. In the remainder of this paper, I shall try to discuss the fundamental framework of the laws of nature from this standpoint.

## 2. THE FIRST LAW

Let us start with a well known fact: the relation between the symmetry and the conservation law. The relation can be stated as follows:

*Corresponding to any symmetry of a dynamical system there exists one conserved quantity.*

As this fact is so familiar to every physicist, there is no need of detailed explanation here. The number of independent conserved quantities is fixed by the mathematical properties of the group describing the symmetry of that system. For example, in classical mechanics, if we denote the Hamiltonian as $H$, one of the generalized coordinates as $q$, and the momentum conjugate to $q$ as $p$, then, as

$$\frac{dp}{dt} = - \frac{\partial H}{\partial q}$$

if $H$ is invariant under the translation in the direction of $q$, the time-derivative of $p$ vanishes. Therefore, $p$ is a conserved quantity.

*Figure 1*

Figure 1 shows a sheet of paper with spots of spattered ink on its surface. The way these spots were made is as follows. I placed this sheet on a desk. A metal net screen of 1.5 mm mesh was held horizontally at the height of about 15 cm above the sheet. Then, a drop of ink was let fall vertically on the net screen from the height of several tens of centimeters. The drop of ink, striking the surface of the screen, was spattered by the mesh. And the splashes, falling on the sheet, formed on it the spot pattern shown in the figure. This phenomenon is one of the typical examples showing the relation between the symmetry and the conservation law.

A drop of ink falling freely along the vertical line under the influence of gravity has axial symmetry around the vertical axis. In its path, a metal net screen is placed as an obstacle. The drop of ink falling downward loses its initial kind of symmetry by collision with the screen, and changes into splashes distributed with poorer symmetry than that it had initially. The latter symmetry becomes visible to us as the spot pattern on the surface of the sheet. To what extent is the initial symmetry broken? In this example, we clearly recognize the same tetragonal symmetry in the spot pattern on the sheet that we also see in the obstacle. Though tetragonal symmetry is more limited than axial symmetry, there occured no further breaking of symmetry.

Axial symmetry means invariance under any rotations around a certain axis. Tetragonal symmetry means invariance under those rotations among them which are of order 4. Tetragonal symmetry is a part of the axial symmetry. But there is a more important relation between these two symmetries.

The totality of the rotations corresponding to all the values of rotational angle $\theta$ forms a group. The group is called the two-dimensional rotation group. That is the group describing the axial symmetry. To the rotation of angle $\theta$, assign the multiplicative operator $e^{in\theta}$. Then we will have one of the representations of this group. As the rotation of

$$\theta = 2\pi$$

is an identical transformation, the corresponding $e^{in\theta}$ must be 1. By this condition $n$ is restricted to zero or one of the positive or negative integers. Thus we have all the irreducible representations of the two-dimensional rotation group.

For a given $n$, the totality of those rotations for which

$$e^{in\theta} = 1$$

forms one of the subgroups of the two-dimensional rotation group. This group is called the kernel of the representation $n$. The kernel is the group formed by the totality of the rotations of order $n$. In other words, the kernel is nothing but the group describing the regular $n$-gonal symmetry.

In the spot pattern of the splashes of ink, we clearly recognize the same tetragonal symmetry as that of the net screen. That is, both the spot pattern and the net screen have the common symmetry described by the kernel of the representation $n = 4$. In other word, what is conserved here is the representation to which each phenomenon belongs of the group describing the symmetry of the dynamical system.

The relation I have just shown between the symmetry, the group describing the symmetry, its representation, and the conservation law is one which holds in general. In classical mechanics there are not many examples which show it as clearly as that mentioned above. But in quantum mechanics, whose theoretical form is very appropriate for treating a problem of this kind, the relation between the symmetry and the conservation law is effectively used for the treatment of all sorts of problems.

However, the relation between the symmetry and the conservation law does not require quantum mechanics as the inevitable premise. I dare say this relation is, on the contrary, a premise for every theory, and should be regarded as the criterion to judge its adequateness. We may consider this relation as one of those parts in present theory which will survive the Hamiltonian formalism.

## 3. THE SECOND LAW

In dealing with fundamental problems it is very probable that cases arise where the knowledge we have about the symmetry of a system is only partial, while the true extent of the symmetry the system has is wider than we yet know. Therefore, it might be interesting to search for principles which enable us to enlarge the symmetry to a certain extent beyond that already established. In this section, I would like to treat this problem.

I have said before that the border between kinematics and dynamics is not very clear. The same is true about dynamical systems and laws of nature. In the previous section I treated a drop of ink falling downward under the influence of gravity. This system has axial symmetry around the vertical axis, which is smaller than the three-dimensional rotational symmetry that the laws of nature have in general. However, if we imagine the symmetry of the laws of nature as the upper limit of the symmetry of an arbitrary physical system, we are not right. For example, the two-dimensional harmonic oscillator has SU(2) symmetry, which is richer than the axial symmetry defined by its geometric form. But this transformation group is rather abstract, and is not a subgroup of the three-dimensional rotation group. Thus, in classical mechanics, the relation between the symmetry of a dynamical system and that of the laws of nature is not very simple. However, the situation is different in elementary particle physics. In elementary particle physics, we cannot imagine any law of nature separately from a certain definite dynamical system. As a result, for example, the symmetry of the system composed of electron and electromagnetic field is at the same time both the symmetry of the given dynamical system and that of the law of interaction between electron and electromagnetic field. Therefore, though the present consideration is about the symmetry of dynamical systems, we must understand that it also refers to the symmetry of the laws of nature at the same time.

As the starting point of our consideration, let us adopt the empirical fact that all the fundamental laws of nature are invariant under three-dimensional rotations as well as under Lorentz transformations. Hitherto, these two invariances were considered as independent. Of course, three-dimensional rotational invaiance is included in Lorentz invariance. But the contrary is not true. There are many groups which include the three-dimensional rotation group as one of their subgroups. Therefore, considering the case in which we know the three-dimensional rotational invariance but do not know Lorentz invariance, there are many ways to imagine, as the parent symmetry, some larger invariance than that established. The object of this section is to search for a general procedure which makes it possible for us to select out of many alternatives the true one, that is, starting from the established three-dimensional rotational invariance, to enlarge the invariance precisely to the Lorentz transformation. Thus, the main job is to search for a relation between the three-dimensional rotation group and the Lorentz group that allows the existence of a general procedure having the desired property.

Let $G$ and $G_0$ be two differentiable continuous groups and $G_0$ be a subgroup of $G$. Let $k$ and $k_0$ be the Lie rings of $G$ and $G_0$ respectively. If $k$ and $k_0$ have the same base in common, and $k_0$ is a real space while k is a complex space, we say $k$ is the complexification of $k_0$, and $k_0$ is the real form of $k$. Complexification and real form are the terms usually used only to describe the relation between linear spaces. However, let us use for a moment the same terminology in describing the relation between two groups like $G$ and $G_0$ mentioned above. That is, if

$$G \supset G_0$$

and their Lie rings are in the relation of a real form and its complexification, let us say $G$ is the complexification of $G_0$, and $G_0$ is the real form of $G$.

The Lorentz group and the three-dimensional rotation group are exactly in this relation. That is, the Lorentz group is the complexification of the three-dimensional rotation group, and the three-dimensional rotation group is the real form of the Lorentz group†. Based on this fact, I would like to postulate the existence of the following law:

*If a dynamical system has the symmetry described by a transformation group $G_0$, that system is also symmetric under the complexification $G$ of the group $G_0$.*

Let us for a moment call this law the complexification law.

---

†Precisely speaking this relation holds between their covering groups. See Appendix.

For example, let us apply this law to gauge invariance. If we denote the wave function by $\phi$, then nature has the symmetry represented by the transformation

$$\phi \rightarrow \phi' = e^{i\chi}\phi$$

where $\chi$ is an arbitrary real function of the real arguments $x$, $y$, $z$ and $t$. This symmetry is called gauge invariance, and the corresponding transformation is called a gauge transformation. As the Lie ring of the gauge transformation is the linear space of the real function $\chi$, we obtain the complexification of the gauge transformation by extending the region of $\chi$ from the real function to the complex function of the real arguments $x$, $y$, $z$ and $t$.

$$\phi \rightarrow \phi' = e^{i\chi}\phi$$

$$\bar{\phi} \rightarrow \bar{\phi}' = e^{-i\chi}\bar{\phi}$$

As the complexification of the gauge transformation is not unitary any more, we must be careful to distinguish between the covariant and the contravariant transformational characters of the quantity. For example, $|\bar{\phi}'|$ is not always equal to $|\phi'|$ and the probability of existence is given not by $|\phi'|^2$, but by $\bar{\phi}'\phi'$, etc. However, though it is not unitary, we can easily see that all the theory is invariant also under complexification of the gauge transformation. That is, the law of complexification holds in this case.

If the law holds in general, it bases Lorentz invariance on three-dimensional rotational invariance. In other words, it answers for the first time the primitive but fundamental question, why is it the Lorentz transformation and not the four-dimensional orthogonal transformation that keeps the laws of nature invariant?

Of course, Lorentz invariance is an empirical fact. But, to be an empirical fact does not makes us understand its internal inevitability. A law makes us convinced of its inevitability when it becomes one of the examples of a more general law. There are many ways to deduce Lorentz invariance from some empirical facts like the invariance of light velocity, but they are too arithmetical, and cannot persuade us to understand its internal inevitability.

As for the generalization of Lorentz invariance, one instantly calls to mind the theory of general relativity. Of course, from one point of view, we may say that general relativity is the immediate generalization of special relativity. But, if we consider them from methodological side, it is better to understand them as two independent theories. Special relativity is a theory about the symmetry of the laws of nature, while general relativity is a theory about the geometrization of the laws of nature. The former is the theory about invariance, while the latter is the theory about covariance. In order to geometrize the laws of nature, we must use affinely connected space. But in affinely connected space, even rotation is not allowed. It is the product of thought standing at the opposite pole to symmetry.

The most perplexing point for me in the theory of general relativity is that it does not admit the distinctness of time. The asymmetry between time and space in special relativity is perfectly forgotten in general relativity.

Probably I am not making a mistake to say that the law I propose in this section is the true generalization that leads to special relativity. The complexification law not only bases Lorentz invariance on three-dimensional rotational symmetry, but also leads to the existence of the freedom of time itself. For Lorentz invariance requires the existence of Lorentz transformation as a premise. But the existence of the Lorentz transformation necessitates the existence of the fourth freedom outside the three freedoms of physical space. In other words, in my theoretical construction time is a freedom which exists in order to accomplish the requirement of Lorentz invariance that inevitably follows three-dimensional rotational invariance. As is known, combining Lorentz transformation with translation in three-dimensional space, we can obtain translation in the direction of time. Therefore, if the existence of the Lorentz transformation is assured by the complexification law, it is possible for us to construct the freedom of time.††

The concept of the complexification of a group corresponds to the concept of the analytical continuation of a function. One of the differences between them is that the procedure of complexification can be repeated any number of times. We can make the complexification of complexification repeatedly. And we may expect that the law of complexification will hold also for the repeated complexification. However, such a formal enlargement of symmetry will bring us no significant results. Therefore, there may be no need to consider this possibility of repetition as an important difficulty. Of course, it is a great problem to represent by word the criterion for distinguishing between physically significant and insignificant results. And my expression of the law does not contain this part. In this sense, we may say that my expression of the law is not logically complete.

Today's physics adopts the theoretical form which uses time and space as a canvas upon which to picture the laws of nature. Therefore, it is impossible for today's physics to treat time or space by itself. If and when physics will take up time or space as an object of study, it will become necessary for fundamental laws to be not time-spacelike. It is a very interesting problem as to what theoretical forms will play the role of equations of motion or field equations at that time. Perhaps we might consider the complexification law as a prototype of such future theoretical forms.

## 4. CONCLUSION

There are several problems in connection with the law proposed in the previous section.

---

††Here time is expressed in the unit of length. The conversion factor between the unit of length and that of time is given by the velocity of an entity whose velocity is independent of the coordinate system.

The first problem is whether or not the complexification law holds in every case, and if not, how shall we behave when the law does not hold? In my opinion, those cases would be the most interesting in which the law seems to be broken. We should try to reform the known theory using the complexification law as the guiding principle like e.g. the principle of relativity. In that process, we might expect to find an unexpected relation between freedoms which are hitherto considered perfectly independent, or to find a new natural constant or a new meaning of a known constant.

The second problem concerns the case when the assumed symmetry is not rigorous but approximate. In this case we may expect that also the complexification law will hold approximately. However, if we extend an approximate relation, the degree of approximation is in general immediately made worse. Therefore, when the premised symmetry is approximate, though we apply the law mechanically, we may obtain no significant result. So what comes into question is, what way shall we choose to apply this law in order to obtain a significant result? As almost all the symmetry we treat in practice is approximate, we may say that the law of complexification has no utility until this problem is solved.

The raison d'être of the complexification law at present is purely theoretical. This law leads to Lorentz invariance from three-dimensional rotational invariance as the premise. It makes clear for the first time the reason why it is the Lorentz transformation and not, for example, the four-dimensional orthogonal transformation that describes the symmetry of the laws of nature. Or, in other words, it makes it clear for the first time that the role of time and that of space are different in the time-space manifold. Moreover, combining the Lorentz transformation with translation in three-dimensional space, we can construct the freedom of time itself. In other words, owing to the complexification law, the existence of time becomes subordinate to that of space.

Thus, what is left to us finally is the problem why physical space is three-dimensional and why the laws of nature are symmetric under rotation and translation in physical space. To my sorrow, I cannot answer this part of the problem. So, I would like to conclude this paper with my answer to the former part of the problem, why physical space is three-dimensional.

This problem, in old times, was treated by Aristotle in his *De Caelo*, and more recently a mathematical proof was tried by Galileo in his *Dialogo*.[3] Though Galileo's argument is no more than the explanation of the mathematical meaning contained in the common understanding that space is three-dimensional, and cannot be its proof in any sense, judging from the context of his argument, we may be sure that he himself regarded it as a mathematical proof.

In order to solve the problem of dimension, we must first of all put the problem itself in order. There are infinite numbers of entities forming the object of our physical congnition. We consider them not as a mere point set, but recognize them as being displayed in three-dimensional arrangements. Therefore, if we can answer the question, why they are not allowed to be left as a mere point set -- what is the merit of arranging them three-dimensionally -- then the properties of the field used to arrange them will be defined automatically.

One of the most remarkable properties of the physical world is the fact that there exists no action at distance. All action takes place in contact. In order for two separate entities to interact, the existence of a medium transmitting the action is essential. I think this empirical fact is the most basic property of physical world. But why? What is the reason of there being no action at distance?

In my opinion, that is the very reason for piling up physical entities in three-dimensional arrangements. We may consider space as the container used to arrange things in such a way that those which can perform direct interaction are placed in contact, while those which cannot are placed distant from each other. In other words, I think the two propositions that things are in contact or not and that they can interact directly or cannot are synonymous with each other. If we define space as such, the fact that space is three-dimensional is reduced to the fact that in order to arrange physical entities in such a way that things which can interact directly are placed in contact, it is necessary and sufficient to pile them up in a three-dimensional arrangement. If we may formulate the problem so, we can explain the three-dimensionality of space as follows.

Among the physical entities given as a mere point set, let us join those which can interact directly to each other with lines. Then we obtain a figure composed of vast numbers of points and lines joining them suitably. In topology such figure is called a polygon (one-dimensional polyhedron). Therefore, the given problem is reduced to the question: in order to picture that figure actually, what dimensional space does it need as a canvas?

There is a theorem known in topology most suitable to answer such questions. The theorem is expressed as follows:

*Any n-dimensional polyhedron can be realized in 2n + 1 dimensional Euclidean space retaining its binding* (Verbindung) *faithfully*.

One familiar example is the electric circuit diagram. If we picture a circuit diagram on a sheet of paper, we generally suffer from unnecessary cross-points. Of course, we plan the picture in such a way that we have the least number of such crossings. But anyhow there remains a certain number of them. Then we show that they are unreal with the symbol of a semi-circular bridge. The above mentioned theorem is the theorem which assures us that if we three-dimensionalize the diagram using the symbol of a semi-circular bridge, we can draw a diagram of any circuit without exception, and there arises no need of four-dimensionalizing the diagram using more complicated symbols.

The figure composed of infinite numbers of physical entities and lines binding them suitably is, like the circuit diagram, an $n = 1$ dimensional polyhedron. So in order to realize it, it is necessary in general and sufficient in all cases to use $2n + 1 = 3$ dimensional Euclidean space.

Thus, the dimension of physical space is three. Or, it may be better to say that, though the dimension of physical space might be larger, the number of freedoms effectively used to pile up the physical entities is three.

The polyhedra treated in geometry have finite numbers of vertices, but the number of vertices of the figures we are treating now is not finite. Still, we might expect that, so long as the binding is not too malicious, no pathological phenomena will arise at the moment of switching over from finiteness to infinity. Moreover, it might need an explanation that in my proof the topological property of binding is substituted for the quantitative property of locality. I hope this substitution will be justified by the fact that it is sufficient for the theorem to hold to restrict the lines binding vertices to straight lines. For if they are straight lines, we can imagine them as rubber strings, and, after they are bound to vertices, as shrinking until the things bound to both ends will come in to contact with each other.

The theorem has the form of realizing the figure in Euclidean space. But this is only because borrowing Euclidean space is favorable for the proof, and does not mean that physical space is Euclidean. What the theorem states is only that the dimension of physical space is three.

APPENDIX: PROOF OF THE THEOREM THAT SL(2), THE COVERING GROUP OF THE LORENTZ GROUP, IS THE COMPLEXIFICATION OF SU(2), THAT OF THE THREE-DIMENSIONAL ROTATION GROUP.

Let us denote the Lie ring of SU(2) as $k_0$, and that of SL(2) as k, where the Lie ring of a group G is defined as the totality of $X$ such that

$$\exp(tX) \in G$$

for an arbitrary real number t.

In order that

$$X \in k_0$$

it is necessary and sufficient by definition that $X$ satisfies the following two conditions:

$$1^\circ \quad (\exp X)^* = (\exp X)^{-1}$$

$$2^\circ \quad \det(\exp X) = 1$$

As the condition $1^\circ$ is reduced to

$$X^* = -X \tag{1}$$

X can be diagonalized by an adequate unitary transformation U:

$$UXU^{-1} = \begin{pmatrix} \lambda & 0 \\ 0 & \mu \end{pmatrix}$$

Then,

$$\det(\exp X) = \det[U(\exp X)U^{-1}] = \det[\exp(UXU^{-1})] = \det\begin{pmatrix} e^{\lambda} & 0 \\ 0 & e^{\mu} \end{pmatrix} = \exp[\mathrm{Tr}(X)]$$

Therefore, the condition 2° is reduced to

$$\mathrm{Tr}(X) = 0 \tag{2}$$

Inserting

$$X = \begin{pmatrix} a & b \\ c & d \end{pmatrix} \tag{3}$$

into Eq.(1) we obtain

$$\begin{pmatrix} \bar{a} & \bar{c} \\ \bar{b} & \bar{d} \end{pmatrix} = -\begin{pmatrix} a & b \\ c & d \end{pmatrix}$$

and inserting into Eq.(2) we obtain

$$a + d = 0$$

Therefore we know that a, b, c, d are of the following shape:

$$a = i\lambda = -d$$

$$b = \mu + i\nu$$

$$c = -\mu + i\nu$$

where $\lambda$, $\mu$, $\nu$ are real numbers. Inserting them into Eq.(3) we obtain

$$X = \begin{pmatrix} i\lambda & \mu + i\nu \\ -\mu + i\nu & -i\lambda \end{pmatrix}$$

$$= \lambda\begin{pmatrix} i & 0 \\ 0 & -i \end{pmatrix} + \mu\begin{pmatrix} 0 & 1 \\ -1 & 0 \end{pmatrix} + \nu\begin{pmatrix} 0 & i \\ i & 0 \end{pmatrix}$$

In other words, $k_0$ is a real space spanned by

$$\begin{pmatrix} i & 0 \\ 0 & -i \end{pmatrix}, \begin{pmatrix} 0 & 1 \\ -1 & 0 \end{pmatrix}, \begin{pmatrix} 0 & i \\ i & 0 \end{pmatrix}$$

Next, in order that

$$Z \in k$$

it is necessary and sufficient by definition that $Z$ satisfies the following condition:

$$3^\circ \quad \det(\exp Z) = 1$$

As $Z$ is not skew-Hermitian, $Z$ cannot be diagonalized by a unitary transformation. However, using an appropriate operator $A$, we can transform $Z$ to the following shape:

$$AZA^{-1} = \begin{pmatrix} a & * \\ 0 & b \end{pmatrix}$$

Therefore

$$\begin{aligned} \det(\exp Z) &= \det[A(\exp Z)A^{-1}] \\ &= \det[\exp(AZA^{-1})] \\ &= \det\begin{pmatrix} e^a & * \\ 0 & e^b \end{pmatrix} \\ &= \exp[\mathrm{Tr}(Z)] \end{aligned}$$

Thus the condition 3° is reduced to

$$\mathrm{Tr}(Z) = 0$$

For a given $Z \in k$ if we put

$$X = \frac{1}{2}(Z - Z^*)$$

$$Y = \frac{1}{2i}(Z + Z^*)$$

we have

$$X^* = -X \ , \quad \mathrm{Tr}(X) = 0$$

$$Y^* = -Y \ , \quad \mathrm{Tr}(Y) = 0$$

Therefore

$$X \in k_0 \ , \quad Y \in k_0$$

and

$$Z = X + iY$$

that is, any $Z \in k$ belongs to the complexification of $k_0$.

On the contrary, for any $X, Y \in k_0$, we obtain

$$\mathrm{Tr}(X + iY) = \mathrm{Tr}(X) + i\mathrm{Tr}(Y) = 0$$

Therefore, any $Z = X + iY$ belongs to $k$.

REFERENCES


1. Galileo Galilei: *Le Mecaniche* (1599).

2. Leonardo's earliest mentioning on this problem is in Codex A, f22v (c. 1492). For his more detailed discussions see Codex Madrid I (1493-'95).

3. Galileo Galilei: *Dialogo sopra i due massimi sistemi del mondo Tolemaico e Copernicano* (1632).

## DISUCSSION AND COMMENTS

*By David Finkelstein*

In this work Professor Ono recognizes the provisional and temporary nature of our present haywire world models, and courageously attempts to separate what will last from what will die.

This is a speculative and somewhat personal matter at present, and so no great weight should be given to my comments on this work, which also express personal speculations about which path to take next in the maze.

I agree with Professor Ono that his first principle, the relation between symmetry groups and conservation laws, will last. Here a symmetry is any process, not just a reflection, that turns the system of physical laws into itself. The relation Professor Ono is emphasizing is, for example, that between the symmetry under translation of time and conservation of energy. This relation is a consequence of the relation between quantum processes and quantum vectors and operators, which I consider more basic and expect to survive also. But I think the role of symmetry principles is shifting, with fewer fundamental or exact symmetries, and more approximate or dynamical symmetries, and will continue to shift. It is not so much that the fundamental constituents of the world will turn out to be asymmetric as that the physical processes that have to be carried out to define a symmetry, such as rotations or translations, will be found to lose meaning in the microscopic world. Under high magnification, the structure of our rods and clocks turns out to be porous and lacunary, and the idea of a smooth rotation or translation is seen to be an illusion born of inadequate resolution.

But even when the conservation laws hold, the deduction of detailed laws of motion from them seems to be possible only for a small number of variables, not for a collection of many particles or for a field.

Professor Ono's second principle is that the parameters or variables defining the symmetry processes of physics should be complex, not real. This raises the question of why complex numbers are so basic for quantum mechanics in the first place. Where does the $i$ in Schrödinger's equation come from? I think a possibility like that suggested by Stueckelberg might be right: that what comes first might be a law like

$$\frac{d\Psi}{dt} = A\Psi$$

with an operator $A$ and vectors $\Psi$ both real.[1] Then $A$ gives rise to $i$ through a factorization $A = iH$. But at the deeper level no complex quantities might occur at all, and the principle of complexification suggested by Professor Ono would appear as a phenomenological one, with a range of approximate validity that might nevertheless be very large.

The representation of the relativistic transformations of space and time as rotations through angles with imaginary parts, described so beautifully in Felix Klein's theory of the top, even before the discovery of relativity, certainly stimulates speculation in the direction suggested by Professor Ono, but the same extension to imaginary angles does not seem to work, say, for internal symmetries.

# The Theory of Space—like Time

**F. Christensen**

*The Special and General Theories of Relativity have in this century inspired the belief that time is very much like space--or at least, much more like space than had hitherto been common-sensically believed. But this is a rather vague notion; what exactly is involved in the concept of space-like time? This paper marks a number of consequences of that theory of time, with special emphasis on the grammatical features required for its expression: it requires a language without tenses and other "adverbial" forms, replacing them with purely predicative expressions. It is shown rigorously how the common-sense idea that objects persist through time, and that events and objects pass into and out of existence, is replaced by the notion that all of the objects and events of history alike exist, in just the same sense, merely being spread across time.*

Common sense seems to hold that the various events of history are intrinsically different from one another, different in a way that is expressed by saying that some of them are presently occurring, others have already occurred and still others have yet to occur. Certain contemporary philosophers and scientists, however, have made the following claim: pastness, presentness and futurity are *not* intrinsic to events or moments of time, but extrinsic, in the sense that it is only relative to something else that anything is either past, present or future. That is, we may not correctly say of a given event or moment that, over and above being past relative to some events and times, in the future of others and simultaneous with yet others, it is also "in the past" *simpliciter*, or *simply* "occurring now." The events of history are all alike ordered by the relations of simultaneity and precedence, they have their relative positions in time, and that is the end of the story. Such a view has been defended by the philosophers Bertrand Russell, W. V. O. Quine, Donald Williams, Nelson Goodman and J. J. C. Smart, among others.[1]

An analogy with space is almost inevitable in explaining this view of time. Indeed, the claim has been largely, if not wholly, popularized by the Special and General Theories of Relativity, which seem to many to require that space and time be sufficiently alike for us to speak intelligibly of a composite of the two -- "space-time". Now, it seems clear enough that "hereness" and "thereness" are not intrinsic to objects or events. It is only relative to something else that anything is said to be "here" or "there" or "yonder." The sentence 'The island is straight ahead', for example, is just a conveniently abbreviated way of saying 'The island is ahead *of us*', or 'The island is ahead *of this place*', or the like. Such words as 'here' and 'ahead' covertly express relations *between* things, not features intrinsic to any single thing by itself, and the spatial locations which different objects and events occupy are all on an onotological par.

Similarly, the claim now runs, words like 'now' and 'then' and special grammatical features like the tenses (past tense, present tense, etc.) should be understood in the same way as words like 'here' and 'there'. Someone's utterance of a sentence of the type 'Event e has occurred' or 'e is in the past' only reflects the fact that e is earlier than that utterance, or that e's position in time is earlier than that of the utterance. A given tensed sentence may have the appearance of referring to only a single event, but it should be regarded as covertly relational in nature. In a language freed from such "perspectival" elements, there would be no tenses or anything like them; indeed, a truly tenseless language is often recommended by these philosophers as a means of avoiding unnecessary confusion about time. All we really need to express what the tenses ultimately say are such plainly relational expressions as 'is earlier than', 'is later than', 'is simultaneous with', 'is in' or 'is at' (in the temporal sense), etc. -- just as with space we need only 'is to the left of', 'is near to', 'is ten feet from', 'is in' or 'is at' (in the spatial sense), and so forth.

Let us for simplicity call this view of time the "S-theory" -- "S" for "space-like."[2] Now, as it is most commonly presented, the S-theory is a claim of linguistic analysis, a claim of having revealed what certain expressions of ordinary speech "really mean", possible appearances notwithstanding. But an even more important matter, I should think, is what the world itself is like regardless of how ordinary language describes it. So the theory could also be presented by its adherents as a proposed conceptual and linguistic reconstruction: "Whatever we ordinarily intend, here is what we ought to mean, if we're to be correct." Either claim would be -- and has been -- strongly opposed by other philosophers, on the grounds that reducing time to relations alone leaves out something that is essential to it. But the continuing debate has been highly unsatisfactory, in my estimation, in that what is at stake has not been made sufficiently clear. The purpose of this paper is to take a few steps toward correcting that situation. I intend to examine, in greater detail than others have done, the conceptual consequences of the S-theory. In the process, I hope, it will become clear that *as analysis* the S-theory is incorrect. What it represents is a wholly new concept of time, too alien to ordinary speech and thought to be reasonably described as what our temporal locutions at bottom really convey. But I will not attempt to answer the question of whether the ordinary view or the S-theory -- or some other -- is the correct concept of time itself. Hopefully my examination will help pave the way toward more perspicuous discussion of that question, but it is beyond the scope of this paper.

To begin with some clarifying preliminaries, let me point out the following fact: in ordinary speech there are two rather different sorts of entity which are related by the temporal relations of which I have spoken, two different sorts of "relata". On the one hand, there are events and states of affairs: for example, an event such as John's becoming sick, and a state of affairs such as John's *being* sick. John's states of being sick alternate temporally with his states of well-being, and temporally between pairs of these are the events of his becoming sick or well. Both events and states of affairs, then, are spoken of as being earlier than, later than and simultaneous with other events and states of affairs. On the other hand, temporal relations are also predicated of moments and periods of time. We can say not only (a) that World

War I was earlier than World War II, relating two events to one another, but also (b) that 1935 was before World War II, or that the outbreak of World War II was in 1939, each of which relates a time to an event, and (c) that 1939 was later than 1935, which relates two times. (Indeed, times are useful largely because they are conventionally given names -- such as '1935' and '1939' -- that allow us to infer the temporal relations -- such as being four years apart -- that each time and its events bear to other times and their contents). Similarly, of course, both events and states of affairs on the one hand and times on the other can be described as being in the past, in the present or in the future.

Now, moments and periods of time are rather ethereal-seeming entities. Some would regard them as mere fictions, abstracted out of concrete happenings -- or at least as derivative, in some sense *dependent* upon those concrete things. Are there, in addition to the physical and mental entities that bear temporal relations to one another yet a second independent class of particulars that bear such relations, and which constitute the temporal "positions" of the concrete individuals? The same question applied, of course, to "time" itself, if that term is taken not to refer collectively to the temporal features of concrete things but to that single huge (if not indeed infinite) "thing" which has moments and time-periods as its parts. The similar old debate over whether there exists any such (independent) "stuff" as "space itself", or any such particulars as "places", may be familiar to the reader already. Whatever the answer in each case may be, I hope it is obvious that which position one takes is not important vis-a-vis the S-theorist's basic claim -- he can readily go either way My reason for mentioning the issue here is to point out that it is the temporal *relations* that are most essential to the notion of relative temporal location, hence to the notion of temporal "perspective". What sorts of particulars are the ultimate *bearers* of those relations is irrelevant to the present issue.

One especially fruitful way of getting clearer about the concept of time, I believe, is to get clearer about the language in which the concept is expressed -- about the "grammar" of time. With this in mind, I will begin my scrutiny of the S-theory with a closer look at the tenses which that theory takes to be eliminable. Just what are tenses anyway? Well, for one thing, they are like a sort of adverb -- after all, they modify verbs. One can see this by reflecting on how the role of tenses in a sentence is similar to that of such temporal adverbs as 'formerly' (past tense), 'presently' and 'now' (present tense), and 'eventually' (future tense). In fact, I'm told that the Chinese language doesn't use tensed verbs at all, but does the same job by adding a separate word to the sentence -- a word that is readily described as an adverb. To be neutral between different languages, and to stress this adverbial role, I will sometimes speak hereafter of "tense-adverbs."

Let me develop this point a bit further. A word that is used to ascribe a *property* to a single individual -- such as the property of being red, or round, or ten feet long -- is by logicians traditionally called a "monadic predicate". A term that is used to signify a *relation between* two or more individuals -- such as one thing's being to the left of, or longer than, or the father of something else -- is called a "polyadic predicate". Using the forms of modern logic, we can symbolize 'Bill is red-haired', say, by the expression '$R_b$', and 'Bill is to the left of Carl' as '$L_{bc}$'. But such formalisms give us no way to distinguish 'Bill *is* (presently) red-haired' and 'Bill *is* to the left of Carl' from 'Bill *was* red-haired', 'Bill *will be* to the left of Carl', and so on. This limitation on standard (Russell-Frege) symbolic logic has in recent years been recognized by the developers of what is called "tense logic". What tense logic does is just to represent the tense in a sentence formally as an adverb. Actually, 'adverb' is a rather imprecise term; it is standardly applied to all sorts of words and phrases that have little in common. (Though most of them are quite different from *predicates*). It is hence preferable to speak of the tense-terms as a logician might, as "monadic sentential operators", formally similar to the negation and necessity operators. But I won't dwell on fine points here; suffice it to say that the usual formalization requires the "atomic" sentences of the language to be in the present tense, and adds two "operators", 'P' for past tense and 'F' for future tense. So if the formal expression '$Q_b$' is read 'b is (presently) Q', then '$PQ_b$' becomes 'Formerly, b is Q', or 'It was the case that b is Q', or simply 'b was Q'. Moreover, we can write "$FPQ_b$" for 'It will be that it was that b is Q', or 'b will have been Q'. And '$\sim FQ_b$' becomes 'It is not the case that it will be the case that b is Q', or 'b will never be Q', while '$\sim F \sim Q_b$' is 'b will always be Q', and so on.

For those not already acquainted with the symbolism of tense logic, this will take some time getting used to. But I have an important reason for making this excursion into logical formalism, namely to reveal more sharply the grammatical contrast between the tenses, on the one hand, and on the other, the relational predicates which are adequate for the concept of space, hence also for the S-theory of time. Though the S-theory evidently treats the tense-adverbs as at best a sort of truncated polyadic predicates, reporting temporal relations in a "perspectival" way, they are actually radically different from predicates of any variety. In order to tell when a given individual bears the property or relation which is predicated of it, a tense-adverb (as a logician might say) "operates on" the combination of subject and predicate. (Recall the symbolization: '$PQ_b$' says that b has had the property Q, '$FR_{bc}$' says that b and c will bear the relation R to one another, etc.) Hence the role of the tense in a sentence is very different from either that of a subject *or* that of a predicate. A tense-adverb may be used (as a grammarian might say) to "modify" the assertion that there is a certain relation between two things, but it does not *itself* express a relation of any sort. Terms like 'here' and 'ahead' do have a basically predicative nature -- or, we might also say, an *adjectival* character; they are indeed merely truncated expressions signifying relations. But the tense, with its adverbial nature, is very different from spatial terms of any kind, in spite of certain superficial similarities.

One purpose of my paper is to demonstrate this claim. A good way to do so, I think, is to reveal the conceptual role of the tense-adverbs in statements that do not mention any of the properties or relations that a thing has, but only assert its existence. With this in mind, I will now point out a few things about existence and its verbal expression. Notice first of all that even the words 'happen' and 'occur' might readily be classed as existence-words: to ask whether the Homeric wars really *occurred* is much the same sort of thing as asking whether Homer really *existed*. Of course, we apply the word 'occurs' to events, and apply 'exists' primarily to what philosophers sometimes call "continuants" -- which are just the things that events happen *to*, namely physical objects, people, minds, etc. As for states of affairs, here too ordinary speech usually uses 'exists', as in 'That sad state of affairs existed for several days'. But we use the "existential quantifier", 'there is', in all three cases; for example, we can say both 'There was once a great war' and also 'There was once a great poet'. (In symbolic logic, either could take the form '$P(\exists x)G_x$'.) As for instants and periods of time, they are once again too abstract-seeming, perhaps, for either 'occurs' *or* 'exists' to be very appropriately used in reference to them. But we do apply the phrase 'there is' to times, as in 'There was a time when man was a hunter'. We also have the related form '*it* is': 'It is presently 2 o'clock' tells us which moment presently "exists", and 'It was the night before Christmas' tells us that a certain time once *did* "exist."

Here is the point that I now wish to call attention to: in each of these different cases, at least in ordinary English, the existence-verb is "modified" by a tense. The role played by tense-adverbs is of such a nature that it affects what is said about the *existence* of entities mentioned in the sentence. And *different* tenses allow us to say something *different* about existence. We distinguish, for example, between things that did exist but don't any longer, those that do exist, and those that will exist but don't exist yet. For the sake of simplicity, let me lump the first and last of these three categories together. (This blurs an important distinction but allows a distinction that is more crucial here to be enhanced.) Then we can say the following: in ordinary temporal talk and thought, there is a huge difference between certain of the events and states of affairs of history and all of the others, namely the difference between existing and not existing, between occurring and not occurring. For instance, according to common sense, World War II is not occurring -- it *was* occurring but it is *not* occurring, in any sense of the word -- whereas certain other armed conflicts *are* happening. It is as true to say of World War II as of the battle between the Titans and the Gods that it does not exist. The difference between the two wars is that the former once *did* occur whereas the latter did not.

In this we now have a clear conflict between the view of common sense and that of the S-theory. For the latter view explicitly denies that there is any *difference in regard to existence* (occurrence) among the events, states of affairs and moments of history. They are held to differ from one another only in regard to their temporal *locations*, and *not* in respect of their *existence*!

Let us make this clear by returning to the spatial analogy. Consider any two spatially separated things -- say, London and Paris. They occupy different locations in space, so that relative to certain people and objects, London is "here" and Paris is "over yonder". And equally well, to other people and objects, it is Paris that is "here" and London that is "over yonder". But this spatial *distance* between the two cities requires no *difference as regards existence* between them. (To the contrary, in fact, the distance requires that they both alike *exist*. The land of Oz isn't *any* particular distance from London or Paris, for the simple reason that there is no such place.) Words like 'here' and 'yonder', applied to either city, are not meant to express an existential difference, but only a difference in the relations that each bears to some third thing.

Similarly, if time is purely "relational" (in the sense of consisting solely of relations among entities), then World War II and the P.L.O.-Israeli conflict do not differ from one another in regard to existence or occurrence, though they *are* at different temporal locations: World War II is occurring, and the Palestinian conflict is occurring, and they are merely temporally distant from one another. Relative to certain events and states of affairs (including certain human experiences) the Palestinian conflict is "here" in time; but just as well, relative to yet other -- and *equally real* -- events, it is World War II that is temporally "here". And so on for all the other events of history, according to the S-theory: all alike exist, all alike are happening.

What all this begins to reveal is that the S-theory differs radically from the common sense concept of time. Yet further differences will emerge as we continue, but this one is very fundamental. There is more to time, as ordinarily conceived, than merely temporal location. (Indeed, I would even hold that the notion of temporal location, of temporal relations, is itself only a derivative construction, but I can't pursue the issue here.) For in ordinary thought, time is inseparably connected with *existence,* in a way that spatial location, color, size, mass, and other properties and relations are *not*. Time is different. And the feature of grammar that makes this conceptual difference expressible, once again, is the role played by temporal adverbs, in contrast to that of all sorts of predicates, signifying all those kinds of properties and relations. Notice moreover that it is just this connection with an entity's very existence, which presumably is intrinsic to it, that makes being past, present or future intrinsic to the entity rather than merely relative, as the S-theory would require. Because the tense-adverb can modify a sentence which refers to only a single event, it is capable of expressing information *about* that single event that is intrinsic to it.

Now, just because the S-theory is alien to common sense, it is easy to misunderstand what the theory says, by reading common-sense ideas into it. For example: one might understand the claim that all the events of history exist as saying that those events exist *at different times*. And this is evidently compatible with the ordinary way of thinking, since to say that some events are occurring and others were occurring *is* to say that they occur at different times. Note well, however, that the prepositional phrase 'at different times', taken as a whole, acts *adverbially* in these statements. Hence 'at different times' *modifies* the existence-verb here, just as the tenses do. Unfortunately, I cannot in this brief paper discuss the nature of this more complex sort of adverb, and how it relates to the tense-adverbs. But I can point out that *all* such adverbs are out of place in the theory that time is like space. For such a view limits temporal facts about events (and "times") to temporal relations among them -- and relations are expressed using predicates, not adverbs.[3]

This latter point is sufficiently tricky, and sufficiently important, to warrant careful scrutiny; and as usual, the spatial analogy should prove helpful. Suppose someone were to make the statement that London and Paris exist *at different places*. Would we understand that expression to imply that there is a difference, between London and Paris, in their existential status? Surely not. The word 'exists' in this instance is not genuinely "modified" by the phrase 'at different places'. At best, 'exists' appears here gratuitously; we should for clarity drop it from the sentence, and say merely that London and Paris *are* at different places. Or, if for some reason we do wish to stress that both cities exist, we could say something like this: 'London exists, and Paris exists, and they are at different places'. Such a sentence asserts the existence of the two cities and independently *adds*, via a predicate, the information that they are spatially separated, rather than modifying 'exists' with any sort of spatial adverb.

And so it is in the S-theory's concept of time. We should not say that World War II and the Palestinian-Israeli conflict occur *at different times*, unless the prepositional phrase is not intended as a genuine adverbial modifier. "Times", if they are regarded as real at all, are only the locations of events in that theory, and hence cannot appear in expressions designed to signify an existential difference between events. We should say instead that the two conflicts, together with all the other events *and* times of history, both exist *and* bear various temporal relations to one another. For the same reason, the S-theory does not say that each event occurs *at all times*, that it is *always* occurring. This too modifies the word 'occurs' with a temporal adverb. It is difficult for people used to modifying all statements about objects and events with temporal adverbs to get used to the idea of not doing so, but it is essential to understanding the theory of space-like time. We must frame all of our S-theory statements not only without tenses but without temporal adverbs of any sort.

Thus far, I have discussed the S-theory in terms of what it says about events and states of affairs. But what about the status of objects? What are the consequences of the S-theory in regard to continuants? Fortunately, the relationship borne by events and states of affairs *to* continuants readily reveals the answer. Let us begin with a concrete example, in the S-theorist claim that all the events of the life of Henry VIII are happening. Now, events don't just happen, so to speak, in a vacuum; they happen *to* continuants: a collision of two objects happens to those objects, and the birth of Henry VIII happened to him. Or, as the S-theory would have it, the events of his life *are* happening to Henry VIII. But from this, surely, we must conclude that what those events are happening to *also* exists, just as they themselves do. Hence Henry VIII himself exists; Henry VIII is alive and is experiencing all of the events of his life! There is *no difference in existential status* among Henry VIII, Elizabeth II, and (perhaps) Henry IX, just as there is no existential difference among the events and states of affairs of their respective lives.

So all of the animate and inamimate objects of history alike exist, in just the same sense. This sounds startling to common sense, which distinguishes between those continuants that exist in contrast to those that did exist but don't any longer -- their materials having been "re-cycled" -- and those that merely will exist. Yet it seems a clear consequence of the S-theory:. To say that Henry VIII's being (or becoming) King of England exists (or is occurring) is another way of saying that Henry VIII is (or is becoming) King of England. And this surely implies that Henry VIII exists, just as to say that Elizabeth II is Queen of England implies that *she* exists. (We must resist the temptation, once again, to say that the events of their lives are happening to Henry VIII and Elizabeth II *at different times*, hence that the two monarchs *exist* at different times.)

But such a conclusion raises puzzles. "If Henry VIII is living, just the same as Elizabeth II", it might be asked, "then why is it that he is not equally available for observation by us? Surely there must be some difference or other between the two monarchs, to account for this; if it isn't a difference in regard to existence, then what *is* it?" This question is a serious one, and it has been taken by some to reveal a clear empirical refutation of the S-theory. But there is a possible answer, and at least some "S-theorists" explicitly embrace it: There *is* a temporal difference between Henry and Elizabeth, and it isn't a difference in regard to existence; the difference is one of temporal location. Henry VIII simply isn't "*here*", where we are, *in time*. He is, in a temporal sense, elsewhere -- or *elsewhen*! Equally well, of course, *we* are "elsewhere" to *him*. Our temporal perspective is in no way privileged over his.

On the S-theory, then, an object has not only a spatial location (a place) but a temporal position as well (a time) -- or perhaps just a single spatio-temporal location (a place-time). In other words, objects bear both types of relations to one another, spatial *and* temporal, just as events are commonly supposed to do. Each animate or inanimate object is temporally distant from all the others of history by various amounts. Indeed, the fact that it is continuants that events happen to suggests that objects be located just where their events are located, in time as in space. Not only is the life of Henry VIII some 400 years earlier than my life, but Henry himself is earlier than I myself, by that same amount. (And he is some 1600 years later than Julius Caesar, roughly simultaneous -- or contemporaneous -- with his wives, and so on.)

This view of the world of objects as "four dimensional", spread out across time as well as across space, is a notion that is easily misunderstood, so I will do well to describe it a little further.[4] An important corollary, evidently, is that objects have *parts* that are various temporal distances from one another. Every object *in itself* is "four-dimensional", in the sense that its parts bear temporal relations, as well as spatial relations, to one another. (Notice that to say this involves a *temporal* notion of "part" and "whole". For in general, we may say that two things can count as parts of one whole if they are contiguous -- either directly or via others in between them. And if the sort of "contiguity" and "betweenness" involved are temporal, we can speak of temporal parts and temporally extended wholes). So objects are not only located in time but also extended in time. They can be conceptually "cross-sectioned" to yield "time-slices" as well as ordinary spatial slices. And on a space-time diagram, we can represent the four-dimensional "shape" of Henry VIII as trapezoidal: fat at his later temporal "end" and slim at the earlier one!

This notion of temporally extended continuants is needed by the S-theory in order to avoid what would otherwise evidently be a logical inconsistency. For to claim, without any qualification, that (say) all the events of the life of Henry VIII are happening to him -- his birth and his burial, winning at cards and losing at cards, etc. etc. -- surely sounds self-contradictory. Henry's life is occurring *and* his burial is occurring -- or in other words, Henry is living his life *and* is being buried -- how can both be true? But the contradiction disappears, *if* the notion of "coexisting" events that are spread across time is augmented by that of objects that are temporally extended. For in that case, these mutually incompatible events and states of affairs are seen as happening to *different temporal parts* of Henry VIII! There is no contradiction in saying that some of his temporal parts are experiencing wedding ceremonies whereas another is undergoing burial, that parts of him are living but other parts are dead. There is no conflict in saying that the reigns of Henry VIII and Elizabeth II over England are both occurring, that Henry and Elizabeth are both reigning over England, since they are reigning over different "time-chunks" of England.[5]

For reasons already discussed, the consistent S-theorist would not attempt to avoid the apparent contradiction here by saying that different events are happening to Henry VIII *at different times*, if the phrase 'at different times' is taken to be genuinely adverbial, modifying 'are happening'. Interestingly enough, however, this *is* exactly what he wants to say, if 'at different times' is understood as being *non*-adverbial! For compare "Henry is fat and thin at different times' to, say, 'Henry is hairy and hairless at different places'. The phrase 'at different places' might be called adjectival rather than adverbial; i.e., it modifies 'Henry', not 'is' (or 'is hairy'). What the spatial modifier does in *this* sort of case is to give us one way of talking about different parts of his body, as a spatially extended whole: some parts have hair and some do not. And for the S-theory, the temporal modifier would be read in the same way; to say that different events or states of affairs are happening to Henry VIII at different times can be taken to mean that they are happening to different temporal parts of him. Some time-chunks of Henry VIII are (spatially) thin and some are not.

But this latter interpretation is emphatically not the intention behind use of such phrases in ordinary speech. The concept of "four-dimensional" *objects* is alien to ordinary thought -- and this reveals even more clearly that, whatever may be true of time itself, the S-theory fails as an analysis of the ordinary language of time. In such talk, objects do not extend across time; instead, we might say, they "persist through" time. That is, we say of one and the same *entire* thing that it exists at different times, rather than that different *parts* of the same thing *are* at different times. To say "The leaf was green but now it is red", for example, is not to speak of two different entities -- two temporally separated parts of a four-dimensional leaf, of which one is green and the other red -- but only of one entire three dimensional entity. It is one and the same leaf that both did and does exist, and it is numerically the same leaf that is now different in color than it was. (Modern speakers may think of it as having gained or lost a few million molecules, of course, so that it is the same object only in part. But even to say this is to speak of entities, namely the molecules, that are identical through time. And under the S-theory, the later leaf cannot even be *partially* the same object as the earlier leaf.) So we have now seen yet another way in which the time of common sense is radically different from space. Objects are conceived of as extending across space, but nothing is taken to "persist through" space. (No one, for example, supposes that one end of a table is the same entire thing as the other end, or that his elbow is his wrist!)

Notice carefully the temporal adverbs that I have had to use in expressing the concept of identity through time: 'at different times', 'did and does', and the like. To make as clear as possible the role of the adverbs in this respect, let me represent a sample sentence -- say, 'Bill did exist and he still does', or 'Bill both was and is overweight' -- in the following formalized fashion: '$PB_b \cdot Qb$'. Now, the two conjoined parts of this sentence are modified by different tense-adverbs. Yet *the same singular term 'b'* appears in both conjuncts, referring to the same individual in each case. And that is what enables us to express a "time lapse" without having to speak of two *different* individuals (at its "ends"). For if we have no temporal adverbs but only relational predicates to work with, the best we can get is something like 'c is Q and d is Q and c is earlier than d' ('$Q_c \cdot Q_d \cdot R_{cd}$'), which has two different particulars -- at best different parts of Bill as a temporally extended thing -- at the extremities of the lapse of time. (Note that '$R_{bb}$' could only say that Bill or some part of him is temporally separated from itself, which will not do!)

So the persisting continuants of ordinary speech require temporal adverbs. Unlike the concept of space, and unlike the concept of time as "space-like", the ordinary concept of time requires for its verbalization something grammatically very unlike the relational predicates. And once again, words like 'here' and 'there' are revealed as being radically different from 'now' and 'then', both grammatically and in the kinds of concepts their grammatical structure expresses. In the same vein, it is worth noting that temporal adverbs are required to express coming into and going out of existence, as well as continuing existence through time. To say, for example, that the state of Israel *once did* not exist but *now does* exist is to say that it has come into existence. (Note the form here: $P{\sim}Q_b \cdot Q_b$, letting 'Q' = 'exists'. And note the adverbs in the more general expression 'x first exists and subsequently does not exist'.) For as we have already seen, the temporal adverb-less S-theory has it that every object (and event) in the history of the universe is in existence -- which means that nothing comes into existence or goes out of existence.

There is, however, an S-theory counterpart of beginning and ceasing to exist, as is evident from considering the spatial analogue. We might be willing to say that an object "begins" (or "ends") -- though not that it begins *to exist* -- at its edges, or where its spatial extremities are. And similarly we might say that the two temporally furthermost points of an object or state of affairs, even though they coexist, can conceptually "stand in" for its going in and out of existence. Once again, the theory of space-like time is led to replace the ordinary concept of a thing's numerical identity time by the notion of the continuity across time of the stuff it's composed of; and similarly, change in regard to an entity's existence or non-existence is replaced by appropriate *discontinuities* in the temporal "dimension". (Actually, conservation of matter would imply that it is only the object itself, and not the stuff of which it is composed, that ceases to exist. So in the S-theory, instead of sharp "edges" for an object on its temporal ends, we will expect a point at which parts of it separate spatially from one another, trailing off like the arms of an octopus.)

In this paper, I have discussed two significant aspects of the S-theory: in regard to existence and in regard to identity through time. Yet there is much, much more that could be said about both the S-theory and the ordinary concept of time; the surface has barely been scratched. And I have not at all discussed the Big Question: which view, if either, is right? Relevant to this problem are such highly involved questions as whether empirical experience favors one view over the other, and what our present scientific theories tell us about time. (Does Relativity really require a four-dimensional world?) All these queries will just have to wait, I'm afraid, for another time.

NOTES

1. Excerpts from and references to the relevant writings of these philosophers, and others with similar views, can be found in *Problems of Space and Time*, part IV, edited by J. J. C. Smart (Macmillan, New York, 1964) and in *The Philosophy of Time*, edited by R. M. Gale (Anchor Books, Garden City, N.Y., 1967).

2. Gale's name 'B-theory', taken from McTaggart's "B-series", has gained some currency for this view of time. Unfortunately for my purposes, Gale directs his remarks primarily toward Grünbaum's notion that "nowness" is mind-dependent. Consequently, his characterization of the "B-theory" includes not only the view that "now" is perspectival, like "here", but additionally this feature of mind-dependence, which is not part of the view as it is commonly held.

3. It is implicit in my way of saying this that I am using the term "predicate", and its object-language correlates 'property' and 'relation', in a narrower way than is often done in pure symbolic logic, where any expression whatever that contains two free variables is apt to be called a dyadic predicate, and said to represent a relation -- even, say, one of the form '$O_x \cdot Q_y$'. Hence, an open sentence such as 'x is red at t' could be said to express a relation between x and t, just as much as do 'x is earlier than t', 'x is at t', and the other phrases that I have listed here as paradigms of relational predicates. But surely the former is very different in grammatical structure from the latter two; lumping both types under the same rubric obscures important distinctions between them. (Moreover, 'x is red at t' is commonly symbolized as '$R_{xt}$', the same as would be 'x is at t', in spite of the difference in structure that this obliterates.) It is the desire to stress these differences that leads me to ignore logicians' usage in favor of terminology that seems much more natural to me: I find it highly strained to say, for example, that being red (or being red *at*) is a relation,

which a thing bears to a time. Being red is a property, to be signified by a *monadic* predicate, and 'at t' is an adverbial phrase which modifies that monadic predicate.

4. The most common misunderstanding being to visualize objects as *moving* across space-time, rather than as being extended across space-time. The idea of (three-dimensional) objects that persist through time but also move constantly from one time or event to another is a carry-over from certain ordinary ways of talking. I maintain that this "passage of time" notion cannot be taken literally even within the ordinary concept of time, and it most certainly is out of place in the S-theory. See my paper "The Source of the River of Time", *Ratio,* Dec. 1976.

5. Some philosophers identifiable as S-theorists give the appearance -- as do also some of their opponents -- of not realizing that a four-dimensional world of events carries a commitment to a four-dimensional world of objects. But others are admirably clear in this regard, notably Quine, Williams and Smart. (See Smart, *op. cit.*)

## DISCUSSION AND COMMENT

Charles Sherover

One never finds it a happy occasion to be highly critical of a paper which obviously represents a good deal of work and aims at rigorous thinking. The difficulty is compounded when the paper appears to be endorsing some of the critic's own biases. If I read it correctly, this paper points out some of the incongruities of the current attempt by some logicians to construct an artificial tenseless language based on a spatial analogy and seek to apply it to temporal events. But I cannot applaud his effort; my chief reasons are enumerated in what follows. I am also troubled by the fact that his criticism judges such a theory as incorrect but, for no discernible reason, leaves it at the end as an open option.

The paper presumes too much without justifying, or even recognizing its presumptions, and is built upon two fundamental ambiguities. It compares this so-called S-theory to what is repeatedly named as the "ordinary view" which is never defined, described or certified as such. We do not know, at the end, among what population this view is "ordinary" or why its supposed generality is important. It augments this ambiguity by pairing it with equally ambiguous use of the word 'existence'. We are left with the reiterated thesis: the ordinary view of time involves existence.* All this really amounts to, in view of the consistent neglect of definition is the assertion "X involves Y" without any indication of the kind of involvement that may be meant. I, for one, do not feel enlightened.

---

*This is, I think, *prima facie* false. 'Ordinary' theology, for example talks of the 'existence of God' while simultaneously insisting that God is *not* in time. Would the author claim that it is meaningful in 'ordinary' discourse to posit some kind of non-temporal existence? Or does he presume an equivalence between time and existence?

The paper presumes a substance metaphysic; it does not consider the possible alternative that 'things' are intrinsically events with the consequent that time is inherent in them. It presumes a container theory of time; it ignores the possibility of a relational view except in a purely external way that begs the issue; it also ignores the possibility of a theory that sees time and being as mutually implicatory. It presumes that logical formalism can authentically deal with time (although it is not clear just how its invocation is clarificatory); it ignores the crucial issue which Kant, for one, raised -- whether time does not itself ground logic and is thereby not subject to analysis by what is dependent on it. It does not take the perspectival distinction -- between what is perceiv*ed* and the perceiv*ing* itself -- seriously enough to refrain from constantly jumping back and forth from one to the other. It presumes that all languages report the world,or describe reality, in exactly the same way; it ignores the lack of one-to-one correspondence between words and phrases in different languages and, more important, the radical differences between grammatical structures (and thereby the linguistically framed structures of human thinking).

The paper seeks to develop the notion that tense is essentially adverbial in nature. Such a view strikes me as untenable. Its systematic critique would take us into an extended metaphysical and epistemological discussion. But it can at least be said here that it seems to presume that semantics can be studied outside of syntax. A language is not just a list of separate words each of which has an intrinsic meaning unsullied by context. Both are culturally conditioned as they reflect and are reflected back into that cultural ethos out of which they emerge and to which they give expression in every pronouncement. It would seem that any linguistic analysis that claims descriptive import must be conducted within the context of its anthropological setting.

One can at least suggest that his thesis regarding adverbs embodies a strange philosophy of language that perhaps reflects the parochialism of presuming the universal applicability of the English language, which centers on static nouns rather than time-centered verbs. But even here a noun without a verb cannot comprise or produce a sentence, yet we can have a sentence by using a form of the verb itself as the grammatica subject. The verb -- the action-word, being-word, time-word -- is the keystone of any statement. The issue is not new. Aristotle already pointed out that a noun "has no reference to time ... [whereas] a verb is that which, in addition to its proper meaning, carries with it the notion of time." (16a10-20, 16b6-7)

This consideration points us to the fundamental problem. While comparing two views about time this paper carries with it no sense of time. The issues raised are not new. The questions we ask and the formulations we develop arise out of previous discussions and the accomplishments and useful failures they provide. These should not be wasted by being thrown aside or ignored. The paper would have been helped, for example, by some attention to the issues to which the S-theory that is criticized was directed. This might help us understand what issue its proponents think is involved and why it is presumably subject to such strange consequences which are described but not explained and why their defenses are not acceptable.

This is to urge that responsible discussion should attend to the fact that a discussion of time, as of any other topic, is intrinsically bound up with its own history, that our thinking and discussion has its being in an historical continuity which gave it birth and meaning. Instead of abstracting a particular dispute from this continuity, the paper would have been more helpful if it had clarified the questions to which his S-theory proponents directed their answers and the problems they believed they had solved. The issues to which the paper is directed would then have been explicated and a basis for evaluating its success would have been provided.

All of this is to say that unless we avoid the metaphysical vacuum of unexplicated presumptions, consistently refrain from the use of unexplicated terms, and understand that any theory is an attempt to answer certain questions arising out of previous discussion, we are at a loss to perceive any progress that might be made or the new horizons we seek to open. Particularly with reference to a paper about time, we have a right to ask that it take the time of its own historical context with some seriousness.

# III. LIVING CLOCKS

## Biological Clocks and Their Synchronizers

J.L. Cloudsley-Thompson

*ABSTRACT*

*Biological clocks are interpreted as self-sustained oscillations whose phase can be entrained by an external synchronizer. The prime synchronizer is light, but temperature may occasionally be effective. Other possible factors are also mentioned, and their operation discussed. Circadian, circalunadian and circannual rhythms are described, and the phenomena of frequency multiplication and demultiplication explained. The interaction between exogenous and endogenous rhythms, and the effects of constant ambient conditions are then considered. The synchronization of individual unicellular clocks with their environments, the interactions between cellular clocks within multicellular organisms, and the possible existence of central master clocks, are then discussed. Finally, attention is given to the synchronization of circalunadian and of seasonal rhythms with the natural environment. It is concluded that circadian clocks are probably coupled with circalunadian clocks to measure photoperiod so that seasonal cycles of reproduction, diapause, and other physiological processes, may be synchronized with environmental influences resulting from the movement of the earth in solar orbit.*

## INTRODUCTION

Rhythmicity is characteristic of many natural phenomena, both physical and biological. Most living things reflect their planetary origin in the possession of innate periodicities which are synchronized with the daily, lunar, and seasonal changes that take place in their normal environments. Except for the bacteria, and those algae that lack a discrete nucleus, probably all living organisms possess 'biological clocks'. There may be no selection advantage in measuring astronomical time to an organism whose lifespan is typically less than one day but, to plants and animals that live for longer than 24 hours, there must be a clear advantage in being able to anticipate the cyclic changes which occur during that time. Claude Bernard's (1878) concept of homeostasis should, therefore, be modified: the internal environment of a plant or animal alters rhythmically to mirror the cyclical changes that are continually taking place in its environment.

## THE CLOCK MECHANISM

Few biologists today doubt that biological clocks really exist, for their operation is manifest in phenomena as diverse as the timing of luminescence in marine dinoflagellates and the control of fluctuations in human body temperature (Sollberger, 1965). But there is much active controversy regarding the fundamental mechanisms involved. For 30 years, Professor Frank A. Brown, Jr. has been claiming that the clocks of living organisms are timed by subtle, rhythmic geophysical forces that permeate the Earth. Most other investigators, however, now hold the view that biological rhythms are endogenous and completely independent of the environment for their fundamental timing (see discussion in Brown, Hastings & Palmer, 1970). This intriguing problem lies somewhat outside the scope of the present discussion. Either hypothesis could probably be proved, or disproved, only by experiments conducted in distant outer space.

It is generally agreed that the rhythms of animals and plants must have arisen as cellular phenomena which have subsequently been strengthened my natural selection.

Under experimental conditions, they exhibit certain fundamental qualities that are common to them all. For example, the phase of a 24-hour rhythm -- that is, the position in the cycle at which some particular event takes place -- is not necessarily restricted to any particular time of night or day. Secondly, although biological phenomena are usually extremely sensitive to thermal influences, the periods of biological rhythms are relatively independent of temperature changes. If this were not so, of course, biological clocks could no longer function except in constant environments. At the same time, although the length of the period of a rhythm may be relatively temperature independent (above the minimum threshold below which activity is suppressed) (Kalmus, 1934), nevertheless its amplitude will vary according to the biological temperature coefficient of the process and it may be synchronized by temperature changes. Similarly, although the amplitude of a rhythm is sensitive to metabolic inhibitors, such as sodium cyanide and other narcotizing agents, investigations have shown that the period is normally unaffected. Finally, rhythms are not learned, because apparently arhythmic organisms, raised under constant conditions in the laboratory, may become rhythmic after experiencing only a single, non-periodic stimulus, such as a flash of light (see below). Strict time invariance is never satisfied in living systems because the very basis of a biological process depends upon the operation of an averaging device at the molecular level (Goodwin, 1972).

Biological clocks are thought to be self-sustained oscillations whose phase can be re-set or 'entrained' (Pittendrigh & Bruce, 1959) by an external 'synchronizer' (Halberg *et al.*, 1954; 1959) or *Zeitgeber*, a term proposed by Professor Jürgen Aschoff (1954; 1960). In their natural habitats, most plants and animals display nycthemeral rhythms which are entrained to a frequency of 24 hours by the daily cycles of light and darkness engendered by the rotation of the earth on its axis. Although these rhythms frequently persist under constant laboratory conditions, the free-running periods exhibited are usually either slightly longer or somewhat shorter than 24 hours. For this reason, Dr. Franz Halberg has coined the word *circadian* (from the Latin *circa*, about, and *diem*, a day) to describe them (Halberg *et al.*, 1959). Persistent lunar and tidal rhythms are likewise called *circalunadian* (about a lunar day) or *circalunar*, because the period of the bimodal lunar-day rhythm is usually longer or shorter than the period displayed in nature (Palmer 1973; 1974), while endogenous yearly rhythms are called *circannual* for similar reasons.

Under certain conditions, oscillations can be entrained to show periods which are a multiple of the entraining cycle. This phenomenon is called 'frequency demultiplication' since the entrained period which the rhythm shows is longer than that of the external cycle. Frequency demultiplication -- transformation of the output from an oscillator (the circadian clock) by counting off a certain number of beats -- may be the explanation, not only of circalunar rhythms but also of oestrus cycles and other long-term periodicities such as those revealed in man by the study of psychiatry and medicine (Richter, 1965; 1975). Frequency demultiplication occurs in nerve fibres: it has also been advocated as one possible explanation for the accuracy and temperature independence of circadian rhythms. The latter are thus supposed to be generated through frequency demultiplication from high frequency oscillations on the molecular level (Sollberger, 1965). Although the application of cybernetic principles has sometimes achieved satisfactory physical models that suggest working hypothesis, it would be a grave error to pursue the analogy too closely (Reinberg & Ghata, 1964).

With regard to *circannual* clocks, only a handful of biological rhythms have been shown to persist with a period of approximately 365 days, under conditions held constant with respect to light and temperature for at least two or three years. Examples are provided by hibernation in ground squirrels, and the reproduction of European starlings, cave crayfish and marine coelenterates. (See reviews *in* Menaker, 1971; Pengelley, 1974). Even in such relatively well-documented cases, however, 24-hour light cycles are commonly used and are considered to be 'constant'. They could theoretically, therefore by summated, as they may also be in the case of lunar cycles -- though it would be hard to estimate whether 'frequency demultiplication' of a circadian oscillator, an endogenous circannual clock, or extrinsic timing, provides the most plausible explanation. It is, moreover, difficult to imagine the adaptive significance of circannual rhythms since, in most parts of the world, changes in photoperiod, measured by the circadian clock, provide a reference point for every phase of the calender year.

In higher animals, the circadian clock is responsible for triggering a wide range of responses, both at cellular and multicellular levels of organisation. Throughout the day, whole series of activities are generated in different parts of the body, and numbers of different clock centres have been identified -- such as the mammalian hypothalamus and the pineal gland of birds. As well as central clocks, there is an hierarchy of lesser clocks, some of which are demonstrably independent of one another. Whether the same mechanism is common to all cellular clocks, or whether convergent evolution has produced several different types of cellular clocks, is not yet known. Indeed, it is often difficult to determine whether a particular function, such as enzyme activity, engenders the circadian oscillation, or is being driven by it.

Although the ability to measure time is apparently an innate property of the cell the fundamental nature of biological clocks remains obscure. Feedback regulation of enzyme activation and inhibition, RNA synthesis, a 'chronon' model which proposes a circadian transcription of genes, and ionic diffusion across cellular membranes, have all been proposed as possible mechanisms. In the present paper I shall discuss both the synchronization of individual cellular circadian clocks with their environments, and their rhythmic interaction with one another in multicellular organisms. Finally, attention will be given to the synchronization of lunar and annual cycles.

## SYNCHRONIZATION

Light is the most usual and important synchronizer of circadian rhythms, but temperature, too, may occasionally be effective. Circadian rhythms can sometimes be initiated in a rhythmic organism under non-inhibitory conditions by a single stimulus, such as a flash of light or a brief increase or decrease in the ambient temperature. In other organisms, a series of repeated stimuli may be required before a stable phase-relationship has been reached (Bruce, 1960). In nature, thermal influences probably reinforce or supplement those of light intensity. Light and temperature are the only environmental factors so far conclusively demonstrated to be coupled to the circadian biological clock (Pittendrigh, 1961), but it is by no means improbable that some other regularly repeated stimuli, such as periodic noises, social cues, or even changes in barometric pressure, may also be effective phasing agents (Aschoff, 1962; Bennett, 1974; Cloudsley-Thompson, 1961; Enright, 1965; Harker, 1958). As mentioned below, mechanical agitation and variations in water pressure serve to synchronize the circalunadian rhythms of marine animals. In higher animals and man, the number of possible synchronizers is larger because of the many important correlations to the environment. Thus, it is often difficult to describe the endogenous rhythm as clearly in them as it is in plants and lower animals (Bünning, 1973).

Some biological activities are non-rhythmic, and others can be entrained only with difficulty. The significance of this will be discussed later. A number of attempts have been made to entrain biological clocks to other than 24-hour periods, but they have not been very successful. In most cases, the imposed cycles have either failed to persist under constant conditions even though entrainment was successful, or else have merely reinforced the 24-hour clock (Harker, 1958). The interactions between light and temperature have also been studied on a number of occasions. Temperature cycles have been shown to dominate the rhythm of petal movement in *Kalanchoë blossfildia*, while a light-dark cycle entrains the rhythm of eclosion in *Drosophila pseudoobscura* more strongly than do temperature fluctuations. Wilkins (1965) concludes that the relative influence of light-dark and temperature cycles probably depends on the magnitude of the change in temperature and the incident radiant flux employed.

Environmental synchronizers are not equally effective at all hours, for the sensitivity of an organism to its *Zeitgeber* fluctuates rhythmically, as Professor Erwin Bünning (1936; 1973) has been emphasising for decades. Bünning's hypothesis has been discussed in some detail by Ward (1972) who points out that Bünning began with two postulates. First, that there is a circadian rhythm of some function of plants that

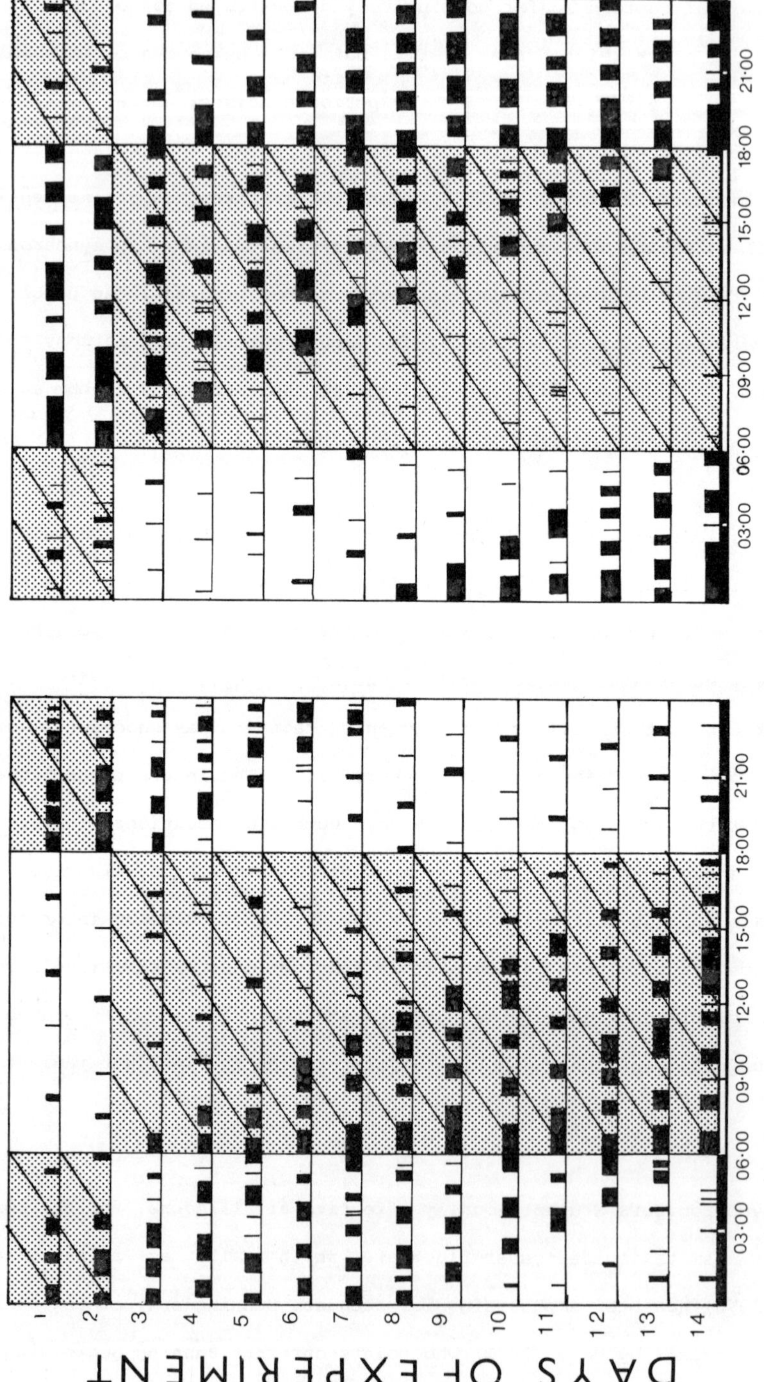


*Figure 1. Effect of a rapid change in the timing of the period of light on the activity of a night-active animal (Left) and of a day-active animal (Right) showing re-synchronization.*

is vitally associated with flower induction in both short-day plants and long-day plants and, secondly, that plants make use of this rhythm for measuring time. The timing mechanism that is responsible for the photoperiodic response of flowering is the same as the mechanism that is responsible for the timing of leaf movements. This timing mechanism has two alternating phases of about 12 hours each which may be distinguished as 'photophil' or 'light-loving', and 'scotophil' or 'dark-loving'. Photophil is equivalent to the day phase and scotophil to the night phase of a circadian rhythm. Consequently, light falling on a plant during the photophil phase will enhance flowering but, during the scotophil phase, will inhibit it.

In a similar way, light shocks of 10 minutes given to flying squirrels (*Glaucomys volans*) which are otherwise maintained in constant darkness, shift the phase of their activity cycles only if presented during the animal's subjective night. As Bennett (1974) points out, however, such variations in the reactions of an organism could equally well be due to perturbations of its cellular clocks, of the clocks' hands, of mediating pathways, or to combinations of all those components.

## 'EXOGENOUS' AND 'ENDOGENOUS' RHYTHMS

An early worker in the field of biological rhythms, Professor Hans Kalmus (1938) divided rhythmic phenomena into two main categories: 'exogenous' rhythms, which are a direct response to physical changes in the environment and do not persist when conditions are kept constant; and 'endogenous' rhythms which continue, at any rate for a time, under constant condition. Later, Park (1938) suggested that the majority of species in their natural environments, appear to show a combination of both types, and such rhythms he designated 'composite'. A composite rhythm, as thus defined, would differ from some endogenous rhythms only in that it would become entrained instantly. Since the rapidity of synchronization may depend upon the intensity of the *Zeitgeber*, there can be no clear distinction between composite and endogenous (Cloudsley-Thompson, 1961).

Many animal rhythms appear to be exogenous and, indeed, do not persist under constant environmental conditions. Nevertheless, they cannot readily be induced by environmental cycles having a periodicity differing markedly from 24 hours. For this reason, I believe that unequivocal examples of true exogenous rhythms, especially of locomotion, are rare. Probably most rhythms which are apparently exogenous, actually represent the expression of endogenous cellular clocks that rapidly get out of phase with one another when removed from the influence of environmental periodicity (Cloudsley-Thompson, 1961). At the same time, of the large number of variable factors in human physiology which oscillate nychthemerally, only a few have been shown to have an endogenous rhythm (Conroy & Mills, 1970).

Professor Philip Corbet (1965) distinguishes between endogenous rhythms and cycles. He defines a cycle as, 'a sequence of events, repeated during the life of an individual, and characterised by a change in physiological condition or behaviour. The events always fall in the same order, but the time-intervals between corresponding ones are not necessarily constant. Cycles of feeding and avarian maturation in blood-sucking Diptera fall into this category'. The separation of rhythms from cycles may, however, cause difficulty. Cyclic events, such as oviposition cycles, naturally tend to become regular in time under constant conditions. For instance, green-bottle flies (*Lucilia sericata*) lay batches of eggs at intervals of approximately three days in the presence of meat. At other times, they will only lay three days after meat has been presented. If meat is given every fourth day, a four-day oviposition rhythm can be produced. Should this be regarded as an exogenous rhythm, induced in a cyclic, but non-rhythmic, event by a regularly appearing stimulus, or as an endogenous rhythm whose phase has been delayed by the absence of the appropriate 'permission'?

The reproduction of certain desert birds is engendered by a combination of two factors -- their innate annual reproductive rhythm and the stimulus of rainfall (Lofts & Murton, 1968). The latter provides the necessary 'permission' to lay, for oviposition is inhibited without it. In other words, an endogenous rhythm must represent the manifestation of a biological clock, but a cyclical event may show exogenous periodicity in the presence of a regularly appearing stimulus (e.g. alternating light and darkness) and 'permission' (e.g. temperature above a threshold value). Centipedes (*Scolopendra* spp.) show a marked endogenous rhythm in constant darkness, but this is suppressed by constant light. By analogy, the oviposition rhythm of *Lucilia sericata* can be regarded as being suppressed by the absence of meat. Alternatively, as suggested above, the presence of meat may be looked upon as 'permission' for a cyclical event to be manifested regularly. Clearly the two concepts coalesce at this point.

Rhythmic changes in the physical factors of the environment may not only synchronise the phase of biological clocks with the time of day, but they may elicit immediate responses from the organism as well. Whether an observed periodicity is regarded as exogenous or endogenous depends upon its subsequent persistence under constant conditions. A problem therefore arises as to whether an observed periodicity which disappears rapidly under constant conditions represents a true, free-running circadian rhythm, as I have suggested, or an exogenous periodicity that has persisted for a short while under its own inertia and is not driven by a biological clock. To use an anology, if the wagons of a railway train are uncoupled in motion, they may follow the engine for a while before coming to a halt. The nycthemeral activity rhythm of the desert locust (*Schistocerca gregaria*) is not clearly marked. It could theoretically represent an exogenous periodicity that persists briefly in constant conditions but is not controlled by a biological clock. Although activity of the desert locust is greater in constant light than in darkness, its periodicity persists better in darkness! To pursue our analogy further, the second condition (darkness) can be likened to uncoupling the wagons while the train is running downhill, the former (constant light) to uncoupling them when the engine is pulling them up a slope. The existence of an underlying biological clock can, in some cases be revealed by the reluctance of a rhythm that is apparently exogenous to come entrained to any periodicity of other than one of about 24 hours. This applies to the desert locust which, in fact, actually possesses an excellent clock to which it pays scant heed under natural conditions (Cloudsley-Thompson, 1977).

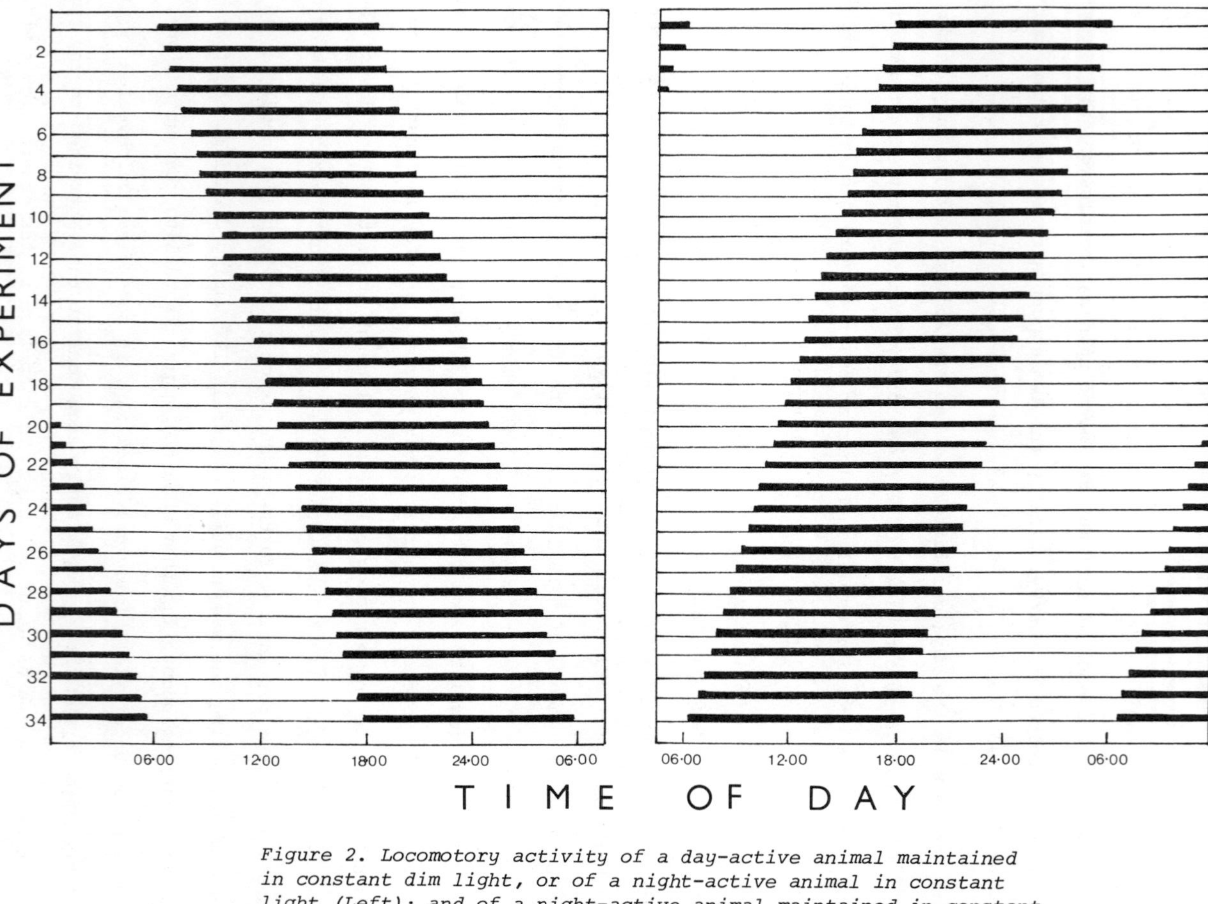


*Figure 2. Locomotory activity of a day-active animal maintained in constant dim light, or of a night-active animal in constant light (Left); and of a night-active animal maintained in constant darkness, or of a day-active animal in constant light (Right).*

EFFECTS OF CONSTANT CONDITIONS.

When circadian biological clocks are free-running under constant conditions; they seldom maintain periods of exactly 24-hours. For instance, although bullfinches kept in darkness show a period of about 24 hours' duration, this changes to 22 hours in constant light. In rodents, on the other hand, the period of spontaneous locomotory activity is longer in light than in darkness. With illumination, the daily period of activity becomes progressively later on successive days and may be shifted steadily round the clock, with no tendency to be fixed at any particular hour of the solar day or night. In general, it seems that the activity rhythms of nocturnal animals are delayed by constant light, while those of day-active animals tend to be accelerated. The extent to which this occurs depends upon the intensity of the light (Aschoff, 1960). Although a number of exceptions are known, it may be significant that many of them are provided by tropical species in whose natural environments the length of daylight varies little throughout the year.

When it does occur, however, this shift in phase allows the daily rhythm of an animal to keep pace with the seasons as the days lengthen in spring or draw in during the autumn; for the duration of daylight in temperate regions varies significantly according to the time of year. Obviously, if an animal is to maintain its regular daily activity, it cannot synchronize both to dawn and to dusk, since the period between them is variable. It seems however, that most nocturnal animals tend to use dusk as the synchronizer, while day-active species use the dawn (Aschoff, 1960).

It might be thought that the existence of 'free-running', circadian periodicity would conclusively invalidate F. A. Brown's hypothesis of exogenous control but, according to Brown (1960) this is not the case. Under so-called 'constant conditions, an organism reacting to a light-sensitive phase in its daily cycle would receive from a constantly illuminated environment a shifting stimulus whose strength would be a function of the light intensity. Thus, constant light would provide rhythmic synchronization as a consequence of the organism's own responsiveness. Brown calls this hypothetical process 'autophasing'. It is instructive to compare this idea with Bünning's (1936; 1973) hypothesis, already discussed, of entrainment through light-sensitive phases of the circadian rhythm.

We have seen that temperature cycles can be used to synchronize the phases of biological clocks, even though they are usually much less effective than are cycles of light and darkness. At the same time, the periods of circadian clocks are relatively independent of temperature: in general, there are only slight although quite significant, differences between the steady-state periods of a circadian rhythm at different ambient temperatures. On the other hand, the amplitude of any particular rhythmic process may depend greatly on the ambient temperature. When organisms are cooled down below a threshold -- usually between zero and 10°C -- their clocks are stopped (Kalmus, 1934). A persistent phase shift is later seen after they have been transferred back to normal temperatures: this shows that the clock itself has been stopped and not merely the processes controlled by the clock. This effect has been described in the movements of bean leaves, plant growth rhythms, the time-sense of bees, pigment migration in fiddler crabs, and the locomotory activity of insects and spiders (Bünning, 1973; Sweeney & Hastings, 1960).

## THE UNICELLULAR CLOCK AND ITS ENVIRONMENT.

Without doubt, the most far-reaching research on this subject has been carried out by Professors J. W. Hastings and B. M. Sweeney, who have investigated circadian rhythms in the marine dinoflagellate *Gonyaulax polyedra*. These authors studied four different rhythms, vis., a flashing luminescence rhythm obtained when the cells are stimulated mechanically, a rhythm in spontaneous luminescent glow, a rhythm in the photosynthetic capacity of the cells, and a rhythm in cell division. These rhythms show circadian periodicity and can be inhibited independently of one another, but are resumed in phase after removal of the inhibitor. At the same time, a relatively brief exposure to light can cause the rhythms to be shifted by several hours (summarized in Brown, Hastings, & Palmer 1970; Sweeney, 1969).

As in the rhythms of more advanced organisms, the endogenous circadian rhythm of stimulated flashing in *Gonyaulax* populations can be initiated by a single abrupt change in illumination. Individual isolated cells behave as the population does, losing all overt rhythmicity in constant bright light, and recovering it when transferred to light of lower intensity. A similar loss of rhythm occurs in constant light at temperatures below 13°C: the rhythm is reinitiated, and the phase determined, upon increasing the temperature. Thus, the biological clock of *Gonyaulax* can be synchronized, or have its phase shifted, by changes in light and temperature. Circadian rhythms have been demonstrated in various functions of other unicellular organisms, such as phototactic sensitivity and swimming in *Euglena gracilis*, sexual reactivity in *Paramecium bursaria*, and so on. The 'chronon' concept of the cellular clock is based on such work (Ehret & Trucco, 1967). Since all the circadian rhythms of a unicellular organism appear in phase (synchrony) and never in allochrony, it must be assumed that they are coupled to a single pacemaker.

## INTERACTIONS BETWEEN CELLULAR CLOCKS WITHIN MULTICELLULAR ORGANISMS

Since every eucaryote cell contains, or is, a clock, the question arises as to whether, in the multi-cellular organism, the cells are synchronized with one another directly or only via the operation of some exogenous *Zeitgeber*. The evidence seems to suggest that both conditions occur, especially as some rhythms appear synchronously, and others allochronously.

Many years ago, I found that the field cricket (*Gryllus campestris*) is normally active during the daytime, the rhythm being endogenous and with its frequency temperature-independent. When the circadian rhythm had died away after several weeks in constant conditions, however, it could be re-established by a single exposure to light, or by a return to higher temperatures after a period at 5°C. The observation was interpreted as implying that the loss of rhythm was due to the fact that the various cellular clocks of the insect had got out of phase with one another under constant conditions, and were re-synchronized by the light and temperature shocks (Cloudsley-

Thompson, 1958). This view was in accordance with an hypothesis proposed by Harker (1958; 1964) and appears to be supported by the more recent work of Winfree (1975).

The nuclei of syncytia, or of multinucleate cells, almost invariably divide in perfect unison, but ordinary cells seldom show such an effect. The mitoses and meioses of animal testes and plant anthers nevertheless often exhibit a very high degree of synchrony as do the early cleavage stages of developing eggs. Although unusual, synchrony of mitotic rhythms is also well known in plants, particularly Algae, and in the root tissues of Angiosperms. The phase may vary in different species, however, with a maximum frequency of mitosis occurring either at night or during the day. Mitotic rhythms also occur in a variety of animal tissues, especially the epidermis. Evidence of synchronization between mammalian cells has been reviewed by Bruce (1965) who points out that a cold shock may induce synchronization of mitosis in tissue cultures. In such cases it is not always clear whether the timing of the rhythm is exogenous or endogenous, but the latter is more likely. Synchrony is probably achieved through the diffusion of metabolites associated with the synthesis of DNA (Ehret & Trucco, 1967).

There may be no need for a central clock if all cells possess clocks which can be synchronized in this way. Nevertheless, certain groups of cells (such as those in the optic lobes of the brain) are better placed than others to entrain with environmental cycles of light and darkness. These might, therefore, logically, be expected to become specialised as 'master' clocks, although few of these have yet been positively identified.

A cell can influence other cells by what it removes from, or discharges into, the common aqueous medium. The ability of many cells to act in consonance depends on the restraining influences they have on one another. It is difficult to conceive of mechanisms, other than metabolic or hormonal ones, by which individual cells can synchronize with one another directly. The responses of an organism to changes in its environment are, in the final outcome, the result of the responses of individual cells to changes in their local environments. Similarly, the overt rhythm of an organism represents the sum of the reactions of its constituent cells to their biological clocks which, in turn, may be synchronized by a group or groups of cellular clocks, forming a master clock (Brahmachary, 1967; Cloudsley-Thompson, 1961). In general, the master clocks which have so far been studied in animals appear to fall into one of two groups: those which stop in continuous light, such as the eclosion clocks of *Drosophila pseudoobscura* (cf. Pittendrigh 1960; 1961) and other insects, and those involved with activity rhythms (Truman, 1971). Clocks of the first type seem to be associated mainly with developmental rhythms and to be under neuroendocrine control: those of the second are the direct product of the central nervous system. Their phase-response curves, in general, are more stable against interrupting light perturbations since the maximum phase shifts are usually small. It is, at present, not known by which type of clock the time-sense and photoperiodic responses of animals are controlled.

Circadian clocks of the second type have been implicated in many diverse kinds of behaviour. Generalized activities, such as locomotion, are influenced by an array of factors so complex that any clock system must interact with a network of other internal and external stimuli. In many instances, the coupling between the master clock and effector organs may be hormonal: testosterone can de-synchronize the circadian rhythms of birds, and mammals. For fifteen years it was accepted that the circadian rhythms of insects were under the control of a hormone secreted by the suboesophageal ganglion (Harker, 1964). Subsequent research having failed to confirm the central importance of this ganglion, it now seems more probable that 'hormonal rhythms are not primary driving oscillators but are driven' (Brady, 1969). Indeed, while the physiology of the oscillator mechanism (which represents the escapement of the biological clock) is not yet understood, its coupling now appears to be primarily nervous (electrical) and only secondarily hormonal.

This line of thought is supported by the following reasoning. The neurosecretory system plays a central rôle in mediating between environmental changes and the responses of the individual. Neurosecretory cells have a capacity for receiving messages from the nervous system and for controlling the activity of other endocrine organs. Thus internal physiological processes are closely related to external environmental events. The adaptive advantages of this form of integration are evident: avian reproductive cycles are geared to coincide with environmental conditions favouring survival of the offspring; metamorphosis occurs in many insects when food plants are most abundant, and so on. By its very nature, the neurosecretory system is able to link internal responses with external stimuli, and is presented in such phylogenetically diverse groups as the Coelenterata, Arthropoda and vertebrates. In the more primitive phyla, neurosecretory structures are situated diffusely and act directly to control processes such as growth and reproduction but, during the course of evolution they have become more localized and concentrated in specific areas of the central nervous system where they are directly influenced by the brain and when their effects are mediated through epithelial endocrine glands.

## ENVIRONMENTAL SYNCHRONIZATION OF CIRCADIAN RHYTHMS

The entrainment of circadian rhythms with daily environmental cycles is achieved mainly through changes in light intensity at dusk and dawn, and the consequent extension or contraction of the photoperiod (Bruce, 1960; Pittendrigh & Minis, 1964). In addition, synchronization may be assisted by those changes in ambient temperature which normally occur at these times. This is suggested by the fact that when the activity rhythms of various insects, including spider-beetles (*Ptinus tectus*), have been gradually lost in constant conditions, they can sometimes be re-initiated by periodic exposure to high and low temperatures. Regular thermal fluctuations also appear to prevent loss of the activity rhythm of the cockroach (*Periplaneta americana*) in constant darkness although they have no power to initiate a rhythm once it has died out. Sweeney & Hastings (1960), have summarized available information on the subject, pointing out that the effects of temperature perturbances depend on the phase at which they are administered: they are greatest when operating in cooperation with the cycle of daylight and darkness. Changes in relative humidity; barometric pressure, food supply and other environmental variables may sometimes support or inhibit the primary *Zeitgeber* (light) and its subordinate (temperature).

## SYNCHRONIZATION OF CIRCALUNADIAN RHYTHMS

Whereas circadian clocks are valuable in most environments, clocks set to the rhythm of the lunar day are chiefly important to littoral forms exposed to tidal action. Since there are two tides during each lunar day of 24.8 hours (the interval between successive moonrises), circalunadian rhythms are necessarily bimodal. Like circadian rhythms they are apparently important in that they give advance warning of cyclic environmental changes. Circalunardian clocks are illustrated by tidal rhythms of migration in diatoms (*Hantzschia virgata*) and flatworms (*Convoluta roscoffensis*), of locomotory activity and colour change in fiddler crabs (*Uca* spp.) and shore crabs (*Carcinus maenas*), by the rhythmic opening and closing of the valves of oysters (*Crassostrea virginica*) and quahogs (*Venus mercenaria*), and in the lunar time-sense of sand-hoppers (*Talitrus salvator*), (reviewed by Fingermen, 1960).

In addition, great numbers of marine animals and plants have bi-monthly or monthly lunar breeding cycles, in which all members of the species within a particular region become sexually active. This synchronization is essential to the maintenance of the species because it ensures that the gametes are discharged in sufficiently high concentrations to provide a reasonable chance of fertilization taking place (Cloudsley-Thompson, 1961). Examples are afforded by the breeding rhythms of palolo-worms (*Eunice* spp.) and *Platynereis dumerilii*. Rhythms of eclosion and mating in may-flies (*Povilla adusta*) and midges (*Clunio marinus*) are also synchronized by the lunar cycle (Caspers, 1951).

The grunion (*Leuresthes tenuis*), a small pelagic fish which spawns on the beaches of southern California between late February and early September, provides a striking example of lunar rhythm. The spawning runs occur only on three or four nights follow-each full or new moon, and last for a period of from one to three hours immediately after high tide. The eggs mature in about 15 days and are just ready to hatch when the next spring tides lap them. This, and the often described spawning of palolo-worms, are probably synchronized by moonlight, but the lunar periodicity of breeding in oysters (*Ostrea edulis*) is entrained by the rhythmical sequence of differences in water pressure from neap to spring tides.

Under natural conditions, most littoral organisms display both circadian and circa-lunadian rhythms. For instance, the solar rhythm of locomotory activity in crabs is represented, not as an individual peak but as a decrease in the amount of activity at the crest of the daytime tidal peak. The combination of solar-day and lunar-day rhythms is frequently seen in inter-tidal organisms, and it raises the question whether such organisms have a solar-day clock for one rhythmic component and a separate lunar-day clock for the other, or whether a single clock drives both mechanisms. The fact that about one third of the total force producing the tide is solar, is an additional complication.

The tidal cycle on the home shoreline sets the phase of the inhabitants' rhythms. Paradoxically, as Palmer (1973; 1974) reminds us, periodic wetting by inundation is not an important entraining factor for most littoral organisms. Instead, the effective portions of the tidal cycle include one or more of the following: mechanical agitation due to the pounding of the surf, temperature cycles, and the pressure of the water. The last is not generally important for most inter-tidal animals, but it is so in the case of the shore crab (*Carcinus maenas*). Although light-dark cycles have no effect on entrainment, a 24-hour cycle maintains a circalunadian rhythm at strict tidal frequency. Moreover, in rhythms with both daily and tidal components, when the former is shifted by light stimuli, the latter is affected in a nearly identical manner. This suggests that both rhythms are generated by a single biological clock *via* specific coupling mechanisms.

Although few terrestrial animals are known to show lunar breeding rhythms, the fact that some do so suggests very strongly that the synchronizer is moonlight itself. In a few instances, lunar rhythms of reproduction have been demonstrated among birds and mammals; and it is not impossible that the precise timing of the breeding seasons of bats and other inhabitants of the equatorial rain-forest may be ensured by a lunar rhythm imparting great accuracy to an internal circannual rhythm.

## SYNCHRONIZATION OF SEASONAL RHYTHMS

The reproductive physiology of many plants and animals responds to fluctuations in photoperiod or day-length. This response enables them to breed at the period of the year when food for the young is most plentiful and other environmental conditions favourable. At the same time, the sexual cycle often responds to other environmental stimuli. Especially in equatorial regions, where changes in photoperiod are slight, the traditional response to photostimulation is frequently abandoned in favour of other timing devices which ensure that the young are produced at the season most propitious for their survival. The partly endogenous and partly exogenous reproductive cycle involves successive phases of post-nupital regeneration (which is reflected in subsequent recovery after sudden loss of breeding function), acceleration (characterized by sex-hormone production and gametogenesis), and culmination (involving ovulation and insemination). The circannual clock is the primary seasonal initiator and, until post-nuptial regeneration is past, male birds, and probably also females, are not influenced by the external stimuli that would cause gametogenesis at other periods of the cycle. After the spontaneous progression from regeneration to acceleration, the neuro-endocrine machinery comes under the influence of two antagonistic sets of external factors, accelerators and inhibitors. For example, among many tropical species, the advent of dry weather often acts as an inhibitor. Many savanna birds habitually breed as soon as the wet season begins, but the acceleration phase is usually under way long before the rains come (Lofts & Murton, 1968).

In equatorial regions, the continuous abundance of food and relative absence of environmental inhibitors of breeding often permit the abandonment of a more or less precisely timed annual rhythm, while the innate periodicity of the sooty tern (*Sterna fuscata*) permits reproduction four times every three years on Ascension Island in the Atlantic Ocean. Elsewhere circannual clocks are entrained by external synchronizers at least once every year (Marshall, 1960).

BIBLIOGRAPHY

In view of the inordinate amount of relevant literature, much of which was cited by Sollberger (1965), the following list of publications has been restricted to include only a few basic references, key monographs and substantial review articles.

Aschoff, J. (1954) Zeitgeber der tierischen Tagesperiodik, *Naturwiss.*, 41: 49-56.

Aschoff, J. (1960) Exogenous and endogenous components in circadian rhythms. *Cold Spring Harb. Symp. Quant. Biol.*, 25: 11-28.

Aschoff, J. (1963) Comparative physiology: diurnal rhythms. *Ann. Rev. Physio.*, 25: 581-600.

Aschoff, J. (ed.) (1965) *Circadian clocks*. Amsterdam: North Holland. xix + 479 pp.

Baker, J. R. (1938) The evolution of breeding seasons. pp. 161-77 *in* G. R. de Beer, (ed.) *Evolution. Essays on aspects of evolutionary biology*. London: Oxford Univ. Press.

Beck, S. D. (1968) *Insect photoperiodism*. New York: Academic Press. viii + 288 pp.

Bennett, M. F. (1974) *Living clocks in the animal world*. Springfield, Ill.: Thomas. xiii + 221 pp.

Bernard , C. (1878-9) *Leçons sur les phénomènes de la vie communs aux animaux et végétaux*. Paris: Baillère (2 vols).

Brady, J. (1969) How are insect circadian rhythms controlled? *Nature, Lond.*, 223: 781-4.

Brahmachary, R. L. (1967) Physiological clocks. *Internat. Rev. Cytology*, 21: 65-89.

Brown, F. A. jn (1960) Response to pervasive geophysical factors and the biological clock problems. *Cold Spring Harb. Symp. Quant. Biol.*, 25: 57-71.

Brown, F. A. jr., Hastings, J. W. & Palmer, J. D. (1970) *The biological clock. Two views*. New York & London: Academic Press. viii + 94 pp.

Bruce, V. G. (1960) Environmental entrainment of circadian rhythms. *Cold Spring Harb. Symp. Quant. Biol.*, 25: 29-48.

Bruce, V. C. (1965) Cell division rhythms and the circadian clock. pp. 125-38 *in* J. Aschoff (ed.) *Circadian clocks*. Amsterdam: North Holland.

Bünning, E. (1936) Die endogene Tagesrythmik als Grundlage der photoperiodischen Reaktion. *Ber. dt. bot. Ges.*, 54: 590-607.

Bünning, E. (1973) *The physiological clock* (3rd ed.) London: English Universities Press. 258 pp.

Caspers, H. (1951) Rhythmische Erscheinungen in der Fortplanzung von *Clunio marinus* (Dipt. Chiron.) und das Problem der lunaren Periodizität bei Organismen. *Arch Hydrobiol*. Suppl. 18: 415-594.

Cloudsley-Thompson, J. L. (1958) Studies in diurnal rhythms -- VIII. The endogenous chronometer in *Gryllus compestris* L. (Orthoptera: Gryllidae). *J. Insect Physiol.*, 2: 275-80.

Cloudsley-Thompson, J. L. (1960) Adaptive functions of circadian rhythms. *Cold Spring Harb. Symp. Quant. Biol.*, 25: 345-55.

Cloudsley-Thompson, J. L. (1961) *Rhythmic activity in animal physiology and behaviour*. London: Academic Press. vi + 236 pp.

Cloudsley-Thompson, J. L. (1966) Time sense of animals. pp. 296-311 *in* J. T. Fraser (ed.) *The voices of time*. New York: Braziller.

Cloudsley-Thompson, J. L. (1977) Diurnal rhythms of locomotory activity in isolated desert locusts (*Schistocerca Gregaria* (Forsk)). *J. Interdiscipl. Cycle Res.*, 8: 27-36.

Conroy, R. T. W. L. & Mills, J. N. (1970) *Human circadian rhythms*. London: Churchill. ix + 236 pp.

Corbet, P. S. (1965) The role of rhythms in insect behaviour. *in* P. T. Haskell (ed.) *Insect behaviour. Symp. Roy. Ent. Soc.*, 3: 13-28.

Ehret. C. F. & Trucco, E. (1967) Molecular models for the circadian clock, I. The chronon concept. *J. Theoret. Biol.*, 15: 240-62.

Enright, J. T. (1965) Synchronization and ranges of entrainment, pp. 112-24 *in* J. Aschoff (ed.) *Circadian clocks*. Amsterdam: North Holland.

Fingermen, M. (1960) Tidal rhythmicity in marine organisms. *Cold Spring Harb. Symp. Quant. Biol.*, 25: 481-9.

Goodwin, B. C. (1972) Temporal order as the origin of spatial order in embryos. pp. 190-9 *in* J. T. Fraser, F. C. Habner & G. H. Müller (eds.) *The study of time, I*. Berlin: Springer.

Halberg, F., Halberg. E., Barnum, C. P. & Bittner, J. J. (1959). Physiologic 24-hour periodicity in human beings and mice, the lighting regimen and daily routine. pp.

803-78 *in* A. P. Wittrow (ed.) *Photoperiodism and related phenomena in plants and animals*. Washington: Amer. Ass. Adv. Sci.

Halberg, F., Visscher, M. B. & Bittner, J. J. (1954). Relation of visual factors to eosinophil rhythms in mice. *Amer. J. Physiol.*, 179: 229-35.

Hamner, K. C. (1966) Experimental evidence for the biological clock. pp. 281-95 *in* J. T. Frazer (ed.) *The voices of time*. New York: Braziller.

Harker, J. E. (1958) Diurnal rhythms in the animal kingdom. *Biol. Rev.*, 33: 1-52.

Harker, J. E. (1964) *The physiology of diurnal rhythms*. Cambridge: Univ. Press. vii + 114 pp.

Hastings. J. W. (1960) Biochemical aspects of rhythms: phase shifting by chemicals. *Cold Spring Harb. Symp. Quant. Biol.*, 25: 131-43.

Kalmus. H. (1934) Über die Natur des Zeitgedächtnisses der Bienen. *Z. Vergl. Physiol.*, 20: 405-19.

Kalmus, H. (1938) Über das Problem der sogenannten exogenen und endogenen, sowie der orblichen Rhythmik und über organische Periodezität überhaupt. *Riv. Biol.*, 24: 191-225.

Lofts, B. & Murton, K. R. (1968) Photoperiodic and physiological adaptations regulating avian breeding cycles and their ecological significance. *J. Zool., Lond.*, 155: 327-94.

Marshall, A. J. (1960) Annual periodicity in migration and reproduction of birds. *Cold Spring Harb. Symp. Quant. Biol.*, 25: 499-505.

Menaker, M. (ed.) (1971) *Biochronometry*. Washington D.C.: Nat. Acad. Sci. x + 662 pp.

Palmer, J. D. (1973) Tidal rhythms: the clock control of the rhythmic physiology of marine organisms. *Biol. Rev.*, 48: 377-418.

Palmer, J. D. (1974) *Biological clocks in marine organisms*. New York: Wiley. xi + 173 pp.

Park. O. (1940) Nocturnalism -- the development of a problem. *Ecol. Monogr.*, 10: 485-536.

Pengelley, E. T. (ed.) (1974) *Circannual clocks*. New York: Academic Press. xiv + 523 pp.

Pittendrigh, C. S. (1960) Circadian rhythms and the circadian organisation of living systems. *Cold Spring Harb. Symp. Quant. Biol.*, 25: 159-84.

Pittendrigh, C. S. (1961) On temporal organisation in living systems. *Harvey Lecture, Ser.* 56: 93-125.

Pittendrigh, C. S. & Bruce, V. G. (1959) Daily rhythms as coupled oscillator systems and their relation to thermoperiodism and photoperiodism. pp. 475-505 *in* A. P. Wittrow (ed.) *Photoperiodism and related phenomena in plants and animals*. Washington: Amer. Ass. Adv. Sci.

Pittendrigh, C. S. & Minis, D. H. (1964) The entrainment of circadian oscillations by light and their role as photoperiodic clocks. *Amer. Nat.*, 98: 261-93.

Reinberg, A. & Ghata, J. (1964) *Biological rhythms* (Trans. C. J. Cameron). New York: Walker. xi + 138. pp.

Richter, C. P. (1965) *Biological clocks in medicine and psychiatry* Springfield, Ill.: Thomas, viii + 109 pp.

Richter, C. P. (1975) Astronomical references in biological rhythms. pp. 39-53 *in* J. T. Fraser & N. Lawrence (eds.) *The study of time II*. Berlin: Springer.

Sollberger, A. (1965) *Biological rhythm research*. Amsterdam: Elsevier. xx + 461 pp.

Sweeney, B. M. (1969) *Rhythmic phenomena in plants*. London: Academic Press. ix + 147 pp.

Sweeney, B. M. & Hastings, J. W. (1960) Effects of temperature upon diurnal rhythms. *Cold Spring Harb. Symp. Quant. Biol.*, 25: 87-104.

Truman, J. W. (1971) Circadian rhythms and physiology with special reference to neuroendocrine processes in insects. *Proc. Int. Symp. Circadian Rhythmicity* (Wageningen, 1971): 111-35.

Ward. R. R. (1972) *The living clocks*. London: Collins. 319 pp.

Wilkins, M. B. (1965) The influence of temperature and temperature changes in biological clocks. pp. 146-63 *in* J. Aschoff (ed.) *Circadian clocks*. Amsterdam: North Holland.

Winfree, A. T. (1975) Unclocklike behaviour of biological clocks. *Nature, Lond.*, 253: 315-19.

## DISCUSSION AND COMMENTS

*By H. Kalmus*

I do not think I should add much to the exposition of research in biological rhythms which we have just heard, and will thus confine myself to a few remarks concerning the entrainment of circadian rhythms.

The causal relations between external (physical) synchronizers (Zeitgebers, cues) and the manifest oscillatory responses of biological systems cannot be analysed by observation and correlation calculations, but require experimentation. These relations are often more complex than one would at a first glance assume. A change from darkness to light may, for instance, have multiple effects on a sleeping bird; it can directly awake it, but it then also sets an internal mechanism going, which will, after about 24 hours, make the sleeping bird more prone to awake even in the absence of another such dawn, or in many instances slightly before it. Finally the increase in illumination may induce the well known "dawn chorus" in other birds, which will arouse our sleeper. Using the analogy of an alarm clock: the same external cue (the dawn) will (1) wake a man, let us say, at 6 a.m. and make him at the same time (2) wind up an alarm clock (3) set its hands at 6 o'clock and also (4) set the alarm at 6 o'clock. In this way the alarm clock will show and ring -- not of course at 6 a.m. the next day -- but at 6 p.m. But I suppose you get the analogy.

Frequently the phase relations between external synchronizers and manifest biological rhythms are more complex: an alarm clock need not be wound and set at the same time, nor need the hands of the alarm be set by the same agents. The "hands" of the circadian system of a honey bee are probably also set by the light-darkness change -- directly or indirectly, but its internal "alarm" for gathering nector or pollen is set to the hour during which the forages are available -- sometimes to separate hours if several crop species open at different times.

This kind of complexity necessitates in any special situation to find out by experiment, which phase of which external rhythm (the change dark/light or bright/dark, or both, or yet another phase) provides the Zeitgeber, and which phases of the internal rhythm are sensitive to synchronization.

Finally as Prof. Cloudsley-Thompson has mentioned we do not know the cellular machinery which is receptive of entrainment. On the multicellular level we can discuss centralized and multiple clock systems. In vertebrates and insects the neurocrine system probably supplies most of the circadian information to peripheral effectors. Epithelial cells from the ear of a mouse lose circadian patterns of cell division, and cannot be entrained, when severed from the rest of the mouse, but the leaves of a plant -- even small parts of a leaf -- maintain various circadian functions in isolation. It would therefore be futile to search for a "clock" in the cells of a mouse ear, but such a mechanism must exist in the leaf tissue.

# The Living Clocks of Marine Organisms

J.D. Palmer

*ABSTRACT*

*Many facets of organismic physiology and behavior repeat themselves with such* beat-*like regularity, that the patterns are referred to as being* rhythmic. *The peaks and troughs of a major category of these rhythms are synchronized to prominent events in the earth's cyclic geophysical environment, e.g., day or night. However -- and this is their most fascinating property -- the persistence of the rhythms is not dependent on periodic changes in the environment, it is controlled instead by a "living clock" amalgamated with the physiochemical components of protoplasm. Almost all plants and animals, including man, possess these horologes.*

*The biorhythm most commonly studied in the past is the one whose period approximates the interval of the rotation of the earth on its axis. This rhythm has come to be called a* <u>circadian</u> *one, and is discussed in other sections of this volume.*

*A category of biorhythm much less studied than the circadian one, but which shares many properties, has a period length equal to the duration of a lunar day (the 24.8-hour interval between successive moonrises). As might be expected, this rhythm is characteristic of marine plants and animals inhabiting the intertidal zone along seacosts, and there-*

*fore usually displays a bimodal waveform with the peaks being locked to specific epochs of the local tidal cycle. When these rhythms are studied in organisms removed from their seaside habitat, and placed in the nontidal setting of the laboratory, they persist, often with a slightly altered period. They are therefore referred to as being* <u>circalunadian</u>. *It is this category of rhythm that is discussed here. The properties of tidal rhythms are described, as are the means by which the environment sets the "hands" of the living tidal clock. Because both solar-day and lunar-day rhythms have several properties in common, it is speculated that a single clock may drive both rhythms. Nothing is as yet known about the actual clockworks of this organismic horologe.*

Organisms govern their lives in such a way that the rates at which their body processes run, change in a periodic fashion: most commonly, they oscillate with a period of a day. A few common examples are: song birds which are active during the daylight hours and sleep at night (Palmer, 1966); mice and rats which have just the opposite schedule (Dowse & Palmer, 1972); and man, whose body temperature is highest during the early evening and falls to a minimum at night (Palmer, 1977). These oscillatory changes in physiology and behavior have come to be called "biorhythms".

Daily rhythms follow the alternations in day/night cycles of light and temperature with such precision, that it seemed at first absurd to even speculate that they were not directly driven by these prominent environmental changes. However, this is not the case, for organismic rhythms were found to persist almost unchanged when plants and animals were studied in laboratories in which day/night cycles were precluded. This persistence demanded the conclusion that organisms were somehow able to measure time autonomously, and the capability has been ascribed to the presence of a "living" timepiece within their bodies. The latter has come to be called by scientific clock-watchers, a "bioclock". To date, very little is known about the workings of this clock (Palmer, 1977a).

The most commonly studied category of biorhythm is that with a period equal to the length of a solar day (see Cloudsley-Thompson in this volume, and Palmer, 1976); I will begin therefore -- as background for the primary subject of the talk (bimodal lunar-day rhythms) -- by briefly describing the major properties of daily rhythms. *Persistent* daily rhythms, i.e., those that continue to be displayed in the laboratory in the absence of day/night cycles, almost always manifest a period length that is slightly altered from the one repeated in the natural habitat. They are usually slightly shorter or longer than 24 hours (seldom by as much as ± 20%). To describe this change, which is a fundamental property of daily rhythms, the term "circadian" (meaning, about a day) was coined. The circadian property is only displayed in the constancy of the laboratory; in nature, the biorhythm to a strict 24-hour period, daylight and warmth alternating with darkness and cooler temperatures force, or "entrain". The entraining role of might and temperature cycles may be vividly confirmed by transporting experimental organisms to new time zones and observing them rapidly adjust to the new light-dark regimen there. [I might add *en passant*, that the body rhythms of the scientist accompanying the organisms are similarly molded to the new locale (Palmer, 1977)]. The hands of the living clock may therefore be set to any time of the day.

An unexpected property of the bioclock governing the solar-day rhythms is that its rate resists change over a whole range of temperatures and when subjected to a great variety of chemical substances. This virtual immutability is not expected of a clock constructed from an amalgamation of chemical reactions.

The last important property to be mentioned is that daily rhythms are innate, meaning that they are not learned from, or are instilled by, the rhythmic fluctuations in the environment. Birds have served to illustrate this point especially well. Eggs removed from the nest immediately after being laid, and hatched in the constancy of an incubator, produce tiny fledglings with a complete coterie of rhythms, in spite of the fact that the animals have never been exposed to the light and warmth of the sun (Aschoff and Meyer-Lohmann, 1954).

A class of rhythms that has been studied in much less detail than daily rhythms, is displayed by organisms living in the *intertidal zone* (the narrow band of shoreline along our coasts that is periodically exposed and then inundated by the ebb and flow of the tide). These organisms adjust their behavior and physiology so as to keep them in synchrony with the regular flooding (Palmer, 1973). For example, the common fiddler crab, an easily recognizable animal because the male has one egregiously large claw (which suggested to a sun-crazed naturalist of bygone days, a fiddle tucked under the chin of a performer) sits out each tidal submersion in the bottom of its burrow, but emerges during low tides to scurry around the exposed sand flats of its habitat. To the casual observer or beachcomber, the behavior pattern would appear to be entirely controlled by the coming and going of the tide. In fact, it is not, but is instead ruled by the organism's bioclock which is this case, measures off intervals equal in length to the lunar day (the interval between successive moonrises: 24 hours and 51 minutes). This fact is easily demonstrated by bringing the crabs into the laboratory and measuring and recording their spontaneous locomotor activity (automatically) in an incubator. Thus isolated from the tides, and exposed to constant darkness and an unvarying temperature for weeks at a time, they continue to display approximately the same rhythmic patterns of activity (Bennet *et al.*, 1957; Barnwell, 1966; Webb & Brown, 1965). This is seen in Figure 1. This persistent rhythm is formally described as being a bimodal lunar-day one -- or, in the vernacular, it is called simply a "tidal rhythm".

In constant conditions in the laboratory, the period length of these bimodal lunar-day rhythms changes slightly, just as do the unimodal rhythms that in nature match in length the solar day (Palmer, 1963; 1973). This change can be seen in Figure 1, if you draw in your mind a line connecting the left hand dots on the upper and lower frames of the graph, and a second line, parallel to the first, through the upper and lower dots to the right on the frames. The points where these two lines intersect the daily activity curves are the times of the midpoints of low tide in the crab's old habitat, and are where the peaks of its activity rhythm would fall if the animal was back on the shoreline. It is obvious therefore, that in captivity, this crab's period has lengthened significantly from a natural one of 24.8 hours, to one of about 25 hours and 40 minutes. This feature of lunar-day rhythms has been given the parallel appelation of "circalunadian" (Palmer, 1973; 1974).

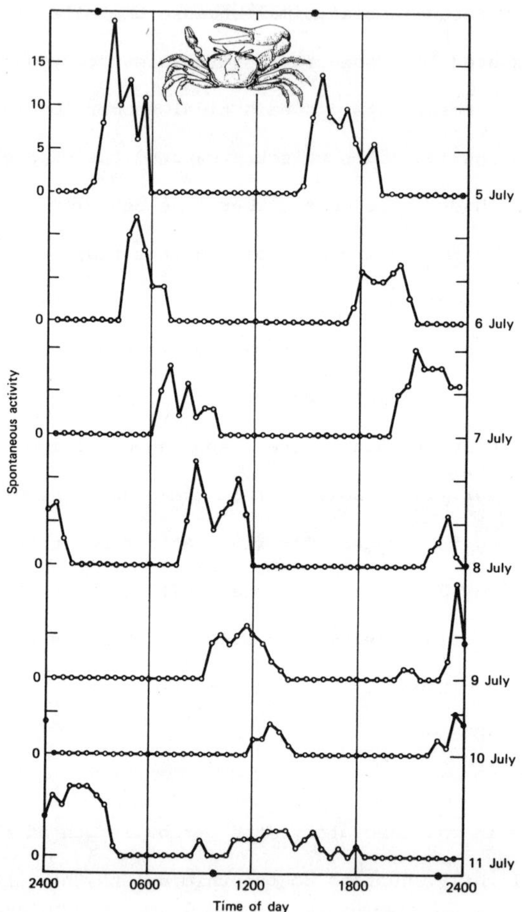


*Figure 1. The rhythmic locomotor activity pattern of one fiddler crab (Uca pugnax, pictured at the top) maintained in constant darkness and 20° C. in the laboratory for 7 consecutive days. Note that the 2 daily bursts of activity appear successively later on subsequent days, thus mimicking the form of the ebb and flow of the tides on the crab's home beach. Because the rhythmic pattern persists in the laboratory it is thought to be under the control of the organism's bioclock. The period of this bimodal, lunar-day rhythem lengthens from 24 hours and 50 minutes (the period displayed in nature) to about 25 hours and 40 minutes under the aperiodic conditions in the laboratory (Palmer, 1973).*

While the ebb and flow of the tide is obviously not necessary in the genesis of the animal's rhythm, it does play an important role in setting the phase. This has been demonstrated by transplanting crabs to different coastlines, where the timing of the tides differs from the home locality, and exposing them to the location in screened cages partially sunk into the intertidal sediments. Usually, only a few days in the new habitat are required to reset the phase of the crabs' rhythms to the new tidal schedule. If the crabs are then placed in constant conditions in the laboratory, the new phase setting is the one displayed. The extremes of this phase lability were demonstrated by translocating crabs from the Pacific side of the Isthmus of Panama, where the usual twice-per-day tide situation obtains, to the Caribbean side, where the shoreline has only one flood tide per lunar day. Within a few days the crabs adopted the latter and then displayed this unimodal lunar-day period when studied in the laboratory (Barnwell, 1968; 1976). The means by which the tides set the phase of the animals' rhythms will be discussed later.

Some of the intertidal crabs also have solar-day clocks (Bennett *et al.*, 1957; Naylor, 1958; Webb & Brown, 1965; Palmer, 1967; Webb, 1976). These timepieces must be quite useful to a crab in the bottom of its dark burrow, for by consulting it rather than venturing out of the safety of the burrow, the animal could be apprised as to whether it was day or night on the surface above. The green shore-crab is an especially interesting case in that its activity rhythm contains both lunar-day and solar-day components as is seen in Figure 2. As is clear from the figure, this crab, unlike the fiddler crab, sallies forth underwater during the times of high tide. The basic tidal pattern in the activity rhythm is modified by the diminished amplitude of the daytime tidal peaks (Naylor, 1958). Another interesting facet of this crab's rhythm is that its period length is virtually unchanged by maintaining the crab for days at a time under different constant temperatures between 10° and 25°C (Naylor, 1963). The period of a tidal rhythm is, therefore, just like that of the solar-daily rhythm -- it is "temperature independent".

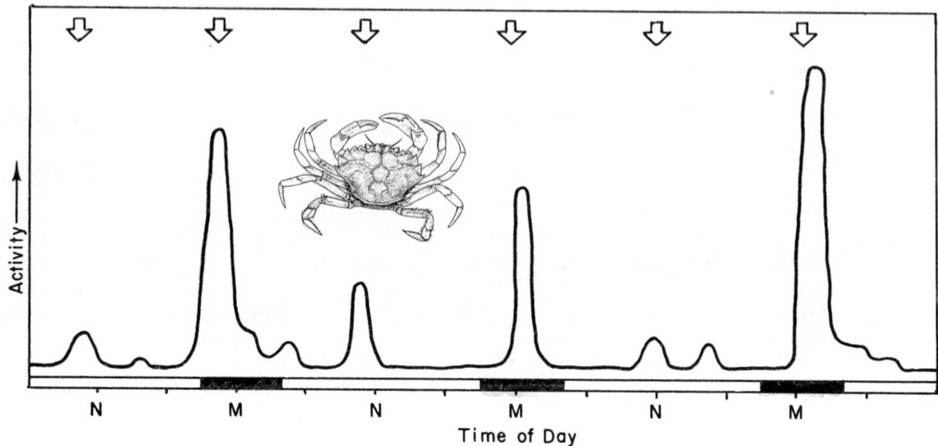


*Figure 2. The rhythmic activity of the green shore-crab (Carcinus maenas, see inset) in constant conditions. The shaded portions along the abscissa signify the hours of darkness, and the falling arrows the midpoints of high tide, outside the laboratory. The difference in the height of the tidal peaks is a function of the time of the solar day that they occur, indicating that a daily clock is modifying the tidal pattern (drawn from the data of Naylor, 1958).*

The green shore-crab has proved to be a very useful and interesting organism to study in the laboratory. In 1966, Dr. Barbara Williams, then a graduate student in the laboratory of Dr. Ernst Naylor at the University of Swansea, performed a very difficult task. She raised crabs from eggs to adults in the laboratory. During their growth and maturation they were exposed to day/night cycles. After many weeks, when they were finally large enough to be used in the apparatus which measured their spontaneous activity, it was found that only a 24-hour component was present in the data (Figure 3a). The data gave no indication of the presence of a tidal component. Dr. Williams then subjected the crabs to one brief chilling -- 15 hours at 4°C -- and returned them to constant conditions for further activity measurements. Computer analysis of these results revealed that the treatment had instilled a tidal component in the animal's rhythm (Figure 3b). The conclusion drawn from this fascinating result is: because no periodic or time-interval information could have been given to the crabs by a single *cold* pulse 15 hours in duration, the 12.5 hour tidal interval must be part of the animal's hereditary makeup. Somehow, the cold shock had served to start the clock running. (As described, the situation would be analogous to you winding for the first time, a newly purchased wristwatch.) Therefore, tidal clocks, just as daily clocks, are innate.

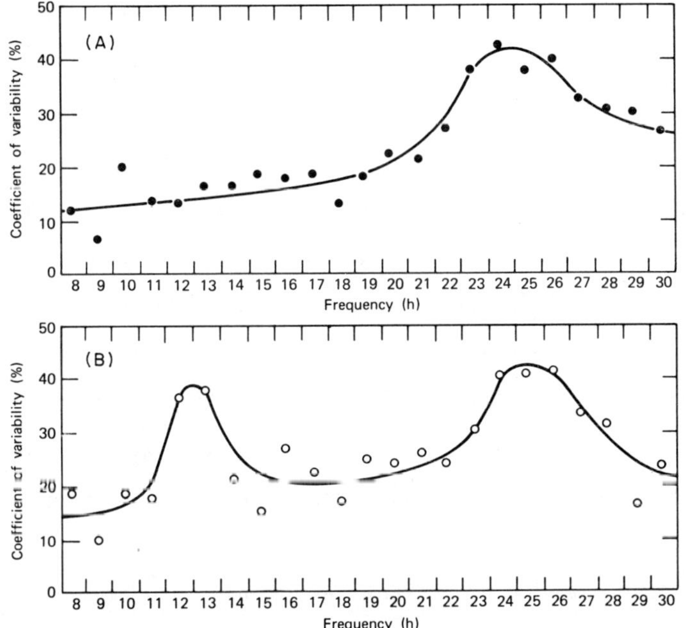


*Figure 3. Printouts of computer scans of the green shore-crab activity data. The program used produces a plot depicting the frequency of different cycle lengths present in data. The crabs used here were raised from egg to adult in natural day/night cycles in the laboratory before their spontaneous locomotor activity was measured in constant dim light. As indicated by the broad peak centered over hours 24 and 25, (curve a), only a circadian frequency was present in the data. The crabs were then given a single 15-hour cold (4°C.) shock and returned to their actographs. Periodogram analysis of this data (b) produced a second peak over hours 12-13, indicating the a tidal rhythm had been initiated by the chilling. These data demonstrate that tidal rhythms are innate (from Williams and Naylor, 1967).*

To make the next point we must turn from crabs to the plant kingdom, and a single-celled brown alga -- the commuter diatom. This microscopic motile plant lives buried in intertidal sediments during high tides, but moves up onto the sand surface during daytime low tides. At these latter times, in spite of the tiny individual size, population numbers are so enormous that large expanses of exposed sands appear golden brown, the color of the predominant pigment of the organism. Just in advance of the returning flood time, the diatoms complete their commute and glide back down into the interstices between subterranean sand grains. By the time the first few wavelets of the tidal front advance over the area, the cells have completely disappeared into the sediment (Palmer, 1976a).

To study the phenomenon under controlled conditions, samples of the diatom-bearing sand were collected in Petri dishes, carefully returned to the laboratory, and placed in the unvarying conditions of an incubator. When the tide ebbed in nature, the diatoms isolated in the incubator appeared on the surface of the sand in their Petri dishes. Just before the flood tide inundated their old habitat, they reburrowed again (Palmer and Round, 1967). This persistent rhythm has been followed for as long as 11 days in the laboratory (Figure 4). This observation demonstrates quite conclusively, that the living clock controlling tidal rhythms needs only the single-cell level of organization for expression. The same is true for the clocks controlling circadian rhythms (Pohl, 1948; Sweeney, 1972; Palmer and Round, 1965; Round and Palmer, 1966), and rhythms are known to persist even in enucleated cells (Sweeney and Haxo, 1961; Mergenhagen and Schweiger, 1975; Karakashian and Schweiger, 1976).

Having discussed some of the fundamentals of tidal rhythms, I will return to the subject of phase setting. Because of the changing topography of a coastline, the tidal cycles of neighboring beaches may be several hours out of phase with one another. Since the phase of each organism's rhythm mimics precisely the times of the ebb and flow on its home beach, it must be the local tides which produce this synchrony. We return again to the green shore-crab for the verification of this point.

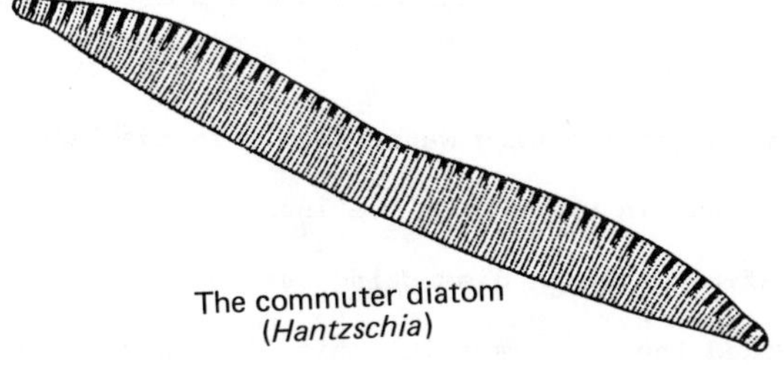


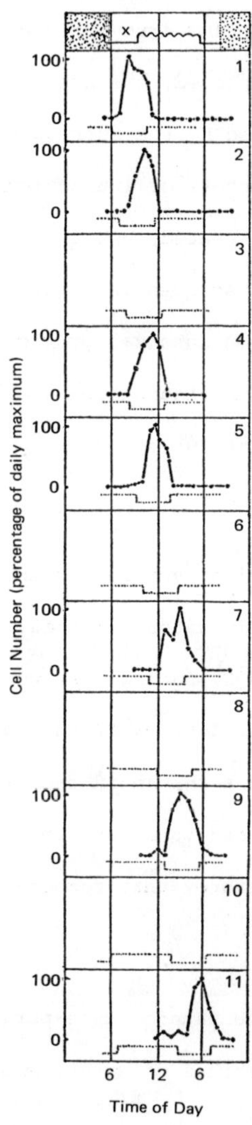


*Figure 4. The persistent vertical-migration rhythm of a laboratory culture of the commuter diatom (Hantzschia) (shown) in constant conditions. Curves are cell counts of the number of organisms on the surface of the sand. Consecutive days are aligned beneath each other; the strippling indicates the hours of darkness on the day of collection; and X indicates the moment the diatoms were collected. The wavy lines signify the times of high tide, and the depressed segments of the dotted lines signify intervals of low tide in the diatoms' natural habitat (modified from Palmer, J. D. and F. E. Round, 1967).*

After several days of incarceration in the laboratory, the tidal activity rhythm of this crab gradually damps and finally disappears (Naylor, 1958). This makes the animal an ideal subject for studies concerned with reinitiation and phase setting of tidal rhythms. An artificial tide machine was built by Drs. Williams and Naylor (1969) and arrhythmic crabs subjected to its changing water levels in the laboratory. As expected, the rhythm reappeared and was in phase with the inundation cycles offered by the surrogate ocean. As a first step in dissecting out just what physical parameters of inundation cycles provided the phase-setting stimuli, the experiment was repeated, but this time the air and water temperatures were kept identical at 19° C. As seen in Figure 5, although the crabs confined their activity to the submersion interval provided by the tide simulator, no carryover effect was seen when the inundation cycles were stopped and the crabs were switched to just moist air held at 19° C.

The final version of the same general experimental design precluded periodic immersion in water. Instead, the crabs were treated to cycles consisting of a temperature of 13° C. during what would have been an immersion time, and exposed to a temperature elevated to 24° C. during other times. This treatment was quite effective in initiating a rhythm in the crabs, and this rhythm would then persist when the crabs were switched to moist air held at a constant temperature of 13° C. These results show, therefore, that temperature cycles serve as phase setters.

In the inundation experiments just described, the crabs were submerged under just a few inches of water, meaning that pressure could not have been a factor. In the natural setting, however, the crabs are repeatedly covered by several feet of water during each high tide deluge. Experiments were therefore carried out by Drs. Naylor and Atkinson (1972) at the Marine Station on the Isle of Man, in which arrhythmic green shore-crabs were exposed in the laboratory to intervals of high pressure (ambient + 0.6 atmospheres) equal in length to a high tide interval, followed by identical intervals at an ambient pressure level. On exposure to six of these cycles,

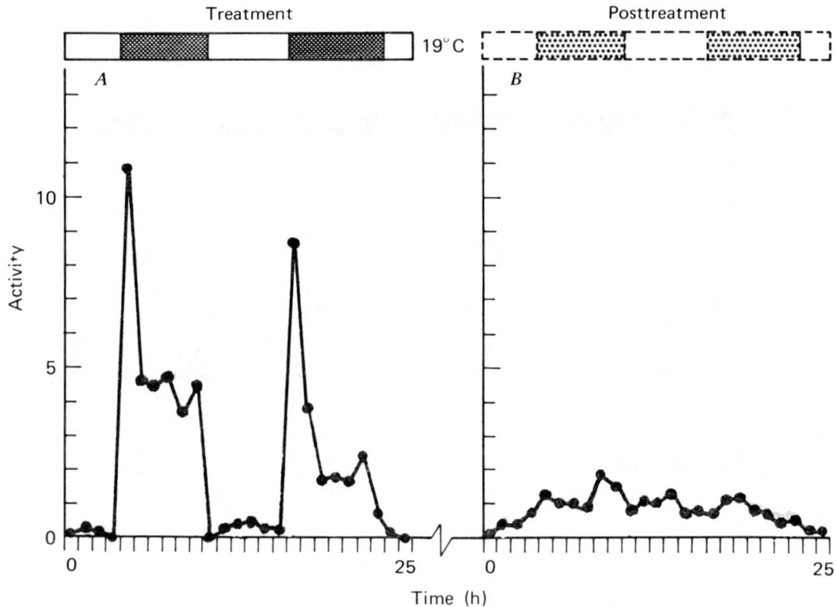


*Figure 5. The ineffectiveness of periodic inundation as an entraining agent for the green shore-crab* (Carcinus) *activity rhythm. The left-hand curve depicts the average activity pattern of several crabs during 5 days of periodic inundation in a tide machine. The dark portions of the overhead bar signify the times the crabs were submerged, the open portions when they were exposed to moist air. Both air and water temperatures were held constant at 19° C. Note that the crabs were active during the times of submergence. The curve on the right hand side represents the posttreatment activity pattern (3-day average) of the same crabs maintained in moist air. The previous times of inundation are signified by the strippled segments of the overhead bar. Note that there is no carryover effect from the pretreatment (modified from Williams and Naylor, 1969).*

arrhythmic crabs became rhythmic again, and, and rhythm persisted in conditions in which the pressure was held constant (Figure 6).

The conclusion of these last two experiments, is that the local tide sets the phase of the animals' rhythms not be the periodic inundation *per se*, but by the temperatur and pressure changes it delivers to the animals at the times of each flooding.

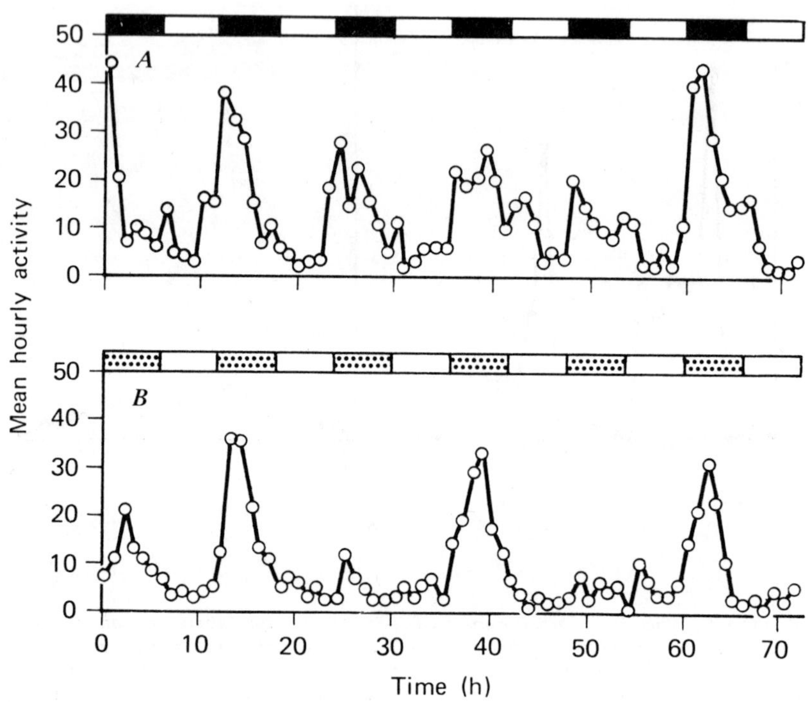


*Figure 6. The induction of rhythmicity into arrhythmic green shore-crabs by subjecting them to pressure cycles in the laboratory. The top curve represents the average activity pattern of 6 crabs while being subjected to 6 cycles consisting of 6 hours of pressure (ambient + 0.6 atmospheres; signified by the darkened portions of the overhead bar) alternating the 6 hours at ambient pressure (open portions of overhead bar). Note that the treatment molds the activity pattern into an apparent rhythm. The bottom curve shows the persistence of this rhythm in the absence of the pressure cycles (strippled sections of the bar signified the previous times of treatment with high pressure) (modified from Naylor and Atkinson, 1972).*

As I mentioned in the introduction, the light/dark cycle is the prime geophysical parameter that sets the phase of daily rhythms. It, of course, could not be expected to have a similar phase-setting role on tidal rhythms, since entrainment to this cycle would mean the destruction of the tidal periodicity itself. There is however, one category of tidal rhythms -- the one that has a 24-hour component inextricably mixed in with it (as was described earlier for the green shore-crab) -- that does respond to day/night cycles. An early demonstration of this was made by Prof. Franklin Barnwell, now at the University of Minnesota. He used the fiddler crab, which, although I did not mention it before, also has a low amplitude daily rhythm in locomotion mixed in with the predominantly tidal locomotory rhythm. He found that if the fiddler crabs were maintained in the laboratory away from the tide but exposed to natural day/night cycles (which, of course, entrained the daily rhythm to a strict 24-hour period), that the tidal rhythm displayed a precise 24.8 hour periodicity, just as it did in the natural environment. However, when the light/dark cycles were replaced with constant illumination, the tidal rhythm became circalunadian (Barnwell, 1966)! It appears therefore, that if the daily rhythm is prevented from becoming circadian, the tidal one does not become circalunadian.

In another experiment along these lines, this one done by Profs. Miriam Bennett and Frank Brown, working at the famed Maine Laboratory at Woods Hole, fiddler crabs were maintained in a light/dark regimen which had been suddenly advanced relative to the natural one. The new schedule called for dawn to come at midnight, and sunset to occur at 6 A.M. Three days of this treatment advanced the daily component of the crabs' activity rhythm about 5 hours; it also advanced the tidal rhythm by approximately the same amount (Bennett and Brown, 1959).

Both of these findings suggest that tidal and daily rhythms are intimately associated, and provide a basis for speculating that possibly just one living clock may control both solar-, and lunar-day rhythms. Without going into the experimental evidence supporting the fact (see Palmer, 1974 for details), I ask you to accept first that the clock is an entity to itself and is in some as yet unknown way (or ways) coupled to processes that it causes to be rhythmic; and second, that evidence exists indicating that a single clock can drive several processes simultaneously (McMurry and

Hastings, 1972). Given this, a single clock provided with at least two coupling mechanisms, one of which can alter the frequency delivered from the clock to the process it causes to be rhythmic, would be sufficient to run both daily and tidal rhythms (Palmer, 1973). The idea is spelled out diagrammatically in Figure 7. This living complex would be analogous to the wristwatches worn by surf fishermen -- timeieces that, via different gear drives coupled to a single escapement, signal time of day and time of tide on the watch dial.

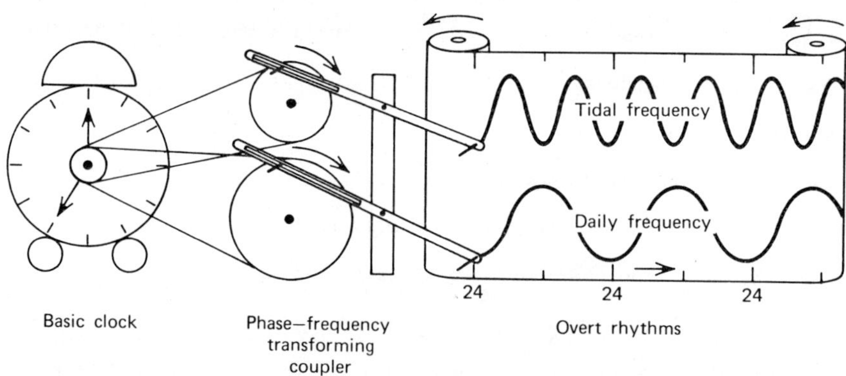


*Figure 7. A physical analogue model of frequency-transforming couplers between a "biological" clock and the rhythms it drives. As portrayed, the clock runs at one speed, but the rate delivered to physiological processes may be altered by the size of the belt driven pulleys of the couplers. Thus, a single clock could drive both solar-day and lunar-day rhythms (Palmer, 1973).*

I emphasize here, that this dual-role scheme for a single clock is highly speculative, but it is consistent with the Law of Parsimony. Why should an organism have two separate clocks whose basic periods differ by only 3% and can drive rhythms whose *circa* periods easily and commonly overlap one another? Mother Nature is known for adopting the simplest solutions to her problems.

## SUMMARY AND CONCLUSIONS

1. The physiology and behavior of intertidal organisms is often molded into a waveform pattern called a *bimodal lunar-day rhythm* -- or more simply, a *tidal rhythm*. The rhythm has an overall length of 24.8 hours in nature, with the peaks synchronized to some specific point of the tide, such as high water.

2. These rhythms persist in the laboratory, meaning that they are driven by an internal "bioclock".

3. The following properties of tidal rhythms have been well documented.
   A. The period either lengthens or shortens slightly in the laboratory; and, after doing so, is referred to as having become *circalunadian*.
   B. The rate at which the bioclock runs is virtually unaffected by maintaining the organism at different constant temperatures.
   C. Tidal rhythms are not learned from, or imprinted by, the rhythmic environment. They are innate.
   D. These rhythms are entrained to the tidal schedule of a particular coastline by the temperature and pressure cycles delivered with the ebb and flow of the local tide. Inundation *per se*, has no entraining effect.
   E. The single-cell level of organization is sufficeint for the expression of tidal rhythms.

4. A tidal rhythm cannot be entrained by light-dark cycles. However, some intertidal organisms possess in a single process, both 24-hour, and 24.8 hour, waveform components. When a 24-hour component is also present, then the tidal component can be "entrained" or "phase-shifted" by light-dark cycles. This observation gives rise to the speculation that possibly a single clock, functioning via frequency-transforming couplers, can drive both the daily and tidal components of the rhythms of these organisms.

LITERATURE CITED

Aschoff, J. and J. Meyer-Lohmann. 1954. Angeborene 24-Studen-Periodik beim Kuecken. *Pflügers Arch.*, 260:170-176.

Barnwell, F. H. 1966. Daily and tidal patterns of activity in individual fiddler crabs (Genus *Uca*) from the Woods Hole region. *Biol. Bull.*, 130:1-17.

Barnwell, F. H. 1968. The role of rhythmic systems in the adaptation of fiddler crabs to the intertidal zone. *Amer. Zool.*, 8:869-583.

Barnwell, F. H. 1976. Variation in the form of the tide and some problems it poses for biological timing systems. pp. 161-187. In: *Biological rhythms in the marine environment*. P. J. DeCoursey, editor. South Carolina University Press.

Bennett, M. F. and F. A. Brown, Jr. 1959. Experimental modification of the lunar rhythm of running activity of the fiddler crab, *Uca pugnax*. *Biol. Bull.*, 117:404.

Bennett, M. F., J. Shriner and R. A. Brown. 1957. Persistent tidal cycles of spontaneous motor activity in the fiddler crab, *Uca pugnax*. *Biol. Bull.*, 112:267-275.

Brown, F. A., Jr. 1976. Biological clocks: endogenous cycles synchronized by subtle geophysical rhythms. *BioSystems*, 8:67-81.

Dowse, H. B. and J. D. Palmer. 1972. The chronomutagenic effect of deuterium oxide on the period and entrainment of a biological rhythm. *Biol. Bull.*, 143:513-524.

Karakashian, M. W. and H. G. Schweiger. 1976. Circadian properties of the rhythmic system in individual nucleated and enucleated cells of *Acetabularia mediterranea*. *Exp. Cell Res.*, 97:366-377.

McMurry, L. and J. W. Hastings. 1972. No desynchronization among four circadian rhythms in the unicellular alga, *Gonyaulax polyedra*. *Science*, 175:1137-1138.

Mergenhagen, D. and H. G. Schweiger. 1975. Circadian rhythm of oxygen evolution in cell fragments of *Acetabularia mediterranea*. *Exp. Cell Res.*, 92:127-130.

Naylor, E. 1958. Tidal and diurnal rhythms of locomotory activity in *Carcinus maenas*. *J. Exp. Biol.*, 35:602-610.

Naylor, E. 1963. Temperature relationships of the locomotor rhythm of *Carcinus*. *J. Exp. Biol.*, 40:669-679.

Naylor, E. and R. J. Atkinson. 1972. Pressure and the rhythms of inshore animals. pp. 395-415. In: *The Effects of Pressure on Organisms*. Academic Press, N.Y.

Palmer, J. D. 1963. "Circa-tidal" activity rhythms in fiddler crabs. Effect of light intensity. Biol. Bull., 125:387.

Palmer, J. D. 1966. How a bird tells the time of day. *Nat. Hist.*, 75(3):48-53.

Palmer, J. D. 1967. Daily and tidal components in the persistent rhythmic activity of the crab, *Sesarma*. *Nature*, 215:64-66.

Palmer, J. D. 1973. Tidal rhythms: the clock control of the rhythmic physiology of marine organisms. *Biol. Rev.*, 43:377-418.

Palmer, J. D. 1974. *Biological Clocks in Marine Organisms: the Control of Physiological and Behavioral Tidal Rhythms*. 173 pp. John Wiley & Sons, New York.

Palmer, J. D. 1976. *An Introduction to Biological Rhythms*. 375 pp. Academic Press, New York.

Palmer, J. D. 1976a Clock-controlled vertical migration rhythms in intertidal organisms. pp. 239-255. In: *Biological Rhythms in the Marine Environment*. P. J. DeCoursey, editor. South Carolina Univ. Press.

Palmer, J. D. 1977. Human rhythms. *BioScience,* 27:93-99.

Palmer, J. D. 1977a. *Biological Rhythm and Living Clocks*. Carolina Biology Reader. South Carolina.

Palmer, J. D. and F. E. Round. 1965. Persistent, vertical-migration rhythms in benthic microflora. I. The effect of light and temperature on the rhythmic behaviour of *Euglena obtusa*. *J. mar. biol. Ass.,* U.K., 45:567-582.

Palmer, J. D. and F. E. Round. 1967. Persistent, vertical-migration rhythms in benthic microflora. VI. The tidal and diurnal nature of the rhythm in the diatom *Hantzschia virgata*. *Biol. Bull.,* 132:44-55.

Pohl. R. 1948. Tagesrhythmus im phototaktischen Verhalten der *Euglena gracilis*. *Z. Naturf.,* 3b:367-378.

Round, F. E. and J. D. Palmer. 1966. Persistent, vertical-migration rhythms in benthic microflora. II. Field and laboratory studies of diatoms from the banks of the River Avon. *J. mar. biol. Ass.,* U.K., 46:191-214.

Sweeney, B. M. 1972. Circadian rhythms in unicellular organisms. pp. 137-156. In: *Circadian Rhythmicity,* pp. 137-156. Centre for Agricultural Publishing and Documents, Wageningen, Netherlands.

Sweeney, B. M. and F. T. Haxo. 1961. Persistence of a photosynthetic rhythm in enucleated *Acetabularia*. *Science,* 134:1361-1363.

Webb, H. M. 1976. Interactions of daily and tidal rhythms. pp. 129-135. In: *Biological Rhythms in the Marine Environment*. P. J. DeCoursey editor, Univ. South Carolina Press.

Webb, H. M. and F. A. Brown, Jr. 1965. Interactions of diurnal and tidal rhythms in the fiddler crab, *Uca pugnax*. *Biol. Bull.*, 129:582-591.

Williams, B. G. and E. Naylor. 1967. Spontaneously induced rhythm of tidal periodicity in laboratory-reared *Carcinus*. *J. Exp. Biol.*, 47:229-234.

Williams, B. G. and E. Naylor. 1969. Synchronization of the locomotor tidal rhythm of *Carcinus*. *J. Exp. Biol.*, 51:715-725.

## DISCUSSION AND COMMENTS

*By J. L. Cloudsley-Thompson*

Dr. John Palmer has postulated a single clock to control both circalunadian and circadian rhythms. In my paper, I postulated two cellular clocks whose interaction, I suggested, might generate the circannual rhythm. It should be remembered that not only does the Law of Parsimony (or the principle of 'Occam's razor') have no predictive power but, in fact, the concept of two clocks may even be simpler than that of one. Furthermore, the existence of a single clock driving two different endogenous rhythms has seldom been established in nature. At the present time, it is impossible to determine which, if either of our views, is the more correct.

The central problem of biochronometry is to understand the mechanism of the cellular clock. Short-term rhythms, such as that of heart beat or the alpha rhythm of the brain, may represent relaxation-oscillation phenomena that are dependent on refractory periods; but circadian and circalunadian rhythms seem to be associated with a quite different type of clock. It is difficult to interpret them in physiological terms either on the 'hourglass' or 'self-emptying cistern' principle, or as temperature-compensated enzyme-substrate reactions. Perhaps D.N.A. transcription along a chromosome may be the most plausible hypothesis. If so, it removes the problem from the field of biology to that of biophysics. Moreover, it has not yet been determined whether the cell is itself a clock or merely contains one. This question takes the subject to the very borders of science or, perhaps, even beyond into philosophy and metaphysics.

# The Measurement of Biological and Social Changes

H. Kalmus

*ABSTRACT*

*Adopting Aristotle's idea of time as just one aspect of processes, it seems logical to consider the time span necessary for any change in a system as constrained by the properties of this system. Conversely, we can, from an observed rate of a change, exclude certain processes from attempts to explain the change. Considering the whole range of organisms, demonstrated evolutionary changes as defined by changes in gene frequency, can vary from days to millions of years. But as far as man is concerned, such changes are, as a rule, rather slow and must in any case take several generations, while some behavioural and social changes can proceed at a higher rate.*

INTRODUCTION

I hope the beauty of the mountains of Alpbach, which look through the windows at our deliberations, will excuse my reason for starting this paper with a medieval fairy tale. It conveys more charmingly than I could the feeling of geological time and, together with a short addition, summarizes a great deal of what I have to say:

> Beyond these hills there lies a huge mountain of diamond - glistening in the sun.
> Every hundred years a little bird comes, settles on the crystal peak of the mountain, sharpens its little beak, sings a little song - and flies away.

And when the little bird has completely ground away the huge mountain, a small part of a second of eternity will have passed.

One day on some time scale or ladder a man - Darwin - climbs the mountain to find out, whether it is still the same little bird, as described in great detail in some old books. He finds that it is not quite the same bird he had expected, and being a good naturalist, he describes the bird, and also how it sharpens its beak and the melody it sings.

A hundred years later, when the little bird is again expected, some other man - perhaps one of us - also climbs the mountain to look at the bird and the mountain and also at the scale on which Darwin had proceeded. And he find the mountain and the bird quite unchanged, but the way it sharpens its beak is somewhat different from the way Darwin has described it, and the bird also sings a new melody.

As far as the time scales are concerned, he takes them down from the heights, to show them to his friends and to talk about them.

Speaking to a multi-disciplinary gathering such as the present one, it is useful to be pedantic and to start by defining the use of some of the terms in one's presentation, as the same words are used for a variety of more or less different concepts by the listeners.

"Measurement of changes" does not provide great difficulties, as it merely indicates an application of Galileo's principle - "To measure what can be measured and to make measurable what as yet is not" - to Aristotle's concept of time as a sort of numerical adjunct to processes. You will see from what follows that the art of measuring biological and social changes is still in its infancy. Nevertheless some important conclusions can already be derived from such measurements.

The idea of time used in this discourse is mainly one of the commonly held "naive" notions, namely that time - whatever it may be - has continuity and direction and that also it always "proceeds" more or less at the same pace.

"Biological change" will be used in a restricted technical sense, meaning genetical change in subsequent generations and their manifold phenotypical manifestations, which used to be called "organic evolution". Not included among these changes, though considered in other ways, will be the processes of individual development, such as growth, differentiation, or decay, and physiological responses. Behavioural changes in some ways bridge biological and social changes.

TIME AVAILABLE AND NECESSARY

Popular views concerning the time spans necessary and available for evolutionary changes vary a great deal and are based on very little fact. By contrast, on the one hand, much more is now known about the amounts of time certain historical developments have taken, and, on the other hand, human pre-history seems to grow all the time as a consequence of new discoveries.

Radio-chemical methods indicate that life on earth has existed for about 2000 to 3000 million years, and that some animal species, for instance certain brachiopods (lingulids) have persisted more or less unchanged since Cambrian times, while other animal and plant species have shown gradual changes over much shorter periods.

It is difficult to acquire a feeling for the enormous dimensions of geological time. Extrapolations from what a person can observe during his lifetime, or even from historical accounts of what has happened in the processes of long time evolution need a great deal of caution. Lyell (1830-1833) was quite justified in explaining such geological processes as erosion or sedimentation in terms of the observation of those forces in action. But the forces which mould organisms are never so obvious, and what in detail happened in the past and will happen in the future is therefore rather obscure. Various attempts have been made in the past to make the geological time dimensions comprehensible, mostly by "contracting" the scales. If in one's mind one reduces the age of the earth, about 4000 million years to one year, the relative duration of the various geological and historical periods would be as follows: If the earth had been formed on the first of January last year, some sort of life, possibly blue-green algae, might have appeared perhaps in May or June, an abundance of marine life in October, reptiles in mid-December, mammals around Christmas, and man about five minutes before the New Year. Recorded history would have started just before the clock struck midnight on New Year's Eve.

While this transformation conveys the relative durations of the phases in organic evolution, another less severe contraction of scale is more useful for getting the feel of the relative duration of one's own experiences and the time spans involved in evolution. If we contract a calendar year to a heartbeat, slightly less than a second, our life expectation of about 70 years, roughly 2.3 giga-seconds is reduced to roughly one minute. Recorded history of some 10 thousand years would have shrunk to not quite three hours. One year in our model would bring us back 31.5 million years into the tertiary, and the reign of Queen Victoria to the beginning of life. If one considers some of the time relations just illustrated it becomes clear how hazardous it is to extrapolate from one second or even one minute or a few hours to what was going on years ago.

Nevertheless, the urge to argue on such meagre evidence is ineradicable, as one can see from the pronouncements of amateur climatologists who happily predict from a succession of a few severe winters or cool summers that another ice age is imminent. A cynic might say that the fact that you listen to my exposition is another proof for the existence of this urge.

What palaeontologists consider organic evolution has certainly taken place very slowly, as we shall see later. But by no means has all biological change needed to take so long. Indeed certain genetical changes, like the substitution of a gene by a mutant allele in a bacterial culture, can happen overnight (Ryan, 1953). Large-scale genetical innovation in plants can also occur within one generation. Our red-flowering chestnut trees are the offspring of one single cross-pollination between two very different species from far distant regions, which happened to grow side by side in a botanical garden. The red chestnut is a perfectly stable and fertile new species. Similar "allopolyploid" new species are known in many families of flowering plants.

There is thus no such thing as a rate of evolution - with a capital "R." Genetical change may proceed extremely slowly and also extremely quickly. Most interesting for the purposes of our discussion are those evolutionary changes whose rates overlap those of social changes.

## MEASURES OF EVOLUTIONARY CHANGE

Evolution can be described in two fundamentally different ways: 1) in terms of changing traits (characters) such as body size or skull capacity or 2) in terms of gene frequencies, for instance, the blood group frequencies. The difference between these two kinds of descriptions derives from the difference of criteria, the choice of which is determined by practical considerations. Traits such as stature, longevity, the components of intelligence, as well as the parameters of breeding for economical reasons, are measured and are called "quantitative". The measurements applied to the members of a sample population show a continuous distribution, usually without any sign of a subdivision. To divide the boys of a school into tall, medium and short ones is an arbitrary process which can be done in many different ways. By contrast, the possession by the individuals in a population of different allelic genes, for instance those determining polymorphic enzymes, is discontinuous, and the enzymes are called "qualitative" characters. Sometimes one can infer qualitative differences from quantitative measurements. The "taster" status of an individual is ascertained by a quantitative method, namely, the threshold value at which he tastes a bitter substance, phenylthiourea. But the assignment from a bimodal threshold distribution of any individual to either the taster or the non-taster class results in a discontinuous distribution of a qualitative nature (Harris and Kalmus, 1949).

Populations investigated for allelic differences fall naturally into two or more classes and are characterized by their relative frequencies.

The complexities of biological structures are such that any particular measure of change is only an aspect of a more complex evolutionary process. The connection between different measures is not often clear, so that some changes may be highly correlated while others are not. Therefore, only measures on similar kinds of material, for instance, the length of bones or the height of teeth can be usefully compared.

In the early days of genetics, a one-to-one relationship between a gene and a character was thought to be the rule. We now know that this only applies to characters which epigenetically are near to the genes, in particular, to such proteins as haemoglobins and enzymes, which are uniquely determined by nucleotide sequences. No single gene determines stature, longevity or intelligence, and most genes, possibly all, affect many traits, This becomes very obvious if one observes the multitude of symptoms which characterize any well-researched hereditary disease.

Very few instances have been described where gene frequencies could be inferred from fossil material. It is true that a few polymorphisms of shell colours and patterns have, with some confidence, been ascribed to genetical diversity, but changes in the frequencies are almost impossible to establish.

Evolution was originally conceived of as creating new species from old ones, either by transformation or by splitting into two. Accordingly, the rate of evolution was estimated by the number of new species arising in, or rather recovered from, various geologic epochs. Now, every taxonomist knows how difficult it is to define a species, especially from fossil material; thus, this method is of necessity rather arbitrary. Moreover, a species in a flowering plant is not obviously comparable to a species in a mammal. Nevertheless, a general statement concerning this kind of evolutionary diversification can be made, namely that the speciation of certain types of organism has proceeded at very different speeds in the course of their history. The number of reptile species "exploded" during the mezozoic age, while the numbers of species of horses, elephants and flowering plants greatly proliferated during the tertiary.

A more objective - if also more limited - method of investigating evolutionary change relies upon measurements of the hard structures, which, with few exceptions, are the only ones preserved in fossils. If one can arrange bones or teeth according to geological age, and if one has reason to believe that they present a "genealogical" lineage, one can measure comparable dimensions. Most data in use are linear measurements such as width, length and breadth, as well as a multitude of combinations of these, which are called "indices."

Measurements on structures which do not grow during an individual's life, such as the protoconches (first shells) of molluscs, the inner chambers of ammonites, or the adult teeth of mammals, can be directly used for estimates of rates of change. But bones which increase in size through growth are better compared by indices, because the proportions of many bones are altered less by growth than the absolute dimensions are. Examples are the quotient between the length and the width of a femur, or the angle of the lower jaw. It is, of course, nonsensical to compare, in absolute measure, changes in large and small structures, such as for instance, the lengthening of a skeletal part in a lineage of rodents with that in a series of elephants. Instead, one has to compare relative increases (percentages). The use of this kind of measurement is limited because in the same series of organisms some structures may change while others do not.

Nevertheless, Haldane (1947) has proposed a unit for evolutionary metric changes, which he called a "darwin" and which for convenience of calculation he based on $e$, the basis of natural logarithms. It is roughly 1/1000th of an original linear measurement per 1000 years. An example will illustrate the way in which such metric changes are estimated. It is well known that during the mesozoic period, not only did the reptiles multiply in species numbers, but also many species attained extraordinary sizes. Simpson (1944) reports that adult representatives of six suborders of dinosaurs increased manyfold in body length during periods of between twenty-two and sixty million years. The fastest of these lines, the sauropoda, changed from an average length of six meters to 17 m in about 35 million years. Assuming that this increase was steady and proportional, its rate would be

$6.1 \times 10^{-8}$ of the original value (6 m) per year. The metric evolutionary change of the body length of the sauropoda would thus have proceeded at a rate of about 61 milli-darwins. This is higher than most "natural" evolutionary rates, but is exceeded by some measurements on hominid skulls. These measurements show a rapid increase of cranial capacity and brain growth of the order of 1 darwin. Metric changes of the order of kilo-darwins have been observed in animals under domestication and in cultivated plants. To this we shall return later.

As we cannot breed from fossils, arguments on changes of gene frequencies, which might underline observed metrical changes are highly speculative. It is, however, most unlikely that the changes in reptiles, horses or elephants mentioned earlier were brought about by single mutations, that is, by gene substitution in one particular chromosomal locus. An increase from 6 to 17 m in length by a single gene mutation would then occur in one step and not gradually, as observed. Such a giant would be quite abnormal and the type not viable. Thus, alleles in many loci must have been substituted through long periods of time before the huge species finally emerged. During this evolution a changing co-adapted system had to be kept functional all the time. We do not really know how such a process is maintained, but Haldane (1947) has also shown that, making certain plausible assumptions, gene substitutions in many loci need not take much longer than substitution in one locus.

Evolutionary speed is not controlled by mutation rate, but by the recombination of pre-existent mutant genes through meiosis and fertilization in every generation. Other circumstances being comparable, organisms having a shorter life cycle will thus evolve more quickly than longer-lived organisms. Thus, parasitic microorganisms and insects, which have a generation turn-over many times faster than their animal or plant hosts, can respond genetically to man's efforts at chemical protection, for instance, by improving their detoxifying mechanisms. As a result, many kinds of bacteria have become resistant to antibiotics and insects resistant to insecticides.

Evolutionary speed may be decisive for the survival of any lineage. In spite of its scarcity, the fossil record shows that many more species have become extinct in several plant and animal groups than have survived. One can assume that the extinct species were not able to change their genetical constitution speedily enough to cope with changed circumstances. Whether these circumstances consisted in a general change of climate or in the evolution of new pathogens or in increasingly competent competitors, is a matter of conjecture.

RATES OF SOCIAL CHANGES

Many of the difficulties of the present generation of our species derive from the rapidity and unequal pace of change with which it has to cope. These changes are of the most varied kind and only a few categories will be mentioned.

Almost all of us eat different food, live in different places, do different things, die from different diseases and hold different opinions from those of our parents. Within our own lifespans, even within a few years things may have drastically changed. For the last decades before I retired, I hardly taught anything that had been discovered when I was a student, and now I have to work hard to keep up with what is going on in my own old department.

While these kinds of changes occur in the developed world, far more traumatic upheavals are experienced by the peoples of the developing countries. Among my much-travelled colleagues, I have friends whose parents were illiterate and whose grandparents were slaves in Africa, people who have never left their village. The children of one of these colleagues watch television and learn computer science; they also visit the illiterate grandparents, and, in this perhaps exceptional family, everybody copes. Transformations of a similar kind, if perhaps not quite so extreme, affect hundreds of millions of people currently. The syndrome of "becoming modern" (Inkeles and Smith, 1974) is a characteristic feature of present-day human life all over the world.

All this explains why some people in the old and many more in the developing countries are bewildered, wondering what is happening and where it all will lead. The more sophisticated, in particular, wonder whether the ubiquitous changes and adaptations which they see happening are acquired individually by learning new skills and forming new habits, or whether the answers to the changes are "racial," that is, whether they occur through the replacement in the population of people by individuals of different ethnic origins, or whether it is brought about by movement of people among the social strata. In any case, compared with the evolutionary changes observed in the fossil record, any change on the social scene happens extremely rapidly: in years or decades rather than in millions of years. This alone should make one suspicious of glib genetical explanations. However, as we shall see later, genetical changes of similar rapidity have been also observed and therefore, the question must in many cases remain open.

## SOME OBSERVED CHANGES IN ANIMAL BEHAVIOUR

Social changes always implicate changes in individual behaviour, as is obvious when considering the interactions between humans. But before discussing the causes of changes in human behaviour it is useful to describe some changes in the behaviour of certain animals, which have a short enough generation time so that genetical changes may occur within the working life of an observer. In all of these changes man has had a hand and, while all have proceeded at comparable rates, two have been shown to be genetical in nature, while three were not.

The genetical base of industrial melanism is well known. It consists in the replacement of formerly light forms by dark forms in several moth species in areas polluted by soot. Kettlewell (1956) has shown that this colour change is due to mutants, and also that the dark forms are cryptically protected against predation by birds, which pick them less frequently from the darkened bark of trees than the light forms. It took about a century - one hundred generations or perhaps more - in some species, to increase the originally rare melanic mutants to their present high frequencies. Kettlewell (1955) has also discovered an additional behavioural change in one of the melanic moths of the species *Biston betularia*, the peppered moth. The dark forms also settle preferentially on dark surfaces, which, of course, enhances their cryptic protection in areas where not all surfaces are dark. This additional behavioural adaptation which is also genetically determined can only have developed after the "melanic" colour genes had reached a certain frequency. In any case, the replacement at the behaviour gene locus cannot have taken more than a hundred generations. Similar behavioural adaptation has also been found in other melanic moth species (Steward, 1977).

While industrial melanism originated from pre-existing rare mutants in the areas where it arose, another drastic - even painful - change of behaviour occurred as the consequence of the introduction of genes from an alien population. About 30 years ago, a bee keeper in Piracicaba in Brazil thought that African honey bees, being products of a tropical environment, might be more suitable for Brazilian apiculture than the races from the temperate zones of Europe which were then in general use. Not having experienced the fierceness of the African "bush bee," he incautiously imported a few colonies from Africa, with disastrous effect (Nogueira Neto, 1964).

First, the bees in the apiary became so fierce that they were almost impossible to handle. Their aggressive stinging habit gradually spread over vast distances in several directions making bee keeping a hazardous occupation. The habit has now spread to the Southern States of the United States. Direct observation and also indirect evidence of "African genes" in the aggressive workers showed that - not unlike the Spanish Conquistadores - the African drones and their male descendants had, by their aggressive behaviour, ousted the local drones of European descent and thus gradually Africanized the bee population.

A more harmless but also annoying new habit is the opening of milk bottles by tits and other small birds. In Britain milk is still being delivered in bottles, which in the country and the suburbs are put in the early morning in front of the kitchen doors. These bottles had for many years been closed with thin metal or cardboard caps without any interference, when sometime after the Second World War in a village near Belfast (and subsequently over wider areas) these caps were found to be holed or removed and some cream siphoned off of the milk (Fisher and Hinde, 1949). Observation easily showed that the culprits were great tits, *Parus major*, who were stealing the milk every morning. The question was then asked whether a mutation had occurred in an ancestor of these cream addicts, which conferred the bottle opening skill genotypically upon his progeny, or whether some time ago a "genius" among the tits, or perhaps just a lucky one, discovered the useful art of bottle-opening, which then, by imitation or learning, had spread over the area. Either explanation seemed at the time possible, as far as the speed was concerned with which the habit spread. If gene diffusion was responsible, the fact that in passerine birds on the average only about 1/5th of the offspring of a pair survives to maturity makes the necessary strong selection just about possible. However, it is difficult to visualize that the consumption or non-consumption of a little cream should be the main factor determining the survival of a tit. A second constraint which obviously must limit the speed with which a new mutant can spread geographically is the area over which individual birds range. While something is known concerning the territoriality of tits, it is difficult to assess how far pairing is limited by distance. In any case, spreading of the habit by learning would also be limited by the distances individual tits cover.

On balance, the hypothesis that the opening of milk bottles was the result of an individual's invention and its subsequent spread by learning seemed the more likely and this conclusion was clinched by the observation that individuals of another tit species, *P. ceruleus*, the blue tit, also had acquired the bottle-opening habit. As no hybridization has ever been observed in nature between the two species a hypothetical gene cannot have jumped the sexual barrier. On the other hand, both species frequent the same sites and each has ample opportunity to see what the other does. More recently even other birds than tits have occasionally been observed to open milk bottles.

A similar new habit seems to have developed in the green finch, *Chloris chloris*. In Europe this bird has some time ago taken to stripping the green, unripe berries of *Daphne mezereum*, a shrub flowering in early spring in many gardens. Bird and plant have for thousand of years inhabited vast common areas in Europe and Asia and one might guess that, if the berry-stripping had evolved in the wild, the shrub would have been exterminated by the finches' depredation. Now gardening firms keep it going. It is interesting (Petterson, 1956) that in Australia and New Zealand, where both species have been introduced from Europe and again live in the same gardens, the berry-stripping habit has not yet been evolved. While the situation has not been as thoroughly explored as the bottle-opening, we may safely assume that transmission by imitation is the likely explanation.

My last example brings us nearer to our own species and to behaviour which resembles more our own actions. Japanese investigators have for several decades made studies of monkey societies and among them one on an isolated artificial colony on an island in the sea (Kawai, 1963, 1965). Among the many behavioural features studied were also a few startling new habits which show the opportunistic nature of primate behaviour. Many individuals, for instance, took to washing their food in the sea before consumption, much as racoons do, but which they could never have practised as they had not lived previously near any open body of water. The habit spread among the younger macacos, but apparently not among the older ones. Even more staggering was the development of large-scale "watersports" like diving from trees, chasing each other in the water, etc., all activities which had been impossible for their ancestors. Without going into details as to how these habits originated one must, from the short time it took them to appear, conclude that they were the result of individual experimentation and subsequent spread by "cultural transmission". Anticipating some points to be made later I should also say that the monkeys were preadapted for their innovative habits.

Developments of the kind just described must have been frequent in human social history, though direct proof is, of course, impossible. Examples would have been the uses of fire, the acquisition and perfection of weapons and tools, and the development of such means of communication as spoken language and script. Dissemination of new skills on a large scale can, of course, be observed at present and, while locally some of these achievements are sometimes lost, one sees a steady accumulation of new skills as far as the totality of mankind is concerned. The speed and comparative ease with which numerical and technological manipulations can be acquired by primitive peoples makes one suspect that the human sensory motor system and other portions of the brain have - presumably in adaptation to other tasks in the past - been ready to perform modern operations for a considerable time. Only the opportunities were lacking. The possibility of adaptation transfer or preadaptation has a considerable bearing on ideas of evolution and also, of course, on estimates and measurements of the rates at which adapative changes occur. Thus, if genetical adaptation for a particular situation had already occurred before a new similar situation arose, it could come into operation at once, though the previous changes may have been gradual and taken considerable time. An apparently quite novel faculty may thus be only a minor step of "transfer" in changed circumstances - from a long practiced activity to a new one. Probably most human inventions arise in this way. Many forms of ritualization may have also developed by some sort of transfer. Combat can change into competitive play, chase into racing, intentional movements into signaling. Thus, it is hardly possible to put a definite date to the genetical changes which preadapted people for football, car racing or the "three R's." It was, in any case, very many generations before the tools used in these activities were invented.

The galloping speed with which these and thousands of similar achievements of our civilization are spreading among undeveloped populations would be difficult to explain in ways other than preadaptation. However, there remains the problem whether the first invention or transfer - or maybe several such independent events - stem from the genetical "superiority" of an individual or from propitious circumstances, i.e. from chance. Script, the wheel, the true arch, only developed in one or very few places, and I would be loath to say why. On the other hand, many primitive technologies like pottery, basket making, spinning and weaving probably had multiple origins. In conclusion, if we take transfers of adaptation to new situations into account, no starting point and thus no rate of evolution can at present be put on these and similar developments of skills, only sometimes rates of elaboration and of geographical spread.

## COMMUNICATION: LANGUAGE AND SPEECH

Social organization is dependent on communication between the members of the society; so the growth of social interactions is to some extent controlled by the rate of development of the means of communication. We have no time here to deal with the interesting field of animal communications, or with pre-linguistic interactions between humans. I can only deal - and that very briefly - with some ideas concerning the emergence of verbal communication. Unfortunately, while we have considerable documentation of the scripts of early societies (Gordon, 1968), we do not have fossil speech and thus, our ideas concerning the history of language are necessarily conjectural, and certain aspects of both its development and its rate are controversial.

Most people would agree that there was speech before script. This conviction is supported by the observation that many highly sophisticated societies exist which neither write nor read. On the other hand, individuals from these societies, especially as children, can be quite easily taught both these skills; an important part of their pre-adaptation must be the fact that they can speak. Why, then, can we not teach non-human primates, and in particular our closest surviving relative, the chimpanzee, to speak? Until recently, there were two schools of explanation: some people argued that the limiting factor was the chimpanzee's anatomical structure and, in particular, the primitive formation of its speech organs. Others thought that it was the lack of abstract or conceptual thought which made language impossible. It seems that these simple alternatives do not exhaust the possibilities and that a more complex explanation must be attempted. To the assertion that as a consequence of a chimpanzee's non-erect posture, his larynx, tongue and upper air cavities are so different from the analogous human structures (Denes and Pinson, 1973) that they could not produce speech, one can object that birds, such as parrots or Minah birds having sound-producing structures far more different from many than the chimpanzee's, can yet produce very accurate imitations of human speech, albeit without connecting them with their conceptual content. This faculty obviously derives from the mocking habits of birds, which in nature determine the songs of many species in detail, while in other species these are fixed genetically (Thorpe, 1961). In the birds that imitate, the song dialect of an individual fledgling can, by exposure to the song of a bird from a different region, be determined much as is the language of a child by the people who are bringing him up. In the non-mockers, such an attempt is futile; the young bird sings in the way his parents have sung, even though he has never heard them, having been hatched in an incubator. The development of song dialects in these species must have proceeded at a much lower rate than among the song imitators, presumably by genetical substitution.

Turning to the chimpanzees, one has the impression that they just do not want to speak, and that for an unknown reason. This impression has prompted a number of people to bring up young chimpanzees together with their own children, but, in spite of great patience, nothing more than a few "words" has ever been acquired. Psychologists, following Chomsky (1972), might argue that non-humans lack the innate deep structure which enables *homo sapiens* to develop grammar, syntax, and thus conceptual thought. However, it has been shown that chimpanzees, and recently gorillas, not only have quite considerable conceptual faculties, but also can develop a sort of syntax by which to organize visual signals into meaningful sequences, for instance, into commands for food, water etc. (Gardner, 1969). Some of you may have seen a most impressive film in which a chimpanzee operated with great speed a panel of knobs, controlling coloured lights, thus producing sequences which brought him the desired reward. I must, however, admit that it was sometimes difficult to avoid the impression that the ape was just playing. Nevertheless, whatever the interpretation of a particular sequence of actions, the interaction between the chimpanzee, the machine and the rewards can only be interpreted as made possible by an innate genetical structure, the product of long, slow evolution brought suddenly into play by an entirely novel situation.

If we can accept neither anatomical imperfection nor the lack of conceptualization as explaining the inability of chimpanzees to speak, we may perhaps ascribe it to the inability to give arbitrary assignments of specific meaning to certain speech elements. This faculty must be acquired anew by every child. We may, thus, accept Chomsky's hypothesis (1959, 1972) that the genetical evolution of the faculties on which these coding systems depend has been the factor which determines the rate at which speech has developed. But what sort of interactions, genetical changes, and cultural traditions took place during the early days of speaking, we cannot even guess. Neither linguistics nor the study of speech defects or language deprivation provide any cues.

## THE RELATION BETWEEN INDIVIDUAL ADAPTATION AND SELECTION

So far we have described evolutionary (genetical) and social (non-genetical) changes, as if they were separate processes and have only hinted at possible interaction. But while sometimes one or the other process predominates, interactions always exist and are in many instances fundamental.

Selection can only transform the gene pool of a species if it is not so severe as to eradicate it. A sufficient number of individuals must be able to adapt successfully to the novel stress and to leave offspring, while other individuals will succumb with ever-diminishing progeny. Differential adaptabilities of the individuals in a population are thus a prerequisite for selection. If in the course of time a particular selective force may increase in severity, e.g. if the climate *slowly* deteriorates or competitors *gradually* increase, selection also will gradually extend the genetically based tolerance of the population, and thus make it capable of surviving in circumstances, in which, at the beginning of the process, not a single individual would have survived. This continuous interaction between a changing situation, adaptive individual reaction, and the resulting genetical transformation of the population has been called "canalization" (Waddington, 1957). It is sometimes presented as a new version of neo-Lamarckism, but this is a spurious claim, as it is not an acquired tolerance of the surviving individuals which is transmitted to their offspring, but their genes, which enabled them, unlike others, to acquire their tolerance. One could describe canalization as a succession of steps where preadaptation is made use of. Again, this does not always work.

Examples for the extinction of populations by the too rapid intrusion of new environmental factors, as well as examples for successful canalization, can be found in many groups of organisms. Preventive methods have in a few decades extinguished small-pox and bubonic plague in most areas where they were formerly prevalent; the European (red) squirrel in Southern England has been displaced by the importation from Pennsylvania of the grey squirrel; tribal populations have rapidly perished from the impact of Western civilization, sometimes from imported diseases. Other indigenous groups succeeded in surviving.

Canalization has occurred in microorganisms which have invaded hot springs, for instance, in Yellowstone Park. Here they survive at temperatures up to 70° C, which would instantaneously kill conspecific individuals from colder waters. It is believed that this heat tolerance has been acquired by the stepwise substitution at many gene loci of "heatresistance genes" during a gradual invasion from the cooler waters, downstream from the hot springs. It has been possible to some degree to imitate this evolutionary process in the laboratory (Brock, 1969). Gradual heritable increases in the drug resistance of pathogenic microorganisms may also proceed in a similar fashion.

Also gradually acquired may be the genetical resistance to infectious diseases in certain environments. Populations which, for generations, have lived in towns and were particularly exposed to tuberculosis have acquired an increased genetical resistance to this disease, while newly urbanized people succumb to it much more frequently; the natives of malarial areas were, even before the introduction of the anti-malarials, less prone to suffer and die from this disease than immigrant whites (Harrison et al, 1977).

A particularly instructive situation, illustrating the complexity of interactions between individual adaptation (tolerance) and selection, exists in West Africa, where the severest form of malaria is endemic. A particular mutant, the sickling gene, which must have appeared some considerable time ago in the area, can be considered to be a successful "single" step in increasing malarial resistance. But in this instance, the adaptation has been achieved at a very high cost of lives for the population (Allison, 1954). It is also a situation where strong selective forces do not result in any shift of gene frequencies but in equilibrium. Selection acts here as a conservative force and there is no evolutionary change which could be measured. In real terms what happens must be described as a gruesome balance of death. The babies in the West African villages, where there is the highest risk of malarial infection, are in respect of the sickling gene of three kinds: homozygous for the "normal" allele, homozygous for the sickling allele, and heterozygous, i.e. carrying one of either. In primitve conditions all these infants are constantly exposed to the bites of the malaria-transmitting anopheles mosquitoes; the "normal" homozygotes are the most likely to die from the infection and the "sickling" homozygtes which are fairly immune against the malaria parasite are prone to die from the sickling disease - a complex syndrome named so, because of the sickle shape their red blood cells assume when they are de-oxygenized. The best chances for survival are enjoyed by the heterozygous babies, which have an increased malaria resistance and also are free from the incapacitating symptoms of the sickle cell anemia. If one simplifies this situation one arrives at a model, in which the population consists entirely of heterozygous couples, who produce "normal", heterozygous and "sickle diseased" children in the proportion 1:2:1.

Half of these children die, either from malaria or from the anemia, and only the heterozygotes survive to carry on the sad system. Of course, recently the situation in many areas of West Africa has been fundamentally changed by the modern anti-malarials and the fight against the mosquitoes. If malaria disappears in West Africa, the balance of death will be upset, and the normal gene will get the upper hand; but the sickling gene and the anemia will linger on for many generations, as it does among the progeny in North America of West Africans, who for generations have not been much exposed to malaria. The rate of extinction of the sickling gene will follow a kind of exponential curve approaching zero.

## ENVIRONMENTAL CHANGES AND PREDICTABILITY

A few years ago, futurology was fashionable amongst scientists. Books, lectures and interviews devoted to this theme provided splendid opportunities for some of my eminent colleagues to make fools of themselves. The reasons for this - why, in fact, apparently plausible extrapolations of biological and social trends are so hazardous - are of the greatest interest to anyone trying to assess trends in human affairs. I suggest that there are two main causes: (1) the complexity of the effects of selective agencies on man, and (2) the impermanence of many of these agencies.

Erroneous extrapolations, due to unforeseen rapid changes in the system, are, of course, commonplace in economics, but the apparently simpler science of demography also provides striking examples. Before the First World War the European powers, and especially France, got frightened by falling birth rates and expected a decrease in their numbers with adverse consequences to their military strength. Some measures to increase fertility were introduced. Whether because of these measures, or not, most European populations increased. After the Second World War the general fear was that, in spite of the war losses, Europe - as well as North America - would take part in the universal, dreaded population explosion. But this also did not happen. In Britain, for instance, where the number of teachers was increased in the expectation of greater numbers of children, there was a short fall of births by several hundred thousand, so that the teachers now can find no work. For the moment the population of Britain, like that of many other European countries, is almost in numerical equilibrium, but this also is unlikely to last. The reasons for the erratic behaviour of birth rates and population sizes are manifold and, of course, interconnected. Changes of attitude, the availability of contraception, the employment situation, and many others, may all influence, both the willingness of women to bear children and the preferred age for doing so. Other factors, such as the incidence of lethal mutants, and social or medical care, control the children's survival. Death rates, though less erratic, nevertheless add to the hazard of guessing population trends.

Another demographic variable, the relative contribution of the various social classes to the next generation has greatly agitated the old eugenists, who considered it as self-evident that the lower classes were, on the whole, less intelligent and generally less desirable. As these classes had in Victorian times more children than people from the higher classes, it seemed to follow from an assumed heritability of intelligence that, in the total population, the general level of intelligence and social worth must decline. This antiquated model of the intelligence problem is still widely used and will be discussed later. In the context of this section I will only note that this kind of differential class fertility is not a universal phenomenon in all societies, and that it also varies with time. In contemporary Sweden the middle class is reported to produce at least as many children as the workers and, in any case, the class structure there is undergoing profound and rapid changes. This probably applies to other countries as well. Calculating long time trends in such rapidly changing circumstances is not a useful exercise.

During the last half-century progress in medicine, in particular the invention of the sulpha drugs and antibiotics, has profoundly changed the life expectations of many millions of people. Other drugs have also played a role. Severe diabetics, who formerly died before procreation, now survive as a consequence of modern treatment, lead a relatively normal life, and produce children. These carry various "diabetes genes", which thus increase in frequency. The fear is that, should modern conditions break down for whatever reason, a sudden resurgence of severe, juvenile diabetes would occur and many people would die. So they would, but by the same token the renewed selection against diabetes would then again start reducing the frequencies of the responsible genes. If, as is likely, the break-down were to be only temporary, the short burst of deaths would cause a good deal of personal tragedy, but would not be a threat to humanity. Meanwile, modern therapy keeps great numbers alive who would otherwise have died.

If we now return to the intelligence situation, somewhat different fears are being voiced by people who feel that egalitarian policies and an increased support for the weak must lead to the erosion of the more valuable genetic traits and then, in the end, to general social decline. Their arguments depend on three assumptions: (1) that intelligence tests are measures of genetically determined qualities and are independent of the environment; (2) that the lower classes are intellectually inferior and (3) that their contribution of children to the next generation is higher than that of the other classes.

Since we have already pointed out that different class fertility is not a ubiquitous and permanent phenomenon, we need only discuss points (1) and (2). Before doing that, however, we might as well point out that two attempts to measure an actual decline in intelligence under controlled conditions have, in fact, shown a slight increase (Penrose, 1967). This result, which was found in Scotland as well as in the United States, has been explained away by the protagonists of intellectual doom by saying that the increase in intelligence is only apparent and produced by improved living conditions and teaching methods. But this, of course, invalidates point (1), namely that intelligence tests are independent of environmental factors; so the whole argument collapses.

There is, however, yet another line of arguing against the inevitability of intelligence loss, which is of greater interest to our considerations of evolutionary trends and rates and which attacks the validity of the naive model on which the case for the intelligence scare is based. Penrose (1967) has shown that, even accepting points (1) and (2), it by no means follows that there must be a general decline in intelligence. There is good evidence that a decreased fertility of the highly gifted is counter-balanced by low fertility of the subnormal. By considering fertility and intelligence as two pleiotropic manifestations of one gene pair, Penrose has shown that, by choosing various parameters for fertility and intelligence, a model can be constructed which according to these parameters produces rises, falls or shows no change in the intelligence level. This model liberates us from the naive assumptions of primitive eugenics, but is, of course, not meant to represent the total situation.

## EVOLUTION, HISTORICAL CHANGE AND REVERSIBILITY

In discussing the diabetes and sickling disease situations we have shown that gene frequency equilibria can be reversed. But complex evolution, inasmuch as it is a stochastic process of many steps, cannot be reversed, nor can it be repeated in every genetical detail, as experiments have shown (Dobzhansky, 1953). Thus, recurrent cyclic changes, such as the succession of generations, adaptive responses to reasons or days, or any "spontaneous rhythms", are not evolutionary events. A similar situation obtains in history. The succession of phases such as growth, maturity and decay in the life of individuals or institutions - though also irreversible - is also not evolution, nor is it history. Confusingly, however, it is often described as a "life history". The terminology used in describing complex changes is altogether most confusing. The word "phase", for instance, is used to describe static equilibrium situations as in physical chemistry (Gibbs, 1876-1878), or as denoting part of a recurrent process, for instance, the systole of the heart beat. Finally, it is applied to the part of an irreversible process as if one talks about the aquatic phase of the vertebrates or the neolithic age. Similarly confusing are the uses of the word "period", which derived from planetary movement and is now applied to any recurrent circumstances; it is even sometimes used synonymously with "phase". Only if comparable phases, for instance, the larvae or the adults of two species, following each other in lines of descent, progressively differ in a measureable way - if we can see a trend - are we dealing with evolution. Historical development also shows changes in time of comparable structures.

Now the processes which effect evolutionary as well as historical changes cannot, in practice, be separated from the processes which maintain individual life or society. Without life there is no organic evolution, without living society no social change. Thus, to understand changes we have to know a great deal about the structures which, while gradually changing, must yet permanently function. Unlike motor cars, where new models are designed on the drawing board, but are not bodily descended from the old models, organisms always have direct ancestors, even if they are occasionally the products of biological engineering. The creation of new life from scratch and the design of radically new kinds of viable organisms, comparable to the novel machines of modern technology belong as yet to science fiction.

What is common to machines and organisms, and sometimes also to societies, is adaptive change. Successive motor car models are meant to be improved, while successive species ought to be more viable, institutions better in some ways. What is different is the mode in which these changes are brought about. Few contemporary biologists or historians believe in a design or blue-print specification for the systems which they investigate, but all engineers are concerned with designs and blue prints. This, of course, is trivial, but is has considerable bearing on the rate at which change can be effected in engineering and in evolution. While, with few exceptions, evolutionary change proceeds slowly in small steps and is subject to trial and error, technological progress can be speeded up by the much faster thought processes. One aspect of the human brain is its power to substitute real time-consuming processes by the fast manipulation of models (hypotheses), thus in some sense to abolish time. It took millions of years for insect, bird or bat flight to evolve, but only centuries for human flight. Similarly with anticipating mechanisms: biological clocks have presumably evolved over millions of years, mechanical clocks during a few centuries. Brains are older than computers, etc.

In the social field we usually find a confusion of processes, mainly interactions between planning and happening, which result in very different rates of change.

Decimalization and metrication or new currencies have in some countries been introduced and accepted overnight, while changes in education or welfare may take generations.

## CONCLUSION

As stated in the Introduction, I have considered time merely as an aspect of processes. To discuss it, it was therefore necessary to describe to you a great variety of very different processes, which must have confused some of you. Nevertheless, I hope to have made it clear that the time characteristics of certain classes of structures and in particular changes in structures like organisms, populations, and societies can be estimated, and their magnitude used, when forming an opinion about the processes underlying observed changes in as yet not analysed situations.

## REFERENCES

Allison, A. (1954) "Protection afforded by sickle cell trait against subtertian malarial infection," *Brit. Med. J. 1*, 290-296.

Brock, T. D. (1962) Microbial Growth under extreme conditions. *19th Symp. Soc. Gen. Microbiol.* p. 15-41.

Chomsky, N. (1959) "Verbal Behaviour," *Language 35*, 26-58.

Chomsky, N. (1972) *Language and Mind* (New York: Harcourt, Brace, Jovanovitch).

Darlington, C. D. (1969) *The evolution of man and society* (New York: Simon and Schuster).

Denes, P. B. and Pinson, E. N. (1973) *The speech chain. The physics and biology of spoken language* (New York: Anchor Press).

Dobzhansky, Th. (1953) "Indeterminate outcome of certain experiments on Drosophila populations," *Evolution* VII, 198-210.

Dobzhansky, Th. (1970) *Genetics and the evolutionary process*, (New York: Columbia U. P.).

Fisher, J. and Hinde, R. A. (1949) "The opening of milk bottles by birds" *British Birds*, *42*, 347-357.

Fraser, J. T. (1975) *Of time, passion and knowledge*, (New York: George Braziller).

Gardner, R. A. and Gardener, B. T. (1969) "Teaching sign language to a chimpanzee." *Science*, N. Y. *165*, 664-672.

Gibbs, J. W. (1876-1878) *Equilibrium of heterogeneous substances*. Yale U. P.

Gordon, C. H. (1968) *Forgotten scripts*. London: Thames and Hudson.

Haldane, J. B. S. (1947) Suggestions as to quantitative measurements of rates of evolution. - *Eveolution, 3*, 51-56.

Haldane, J. B. S. (1957) The cost of natural selectrion.- *J. Genet.* *55*, 511-524.

Harris, H. and Kalmus, H. (1949) The measurement of taste sensitivity to phenylthiourea (P.T.C.). - *Ann. Eugen.* *15*, 24-31.

Harrison, G. A. et al. (1977) *Human Biology*. 2nd Edition. Oxford U. P.

Hollis, J. H. and Carrier, J. K. (1975) "Research implications for communication difficulties." *Except. Children*, *41*, 405-412.

Huxley, J. S. (1949) *Evolution, the Synthesis*. London: Murray.

Inkeles, A. and Smith, D. H. (1974) *Becoming modern*. London: Heinemann.

Kalmus, H. (1943) "Separation and Reintegration as Phases of Evolution." *Philosophy* VIII, No. 70, 1-8.

Kalmus, H. (1966) "Organic evolution and time." In *The voices of time*. Edited by J. T. Fraser. - New York: George Braziller.

Kawai, Masao (1963) "Abstracts of papers read at the 7th annual meeting of the Society of Primate Research." - *Primates, 4,* 114-118.

Kawai, Masao (1965) "Newly acquired pre-cultural behaviour of Japanese monkeys on Koshiu Islet." - *Primates, 6,* 1-30.

Kettlewell, H. B. D. (1956a) "A résumé of investigations on the evolution of melanism in lepidoptera." - *Proc. Roy. Soc.* B. *145,* 297-303.

Kettlewell, H. B. D. (1956b) "Further selection experiments on industrial melanism in the lepidoptera." - *Heredity 10,* 287-303.

Kuczynski, R. R. (1936) *Population movements*. Oxford: Clarendon Press.

Lyell, C. (1830-1833) *Principles of geology*. London: Murray.

Nogueira Neto, P. (1964) "The spread of a fierce African bee in Brazil." - *Bee World, 45* (3), 119-121.

Penrose, L. S. (1967) *The biology of mental defect*. 4th edit. London: Sidwick and Jackson.

Petterson, M. (1956) "Diffusion of a new habit among green finches." - *Nature 117*, 705-710.

Post, R. H. (1962) "Population differences in red and green colour vision deficiency: a review, and a query on selection relaxation." - *Eugenics Quarterly, 9*, 131-35.

Premack, A. I. and Premack, D. (1972) "Teaching language to an ape." - *Sci. Amer.* Octob. p. 92-9.

Ryan, F. J. (1953) "Natural selection in bacterial populations." *Atti. VI. Intern. Congr. Microbiol*. Rome. Vol 1, 649-57.

Simpson, G. G. (1944) *Tempo and Mode in Evolution.* New York: Columbia U. P.

Steward, R. C. (1977) "Preference of melanic moths to dark background." - *J. Zool. 181*, 371-395.

Thorpe, W. H. (1961) *Birdsong: the biology of vocal communication and expression in birds*. Cambridge U. P.

Waddington, C. H. (1957) *The strategy of the genes: A discussion of some aspects of theoretical biology*. London: George Allen and Unwin.

Wilson, E. O. (1975) *Sociobiology, the new synthesis*. Cambridge, Mass. and London: The Bellknap Press, Harvard U. P.

## DISCUSSION AND COMMENT

*by N. Lawrence*

Professor Kalmus's paper is a unique contribution. Professional excellence has made him neither unwilling nor unable to see how our disciplines relate to other disciplines. He shows us how they are alike, and, more importantly, how they are unlike. He both provokes our imagination about principles of biological and social evolution and shows some of the limits of speculation. Too often the ardent researchist is ready to generalize his results beyond their capacity to explain. Consider, for instance, the wild claims of one of the best of invertebratologists, E.O. Wilson, to have found the evolutionary roots of altruism in the social behavior of non-hominids.

Professor Kalmus's paper is unique in another respect. It is not polemic. It embodies research of his own and that of others, but it is a prolegomenon to a continuing dialogue about two problems we can little ignore, yet which we little consider: (1) What are the agencies of change? and (2) What must we look for as we try to understand, to control, and to predict changes?

The subject, then, is evolution in the broad sense, as it applies to organized alterations in both organisms and societies. By sketching the results of widely varying types of "adaptive variation," Kalmus manages to invigorate a sometimes tedious subject. "Adaptation" is supposed to explain almost single-handedly the giant proliferation of living species from what Darwin speculated might be a small original number of primordial types. Evolutionary change and survival is all too often presented as something between a deadly fulfilling of your role in a food chain and the sly minimizing of hazard by finding or making a niche or a disguise. No one can ignore these factors. But what of the tit that "learns" to get at milk bottles by tipping up the cardboard cap, and passes the knack along to other tits, even to other species of tits? Or the imaginative explosion among the Japanese macaques when, living in a colony near the water, they stumbled (perhaps literally) onto dunking their food and soon took to playing in the water, diving, and so on--against an apparently inborn "taboo" carefully maintained, under human observation, for nearly fifty years by their elders? (This colony, incidentally, unknown to the west for many years, is the longest continuously observed primate society in ethological study.)

The interjection of something like human imagination, rapid change, the seizing of a new opportunity, rather than a mere avoidance of death or species disaster presents a real challenge to Neo-Darwinists clinging to the primacy of gradual change. The panorama of evolution thus considered is much more compatible with the temperaments of those who are not merely curious about living things, but are delighted by them. Once the creative aspect of evolution is emphasized, the proposition that beauty is only in the beholder's eye loses something of its grubbiness. And on the less sentimental side it raises serious questions as to whether "Homo sapiens" should be applied to hominids much before Aurignacian times.

And there are warnings. For instance, planning has its limits. Consider the pendulum between too many children and too few teachers, followed by too few children and too many teachers. There is also the "gruesome" price paid for sickle-cell immunity to malaria. Again there are limits to the rate of adaptation that an organism can tolerate to an orthogenetic change. The microorganisms that have adjusted to temperatures of 70° C in hot springs (in Yellowstone Park) live in a medium that would kill their conspecific kin. By risky analogy how far can Homo sapiens adapt to the natureless city with its "pressure cooker" lifestyle? Progress from field to town took a long while. But in the late phase of towns, some towns burgeoned rather quickly into cities, and these, before they really matured, fused into megalopolises covering hundreds of continuous square miles of what ought to be called, not suburbs, but superurbs.

Let me say that these speculative questions are exactly what a good scientist is wary of. They are perhaps saved by the interrogative form. But if we may not find sermons in stones, we are certainly permitted to get a few suggestions from them; and there are more than a few to be gained from Professor Kalmus's fine survey. And is there anyone who can maintain that our curiosity about the world is merely aesthetic, wholly playful or avocational?

I will close with a few demurrers, in the spirit of the open dialogue.

1. Chomsky can not much be enlisted on the side of evolutionists. He does not deny the evolution of languages, of course, but he puts this "diachronic" approach to one side. As Kalmus says, and as Chomsky would agree, we do not have fossil speech. Chomsky's concern, like that of most structuralists (Piaget is an exception), is "synchronic," emphasizing fundamental structures rather than primordial ones. In this he resembles Levi-Strauss. Indeed synchronic analysis is the only serious challenge to developmentalism in the current history of ideas. Moreover, Chomsky's effective work, and that of a tribe of disciples and *afficionadi,* has been in the penetration of deep structures of given languages, with a view to showing equivalence of surface structures transformably equivalent to one another according to rule. Progress toward a deep structure common to all language that is, to the linguistic base in all consciousness (with corresponding universal rules) has been all but insignificant. Moreover, as a matter of personal critique, I shall agree that Chomsky's famous challenge about the inborn competence of children is indeed a great stumbling block to behaviorists of all stripes. It is, howeve, logically independent of his assumption that because there is a deep structure for language, such a structure must be linguistic. Indeed, why ignore the non-linguistic competence of the child? This competence--if his pushy parents would leave him alone, à la Rousseau--appears both both in manipulative aptitudes and in their affective value, which *also* seem more like emergence than acquisition. Why not ask for a deep structure which underlies linguistic, manipulative, and evaluative competence, since these are coordinated? Our civilization allows and encourages the rapid expansion of linguistic competence, which outruns the child's ability to manipulate and evaluate. But no one who teaches is ignorant of how this encouraged verbal facility soon withers to personal incompetence, if it is isolated from other competence.

2. As to chimpanzee communication, this is a field of pure delight. But so far as I know, the true use of the first personal pronoun (and the second, for that matter) is still in abeyance, and while one chimpanzee has asked about the name of something, thus chancing her way from language to metalanguage, it is still a small venture, governed by pretty pragmatic concerns. We use language about language about language with ease. So also with tools to make tools to, etc. It is this infinitizing capacity that makes us homo faber, homo loquens, and above all homo ludens. If we must look for preadaptation in a corticated brain with a fantastically large number of surface connections, the infinitizing capacity (of which mathematical recursiveness is the abstract model) would be the primary object of interest.

(3) Finally--and I hesitate to question a naturalist with whom I have literally hiked and learned much--Professor Kalmus says, in his brief review of bird songs, that only in "imitative" birds does the "subsong" get modified by "learning" from other birds, while in non-imitative birds isolation of the fledgling results in a song no different from that of other conspecifics. One may well ask how "imitative" is to be defined independently of the data it is supposed to explain. Part of the answer lies in the response of young birds isolated from contact with their own natural song and living with the sounds of other birds. But the situation is very complex. Dorst (French 1971, English 1974), after reviewing the work of Thorpe and others, especially on the chaffinch, a notably "innatist" bird, makes the general remark "Song certainly has an innate component: elements composed of notes of a particular pitch and in a certain rhythm are hereditary, forming a sort of framework of the song. However, a bird cannot by itself reconstitute from this the full species song, but must take advantage of the auditory experience and thus learn from contact with other members of the species."

Of what use are such minute considerations? Simply this: Our warm-blooded cousins seem to have inborn behavioral tendencies. Speculators on human nature of one stripe tell use we are virtually instinctless, others that we are inescapably aggressive and always in heat. Perhaps we can learn caution from the problems of ornithologists --if nothing else.

# IV. SUBJECTIVE TIME

## Time, Memory, and Affect: Experimental Studies of the Subjective Past

S. Albert

*ABSTRACT*

*A series of studies are reported in which memory, impression formation, and time estimation are shown to be a function of the passage of subjective time. By unobtrusively increasing or decreasing the speed of a clock by a factor of two an individual is led to believe that either 3 hours or 45 minutes have elapsed. In all cases the real interval, filled with a variety of booklet tasks, is 1½ hours. The results indicate that individuals tend to forget a list of words, and in some cases the order in which they were presented, to a greater extent if they thought that they saw the list 3 hours ago vs. 45 minutes ago. Further, a description of a person is seen as more positive if the subject thought he read the paragraph description 3 hours ago vs. 45 minutes ago. Finally, estimates of a 30 and 90 second interval are reliably foreshortened or elongated depending on whether the subject has been in an experimental condition in which time (the speed of the clock) is going faster or slower than normal. A model of stimulus incompleteness is developed as one possible explanation for the results.*

### I. STUDIES OF MEMORY

In all theories of memory, time is treated as the time of Newtonian physics and is employed as a uniform standard against which to measure the presumably more variable features of cognitive and affective functioning. According to McGeough (1932) and in accordance with the presuppositions of interference theory (Postman, 1961), the passage of time has no effect on memory; rather, we forget because the contents that fill the temporal interval following presentation of a stimulus interfere with memory for the stimulus or because certain time dependent physiological changes diminish the strength of the stimulus. The latter is the basic notion of decay theory (Broadbent, 1958, 1963; Brown, 1958). The general finding, at least since Ebbinghaus (1885), is that memory for an event declines with the passage of time falling off rapidly at first and then more slowly.

The question to be addressed in this paper is whether we forget as a function of how much actual time has gone by, all else being equal of course, or whether we forget in proportion to how much time we think has gone by, if in fact the two are different. Do we forget more of something if we are led to believe (although erroneously) that it occurred in the distant past, and are we more likely to remember something when convinced (although erroneously) that it occurred in the very recent subjective past. To deal with this question experimentally we need to be able to manipulate the subjective remoteness of a stimulus independently of its actual location or time of occurrence. There are three ways of manipulating persons' subjective sense of time; hypnosis (Aaronson, 1968a, b, Zimbardo, Marshall, Maslach, 1971; Zimbardo, Marshall, White, 1972), drugs (Goldstone, Boardman, Litamon, 1958; Frankenhauser, 1959) and altering the speed of a clock (Rotter, 1965, 1969; Craik and Sarbin, 1963; McGrath and O'Hanlon, 1968; Bull, 1970; Snyder, Schultz and Jones, 1974; London and Monello, 1974; Zimbardo, Marshall, White and Maslach, 1971). The difficulty with manipulating time either through the administration of drugs or by hypnosis is that other aspects of functioning may be affected, aspects which may relate to memory in unknown and complex ways. In addition, were an effect of subjective time on memory found using these manipulations, generalization to individuals in a normal state of functioning would be at best uncertain.

Thus, the solution to the problem of manipulating subjective temporal duration without the use of drugs or hypnosis was to unobtrusively alter the speed of a clock that was used by the subject to tell time. In this way 1½ hours could be made to appear to be 3 hours, if the speed of the clock were doubled, or only 45 minutes, if the speed of the clock were reduced in half. In the first series of studies the basic experimental logic was to present a stimulus, increase or decrease the speed of the clock, and then ask the subject to recall the stimulus. Our hypothesis was that subjects should forget more of the stimulus the longer the time interval they perceive to have transpired between its presentation and their attempt to recall it.

*Details of the experimental procedure*. When the subject arrived at the laboratory for an experiment that he though dealt with the relationship between intellectual tasks and physiological measures, he was asked to remove all items of metal including his watch and place them in an envelope. The rational was that the equipment in the experiment was sensitive to metal. Once inside the laboratory, he had to tell time by means of an ordinary looking large GE wall clock, the speed of which, unknown to him, was under the experimenter's control. Allegedly for purposes of calibration, the subject was asked to record the time he began each task in the experiment so that changes in his physiological state can be coordinated to the specific mental state he was in while doing each task. In fact, the only purpose of recording the time was to provide a reason for the subject to look at the clock. No physiological measures were taken, although it would be of interest to do so.

Our intuition was that an affect of subjective time on memory would be mediated by some kind of motivational process. All other things being equal, the utility[1] of a piece of information may depend on its age, the older a piece of information, the less its perceived utility for current functioning, and the less its perceived utility for current functioning, and the less likely an individual is to maintain the information through periodic rehearsal. Information that is temporally remote should therefore receive less rehearsal than more recent information.

*Subjects*. A total of 224 adults participated in the four experiments reported in this paper. They were recruited by newspaper advertisement. All were told that the experiment would last about 3 hours. This procedure was necessary because a subject couldn't believe that the experiment lasted 45 minutes only for him to discover that an hour and a half had gone by when he reemerged from the laboratory and that he had missed an appointment.

*Experiment I*. After entering the laboratory subjects were given one trial of serial learning consisting of two lists, one contaning five threatening or unpleasant words (bowel, suicide, torture, abortion and suck) and five non-threatening words (primary, port, formula, harmonic and gravy). These words were previously scaled for their unpleasant or threatening quality by Bergquist, Lewinsohn, Sue and Flippo (1968).

There was an 8 second interval between lists. The order of presentation of the two lists was counterbalanced and the order of presentation of the five words within each list was randomized. The speed of the clock was then unobtrusively increased or decreased by a factor or two. A control group in which the speed of the clock was not altered was also subsequently run.[2] The subject completed a variety of interpolated tasks which included listening to a speech, making probability estimates, and filling out a series of questionnaires on different topics.

After a subjective interval of either 3 hours or 45 minutes (1½ hours real time) subjects were given a recall period of 90 seconds in which to list the five threatening and non-threatening words in the order they say them. Subjects were then presented with the two lists, but the words in each list out of order and asked to relist the words so as to form the correct input order.

*Results*. Two subjects were suspicious and discarded from the analysis, one in the fast clock and one in the slow clock condition. It should be noted that the usual reaction of subjects to the discovery that they had been deceived was one of surprise and enjoyment. In fact, when one subject was informed about the deception he revealed that he was a magician and proceeded to entertain the experimenter and his assistant with some card tricks of his own, one conjurer to another.

These data are presented in the figure below in the form of serial position curves. These curves plot the probability that the subject recalled the first word he was presented with, the probability that he recalled the second word he was presented with, and so on. As can be seen from the figure the same results hold for both the threatening and non-threatening lists. Subjects were less able to recall the beginning of each list if they thought they saw the two lists 3 hours ago compared with 45 minutes ago,[3] but because the serial position curves cross for the third and fourth words of each list, there is no overall difference in recall.

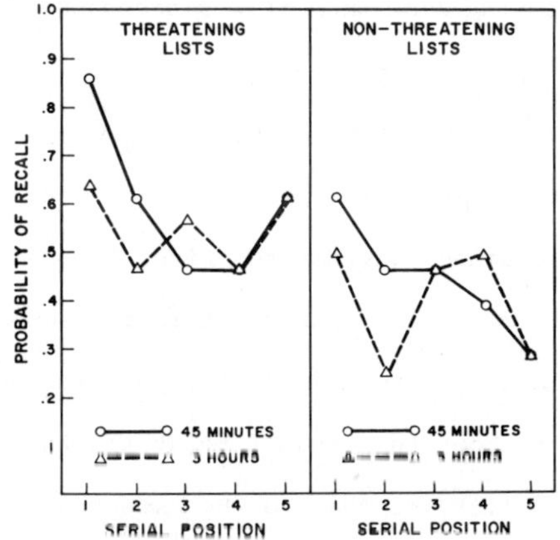


*Figure 1. Serial position curves for the threatening and non-threatening lists as a function of subjective time.*

Subjects were better able to recall the list of threatening words that the non-threatening words which was surprising. In a sense then the list of threatening words might have been inappropriate for our purposes since they were so well remembered. Half of the subjects were presented with a threatening list of words followed by an unthreatening list and half with the order reversed. Let us look at memory for the unthreatening words for those subjects who say the unthreatening list of words first, which is perhaps the simplest case. Did they remember fewer words if they thought it had been 3 hours rather than 45 minutes since they saw them. The appropriate serial position is given below. As can be seen from the figure the results are stronger in

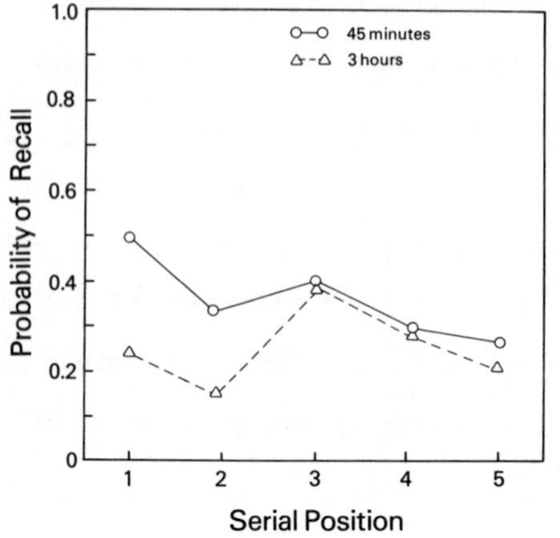


*Figure 2. Serial position curves for the non-threatening list when it was presented first.*

the sense that a difference is observed in the first two positions but the curves do not cross in the third, fourth and fifth positions as in the previous figure. The fact that the effect was obtained only for the first few serial position is somewhat puzzling. It is possible to marshall an argument in its support which in fact motivated our plotting the data in the form of serial position curves; namely, that to the extent subjects thought about the word lists at all they probably thought about the first few words of each list, so that to the extent differential rehearsal was the mediating process, it would affect the first few serial positions only. We don't know whether this hypothesis is true, but it is another reason to attempt to replicate the findings in another experiment.

To examine how well the subject remembered the order in which he saw the words, a correlation coefficient was computed between the actual and remembered order. The results indicate that subjects were less able to supply the correct input order of the five threatening words if they thought they saw these words 3 hours ago *vs*. 45 minutes ago. There was no effect of subjective time on the accuracy of recalling the order in which the non-threatening words were presented.

We sought to replicate these results with a different subject population, different experimenters, different interpolated tasks, a slightly different real time interval, and a different list of threatening and non-threatening words. We also included a control condition in which the speed of the clock was not changed. We would expect subjects in the unchanged clock condition to remember more than the subjects in the 3 hour condition but less than the subjects in the 45 minute condition.

*Experiment II.* This experiment lasted for 75 minutes which meant that subjects in the slow clock condition thought that 38 minutes had gone by at the time they were asked to recall the two lists of words, while subjects in the fast clock condition thought that 2½ hours had gone by. The results can be seen in the figure below.

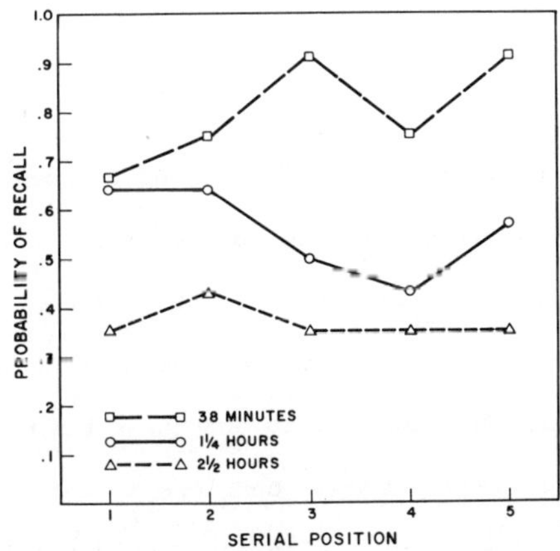


*Figure 3. Serial position curves for the combined threatening and non-threatening lists as a function of experimental treatment.*

The data show a statistically significant linear relationship between recall and subjective time. The greater the subjective age of a stimulus, the less the subject can recall it. We did not notice an especially large effect for the beginning of the lists, as we had previously, but rather a more general effect that held for all the words in the lists. Although the 38 minute and the 2½ hour groups are very different from each other, the 38 minute group is only marginally distinguishable from the 75 minute group and the 2½ hour group. This means that we need a difference in subjective time of at least 112 minutes (2½ hours minus 38 minutes) to yield a reliable difference in memory, at least given our present procedures. A difference of 75 minutes, which is the difference between the normal clock speed and either the fast or slow clock conditions, simply is not large enough to produce a reliable difference in recall.

Understanding the effect of subjective time on memory would be increased if the conditions which eliminate it could be determined as well. If we assume that increasing the subjective age of a stimulus decreases our memory for it because the passage of time acts as a cue that the stimulus is not likely to have current utility, then the effect of subjective time on memory should be eliminated by a procedure which sets the utility of an event or piece of information equal to a constant regardless of its actual historical location. The constant we selected was zero and the procedure which produces this result is as follows.

In two studies just reported, the subject was asked to recall the words he saw only once, at the end of the experiment. If the subject recalls the words twice, once immediately after he is presented with them and then again at the end of the experiment, the second recall should be totally unexpected. When the words are recalled at the beginning of the experiment right after they have been presented, the subject's perception of their future utility should be close to zero. Differential rehearsal of the words as a function of their subjective age should not take place.

*Experiments III and IV*. We have conducted two studies following this logic in which the subject recalls lists of words presented to him immediately after presentation and then again after what he perceives to be a subjective long or short interval. Both studies found no differences in recall as a function of the alteration of clock speed. We present the serial position curves for one of these studies, Experiment III, in the figure below. The fast clock (3 hour) and slow clock (45 min.) curves are

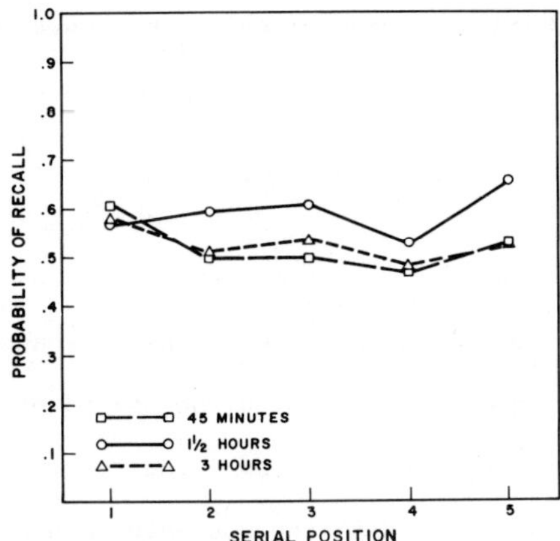


*Figure 4. Serial position curves for the combined threatening and non-threatening lists adjusted by covariance for differences in initial recall.*

virtually identical: statistically the 1½ hour condition (clock unchanged) is not different from either. This study used the same set of threatening and unthreatening words as Experiment I, so that a direct comparison would be possible.

In Experiment I, subjects were less able to recall the order in which the list of five threatening words were presented to them depending on whether they thought they saw the list 3 hours *vs*. 45 minutes ago. That result could have occurred by chance only five times in 1,000. In this study we find the same effect although somewhat diminished: It could have occurred by chance 9 times out of 100. Again the subject's ability to recall the order of the nonthreatening lists of words was unaffected.

## CONCLUSIONS

The results we have obtained should be interpreted with caution and treated as preliminary. The data have suggested, but have not conclusively established, that memory for a stimulus is determined by its subjective remoteness in an individual's past. The results need to be replicated several more times with other stimuli and other time periods.

We turn now to two other findings, for the passage of subjective time appears to influence not only memory but other psychological processes as well.

## II. TIME ESTIMATION

In one study subjects estimated the length of three time intervals: 30 seconds, 5 seconds, and 90 seconds presented in that order. The beginning and end of each interval was indicated by the ring of a bell. Using the method of verbal estimation (Underwood, 1969) the subject was asked to judge the length of each interval in minutes and/or seconds. During this task the subjects were blindfolded so as to prevent them from basing their estimates on the clock what was visible to them. This estimation procedure took place before the speed of the clock was changed, and then again after the subject had been temporally accelerated or decelerated. The results are presented in the table below.

TABLE 1. DIFFERENCES IN TIME ESTIMATION AS A FUNCTION OF EXPERIMENTAL CONDITION

| Subjective Time | Interval (in true sec.) | | |
|---|---|---|---|
| | 5 | 30 | 90 |
| 45 minutes (clockspeed reduced) | -.94 | -5.89 | .45 |
| 1½ hours (clockspeed unaltered) | .02 | -4.32 | 3.64 |
| 3 hours (clockspeed increased) | 1.28 | 1.88 | 18.37 |

Note: *Numbers in the table are mean difference scores based on the subjects estimate of the interval at the end of the experiment minus his estimate the the beginning before time was altered. Thus, subjects in the 3 hour condition increased their estimate of the length of the 90 second interval an average of 18 seconds as a result of being placed in a temporal world in which clocks move faster.*

A minus sign in the table indicates that the interval was judged to be shorter at the end of the experiment than at the beginning. This is the expected result in the 45 minute condition since the reduction in clock speed which produced that condition meant that the same interval would appear shorter; the clock would indicate that only 15 seconds had passed, but in reality 30 seconds had gone by.

In the 45 minute condition subjects estimated that the same 30 second interval contained an average of only 24.11 seconds (30.00 - 5.89) at the end of the experiment. Subjects in the 3 hour condition for whom the speed of the clock was increased judged the same interval as longer. What is particularly interesting is that while the manipulation of subjective duration was accomplished by having subjects believe that 1½ hours was really 45 minutes or 3 hours, the manipulation apparently also affected the subject's estimates of intervals more than 90 times smaller.

The differences between the 45 minute and 3 hour condition was statistically significant. The 1½ hour group fell in between the two other conditions, but the 3 hour group was sufficiently close to the 1½ hour group to be virtually indistinguishable from it. While the pattern of results for the 5 second interval was similar to those of the 30 and 90 second intervals, statistical tests do not allow us to eliminate the possibility that this was due to change. Thus, estimation of the 5 second interval was not reliably affected by the experimental conditions. However, it is likely that subjects did not estimate the length of the 5 second interval so much as directly identify it as the one originally presented, both because the 5 second interval was distinctively shorter than the other two intervals, and because the order of presentation of the three intervals was the same at the beginning and the end of the experiment. Whether the manipulation of subjective time affects the estimation of short intervals is still an open question.

## III. IMPRESSION FORMATION

We have now presented evidence that our experimental procedures influence both memory and the estimation of temporal duration. In this section we describe how the subjective passage of time alters a previously formed impression of another person.

The basic procedure was to present subjects with a paragraph description of a hypothetical person at the beginning of the experiment and ask him to provide his impression of that person at the end of the experiment. In the first study we presented a positive description of an individual at the beginning of the experiment followed by negative information about the same person at the end of the experiment. For half the subjects this order was reversed. We reasoned that the initial piece of information should lose its impact the more it was displaced into the subjective past. Negative information that was subjectively 3 hours old should carry less weight than negative information that was seen as 45 minutes old, resulting in a more favorable overall impression. Similarly, positive information that is perceived as subjectively remote, should have less impact in overcoming more recent negative information. The paragraph descriptions were as follows.

*Positive Description*

He is a pleasant individual well liked by all who know him. He will be successful in his career. In general, one would think of him as warm, outgoing and intelligent.

*Negative Description*

Although cheerful in manner, he is not very sincere, he is a hypocrite and not very well liked. He is unlikely to rise to high executive position. One thinks of him as cold, introverted and not very intelligent.

Subjects used a set of six scales (warm-cold, not well liked-well liked, etc.) to give their remembered impression of this hypothetical individual at the end of the experiment. Negative information that was subjectively 3 hours old *vs.* 45 minutes old did indeed seem to result in an overall more positive impression. Surprisingly, however, positive information that was subjectively 3 hours old seemed to make the overall impression even more positive than positive information that was subjectively more recent. One hypothesis that embraces both results is that information is viewed more positively as it becomes subjectively older. A negative stimulus is seen as less negative, a positive stimulus even more positive. To check this hypothesis we conducted a second experiment in which subjects were presented with either a positive or negative description of a person at the beginning of the experiment but asked to give their impressions of this person only at the end of the experiment.

The results indicated that a description rated after a subjective interval of three hours was seen as more positive than the same description rated after a subjective interval of only 45 minutes. With one exception, the impressions formed by a control group of subjects in which the speed of the clock was not altered fell in between the two experimental groups, as expected.

In the next section we present a conceptual model for understanding the reinterpretation of stimulus events with the passage of time. We are less concerned to advance specific explanations of the results that have been presented than to develop a model that will allow us to think about the reinterpretation of the affective quality of past events in a very general way.

*A Stimulus Incompleteness Model*

The basic premise of the model is that the occurrence of almost any stimulus has future as well as present implications. We call the perceived future implications of a stimulus, its forecast. A forecast need not be complex or well articulated but few stimuli that can be described in social or symbolic rather than purely physical terms do not contain at least some implications that extend beyond the exact moment of their occurrence. Our hypothesis is that when we evaluate or rate a stimulus we take its forecast, or in rare cases the lack of one, into account. To the extent that a person believes a stimulus has future implications, but is uncertain as to their nature, he will feel that the full meaning of the stimulus is incompletely defined, described or understood.

The interval within which a stimulus forecast may be realized we label its opportunity interval, and any prior interval in which the forecast is not expected to occur, its incubation period. The size of both intervals may vary independently.

A long or short incubation period may be conjoined with a long or short opportunity interval. Furthermore, the boundaries of each may be sharply defined in a single point, or only vaguely defined as some interval of time. By definition each forecast will have an opportunity interval, however brief or imprecisely located, but it need not have an incubation period.

We can relate these concepts to changes in the evaluation of a stimulus as a function of the passage of time if we make the following assumption: the longer a potential forecast has not been realized a) the more we will conclude that it was not present in the first place, and/or b) that its opportunity interval has passed, because the more time that goes by the less likely the appropriate opportunity interval for the forecast has not been reached.

Underlying this reasoning is an almost metaphysical assumption that the implications of an event will be immediately apparent unless specifically postponed, delayed, or inhibited. Part of the evidence that people hold this view is that cause and effect are expected to be temporally contiguous. The longer the interval between an event (a stimulus) and its reputed effects (a realized forecast), the less likely the two will be perceived as causally related.

While complex, this analysis can be illustrated quite simply. Consider an individual who fears he may have eaten some food that was spoiled. After what he takes to be a suitable incubation period, the more time that expires with no ill effects, the more the individual will conclude that food was probably not spoiled. He reasons that if it had been, he would be sick by now. The opportunity interval for becoming sick has passed. Our argument is that the same reasoning applies to complex social and symbolic stimuli as well.

Consider a negative stimulus. In contrast to a more positive or neutral one, the occurrence of a negative stimulus almost always gives rise to the fear that it may also contain a negative forecast. The individual to whom such a stimulus occurs typically asks such questions as: Is it over? Will it reoccur? What does it mean for the future? - all of which deal with the nature and probability of a stimulus forecast. If, however, a negative forecast does not materialize within the projected opportunity interval, the individual then has a rational warrant for revising his estimate of the stimulus in a positive direction.

Consider a positive stimulus. It is possible to envision a situation in which a stimulus is so uniformly and intensely positive that the person cannot quite believe that he has seen all of it. He may fear some counter-balancing negative experience in the future. His motivation for this belief need not concern us; it may be guilt, or it may simply be his estimate of the distribution of positive and negative events in the world. In any case a disconfirmed negative forecast can cause him to reevaluate an event that was already quite positive.

In general we hypothesize that the more intense the stimulus, the more the individual will monitor its future to determine whether a forecast was implied, unless of course a forecast was explicit. Thus, the full evaluation of intense stimulus will always be *partially* postponed pending an examination of their future.

The model of stimulus incompleteness is of interest because it challenges the dominant explanation of why the past is reevaluated; namely, the psychoanalytic view. According to this view the past is increasingly seen in a more positive light with the passage of time because of largely defensive if not irrational processes. Negative features of the past are repressed, denied and selectively forgotten; positive features are retained and perhaps amplified. The model of stimulus incompleteness takes a different position. It is not the same stimulus that is being reevaluated with the passage of time, but an incomplete stimulus that is becoming completely defined in virtue of additional information about whatever forecasts may have been implied by its occurrence. Thus, reevaluation is rational, not irrational.

According to the psychoanalytic model we base our view of the past on less and less information, negative information being forgotten. According to the stimulus incompleteness model we change our view of the past because we are in possession of more information. The past is preferred not for its simplicity, but because its full complexity is known. Thus, the past is reevaluated not necessarily because of any deficiency in the mechanisms of storage and retrieval, not necessarily because we are motivated to distort it, for whatever reason, but because the future implications of a past event could not be completely specified at the time that event occurred. This view is congruent with the notion often expressed by historians that the passage of time allows a better view of an event because the shape of its future is more clearly articulated.

The general logic of the stimulus incompleteness model can also conceptualize the effects of the passage of time on memory. The line of reasoning is as follows. If a stimulus contains a forecast of future utility, rehearsal, and hence memory for the stimulus will decline once the appropriate opportunity interval has been exceeded and, the greater the passage of time, the more likely that interval has been exceeded. In the procedures of Experiment I and II, a list of words was presented to subjects with the instructions that the task was a study of memory. However, no immediate recall test was given. With the passage of time, subjects may have thought it less likely that they would be asked to recall the words. In contrast in the procedures of Experiments III and IV, subjects recalled the words immediately after they were represented. Since there was no expectation on the part of the subjects that they would see the words again, there was no forecast of future utility, no opportunity interval to be differentially exceeded according to the passage of time, and hence no differential effect of the modification of clock speed on memory.

*Implications Of This Analysis*

The model of stimulus incompleteness schematizes a general class of informal temporal logics that people use to evaluate and remember past stimulus events. The value of such a schematization is that it allows more precise questions to be asked. Consider the following diagram of the model.

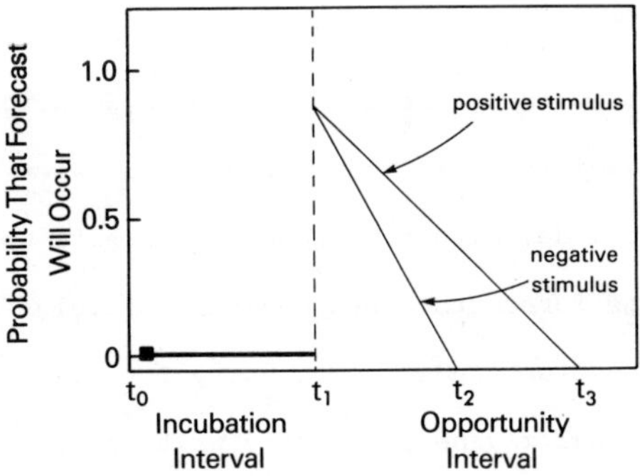


*Figure 5: The stimulus incompleteness model*

A positive or negative stimulus event occurs at time $t_0$ the consequences of which will not be evident except during the opportunity interval $t_1$-$t_2$, or $t_1$-$t_3$. We hypothesize that, in general, the opportunity interval for negative stimuli will be shorter than that for positive stimuli, since an individual should be motivated to extend the time during which a positive forecast may be realized, and to foreshorten the interval during which a negative forecast may be realized. Some of the specific questions that are stimulated by this model are: 1) How does an individual decide that a stimulus has a forecast? 2) How is the length, location, and clarity of the incubation and opportunity intervals determined? 3) At what point, and to what degree, does a reevaluation of a past stimulus take place? These questions will be answered differently depending on a host of factors, and the advantage of the model is that it provides an organizational frame for discovering the different ways in which the past is viewed according to the way these questions are answered. For example, consider the size of a typical opportunity interval as a function of age. The common observation that individuals view the past more positively as they grow older is understood in terms of the model as the result of an increasing probability that either the opportunity interval for previous negative forecasts has been exceeded, and/or this interval is rapidly being reduced in size.

Answers to the questions posed by the model may be a function of individual temperament. For example, one individual may never revise his view of the past. This can happen, according to the mode, either because he correctly predicted and hence took into account all the forecasts contained in a stimulus event, and/or because he characteristically chose unbounded opportunity intervals for his forecasts. By contrast, another individual may be constantly writing a revisionist history of the past. In terms of the model this can occur either because this person tends to see most stimuli as containing forecasts, and/or, he tends to select short and clearly bounded opportunity intervals which make the occurrence or non-occurrence of a forecast readily apparent.

One of the interesting features of the model of stimulus incompleteness is that it directs us to consider as theoretically important certain experiences and phenomenal states that have not received scientific scrutiny; for example, a sense of foreboding, the experience of having a premonition, a belief that something is a good or bad omen. In all of these situations, the individual perceives the stimulus to be incomplete and contain a forecast. What is needed is an account of these situations to know why the individual believes there is a forecast present. To understand how a forecast about the future originates, is, in terms of the model, to begin to understand the basis on which the past may be re-evaluated with the passage of time.

NOTES

1. The fact that apparent duration can provide individuals with important information has also been pointed out by Michon who stated that "Time is most certainly not a neutral variable. It claims on the contrary, equal rights as a genuine source of information; equal to other stimulus dimensions such as brightness, loudness and pitch." ("Time Experience and Memory Processes" *The Study of Time II*, J. T. Fraser and N. Lawrence eds. New York, Heidelberg, Berlin: Springer-Verlag, 1975).

2. The control groups for Experiments II and IV were drawn from the same pool of subjects, and were run after these experiments were completed. Due to evidence that the control groups are not strictly comparable to the experimental conditions they are not reported.

3. While we will not explicitly mention the work of Zeigarnik, this model might be considered an elaboration and extension of the basic insight that whether a simulus event is considered complete or not has implications for the way individuals remember and behave towards it.

REFERENCES

Aaronson, B. S. "Hypnotic alterations of space and time." *International Journal of Parapsychology*, 1968a, *10*, 5-36.

Aaronson, B. S. "Hypnosis, time rate perception, and personality." *Journal of Schizophrenia*, 1968b, *2*, 11-41.

Bergquist, W. H., Lewinsohn, P. M., Sue, D. W., and Flippo, J. R. "Short and long term memory for various types of stimuli as a function of represeion-sensitization." *Journal of Experimental Research in Personality*, 1968, *3*, 28-38.

Broadbent, D. E. *Perception and Communication*. New York: Pergamon Press, 1958.

Broadbent, D. E. "Flow of information within the organism." *Journal of Verbal Learning and Verbal Behavior*, 1963, *2*, 34-39.

Brown, J. A. "Some tests of the decay theory of immediate memory." *Quarterly Journal of Experimental Psychology*, 1958, *10*, 12-21.

Bull, John A. "The influence of appetite Pavlovian CSs on the performance of a discriminated instrumental avoidance response." *Dissertation Abstracts International*, 1970, *30*, 4806.

Craik, K. H. and Sarbin, T. R. "Effect of covert alterations of clock rate upon time estimations and personal tempo." *Journal of Perception and Motor Skills*, 1963, *16*, 597-610.

Ebbinghaus, H. *Über das gedächtnis*, Leipzig: Duneker, 1885. Translation by H. Ruyer and Bussenius, C. E., *Memory*, New York: Teachers College, Columbia University, 1913.

Frankenhauser, M. *Estimation of Time*. Stockholm: Almquist & Uksell, 1959.

Goldstone, S., Boardman, W. K., Lhamon, W. T. "Effect of quinal barbitone, dextro-amphetamine, and placebo on apparent duration." *British Journal of Psychology*, 1958, *49*, 324-328.

London, Harvey and Monello, Lenore. "Cognitive manipulation of boredom." In *Thought and Feeling*, Harvey London and Richard E. Nisbett (Eds.), Chicago: Aldine Publishers, 1974, 74-82.

McGeogh, J. A. "Forgetting and the law of disuse.""*Psychological Review*, 1932, *39*, 352-370.

McGrath, J. J. and O'Hanlon, J. F., Jr. "Temporal orientation and task performance." *Human Factors Research Technical Report*, California, 1968.

Postman, L. "The present status of interference theory." In C. N. Coffer (Ed.), *Verbal Learning and Verbal Behavior*, New York: McGraw Hill, 1961, 81-91.

Rotter, G. S. "Time rate as an independent variable in research." A paper delivered at the American Psychological Convention, Chicago, 1965.

Rotter, G. S. "Clock speed as an independent variable in psychological research." *Journal of General Psychology*, 1969, *81*, 45-52.

Snyder, Melvin, Schulz, Richard and Jones, Edward E. "Expectancy and apparent duration as determinants of fatigue." *Journal of Personality and Social Psychology*, 1974, *29*, 426-434.

Underwood, B. J. "Attributes of memory." *Psychological Review*, 1969, *76*, 559-574.

Zeigarnik, B. "Ueber das Behalten von erledigten und unerledigten Handlugen," *Psychol. Forsch*. 9 (1927), 1-85. The complete translation - "The Retention of Completed and Uncompleted Activities" - is available only from University Microfilms. A fourteen-page abstract may be found in Willis E. Ellis (Ed.), *A Source Book of Gestalt Psychology* (London: Routledge and Kegal Paul, Ltd.). This summary is also a Bobbs-Merrill reprint P-375.

Zimbardo, P. G., Marshall, G., and Maslach, C. "Liberating behavior from time-bound control: Expanding the present through hypnosis." *Journal of Applied Social Psychology*, 1971, *1*, 305-323.

Zimbardo, P. G., Marshall, G., and White, G. "Objective assessment of hypnotically induced time distortion." *Science*, 1973, *181*, 282-284.

## DISCUSSION AND COMMENTS
*by Manfred E. A. Schmutzer*

My comments on Albert's paper begin where his paper finishes: at his discussion of endings. Albert leads our attention to the fact that our lives are structured by distinguishing between certain chunks of time, periods during which distinct modes of behavior are appropriate, whereas others are not. These chunks of time can be called *social times*. They may last for hours, days or for lifetimes.

But the flux of phenomena is usually continuous. Thus, in order to establish the needed correspondence between real time and social time, society is in need of methods for disjoining appearances, as R. S. Brumbaugh said at this meeting. Frederick Turner referred to a similar act in his paper and called it "cutting a blaze." Anthropologists and social scientists talk in this context of rites of passage, linked up a long time ago to Eliade's notion of sacred times and of *illud tempus*[1] , and more recently refined by E. R. Leach's concept of *holy times*[2] . These holy times are chunks of social time segregated by inserting intervals. Holy times are not manufactured according to usually distinctive pattern. They must not only be *made* different to be distinguishable from ordinary time; they *are* different since they are the intervals wherein one ceases to be the one, without being the other yet. This holds for persons as well as for things.

Holy time is the time wherein a thing's property of being mine ceases without having become yours. During holy times one is "either-or" or alternatively "neither-nor". Holy times require, therefore, a different mode of thinking, called *mythological* by Leach. Mythological thinking prevails when separated categories are fused and established distinctions are made obsolete. Seen from the point of view of ordinary time and life, holy times appear dangerous and/or "illegitimate." They are therefore marked as such through rituals at the beginning and end of these exceptional periods. It is, therefore, not surprising that endings, such as Albert analysed, exhibit distinct structures: they serve the function of conveying information about the end and the beginning of social times.

But what corresponds in adult life to Albert's bedtime stories for children? The holy times are clearly times of leisure, holidays, as M. Eliade and others have observed. During holy times a different kind of logic holds, where what is distinct during normal times ceases to be so. Under normal times and conditions most people have a good sense for the length of a period experienced and those who do not, are supported by public devices, clocks and watches. Thus, holy times should be times when distinctions made normally, e.g. between 3 hours and 1.5 hours or between 45 minutes and 90 minutes, should vanish. Everybody who has experienced holidays will willingly testify that this is what happens. During holidays our sense of time seems to observe the rules of the mythologic. In addition, we command certain devices which help to make time fuse, just as we have others for normal times, helping to keep events apart. Amateur photography, for instance, used almost exclusively during the holy times of holidays, makes time stand still and/or reversible. There are also other means to manipulate time during such periods, like alcohol and music.

Albert, in his fascinating experiments, manipulated certain disjoining devices, when he equated 1.5 with 3 hours and 45 with 90 minutes, thereby creating artificially holy times. The rituals - beginnings and endings - which surround any psychological experiment, can therefore be regarded as the necessary social devices which ensure that experiments are what I see them to be: representatives of, and for, holy times.

The conclusion to be drawn from this is that psychological experiments and their findings are lifted outside normal times and hence have little in common with ordinary life in normal times. A further heretical conclusion would be that scientific experiments in general should be regarded in themselves as social settings which have been placed into an interval of holy time during which scientific mythology prevails.

## REFERENCES

1. M. Eliade (1957), *Myths, Dreams and Mysteries*. London-Glasgow Collins, The Fontana Library.

2. E. R. Leach (1976), *Culture and Communication*. Cambridge University Press, U. K.

# Future Time Perspective and Ego Strength

A.I. Rabin

*ABSTRACT*

*Following a brief historical introduction regarding the concepts of time perspective and time orientation, their theoretical relationships to ego functions and ego strength was discussed. It was predicted that there will be a positive relationship between indices of future time perspective and future orientation, and measures of ego strength, internal control and a tendency to delay gratification. A negative relationship to impulsivity was also predicted. The empirical test of these propositions based on the administration of several techniques to 55 subjects, has generally given support to the predictions at a respectable level of confidence. It was concluded that temporality should be an integral part of the definition of the concept of ego.*

## 1. PRELIMINARIES

Temporality and temporal experience have been of interest to psychologists since the inception of their discipline. "Protensity" was considered as one of the fundamental characteristics of sensation in the early development of psychophysics (Boring, 1933). Interest in time per se, especially in the estimation of duration and "time perception", is traceable to the very beginnings of experimental psychology (Fraisse, 1963). In more recent decades, with the development of personality theory and research, the relationship of the experience of time to personality variables has received considerable attention from a large group of investigators (Doob, 1971; Fraisse, 1963; Wallace & Rabin, 1960).

Two major concepts, or variables, of temporal experience have evolved and have become dominant in the empirical research that concerns itself with personality-temporality relationships. These concepts are: Time orientation and time perspective.

## 2. TEMPORAL ORIENTATION

There are several different ways in which the term "time orientation" is used in the literature. Most common is the reference to the person's awareness of the current location in time. It is a demonstration of the functioning of the "time sense", regardless of what its origin may be construed to be. The orientation may refer to conventional units of time such as the day of the week, month, and year. It also refers to the time of the day, awareness of it, without necessarily naming it. "Orientation for time" has been one of the traditional tests used by psychiatrists to diagnose psychopathology. The confusion in many phychotic states as well as in brain injury is marked by such "*dis*orientation".

A less frequent, but nevertheless another use of the term time orientation refers to the preferential tendency discovered in individuals with respect to the past, present or future. In this, more global, sort of orientation persons are viewed as predominantly past-oriented, present-oriented, or future-oriented. Such judgements are arrived at from an analysis of the mental content - fantasy production, verbalization in interviews, or in other specific testing situations. In one study, for example, it was found that persons in psychotherapy tend to alter their primary past orientation to a future orientation as the treatment progresses successfully (Smeltzer, 1969). An analysis of the contents of the interviews indicated numerous references to the past, as compared to present and future, during the earlier sessions. Planning and future orientation becomes more evident when the issues of the past become less salient and the future direction is of utmost concern.

Again, not only do changes occur with respect to temporal orientation as a result of intervention, but also as a function of development and growth. The "temporal horizons" (Fraisse, 1963) expand as the individual gets older and is capable of memory and imaginal activity. It would appear that the temporal orientation of a person may be closely related to his developmental ability or capacity, or willingness to postpone gratification. The impulsive, the "here and now" individual is present-oriented. The planner is future-oriented and the depressed, guilt-ridden is past-oriented (Dilling & Rabin, 1967). Temporal orientation thus evolves as a characterological, though not unmodifiable, trait for there is considerable consistency and stability in observation and experimentation with this aspect of human behavior and experience.

## 3. TIME PERSPECTIVE

A closely related concept of temporal experience, and of the temporal taxonomy, is that of *time perspective*. The discussion of this concept, and, subsequently, its employment as an experimental variable along with time orientation in an actual research project occupy the rest of this presentation.

The term time perspective(s) is traceable to the works of Lawrence Frank and Kurt Lewin, some 40 years ago. Essentially the reference is to "the timing and ordering of personalized events" (Wallace, 1956; Kastenbaum, 1961). The ordering of these events may be from the farthest past to the remotest future. Although time perspective as a concept encompasses the same range as time orientation: past, present and future, the bulk of the research reported and the major concern for personality research has been "future time perspective" (the timing and ordering of future personalized events), (Doob, 1971).

Several related concepts should be briefly considered in this context. By far the most popular and quantifiable characteristic of future time perspective (FTP) is that of *extension* (or "protension"). The reference here is to the time intervening between the present and the most distant "future personalized event". Another term is that of *density*. This is, strictly speaking, not a temporal term; it refers to the number of future events listed, in free response situation, within the given temporal extension.

Still another concept is that of *coherence* which deals with the consistency of the ordering of personalized events, over time, within the future extension period.

Most workers in the field, however, have primarily concentrated on the study of extension of FTP. It readily seems to relate to the degree of planning for the future, to imagery about the future, and to the extent one is able to project oneself in anticipation of future events.

## 4. ON PERSONALITY - THE EGO

Now that we have briefly surveyed some of the issues and concepts in the field of temporal experience, we may consider some aspects of personality. Following a review of the recent history of the concept of personality and definitions of the term, Sanford (1970) writes in his *Issues in Personality Theory* that "the trend of the discipline, as of the city, is toward disconcerting sprawl. The field of personality has expanded in all directions, and of the many different voices heard, none can be called dominant", (p. 131). The same author also discusses the multitude of processes and elements whose patterned organization constitutes what we call personality. The "elements" and "processes" of personality selected to relate to our indices of temporal experience are the ones which stem from theory and from previous work in which we found some leads that justified the expected relationship.

First, we shall consider the rather global term "ego", especially as its meaning has developed within the theoretical framework of the so-called "ego psychology", (Hartmann, 1958; Blanck, 1974). In orthodox Freudian theory it was described as the mediator between the three "harsh masters", the id, superego, and the environment. It was viewed as a derivative of the instincts and born of conflict with them. The functions assigned to the ego involved defenses, perception, memory, attention, judgement, and reality testing. Later with the development of ego psychology, the major functions that have been stressed were those of "perception, motility, anticipation and delay" (Blanck, 1974).

Two of the ego functions just mentioned, are closely related and intertwined with temporal experience. The reference, of course, is to the function of anticipation which points to the future, and to delay (of gratification) which lies at the very root of the development of time awareness.

Cottle and Klineberg (1974) have presented an especially detailed analysis of the "...person's ability to act in the present in the light of his anticipation of relatively distant future events". According to them, there are "entailed three central processes that are uniquely developed in human beings:

(1) the prodigious capacity to manipulate symbolic representations of reality and thereby create images of absent events and believe in their validity;

(2) the ability to integrate these symbolic representations into ongoing problems of action and meaning, being images of the future into an implied continuum with conceptions of past and present experience; and

(3) the present experiencing of pleasure or discomfort generated solely by these representations..." (p. 16).

Thus, part of the ego, might be viewed as closely related to future time perspective, expecially via its anticipatory function: "create images of absent events."

The concept of delay of gratification is, of course, intimately related to the notion or characteristic of impulsivity. Impulsivity, the tendency to express drive immediately upon arousal is the obverse of delay. Delay involved the capacity for self-control, postponement of need gratification, and of drive expression. It is the interposition of a time interval between felt need and its fulfillment. Whereas delay is considered an ego function, impulsivity may be considered an ego malfunctioning; an inadequacy in the adherence to the "reality principle" which is at the basis of ego and its development.

Another "element" or major personality variable which has gained considerable popularity during the past decade or so, stems from an intirely different theoretical orientation. The "internal versus external control" dimension has its origins in socal learning theory. The originator of this dichotomous characterization (Rotter, 1966) explains it as follows: "When a reinforcement is perceived by the subject as following some action of his own, but not being entirely contingent upon his action, then, in our culture, it is typically perceived as the result of luck, chance, fate, as under control of powerful others, or as unpredictable because of the great complexity of forces surrounding him. When the event is interpreted in this way by an individual we have labeled this a belief in *external control*. If the person perceived that the event is contingent upon his own behavior or his own relatively permanent characteristics, we have termed this a belief in *internal control*" (p. 1).

In examining the ingredients of the description of external-internal control, we can readily note the possible relationship of this concept to ego and temporal experience. An important aspect of the differences between external and internal control is the element of predictability. In the former instance, events are essentially unpredictable because they depend on external forces, whereas in the case of internal control, they are predictable for they depend on what the person believes in his own initiative. This involves a certain confidence in planning and visualizing the future; i.e., "timing and ordering personalized events" - future time perspective.

According to Fenichel (1945), "In the early states the weak ego has not yet learned to postpone anything" (p. 39). Impulsivity and lack of ability to delay gratification are earmarks of ego weakness. Conversely, capacity for delay, low impulsivity, ability to anticipate and plan are characteristic of ego strength, of the well-developed ego. Since temporality is involved in the ego functions listed above, albeit indirectly, we shall explore their relationship to direct and explicit temporal dimensions. Furthermore, these component functions and time orientation and time perspective will be related to a global index of "ego strength". By exploring these relationships we may contribute to the construct validity of our measures as well.

## 5. SOME PREDICTIONS

From the foregoing discussion several predictive propositions regarding the relationship of temporal phenomena to personality parameters appear to be justified. We have subjected these predictions to empirical test using some of the most suitable methods of assessment in the field of personality-psychometric, as well as experimental. Some of the predictions formulated are as follows:

(1) There is a positive relationship between indices of FTP and future temporal orientation on the one hand, and the tendency to delay gratification on the other.

(2) Conversely, there is a negative relationship between the temporal indices and impulsivity.

(3) A positive relationship between future orientation and extension of FTP, and an index of ego strength is expected.

(4) Finally, measures of temporal orientation and perspective correlate positively with the tendency toward "internal control".

## 6. THE EMPIRICAL STUDY

A group of 55 university students volunteered for the experiment and were examined individually with the following methods designed to assess temporal experience as well as personality dimensions.

There were three measures of temporal experience:

(1) One method of assessing the extension of FTP consisted of giving the person the following instructions:

"I want you to look ahead and tell me ten things that you'll do or think will happen to you. These don't have to be important things; just anything that comes to your mind."

Consonant with the original procedure (Wallace, 1956), following the enumeration of the ten events, the subject is asked to specify how far into the future he envisions each event. The score for this test is the median time for all events.

(2) The second method for assessing FTP used some of Wallace's (1956) incomplete stories, supplemented by additional ones. It is a less direct measure of FTP. The following is a sample story:

"About three o'clock one bright sunny afternoon in May, two men were walking along a street near the edge of town..."

Following the stories and their completions, an inquiry determines how much time has passed in each story. The score of the FTP extension is the median time transpired in the completed stories.

(3) The third temporal measure is one of orientation (TO). Embedded in a lengthy questionnaire (internal-external control) were five items that involve the determination of a preference for the future (Shybut, 1968). Here is an example:

a. I rarely think of what I will be doing ten years from now.

b. I quite frequently think of what it will be like ten years from now.

The score, in this instance, is the number of sentences in which the future direction is the preferred one.

Two brief methods for assessing impulsivity were employed:

(1) The first approach consisted of five pairs of self-report sentences in which the respondent had to select the one which is most descriptive of him.

a. I sometimes tend to act without thinking out the consequences.

b. I am hardly ever impulsive in my actions.

(2) The second is a performance task used in earlier assessments of "will-temperment". The subject is asked to copy "as slowly" as he can, without lifting the pencil from the paper, the phrase "The United States of America". The time necessary to finish the task is the reciprocal of impulsivity.

Delay of gratification was measured by the subject's willingness to delay receiving credit for participation in the experiment. The length of time he was willing to wait to receive two (instead of one credit) credits for his participation was a measure of delay capacity.

*The ego scale* (Barron, 1953) is made up of MMPI items that assess adaptation and nonpathological behavior and feeling states. It is essentially a measure of normality and adjustment, broadly defined.

Finally, the I-E (Internal-External control) scale (Rotter, 1960) consists of 23 forced choice items in combination with an additional six "filler items" concerned with the dichotomy. Here is a sample item of the scale:

"a. Many of the unhappy things in people's lives are partly due to bad luck.
b. People's misfortunes result from the mistakes they make."

It may readily be noted that the first sentence corresponds to external control, while selection of the second one would bolster the score of internal control. The total score depends on the number of sentences answered in the external direction. Thus, when correlating with ego-strength or temporal experience, a negative correlation coefficient may be expected if the results come out according to prediction.

After all of these methods, described above, have been employed in testing our sample, an intercorrelation matrix, relating each test with all the others, was constructed. In the next sections the result will be very briefly summarized and discussed. Further speculation concerning the developmental and dynamic personality relationship to temporal experience will be offered.

## 7. RESULTS AND SPECULATIONS

With one notable exception all of the measures showed statistically significant correlations, according to prediction. This statement reflects the correlation matrix obtained. Generally, it may be stated that all of the predictions were confirmed by all but one of the instruments employed (see Table 1).

The exception among the methods used is the one that involves the indirect measure of FTP extension - the incomplete stories. This measure does not correlate very positively with the other temporal tests, nor with most of the personality variables included in the study. The other two temporal measures correlate quite highly with each other (r equals .67) and apparently measure the same thing; there seems to be a good deal of commonality in the extension measure of FTP and futurity in orientation.

As predicted, these temporal experience variables correlate positively with ego strength (.79 and .61), with internal control (.66 and .46), and with delay of gratification (.71 and .77). Moreover, the correlations with the two measures of impulsivity are consistently negative; all being significant at better than the .01 level of confidence.

The intercorrelations of the personality variables are also interesting. Ego strength, internal control and delay, form a cluster where the correlations with each member, ranges from .66 to .57. On the other hand, impulsivity correlated negatively with all of these ego-strength-related variables. The coefficients of correlation of both impulsivity measures with the other personality variables range from a negative .29 to a negative .53. All of these coefficients are significant at the .05 level of confidence or better.

The experimental sample employed in this study was about evenly divided between the sexes. It is interesting to note that a separate analysis of the data for each sex yielded no significantly different coefficients of correlation from those obtained with the entire sample. Consonant with the findings reported in the literature, there are no marked sex differences in the assessment of FTP and the relationships to other personality variables.

To be sure, one of the temporal measures did not yield the same level of relationship to the personality variables than did the others. However, the indirect nature of the incomplete stories makes it a different task than the consciously cognitive demands made by the others. Overall, there is consistency in confirming the hypothesized relations and thus, construct validation in relation to the measures that

Table 1 -- Coefficients of Correlation between FTP Measures and Personality Variables

| Time Measure | Impuls.-1 | Impuls.-2 | Delay | Ego Strength | Internal Control |
|---|---|---|---|---|---|
| 1. FTP-1 | -.45 | -.37 | .71 | .79 | .66 |
| 2. FTP-2 | -.20 | .04 | .04 | .08 | .15 |
| 3 TO | -.38 | -.46 | .77 | .61 | .46 |

r = .27 (p = .05); r = .35 (p = .01)

were employed and were consistent with the entire nomological network.

Considering the results, briefly detailed above, there is a very close relationship between temporal experiences and several aspects of the ego. We might almost regard temporal perspective itself as a personality variable, as one of the ego's constituents, rather than anything extrinsic to which variables of personality might be related.

ACKNOWLEDGEMENT

The author is grateful to Alan Maisel for his aid in obtaining the data on which the study is based, and to Dr. Ruben Gur for his assistance with the computer program.

REFERENCES

Barron, F. An ego-strength scale which predicts response to psychotherapy. *Journal of Consulting Psychology*, 1953, 17, 327-333.

Blanck, Gertrude and Rubin. *Ego Psychology: Theory and Practice*. New York: Columbia University Press, 1974.

Boring, E. G. *The Physical Dimensions of Consciousness*. New York: Appleton-Century-Crofts, 1933.

Cottle, T. J. & Klineberg, S. L. *The Present of Things Future*. New York: The Free Press, 1974.

Dilling, C. A. & Rabin, A. I. Temporal experience in depressive states and schizophrenia. *Journal of Consulting Psychology*, 1967, 31, 604-608.

Doob, L. W. *Patterning of Time*. New Haven: Yale University Press, 1971.

Fenichel, O. *The Psychoanalytic Theory of Neurosis*. New York: W. W. Norton & Company, 1945.

Fraisse, P. *The Psychology of Time*. New York: Harper & Row, 1963.

Kastenbaum, R. The dimensions of future time perspective, an experimental analysis. *The Journal of General Psychology*, 1961, 65, 203-218.

Rotter, J. B. Generalized expectancies for internal versus external control of reinforcement. *Psychological Monographs*, 1966, 80 (1, Whole No. 609).

Sanford, N. *Issues in Personality Theory*. San Francisco: Jossey-Bass, Inc., 1970.

Smeltzer, W. E. Time orientation and time perspective in psychotherapy. *Dissertation Abstracts*, 29, 1969, 3922-B.

Wallace, M. Future time perspective in schizophrenia. *Journal of Abnormal and Social Psychology*, 1965, 52, 240-245.

Wallace, M. & Rabin, A. I. Temporal experience. *Psychological Bulletin*, 1960, 57, 213-236.

DISCUSSION AND COMMENT
*by Shiro Imai*

Professor Rabin's study is interesting and attractive to me, since he has taken two of the most fundamental concepts, ego and future time perspective, and found empirically a close relationship between them. Using legitimate reasoning, he has measured quantitatively these important fundamental variables and demonstrated successfully that the ego is closely related to the FTP. This is no doubt a great contribution.

However, there is an ambiguity in his paper. He obtained three different measures of FTP and showed that two of them are highly correlated with the ego measures but the third indirect measure is not. One may wonder whether the relationship between FTP and aspects of the ego are indeed as strong as he infers them to be.

He states further that "We might regard temporal perspective as a personality variable, as one of the ego's constituents..." I disagree with this statement. The reason is the following: What he empirically obtained are high correlations between ego measures and direct measures of FTP, a symmetric relationship, so his statement should be symmetric, assuming both the ego and FTP are multi-dimensional variables.

Finally, I like to argue a weak point of any study that is based on a correlation. When we get a significantly high correlation between two variables, we psychologists mistakenly understand it as if there must be a definit relationship between them. But actually we do not know whether the relationship is direct, indirect, or some other. (Obviously, I am exaggerating the point as a discussant.) In order to make such a relationship clear and definit we must investigate essential cognitive processes during a task performance. For example, we must investigate how a subject gets his associations of 10 events that may occur in his future life. My opinion here is the following: When *S* is given such task he must quickly simulate his future life in his mind. As the result of simulation he finds the required number of associations. It is a very important and fascinating problem to investigate how such simulation is performed and what the underlying cognitive process is. We shall not be able to know a true definite relationship between a personality trait and FTP until we can make clear underlying cognitive process.

# V. PAST, PRESENT, AND FUTURE

## The Objectivity, or Otherwise, of the Present*

K.G. Denbigh

*Exponents of both sides of the controversy concerning whether or not 'the present' is objective have claimed that the issue should be capable of being resolved scientifically. It is here suggested that this is a mistaken view. The t-coordinate of physics has been widely endowed with overmuch ontological significance and there is no scientific warrant for the view, espoused by some of the B-theorists, that past, present and future are necessarily 'equally real'. From an epistemological point of view, 'the present', at any particular location, is simply the terminus of all events which can be known with certainty and thus the temporal order, as it applies to any assumed events later than the present, is no more than a schematic construction.*

### 1. INTRODUCTION

This paper is concerned with the question of the ontological status of 'now' and 'becoming'; the question, that is, whether or not 'the present' is objective and whether or not there is a real 'coming into being' of things or events.

The two main viewpoints on this issue have been aptly named by R. M. Gale as the A- and B-theories respectively in remembrance of the A- and B-series of McTaggart. Broadly speaking the A-theorists (1)-(5) maintain that 'now' (or 'the present') is a real feature of the world as is also 'becoming'. The B-theorists (6)-(10), on the other hand, regard events as occurring tenselessly at certain clock times and are primarily 'earlier than' or 'simultaneous with' or 'later than' each other. 'Past', 'present' and 'future' are taken as mind-dependent.

*Numbers in parentheses are references; small superscripts are notes.

Although both of these theories have been very persuasively presented, they can hardly be regarded as *scientific* theories in Popper's sense. There appear to be no means, apart from linguistic arguments, by which either of them could be refuted. Gale, who is an A-theorist, has rightly pointed out that the B-theory's exponents use only *a priori* arguments, not empirical ones. Nevertheless there remains a lingering feeling that the issue ought to be capable of being resolved on scientific grounds. For example Reichenbach and Grünbaum, although opposed on the substance of the matter, both remarked that if 'now' and 'becoming' are objective this must be capable of being known to physics.[1]

However, as will be seen below, it is difficult to conceive what sort of empirical evidence could possibly count one way or the other. In general the best that can be hoped for, in my view, is a manner-of-talking about 'time' which is as self-consistent and comprehensive as possible and requires the minimum of ontological commitment. In this paper my aim is therefore to enquire whether there is perhaps something wrong with the generally accepted manner-of-talking which has led to the putting forward of two 'theories', neither of them apparently capable of being falsified by any empirical evidence. My belief is that there is indeed something wrong and this is the placing of too much credence, too much ontological reality, on the physically convenient notion of time as a coordinate.

The extent to which many writers on time have been influenced by relativity, in my view unwarrantably, is well illustrated by a passage from Smart. "I shall argue," he says (11), "for a view of the world as a four-dimensional continuum of space-time entities, such that out of relation to particular human beings or other language users there is no distinction of 'past', 'present' and 'future'." And he continues: "It is perfectly possible to think of things and processes as four-dimensional space-time entities. The instantaneous state of such a four-dimensional space-time solid will be a three-dimensional 'time slice' of the four-dimensional solid. Then instead of talking of things or processes changing or not changing we can now talk of one time slice of a four-dimensional entity *being* different or not different from some other time slice." And he goes on to speak of the value, in his opinion, of the corresponding *tenseless* mode of speech in eliminating from our view of the world the anthropocentric reference which is constituted by 'the present.'

Clearly one needs to distinguish between valid conclusions drawn from a physical theory and opinions or interpretations which are really no more than a gloss on that theory. It is an important conclusion from relativity that a 'world-wide now' cannot be defined unambiguously. So far so good. But it is also the case that relativity *neither supports nor disproves* the view that there may be objective[2] 'now' at each location. Relativity, I think, has nothing to say on that particular issue; that is to say concerning the possibility of an objective 'now' at the actual *site* of an event. (Including the type of event which is the receiving of a signal at that site, even though the signal may have arrived there from a distance.) It is very significant that neither Reichenbach nor Whitrow, both of them distinguished authorities on relativity, have regarded Einstein's theory as having denied the objectivity of the present. The question remains an open one.[3]

The next two sections of the paper will be concerned with developing the foregoing view that it may be impossible to bring the A- and B-theories into any real confrontation with each other in regard to empirical evidence. My own positive thesis concerning why this is so will be deferred to §4.

## 2. WHAT IS IT TO BE AWARE OF THE PRESENT?

D. C. Williams has severely criticised the A-theorists for using pictorial language ('time's flow' etc.) although he overlooks the fact that some of the B-theorists have been equally at fault in this respect. Nevertheless it is an important point that he makes. Now the A-theory goes beyond the B-theory in regard to the significance of 'now' and for this reason I shall aim at using a vocabulary of temporal words which are common to both theories (e.g. 'event', 'moment', 'occurrence', 'earlier than', 'simultaneous with', etc.) together with *a bare minimum* of A-theory words - viz: 'past', 'present' ('now') and 'future' plus the corresponding tenses of the verb 'to be'. Various locutions such as 'already', 'not yet', and so on which tend to beg the issue will be avoided and consideration of 'becoming' as an A-theory word will be left to a later stage.

Let's begin with a truism: although clocks can be used to tell us 'the time' they do not also identify 'the present'. For if I were to look at the clock and report, say, "It is 10.15", my evidence for this statement is that the hour and minute hands coincide *now,* at *my present,* with such and such numbers on the dial. In other words, it is the word 'is' in my utterance "It is 10.15" which contains the understanding that I am referring to a present reading of the clock, rather than to any reading in the past or to a possible reading in the future. What identifies 'the present' is not the clock but rather my awareness of the moment which 'is'. For it is conscious awareness which judges that a present reading of the clock is indeed a present reading and the same applies to the reading of any other sort of instrument. Furthermore this situation cannot be circumvented by using a camera; for although a photograph would satisfactorily identify, say, a certain thermometer reading as being simultaneous with a certain clock reading, it would not also contain within itself the evidence that the particular photograph is (or was) 'now being taken' - i.e. at some person's awareness of the present.

In short a statement concerning 'the time' is based on something external - a clock - but the decision that the clock reading is a present reading, rather than one which appertains to past or future, is made within ourselves. And also of course I have no means of reading 'the time' other than at my present and this is because I am, in a certain sense, always *in* my present .

The fixing of 'now' relative to clock and calendar readings, what I shall call its *dating*, thus appears to be a privileged function of conscious awareness. However it does not follow from this as a necessary conclusion that 'the now' or 'present' is mind-dependent (as Grünbaum believes) for it may be that 'now' is objective in some manner which is not concerned with its dating. Neither does it follow that past, present and future "are all equally real", as Smart (12) puts it.[4] These things may or may not be the case; the foregoing provides no more than some small degree of support for these B-theory contentions.

Let's go deeper into the issue by enquiring what it is to be aware of the present. Notice in the first place that we are usually not aware of it at all! When I am absorbed in my affairs or when I am daydreaming it never occurs to me to pick out a distinguished moment. Even when I look at the clock I don't often say to myself "It is 10.15". I notice no more than "10.15" and this is simply to observe a particular clock reading.

To be aware of the present requires a state of awareness of being aware. As Grünbaum (13) has very clearly put it: "*M*'s experience of the event at time *t* is coupled with an awareness of the temporal coincidence of his experience of the event with a state of *knowing* that he has that experience at all. In other words, *M* experiences the event at *t and* knows that he is experiencing it. Thus, presentness or nowness of an event requires conceptual awareness of the presentational immediacy of the experience of the event."

Although I agree that the present is brought into prominence in this way, I believe it owes its particular character to something else - to the existence of memory. This provides the element of contrast which enables 'the present' to be compared with what is not the present. Thus when I examine 'my present' introspectively I find that I have the awareness of the word I am now writing, but also I have the memories of earlier words and of earlier events in general. If I had no memory I should presumably merely have a punctiform state of attention - various clock readings would be experienced during various acts of attention but these would not impress me with the quality of 'being present' precisely because, in the absence of memory, I would have no power for comparing what *is* with what *was*. All earlier experience would be wiped out at the very moment of its ceasing to be 'present' and the present would thus not stand out as being the present.

What is particularly to be noticed about memories is that *there is one which is latest* (for me now the word 'latest'). For clearly I don't have memories of that part of my life which is called 'future'. The awareness of 'now' thus involves the awareness of a *terminus*.

This will be an important point in what follows and therefore, lest the use of 'terminus' may seem to be begging the issue, it is desirable to re-phrase what has just been said by use of my proposed minimum vocabulary. Within my memory there is a 'latest' one - 'latest' in the sense that at the moment *P* which is my present I have a series of memories referring to moments earlier than *P* but none referring to moments later than *P*. This, I think, satisfactorily explicates the notion that the series of memories has a terminal member. It may be noted too that this discontinuity in conscious experience corresponds to the distinction between *empirical facts* and *empirical possibilities*. The former, as recorded in the memory or in some other way, refer to times earlier than the present. The latter refer to times later than the present.[5] When so regarded 'the present' marks a division between factual states of the world and possible states of the world at my own location.

Between memories and present perceptions, on the one hand, and between present perceptions and anticipations of the future, on the other, we do not usually suffer any confusion. They are not mistaken for each other and thus correspond to three distinctive sorts of mental states. Does it not seem reasonable therefore to assume that these distinctive sorts of mental states correspond, in their turn, to different sorts of physical states of the brain? Almost all workers on the mind-body problem seem by now to have accepted the view (although without necessarily subscribing to the Identity Theory) that mind states are indeed dependent on brain states (14). If so it would appear that, *at any moment*, there are three physically distinguishable kinds of brain states having the mental characters of memories, present perceptions and anticipations respectively. Some evidence which has a bearing on this contention is already available, for there are indications that short-term memories depend on short-term electrical excitations within the brain whilst long-term memories depend on changes of molecular structure in the neurones. Memory in humans and in higher animals is perhaps not significantly different from the kind of imprinting which occurs in the 'memory' bank of a computer; except however (and this is a very important 'except') that humans have the ability to bring their memories to a conscious state. (And it may be that it is the synthesizing capacity of consciousness that it can make memory appear as a molar, rather than a digital, phenomenon).

Let us ask then if it is not conceivable that a rudimentary now-awareness could be incorporated in a suitable piece of hardware. Certain items that would appear requisite to the hardware are: (a) a set of receptors, such as TV cameras, which are capable of causing the hardware to react to (virtually) simultaneous states of the environment; (b) a memory store which serially records an abstract of the successive states of the environment, including clock readings; (c) perhaps also a predictor of possible future states of the environment - i.e. states later than the latest recorded in the memory store; (d) most importantly a device capable of distinguishing between the momentary output of the receptors, the content of the memory store and the predictions.

This hardware thus appears to have the means, through its ability to distinguish between memories and perceptions and anticipations, of denoting successive clock readings as having the status of 'being the present'. To be sure this is still very far from having the awareness of what it is doing (remember Grünbaum's point about the two-tiered awareness). But it does suggest a naturalistic basis for how 'the present' is to be understood.[6]

The point of the above discussion has been to indicate that it would be erroneous to think of now-awareness as necessarily being 'non-physical' (in some peculiar sense). Given that conscious awareness corresponds to a physical brain state, it would seem that there are indeed physical states of things whose comparison serves to indicate 'a present'.

Although this may seem to give support to the A-theory it is not very substantial support. Just as my earlier discussion of the dating of 'now' showed that this offered nothing decisively in favour of the B-theory, so also the foregoing remarks about physical states provide nothing decisively in favour of the A-theory.

For consider how the opposing B-theory would deal with the same situation. If the piece of hardware were to traverse an *undifferentiated* time coordinate (such as is assumed in that theory) it would nevertheless succeed in distinguishing each successive moment of its career from the earlier moments whose contents are recorded in its memory store and from the later moments whose contents it predicts. When each successive external event occurs tenselessly, appropriate light or sound waves tenselessly reach the hardware's receptors and each such tenselessly occurring state of perception presumably has the character of a particular present moment P. The hardware cannot experience 'all-of-time-together' since it cannot perceive events later than P because the appropriate light or sound waves have not arrived. Neither can it perceive events earlier than P. Its perceptions therefore have a punctiform character. Although the hardware might indeed be able to report "It is now 10.15" this would not provide evidence that 'now' has an ontological standing since the hardware's report occurs tenselessly like any other sort of event according to the B-theory.

Similar remarks can be made about the intersubjectivity of 'now' - i.e. the truism that different people do in fact agree that they are experiencing *the same* present. For instance that they are in a room together, that they are looking at the same clock and obtain the same reading of the clock. This too may seem at first sight to give strong support to the notion of an objective present as proposed by the A-theory. But consider two people Paul and Simon (or two pieces of hardware) whose now-awarenesses traverse the same sequence of external events, as they would do if they lived at the same location and during a common temporal interval. Consider any such tenselessly occurring event E (i.e. 'tenselessly' as interpreted on the B-theory) such as the actual reading of a clock and calendar. The effect of light waves and nerve transmissions is to create in the brains of Paul and Simon virtually simultaneous imprintings of that time and date. Even so it is not immediately obvious, on the basis of the B-theory, that Paul and Simon must be aware (and presumably in some sense of being *simultaneously* aware) of *the same* imprinting as being 'the present' since according to the theory all such brain imprintings are 'equally real'. Why then do they pick out, apparently fortuitiously, the self-same imprinting as being 'present'? However this difficulty for the B-theory is more apparent than real. It only arises on the tacit assumption (as is indicated by the 'presumably' clause above) that there is some *independent* criterion of simultaneity between Paul's awareness of E being present and Simon's awareness of E being present. On the B-theory there can be no such independent criterion since 'presentness' is entirely mind-dependent. Thus there can be no sense in asking *when* Paul (or Simon) is aware of E as being present *other than* his own awareness of E as present.

Putting the matter a little differently, there will be a sequence of Paul's presents and there will also be a sequence of Simon's presents. Since Paul and Simon perceive the same external events (and necessarily in the same order for physical and causal reasons) each member of the P-sequence can be paired, in regard to its content of perception, with a member of the S-sequence. Since there is no independent criterion for saying that these paired members are *not* simultaneous, there can be no basis for claiming that they are not 'the same present'. Thus the intersubjectivity of 'now' does not disprove the B-theory and by the same token it fails to give any real support to the A-theory.

## 3. QUANTUM INDETERMINACY

Let's see if there is some other area in which the relative merits of the A- and B-theories might be tested. The essential point at issue between the theories is whether 'time' *really is*, in some deep ontological sense, differentiated into past, present and future. If one adopts a relational view of time (time as being no more than a relationship between events) this seems to be one and the same question as to whether or not there is *some unique sort of event* at each successive present - i.e. something quite different from ordinary physical changes such as changes of colour or temperature, or the falling of a leaf from a tree or even the differentiation of a 'present' relative to earlier memory states (and to later predicted states) as discussed above. All such changes or events, it would appear, can be expressed equally well in A-theory language and in tenseless B-theory language. Thus we are looking for a very different sort of event.

What the A-theorists have in mind is a 'coming into existence' of the events themselves; that is to say the 'Absolute Becoming' of the A-theory. As Eva Cassirer (15) has very clearly pointed out this is actually a logically distinct issue from the issue concerning the present: "There is no *logical* relation (as between antecedent and consequent) between the happening of an event and the distinction between future and past. ...it is an *interpretation* that I am putting on the word 'present' when I identify it with the 'moment of becoming'..." However it is precisely this interpretation which Reichenbach and Whitrow have used in their support of the A-theory.

Reichenbach, it will be recalled, says that "if there is Becoming the physicist must know it" (16) and he claimed that it is indeed knowable - through the indeterminacy relation of quantum physics. "Le concept de 'devenir'", he writes (17), "acquiert une signification dans la physique: le présent qui sépare l'avenir du passé, est le moment où ce qui etait indéterminé devient déterminé, et'devenir' signifie la même chose que 'devenir déterminé'." Whitrow (18) expressed a very similar view: "The past is the determined, the present is the moment of 'becoming' when events become determined, and the future is the as-yet undetermined."

Although neither Reichenbach nor Whitrow developed their thesis at any length the general purport of what they meant is clear: there is a basic chance element in nature, at least at the micro-level, and the moment of 'becoming', the present, is marked by a transition from what is merely possible to what is factual.

This important attempt to establish the A-theory is however by no means immune from criticism from the side of the B-theory. A particularly well-known criticism is that which was made by Grünbaum (who also quotes H. Bergmann as having preceded him in this). Grünbaum (19), if I have understood him correctly, takes it to have been Reichenbach's intention that "le moment où ce qui etait indéterminé devient déterminé" can be used as a *dating*, or even as a *definition*, of the present. Grünbaum then quite rightly objects that, on the assumption of indeterminacy, the change from an undetermined to a determined state of affairs has *always* occurred and therefore such a change cannot serve to distinguish what was once Plato's 'now' from what is now mine.

As against Grünbaum's point it may be argued that Reichenbach intended his remark as providing the means, not so much of dating or of definition, as of *elucidation*. That is to say, of making a connection between the notion of 'the present' and the concepts of quantum physics. This reading of the passage is given some support, I think, by the fact that it begins: "Le concept de 'devenir' acquiert *une signification* dans la physique..." It is also given support by Reichenbach's subsequent discussion of 'now' as being token-reflexive and by a further passage: "c'est un fait physique que, si A est la situation *définie par l'acte de parler*, une situation précédent A est déterminée par rapport à A, tandis qu'une situation qui suit A ne l'est pas." (My italics.) Perhaps it may be said that although Grünbaum's criticism shows that Reichenbach's proposal does not provide a sufficient condition for the definition of the present, it does not disprove that it may provide a necessary condition.

It is concerning the latter, however, that a further substantial comment has been made by J. J. C. Smart (20). He points out that indeterminism, when looked at from the standpoint of the B-theory, means no more than that successive 'temporal slices' are not related to each other in a completely law-bound manner. This, on the B-theory, is just as true of what, to us, are 'past' events as it is also true of what, to us, are 'future' events. The real events are those which actually occur, each at a certain clock time, whether they are deterministically related to earlier events or not. In other words indeterministic events can be treated as tenseless occurrences, in the manner of the B-theory, just as readily as deterministic events.

In view of the combined effect of these two criticisms it seems that the Reichenbach-Whitrow thesis gives little firm support to the A-theory. But of course this does not mean that the truth of the opposing B-theory is thereby established! It is simply another instance of what was dealt with in §2 - i.e. the existence of two 'theories' each of them self-consistent and unrefutable within the scope of their own premises but capable of being criticised from the standpoint of the other.

## 4. THE COORDINISATION OF TIME

The issue between the two theories is clearly metaphysical or linguistic, not empirical. Even so, many of the B-theorists, as was seen in the Introduction, seem to hold the view that science is positively on their side. Is there perhaps some tacit metaphysical assumption within the physical scientist's habitual manner-of-talking about time which has given rise to this idea?

In my view there is such an assumption and it resides in the notion of time as a coordinate. That which is shown in the diagrams in the physics books, where $t$ is shown as looking just like $x$, $y$ and $z$, has been accepted as if it were 'real'. And of course I agree that time as a coordinate is an extremely useful and convenient notion. Classical physics, working in the field of macroscopic phenomena, has been wonderfully successful in predicting 'the times' of future eclipses of the sun and innumerable other large scale effects. The consequence of the sheer utility of the t-coordinate is that 'time' is thought of as if it *really were* something like a straight line stretching indefinitely far in either direction.[7]

It is however entirely a gloss on the concept of the t-coordinate to say, with Smart, that past, present and future "are all equally real". Such a conclusion is very far from having been demonstrated. It arises (I suggest) from nothing more than certain aesthetic or metaphysical considerations, such as the desire to attribute to 'time' the maximum of symmetry or to avoid seemingly anthropocentric viewpoints.

In fact the t-coordinate is actually a derivative notion. It is based (as is 'time' itself) on *the prior concept of the temporal order* - that is to say on the empirical observation that all events at a particular location can be placed in a unique sequence. This construction of the temporal order is based, in its turn, on the ability to distinguish between 'what-is-now' and 'what-is-in-the-memory' - i.e. between 'now' and 'earlier than now'. More generally it is based on the ability to place events in a series whose generating relation is 'earlier than'. The t-coordinate thus derives from the asymmetric transitive ordering which is arrived at from direct experience. Which is not to say, of course, that there are not subsidiary physical criteria, such as entropy increase (21).

What is very significant in the present context is that the temporal order cannot truly be said to extend 'beyond' that particular event (or set of events) which constitute the observer's 'now'. The order is a relationship between *known* events, and thus under circumstances where there are no known events, none which can be known *with certainty*, there is no such relationship. In other words the temporal order as applied to any assumed events later than now ('future time') is a schematic construction; it represents no more than an anticipated number of tick-tocks of the clock for the purpose of dating anticipated events; events, that is to say, which may or may not occur.

Consider this point in a little more detail. The Minkowski world-lines are often adduced in support of the B-theory - and in the face of these celebrated world-lines surely one needs to cross oneself! But let us ask in all seriousness how in fact they can be drawn otherwise than schematically and with a flourish on the blackboard. No doubt they can be drawn with very considerable accuracy with regard to a great many sorts of 'already observed' events - i.e. events earlier than the observer's 'now'. But are they not affected by a great deal of guesswork whenever they are extrapolated into the observer's future? Each such line supposedly describes the space-time behaviour of a genidentical body or particle. To attempt to draw the line beyond actually observed events is to assume that the particular entity's future behaviour is reliably and accurately predictable. But in general this is not the case for it cannot be known that the body or particle will not undergo some event which is utterly unforeseeable. If it is a star it may suffer an explosion; if it is a nuclear particle it may undergo a disintegration and thus give rise to two or more divergent world-lines. Since the 'times' of such events cannot be predicted the future world-lines cannot be drawn.[8] Clearly there is an important epistemological distinction between the recorded facts of the past and the non-recorded possibilities of the future and this is a distinction which has been largely glossed over by some of the B-theorists.

It follows that the assumed continuum of the temporal order (its assumed decomposition into 'instants', each of strictly zero duration) differs from, say, the continuum of the real numbers in one very important respect. One real number is related to another by being 'greater than' and similarly one instant is related to another by being 'later than'. Yet this latter relationship is vacuous except by reference to concrete events and thus to *empirical states of the world* (including states of consciousness). For if there were no difference anywhere in the universe between the physical states corresponding to two supposedly different times there would be no basis for believing that they are not one and the same time. The next instant, or the next minute or hour, has therefore a different logical status from, say, the next digit of $\pi$. Even though this digit may not have been worked out, it has a definite value in a way in which the physical content of 'future time' does not. For clearly there is no logical necessity that all change in the universe, including the ongoing of clocks, will not suddenly cease. The extrapolation of the temporal order beyond the present is thus defeated by the logical failure of induction.

What I am saying in brief is that the temporal order, which is the order of known events at a location,[9] extends only up to the observer's 'now' *and there it has a terminus*. All considerations concerning 'time' and the t-coordinate, concepts which are based on the temporal order, must be seen in this light.

These remarks are in no way contrary to the continuum theory of time[10] and neither are they contrary to relativity (22). To be sure as soon as one postulates the existence (in some sense) of 'time', as distinct from the local temporal order, one is adopting a universe-wide concept and this has to be accommodated to the facts of signalling. The t-coordinate must then be assimilated to the space coordinates, as is done in relativity theory. But this does not affect my point which is that the t-coordinate is a schematic construction (invaluable to science though it is). To endow it with overmuch reality is an instance of the false reification of 'time'.

Notice that it would be impermissible, from the epistemological point of view which is being adopted, to pose the question: "How fast does the present move on?" Such a question would be to assume that 'time' is indeed correctly regarded as a coordinate, one which already exists (so to say) ahead of the present. So too if it were said that the present 'advances' into time. There is no 'existing ahead' and no 'advancing' according to the viewpoint which I am adopting.

But of course this doesn't preclude speaking of the time and date of some anticipated event such as an eclipse of the sun. For what one would be saying is simply this: that if the sun and moon continue to move along their present paths and if clocks too continue to behave deterministically, then an eclipse is likely to be observed at such and such a reading on the clocks. This understanding of the t-coordinate as being a convenient tool for purposes of prediction does not carry with it the consequence that past, present and future must be equally real. Indeed, as has been seen, my contention is that the present is the moment P such that there are no moments later than P to which any physical content can be ascribed. In this epistemological sense there is in fact no time later than P; one should not think of future time as 'existing'.

C. F. von Weizsäcker (23) expressed a similar view when he wrote: "One would expect a measurable time not to be a real-number parameter but a counting operator, perhaps counting the facts, that is the events which have happened up till now."

With this idea in mind let us think of any moment *j* during Plato's life. For him that moment was a divide - a divide which separated his factual knowledge of earlier events from his imagined possibilities of later events. But of course, that moment *j* is not a divide for me, it is not one of my 'nows'. For me Caesar's crossing of the Rubicon is a fact, but it could not have been so for Plato. For Plato, and for those who lived contemporaneously, the class of real events was the class $E_j$ of all *known* events - events that is to say whose occurrence was either earlier than or simultaneous with the moment *j*. For me and for my contemporaries a much larger class is real; larger because the class $E_j$ which was accessible to Plato at the moment *j* is now (at my present) a sub-class within my own (or at least potentially so assuming complete recording). Thus each successive 'present' corresponds to a larger class of events which are real.

Before ending I need to deal with an important difficulty. The view I have been advocating is that the relational theory should be taken seriously and no more reality should be attributed to 'future time' than the relational theory warrants. As Mario Bunge (24) puts it: "Time is not out there, by itself and ready-made, as the absolute view of time had it: time is in the making alongside happenings."

So far so good; but what about the remote past before there were humans capable of any awareness of 'the present'? Clearly there was a temporal order at that period and its component events are arrived at by a process of inference, for example from rock strata, moon dust, etc. But was it then a temporal order *without* a terminus and did the terminus make its first appearance with the existence of human beings? If that is a conclusion to be drawn from what has been said above it is clearly unsatisfactory.

However, it should again be stressed that the foregoing has been written from an epistemological viewpoint and the 'terminus' which has been spoken about is a terminus of knowledge. As such it has no ontological standing and to ask when it first *appeared,* as in the previous paragraph, is deceiving since it conveys the impression that a 'something' called 'time' suddenly became endowed with a new property. 'Time', I believe, should not be conceived in that kind of way - it is not some sort of existent but is simply a relational characteristic of events - including those events in the brain and in conscious awareness which provide the sense of a 'present'.

If one wishes to go further and to make an ontological commitment there seem to be two alternatives. One of them is to accept the B-theory and thereby to deny any reality to past, present and future, other than their reality to conscious awareness. The other is to adopt the Reichenbach-Whitrow hypothesis; there is, and always has been, a fully objective terminus, a moment at which there is a coming-into-being, a change of ontological status. On various grounds the latter seems to me the more attractive option. What Reichenbach and Whitrow achieve is a linking up of 'becoming' with quantum indeterminacy - an heuristic linking up which yet falls short (in view of Smart's point) of a logical demonstration.

Let me amplify a little by adopting a manner-of-talking about time suggested by some recent ideas put forward by J. T. Fraser (25). Following Fraser (although differing from him somewhat in detail) I shall here regard 'time' as being a many-tiered concept. At the level of atomic phenomena all that is required is the notion of a directionless coordinate since all such phenomena (with the possible exception of the weak interactions) appear to be t-invariant. On the other hand as soon as we are concerned with largish aggregates of particles and with macroscopic phenomena this simple notion must be enriched by attributing an 'arrow' to the coordinate.[11] 'Time' then takes on an additional quality and becomes a richer concept. This process goes a stage further when 'time' has to be adapted to the phenomena existing at the level of conscious awareness. As has been seen the notion of a coordinate is now seen to have been an over-simplification and it becomes necessary still further to enrich the time-concept by including 'the present' and also 'past' and 'future'.

Far from regarding the limited time-concept, the directionless coordinate, which is used at the atomic level as being 'true' in some sense (for that would be a prejudice based on theoretical physics), what is here being suggested is that we obtain a more comprehensive, although perhaps still very incomplete, understanding of temporal ongoings if we adopt the greatly enriched time-concept which is required to do justice to the entire range of known phenomena, including those which are peculiar to the human level.

ACKNOWLEDGEMENTS

It is a pleasure to record my thanks to Dr Eva Cassirer, Professor N. Lawrence, Professor David Park and Dr J. T. Fraser for many helpful comments.

REFERENCES

1. C. D. Broad, *Examination of McTaggart's Philosophy*, Cambridge 1938.

2. R. M. Gale, *The Language of Time*, Routledge and Kegan Paul, 1968.

3. A. N. Prior, *Past, Present and Future*, Oxford 1967; *Papers on Time and Tense*, Oxford 1968.

4. H. Reichenbach, *The Direction of Time*, University of California, 1956.

5. G. J. Whitrow, *The Natural Philosophy of Time*, Nelson, 1961.

6. A. J. Ayer, *The Problem of Knowledge*, pg. 170, Macmillan 1965.

7. D. C. Williams, *Principles of Empirical Realism*, Charles C. Thomas, 1966.

8. A. Grünbaum in *Essays in Honor of Carl G. Hempel*, ed. N. Rescher, Reidel Publ. Co., Dordrecht; also *Philosophical Problems of Space and Time*, Knopf, 1963.

9. J. J. C. Smart, *Between Science and philosophy*, Random House, 1968; also *Philosophy and Scientific Realism*, Routledge and Kegan Paul, 1963.

10. D. Park in *The Study of Time*, Ed. J. T. Fraser, *et al*, Springer-Verlag, 1972.

11. *Philosophy & Scientific Realism*, pg. 133

12. *Between Science & Philosophy*, pg. 255

13. *loc. cit.*, pg. 155-6

14. See for example J. A. Ornstein, *The Mind and The Brain*, Nijhoff, The Hague, 1972. For a critique of what has been called the 'strong correlation thesis' see R. C. Solomon, *Brit. J. Philosophy of Science*, 1975, *26*, 27.

15. E. Cassirer in *The Study of Time*, ed. J. T. Fraser et. al., Springer-Verlag, 1972. Concerning the notion of 'becoming' see also P. Fitzgerald in *Boston Studies in the Philosophy of Science*, Vol. XX, Reidel Publ. Co. Dordrecht, 1974.

16. *loc. cit.* pg. 16

17. *Annales de L'Institut Henri Poincaré*, 1952-3, *13*, 109-158.

18. *loc. cit.* pg. 295

19. *loc. cit.* pg. 167-8

20. *Philosophy and Scientific Realism*, pg. 141-2

21. My attitude to this particular issue was described in my contribution to *The Study of Time*, ed. J. T. Fraser et al., Springer-Verlag, 1972. Also in my book, *An Inventive Universe*, Hutchinson, London, 1975; Braziller, New York, 1975.

22. On this point see, for example, Lawrence Sklar, *Space, Time and Space-Time*, pp. 272-5, University of California Press, 1974.

23. *The Physicist's Concept of Nature*, ed. J. Mehra, Reidel Publ. Co., Dordrecht, 1973.

24. *Philosophy of Science*, 1968, *35*, pg. 375.

25. J. T. Fraser, *Of Time, Passion, and Knowledge*, Braziller, New York, 1975.

NOTES

1. Grünbaum (*loc. cit.* pg. 159) writes as follows: "...if nowness were a mind-*in*dependent property of physical events themselves, it would be very strange indeed that it could be omitted *as such* from all extant physical theories *without detriment to their explanatory success*." As against this Gale (*loc. cit.* pg. 224) has pointed out that any law or theory "is general: the statement of it is temporally unrestricted since it quantifies over all times. Since the law or theory holds true for *any* time it obviously cannot serve as a criterion for picking out some one time as *the* present: if it holds for all times it cannot hold for just one time." And therefore "...there is no physical criterion for determining what is *the* present." To Gale's point it may be added that although physical laws and theories also do not pick out a spatial location, this analogical situation does not imply that there may not be a distinguished 'present' even if there is no distinguished 'place'.

2. The term 'objective' will be used in this paper in the strong sense - i.e. as referring to whatever may be said to exist or to happen quite independently of man's own presence in the world, or of his thoughts and perceptions. Thus I shall not be concerned with the weaker sense of the term which refers to whatever can be publicly agreed.

3. Hinckfuss is among those who still regard relativity as having disposed of an objective present. He writes: "...if the simultaneity of events is relative to a frame of reference rather than absolute, then there is no such thing as The Present." (*The Existence of Space and Time*, pg. 106, Oxford, 1975). This seems to me an illicit extrapolation from the non-existence of a universal reference frame to the supposed non-existence of a 'now' at each location. It is very significant that no observer whatsoever can signal to me that he has observed an event at my own location *before* I have observed that event myself.

In that respect the A-theorist might claim that there is something absolute about the occurrence of an event here and now.

4. Indeed it isn't at all clear what he could mean by this. Is it that the *physical content* of the future is just as real as the physical content of the present? No doubt at any moment it can reasonably be expected that there will be *some* future and that it will have some physical content. But this seems to be saying little more than the old adage "What will be, will be."

5. Even though the possibilities in question may refer to an earlier present; for instance when it is said "It was a possibility yesterday that he might be coming."

6. It is of interest that Grünbaum in one of his footnotes (no. 13 of ref. 8) remarks that the conceptualized awareness on which 'now-awareness' depends must surely require a physical sub-stratum and therefore this awareness might also inhere in a suitably complex piece of hardware.

7. According to E. A. Burtt, the representation of time as a straight line was first adopted by Galileo and was associated with his concept of natural law as expressing necessity. E. A. Burtt, *Metaphysical Foundations of Modern Physical Science*, Second Ed. pg. 86, Routledge and Kegan Paul, 1932.

8. Mario Bunge has made the further point that the world-line of an elementary particle is necessarily 'fuzzy' because of the Uncertainty Principle. *Philosophy of Science*, 1968, *35*, 355.

9. In this discussion I am referring, of course to events as experienced and not to events at the source of origin of the experienced signals which may be light-years away.

10. Cantorean concepts are, of course just as applicable to a series which is bounded at one or both ends as to a series which is endless.

11. This transition between micro- and macro-concepts of time has been particularly clearly brought out in various papers by P. T. Landsberg; for example in his contribution to *The Study of Time*, Ed. J. T. Fraser et. al.

DISCUSSION AND COMMENT
*by Eva Cassirer*

It is a notable, though regrettable, fact that so much of what is said and written about time seems to depend on our ontology, our philosophical commitment, even our Weltanschauung. Dr Denbigh, for instance, would not have established his theory of the present (moment) as the terminal point-in-time at any particular location, were it not for his profound distrust of induction. He says: "To attempt to draw the world-line beyond actually observed events is to assume that the particular entity's future behaviour is reliably and accurately predictable. But in general this is not the case...". That the sun will rise tomorrow is to him not reliably predictable, because "a star...may suffer an explosion"; that the tree in the Quad will continue to exist unobserved overnight cannot be accurately assumed since its "nuclear particle(s)...may undergo disintegration and thus give rise to two or more world-lines" (ibid.).

We all know that the inductive 'argument' cannot be non-viciously proven; in fact, we know that there is no 'argument'. But the *problem* of induction could not even be *stated*, did we not have a strong belief that there will be events after the present moment. In fact, Denbigh's theory of the present moment as the last one (in a series) might furnish us - finally - with the long-sought conclusive disproof of the possibility of induction.

Actually, I agree with much of what Dr Denbigh says. I share his dislike of the Minkowski block universe in which the future, as well as the past, is firmly determined and we come across future events as we move along our world-line in time. And I think he must be congratulated for stating so emphatically that the choice between the A-theory and the B-theory concerning the character of the present is spurious, since we are faced with a non-exhaustive alternative, and that both theories are really incomplete. I also agree with him that the representation of time in physics as a coordinate has enhanced the belief that "science is positively on the side of the B-theorists", and I think further that many of the 'paradoxes' about Time result from an overestimation of the applicability of this representation.

Unfortunately, however, Denbigh's way out does not seem to me a possible one. He observes that "it is an important conclusion from relativity that a 'world-wide now' cannot be defined unambiguously", and then continues that 'it is also the case that relativity *neither supports nor disproves* the view that there may be an objective 'now' at each location". But he does not explain why this is so - or he would not have set up his theory as he did.

It is built into the concept of modern science that objective descriptions of reality, i.e. physical theories (among others), are time- and space-independent in the sense that the hypothetical observer can be assumed to reside at *any* place and time. Therefore, the scientific 'objectivity', i.e. the inter-subjectivity, of the 'now', becomes a contradiction in terms, the 'now' being always observer-referring. This remark is not to be understood as a linguistic finesse, rather as a logical point: if we set up science in such a way that physical laws hold universally, i.e. for all times and places - which is what we do - then there *can* be no scientific, empirical proof or 'resolution of the problem' which will allow for the objectivity of the 'now'. Since in science time is treated, like space, as a coordinate for physical occurrences, the moment (i.e. the time) *at* which something happens cannot become the subject of scientific 'objective' investigation. For, whose 'now' would we want to investigate? Surely the individual observer's! But then we are begging the question - for who, or what, could function as the universal, albeit hypothetical, observer to determine the simultaneity of all individual observers' 'nows'? - It is precisely this dilemma that Denbigh's solution wants to circumvent. But he could only do so at the price of denying the universality - and continuity, i.e. the legitimate extrapolation - of scientific laws. And he comes dangerously close to doing just that when he says: "the present is the moment P such that there are no moments later than P to which any physical content can be ascribed".

I think that Denbigh himself realises this danger when he admits of an "important difficulty", where he says that in the remote past, before there were humans on earth, there must yet have been temporal order obtaining between the events of inorganic matter and this order must have existed without a terminus, so that the terminus arose together with the first human being. His way out of this difficulty is to accept the view that there has always been a "fully objective terminus, a moment at which there is...a change of ontological status". He thinks that Reichenbach and Whitrow allow for this possibility by linking up the notion of 'becoming' with quantum indeterminacy.

But it is clear that events do not only 'become' by chance or unpredictable quantum jumps. A regular, causally generated, and therefore quite predictable event likewise constitutes an example of 'becoming', and if the ontological status of the world changes through the occurrence of a sporadic event now, it does so also when the event has been successfully predicted earlier. But it can only have been predicted on the assumption of the existence of a future world, or at least, of a future time.

For, surely, no-one would seriously wish to hold that the sun will not rise tomorrow because he cannot know today that there will be a physical sun existing tomorrow!

# Ideas of Beginnings and Endings in Cosmology

J. Merleau-Ponty

*As far as the philosophy of time is concerned, more specifically of cosmic time, the ancient Greek philosophers still provide a basic reference. Out of the small number of possible solutions, they clearly formulated three: those of Democritus, Plato and Aristotle. Among the three, one, at best, that of Plato, if carefully qualified, implied a beginning of the world. By contrast, such a beginning was categorically asserted in the Book of Genesis. It was taken by the Christians as an untouchable dogma. They were at pains to build a philosophy grounded on the Greek tradition and the Judaic dogma.*

*St Augustine, trying to find a solution along Platonic lines, made a deep inquiry into the very concept of time. He conceived of God's eternity as a present that does not extend itself into past and future. That extension, which is time, results from the creation. Thus, if God "precedes" all the time of the world, this precedence is not within the order of time.*

*On the other hand, St Thomas Aquinas accepts the Aristotelian view: the world should be considered eternal if it were ruled only by natural causality, but the creating act of God's will escapes any natural law, and it is indeed an absolute beginning that He gave to the world.*

*In modern times, the natural philosophy of time gave up Aristotle as well as Plato, and revived Democritus. At the highest point of classical science, in the 19th century, Democritean concepts pre-*

*vailed: an indefinite multiplicity of worlds in infinite space and time; no ordering by a final causality; all cosmic processes reduced to local and differential causality plus chance. All concepts of a beginning of the world were excluded.*

*But the rebirth of cosmology at the beginning of the 20th century revived the forgotten problems: if scientific thinking is allowed to consider the universe as a whole, is it possible to conceive it, within the framework of a classical causality, as self-contained and self sufficient? Besides, the assertion of an irreversibility of cosmic processes - supported by so many facts - revives the problem of the beginning, in so far as it seems to exclude the indefinite alternations of building up and destruction of worlds as Democritus had imagined.*

Time seems to have very little effect on the philosophy of time. If you are requested to talk about the idea of beginning in cosmology, and you are bold enough to accept, you soon find out that this very old question is not an obsolete one at all. It is deeply rooted in the theories of contemporary cosmology, as demonstrated by other papers in this volume. Obviously some scientists are interested in the question and obviously they do not agree on the answer; Dr Davies has one "big bang", and Dr Landsberg has at least three. To a philosopher's mind this is not very surprising. Try to pay direct attention to the problem, be it only to elucidate its terms, and you will soon find yourself entangled in conceptual and dialectical questions to which you feel that neither factual evidence nor hypothetico-deductive reasoning are able to give satisfactory answers. That, of course, reminds you of your Greek culture, or of what is left of it; so you take again your *Timaeus* or your *de Caelo*, your anthology of Presocratics or ancient Stoïcs, and you find out that your problems are there, with a few planets and stars, instead of thousands of galaxies, a good deal of myth instead of group theory and topological spaces. Nonetheless, there they are, with very subtle solutions, which usually destroy each other and occasionally destroy themselves.

## 1. GREEK THOUGHT.

My postulate, at least for today, will be that, although nearly everything has changed since the time of Democritus and Plato, the basic metaphysics of time cannot be very different from what it was then. That suggests a method for the inquiry into our problem: precisely because this basic metaphysics appears in ancient philosophy within a context so different from the one we know - mythical representations, inadequate factual information, poor mathematics - it is easier to identify it. Such recognition could at least prevent us from yielding too easily to the temptation of scientific comfort, namely that, with half a dozen more galactic spectra and a couple of new theorems of topology we will be able to swear that the universe had a beginning or that it had not.

Concentrating, for the sake of brevity, on the problem of beginning, we can say that in ancient philosophy we find three solutions, or types of solutions, namely Democritean, Platonic and Aristotelian, together with a fourth one, quite different from the three others, that which is expressed in the first sentence of *Genesis*. The order of enumeration has no particular significance, but a preliminary remark is necessary: each of these views is associated with a definite conception of causality, from which it cannot be separated. That link between the idea of beginning and the concept of causality is probably dependent on some basic fact of the experience of time. Events are certainly an essential element of that experience; but events, as such are irrational, and the concept of causality has always been the response of rational thinking to the idea of an event. As an obvious consequence, any logical representation of the beginning of the world, a superevent, or even any question about it, must be linked to some concept of causality.

*A*. Let us begin with the "Democritean" doctrine. By this I mean the doctrine and its main elements that are usually attributed to Democritus (and possibly Leucippus), though that is no more than a doxographic and conventional designation.

As to our problem, the main Democritean concepts are: infinite multiplicity of worlds made of an indeterminate number of "atoms" eternally moving in a void. Consequently, all concepts of beginning or ending of the world as a whole are completely excluded.[1] The world we see is only one among many and, if it has begun and will end, which Democritus does not seem to exclude, this was only one beginning and it will be one end among an infinity of others. Democritus thought that worlds can destroy each other and be transformed into one another.[2]

Now, what concept of causality underlay these cosmological views? At first sight, one finds a sort of contradiction in the doxography of this point In several fragments Democritus is reported to have said that beings are, and events occur by "necessity" (ανάγκη); but at other places, he is said to believe that chance rules the world and he is sharply criticized by Aristotle for that.[3] In fact, this contradiction is only apparent if one interprets Democritus' "necessity" as something akin to what we would call a mechanical process, taking place locally, at a definite moment of time, when atoms or groups of atoms act on each other. On the other hand, Democritus probably thought that no other type of causality was operating in the world, namely no universal or cosmic purpose, nor any kind of harmonic or unitary principle. Thus, when atoms seem to combine into an orderly world, that is the result of chance as much as when a world is destroyed or born. In Aristotle's terms, causality is reduced to the efficient cause, the final and formal being excluded. And for that reason, Democritus' philosophy of nature could perhaps be described as a non-cosmology.

*B*. Let us now examine the Platonic concepts. They are quite opposite to those of Democritus, though Aristotle mentions some statements common to Plato and Leucippus. In Plato's view there is one world which had a definite beginning but will not end. That world and its beginning proceed from a very different type of causality, in Aristotle's terms both formal and final, analogous to the action of a craftsman. That Plato knew of a mechanical causality, at least akin to that of Democritus' necessity, and thought it inadequate to explain the world is proved by a passage in the *Phaedo* in which Socrates expresses his disappointment about Anaxagoras: he has read in that author that the Mind, the Noũs has put the world in order and that pleased him very much. But reading further, he has found out that Anaxagoras mentioned mechanical and material causes, but did not say more about the action of the Noũs.[4] In the *Timaeus*, the craftsman, the god (ο δημιουργός, ο θεός) shapes the world after an eternal model, which is the world of ideas, with the definite intention of making an image as perfect as possible.[5] It is clear that the myth is here to be taken as convenient language and that Plato's mind was far beyond any naive representation of the process. What did he mean? Obviously, at least, that the world was not self-contained and ontologically self-sufficient, but only an image or a copy. Time itself, and this is the main point for us, was also, as Plato explicitly says, only an image, a moving image of eternity or duration (αἰών).[6] So that the Platonic concept of the beginning of the world seems to imply the paradox that the beginning of the world is also, in some sense, the beginning of time. For, says Plato, future and past do not exist in the eternal being (ἀΐδιος οὐσία) which is the paradigm of the world; of that eternal being, we can only say that it *is*, not that it *was* or *will be*.[7] The statement that the world had a beginning cannot be separated from its ontological evaluation; it implies that temporal existence is but an imperfect substitute for eternity, that time is not fully real.

This must be kept in mind, because it is quite opposite both to the Democritean and the Aristotelian concepts. Aristotle himself seems to have misunderstood this element of Plato's cosmology, taking literally the passage in the *Timaeus* where the god is said to have taken a disordered and chaotic world and brought it to a κόσμος, as if the process took place in time.[8]

*C.* The third concept to be considered is the Aristotelian one. Like Plato and contrary to Democritus, Aristotle asserts the unity of the world and emphasises the cosmic harmony. Although the world as a whole depends on a first cause of its motion, it is clear that the action of the prime mover is more of the final type than of the efficient type. Aristotle's cosmology satisfies the condition that Socrates was disappointed not to find in Anaxagoras's physics, namely the presence of the Noũs as the ultimate cause of world's order. There is also, in Aristotelian cosmology a hierarchy of beings. At the top, we find eternal beings which rule the world and have a direct relationship with the highest parts of the heavens: the prime mover of the *Metaphysics*, the eternal beings referred to in the *de Caelo*.[9] So far, this is not very different from the Platonic doctrines. Time however, is strongly associated with the existence of the world, and hence with a definite cosmic process. In the *Physics*, Aristotle tries to prove that there is only one world, because there is only one time, which would be judged nonsensical in Democritus' cosmology and is quite consonant with Plato's.[10]

Yet, the differences between Aristotle's and Plato's cosmologies are basic enough to make the cosmologies impossible to reconcile. First, although there is some uncertainty in Aristotle as to the relationship between the eternal being or beings and the heavens, this relationship is certainly not what it is in Plato, namely that of perfect reality to imperfect image, or of paradigm to copy. Secondly, there is no sort of creation of the world in Aristotle, nor even any process of διακόσμησις ("putting in order") because actual being is prior to potential being and we cannot conceive of a chaotic world existing before the act of putting it in order.[11] Thus, although the causality of the prime mover is of the final type, it is not that of the craftsman; he did not create the world, nor has he brought it from chaos to order. As final and efficient cause, he produces in the world an eternal motion which has some similarity to that provoked by love. As a final cause, he moves as does the beloved: κινεῖ ὡς ἐρώμενον;[12] but the world is eternal and permanent in the harmony of its motions, and the very idea of a beginning of the world, or of an end, is sheer nonsense in Aristotle. If there are beginnings and endings, generations and destructions, it is only in the inferior parts of the world where, besides the known types of causality which achieve ordinary kinds of regular alternation, there also acts a sort of non-causality or chance, ταὐτοματον. Granted the three basic and incompatible concepts of cosmological time, a great part of the problems which we, in European culture, have inherited from our tradition in this respect, result from the following fact: At a definite period of our history, each of these three concepts has come into conflict, more or less sharply with the basic dogma of the Judeo-Christian concept of creation. This conflict and its consequences are also relevant to our discussion of contemporary cosmology. Before dealing with them, however, two remarks are necessary.

1. One might mention a fourth view of cosmological time in ancient philosophy, that of a cyclic history of the world, determined by a dualistic type of causality. This was the view of Heraclitus and later of Empedocles. The basic idea is that friendship and discord (ἡ φιλία, τὸ νεῖκος) acting as antagonistic causes, alternately condense and disperse the world. This idea is also present in ancient Stoic philosophy: at the end of the Great Year, the world is supposed to be destroyed and reborn in a conflagration (εκπύρωσις). But it seems to me that this view was not worked out with enough detail and accuracy to play a role different from the others, to which it was more or less associated in various combinations. Following the advice of Aristotle, we will not consider it separately.

2. The second remark is of greater significance. As far as science was concerned (using this word in its modern sense) - and scientific astronomy at least existed in the ancient world - the Aristotelian view prevailed, and could not but prevail, over the others. The spherical and geocentric model of the world, though it met great difficulties, was probably the best suited to available observations. The Democritean concept of the plurality of worlds could not but seem very speculative to thinkers wishing to comply with what we call scientific rules. Besides, as Aristotle noticed,[13] there was no memory of any change in celestial appearances above the moon, and consequently, no serious ground for an inference towards a different shape of the heavens in the past. Thus, to a positive mind, the Platonic building of the world faded into an unscrutable and therefore insignificant past.

Now to sum up this brief survey: 1. The idea of the beginning of the world had very little place in ancient Greek speculations. 2. The Aristotelian view, the one which prevailed from the "scientific" viewpoint, excluded explicitly and entirely any idea of the beginning of the world, whereas it maintained its unity and its hierarchical dependence upon an eternal and, in a sense, supramundane entity.

## 2. AUGUSTINE AND AQUINAS.

In very sharp contract to these views we quote the first sentence of *Genesis:* "In the beginning, God created the heavens and the earth." This, of course, could be interpreted in many ways but in the Christian tradition the view prevailed that it meant a definite event of creation, an absolute beginning of the world. The conflict with Greek concepts appeared in full light when Christianity became a public and honored religion. For instance, Ambrosius, at the beginning of his *Exameron* presents, with mixed indignation and irony, the concept of an eternal world as a proof of the conceited extravagance of philosophers. But, not much later, one of Ambrosius' own disciples, Augustine, took the question very seriously. There were not many possible solutions. Democritean philosophies seemed excluded for obvious reasons, and so some compromise was to be looked for, either with Plato, or with Aristotle. The first way was that of Augustine; the second that of Aquinas, and I do not think that a third way could have been found.

We recall the famous passage of Augustine's *Confessions*, relating to the problem:[14] To the question "What was God doing before the creation?" some, says Augustine, ironically answer: "He was preparing punishments for people raising such deep questions." But Augustine did not laugh at the joke. He realized that there was no easy answer and looked for a reasonable one in a keen analysis of the concept of time, along the line traced by the *Timaeus*. This led him to one of the very few discoveries which have been made about time since ancient Greek philosophy.

To the question of creation, Augustine answers that there is no "before" the creation. The creation creates time and that is Platonic: "Nec tu tempore tempora praecedis; alioquin, non omnia tempora praecederes. Sed praecedis omnia praeterita celsitudine semper praesentis eternitatis et superas omnia futura...."[15] The reference to past, present, and future recalls the *Timaeus*, but Augustine pushes the analysis further and makes explicit an ontological structure more complex than the simple Aristotelian ordering before-after. *Present* is in the full sense of the word, *past* and *future* are and are not, they are some sort of non-being, or half-being. The main point in Augustine's analysis seems to be this: the experience of the present, he says, if it did not fall into the past would be eternity;[16] the falling into past of the present, which is time, is a sort of degeneration of eternity. Augustine writes *distensio*, meaning probably more than extension, perhaps some sort of decay.[17] Moreover, we must notice that, in order to express the relationship between the eternal present of God and its *distensio* in the world, Augustine uses geometrical metaphors as though he were trying to refer to a sort of second dimension in the structure of time. "Superas" he says to God; "celsitudine tua"; and in that sort of vertical dimension, God "precedes" even the past. Centuries later, this will lead to the concept of "continuous creation" as it is explicitly stated by Descartes, Malebranche and Leibniz. In a way such a doctrine satisfies the Biblical requirement of the absolute dependence of the world upon God, but the literal meaning of "beginning" is completely forgotten.

At first sight, what Thomas Aquinas tried to do was still more difficult. He tried to reconcile the first sentence of *Genesis* with Aristotle's conception of the eternity of the world. Yet, his solution prevailed, at least in the doctrine of Catholic church.

Aquinas does not want to alter Aristotle's doctrine on this point. In his commentary of the *de Caelo*, he concedes that, as Aristotle says, the world could not have begun, and will not end "per generationem and corruptionem, quasi a natura". But he says that, according to the faith, "incoepit esse", "effluens e primo principio" who was not bound to create the world at any definite time but did it "secundum quod voluit", "postquam prius (mundus) non fuerit".[18] God is an absolute cause of the world and gave it an absolute beginning. Clearly, in Aquinas' concept, *there was* a definite beginning of the world, and that event had a cause, namely an entirely arbitrary will. Not being "natural", the beginning was not determined by any law of causality, which makes unanswerable Augustine's question.

## 3. THE MODERN AGE.

I must just jump over centuries of metaphysics to come to, what seems to me, the basic historical fact which determines the modern form of our problem. The rise of the new philosophy of nature which eventually resulted in the enormous development of what we call "science", was associated with the resurgence and, ultimately, the complete victory of the Democritean concept. Progressively, that concept prevailed over the uncertain and somewhat paradoxical mixture of Aristotelism and creationism which had, for centuries, occupied the scene of natural philosophy.

The notion of a very long, indeterminate, and perhaps infinite duration replaced, through a long and silent process, the belief in a short cosmic history of a few thousand years. Such a replacement could have been compatible with an Aristotelian philosophy, but at the same time, the rest of that philosophy came under fire. The new concept of mechanical causality was more akin to that of Democritus rather than to the ideas of Aristotle. At the beginning of the 18th century ideas of final causation and cosmic harmony, revived by Leibniz and Wolff as against Descartes and Spinoza, were still widely accepted. The popular concept of the clockwork-universe, used by Voltaire among others, helped combine the new scientific and technical requirement of mechanical causality with the notion of a cosmic order.[19] But at the end of the Enlightenment, final causes definitely and forever lost ground, at least among cosmologists; in biology, however, things were, of course, very different.

Along the way, other Democritean concepts, including that of order created by chance, were rediscovered by the scientists. Newton's concept of absolute time was probably grounded in theology, but it was transformed into a Democritean time by his followers who maintained the concept and forgot the theology; time became an empty though real form which was not in any way related to any exceptional event concerning the universe as a whole.

Finally, along the Democritean line, the very concept of the universe weakened conspicuously. The hypothesis of a multiplicity of worlds, naively understood as a multiplicity of inhabited planets and stars, became a very common creed in the 18th century. On the theoretical side, Newtonian theory provided laws and calculating procedures to explain and predict very accurately the local motions of the planets and satellites, but it gave no clue to the understanding of cosmic structure as a whole. The unity of the universe was asserted only in so far as the laws of motion were regarded as universal; moreover, the universality of the law of gravitation was the main cosmological problem of the 18th century. Even when established, as Laplace thought it was, it secured only a formal unity, not an ordered "cosmos". On the side of observation, as a result of the grand, but unsuccessful attempts of William Herschel, the enormous size of the system of stars and nebulae, the difficulty of fathoming and measuring it, of understanding its structure, appeared more and more clearly.

On this point also, Democritus prevailed. This does not mean that all scientists interested in cosmological subjects were, and still less, declared themselves to have been Democritean. In 19th century literature one often finds references to the Creator and the Creation, though probably more so in English speaking countries than in French or German literature. But were these references usually more than a pre-caution to protect religious faith and its moral implications?

So, we may say that at the age of classical science cosmology was Democritean: infinite space, infinite time, no real unity of the world except that formal unity provided by the universality of physical laws, no definite concept or beginning or end of the world, mechanical and local causality, excluding cosmic order and final causality. It is probably not a purely accidental coincidence that the atomic concept, which is usually considered as the most characteristic element of Demo-critus's philosophy was also the favorite hypothesis of 19th century science.

## 4. COSMOLOGY TODAY.

The question I would now raise is this: is contemporary cosmology Democritean? Is it, at least, as easily and completely Democritean as cosmology was a century ago? Contemporary cosmology has inherited its basic concepts and methods from mathematics, physics, astronomy of the last century, and it could not exist without that inheritance. But new observational data and new theoretical ideas have completely transformed its vistas. This transformation results in very deep conceptual difficulties, particularly where the notions of beginning and end are concerned. I would now draw your attention to these difficulties even if only by mentioning and naming them, because their discussion would necessarily be very technical. They were already seen in classical science, but the new trend of contemporary cosmology makes them sharper.

I shall distinguish between two kinds of difficulties: (A) the unity of the universe and its being self-contained and (B) the direction of time.

A. In the Democritean view prevailing in the 19th century, for the reasons we have just recalled, the world, as one and whole, remained, both empirically and theoretically, outside the field of scientific inquiry. In the 20th century, on the one hand, more powerful instrumental techniques have revealed the extragalactic universe and some of its remarkably simple and universal properties. On the other hand, the concept of the universe has been thoroughly transformed by relativity theory. The universe has come back into the field of science as a consequence of (1) the mathematical relationship between the distribution of matter and energy and the structure of space-time and (2) the general hypotheses about that distribution on a cosmic scale as suggested by observation. Thus, there has been unquestionably, since the nineteen-twenties, a rebirth of cosmology.

But the trouble has been that the basic physical concepts of causality, although greatly refined by relativity theory, and still more by quantum theory, still rely on the traditional mathematical structure and therefore are adaptable to local processes, not to cosmic ones. When the universe as a whole is concerned, can we maintain the distinction between universal laws and the particular conditions in which they apply (as Dr Fraser has already asked in connection with the papers of Davies and Landsberg)? If the existing world is a particular case, must we agree that the laws are somehow "out of the world" and that they imply possible worlds, which nevertheless, did not come into existence because ο δημιουργόζ chose the one we know? Must we come back to Plato? Or must we say that above the mathematical causality, but within the world, operates a principle of harmonic and selective causality, a πρῶτου κινήτον? Must we come back to Aristotle? Some 20th century cosmologists, (for instance Bondi, McCrea) are aware of the problem of cosmic, as opposed to local, or differential causality. I understand that Dr Davies is trying in his own way to face questions of that kind. Nobody of course, at least in scientific circles, seems prepared to maintain a Platonic or Aristotelian cosmology. Thus, the question remains open whether and how the concept of the universe can be reconciled with the still prevailing Democritean philosophy.

*B.* The second set of problems which arise about Democritean cosmology is linked with the so-called "arrow of time." The last great discovery about time is probably that of the general principle of irreversibility in physical phenomena. This was achieved, as is well known, in the middle of the 19th century by William Thomson (later Lord Kelvin) and Rudolf Clausius, with the correct formulation of the second law of thermodynamics.

But man did not wait for Clausius before observing the general tendency of natural things to decay. Yet in none of the three conceptions we have mentioned was that fact stated as a universal principle, and in all three, including Democritus', it was more or less concealed either by the alternation of generations and destructions, or by the incorruptibility of celestial beings.

It soon appeared in the course of classical science, even before the great scientific revolutions of the 20th century, that the existence of a general principle of irreversibility was not easily made consistent with a Democritean view of nature; this can be seen in the passage of Boltzmann's *Lectures on Gas Theory* (§ 90) already quoted by Dr Davies, of a purely Democritean vein. Boltzmann accepts the hypothesis of a plurality of worlds and even that of a plurality of times. The direction of time is determined by the increase of entropy, and in a huge statistical system of particles there may be very large fluctuations within which less probable configurations may steadily come out of more probable ones so that, compared with the rest of the system, the direction of time would appear reversed. Boltzmann suggests that in very distant parts of the universe this may take place and time may be reversed relatively to ours. What he does not say is what would happen at the boundary between that distant world and ours.... Here Aristotle's ghost comes in and whispers: "one time, one world."

In the age of Boltzmann, that is, at the beginning of this century, such discussions did not seem to have any direct physical significance except for gases completely isolated in closed boxes. They referred to sets containing very great numbers of invariable atoms in which a standard of rest and equilibrium conditions could be statistically defined. This is obviously an oversimplified model of the real world. On the contrary, in the 20th century very important astrophysical discoveries seem to fit very well with the principle of the universal direction of time and impose upon us, contrary to Democritean concepts, the notion of a cosmic-oriented history.

Consider, for instance, the formation and evolution of the stars, a process of a very common type. This was a problem technically inaccessible in classical physics, to which a general pattern of solution has now been found. Up to a certain point, the process admits of a Democritean alternation: the stars are formed by accretion of diffuse material and, as their life goes on, they undergo more or less violent transformations during which a part of their mass is thrown out into space, providing material for new star formation. But this cannot be a real alternation, and no kind of periodicity is possible. Within the stars basic irreversible transformations are taking place: for instance hydrogen is transformed into helium with a loss of mass released as radiant energy. Moreover, in the most frequent cases, the main part of the mass becomes more and more concentrated. Eventually it reaches a state of equilibrium out of which it could be taken only by some very energetic external stimulation, but the general dispersion of matter and radiation makes such an external action less and less probable.

This leads us to the second very important discovery of modern astrophysics, the red-shift of distance nebulae, generally understood, at least nowadays, as the effect of a cosmic expansion. Now, even if, as some people do, we doubt that this effect results from an expansion, it still seems to offer the evidence of a cosmic "arrow of time," an everlasting and universal criterion to distinguish past from future. For, the universal *red*-shift of nebulae points to a cosmic process which, whatever it is, is oriented in the same direction as the irreversible local processes.

Things being so, two alternatives may be considered: an infinite or a finite past. In both cases, because of the "arrow of time", it seems to me that great difficulties are inevitable; but, as the working cosmologists who are here seem to be interested in "big bang" hypotheses, let us concentrate on the second case. In that case, we have a real beginning and, in a new form, Augustine's question comes again: what was there *before* the beginning? But actually, the question is very different and not only because it concerns the world and not God. In Augustine's Christian view - at least when he opens the discussion - creation is to be understood as taking place at a definite instant, the first of the time series. In modern cosmology the "big bang" is a singularity, clearly expressible in mathematical terms. The existence of a beginning at a finite interval in the past does not prevent the ordered set of instants from being an *open* set, even without a *first* element. Thus an infinity of continuous transformations of time coordinates, preserving the order, could transform that finite interval into an infinite one (Milne was the first to work out such a transformation).

But what is the *physical* meaning of such a situation? To measure the interval we must have a definite unit of time, linked with a periodical process, and to say meaningfully that the interval is finite is to say that the interval contains a finite number of such processes. But what unit can we choose? Years or days? What is a year or a day where and when there is no sun and no earth? Should we choose frequencies corresponding to atomic spectral lines and energy levels of atoms? How can that be counted where and when no atoms exist? How about nuclear periodical processes? But near enough the "big bang" will we find nuclei? Finally, quantum conditions will prevent the use of any definite unit, the consequence being that the history of the world depends on a situation totally unthinkable according to the usual standards of science. The situation analogous to that in which Aquinas, very consciously, wished to place the natural mind when he referred to an absolutely arbitrary act of God's will.

Must we then, in order to remain Democritean, and to go on laughing with Democritus, conceive a sort of weak "big bang" which would allow a physical prehistory? Then we would have to face a new problem: how could, so to speak, the direction of time cross the "big bang"? That is: if we take an event *A*, before the "big bang" and another *B*, after it, what physical criterion can we apply to assert that *A* is really before *B*? That seems difficult to decide for the "big bang" is supposed to destroy any physical structure and, therefore, break any process or evolution continuity.

Finally, let me, at least, ask the question: facing these difficulties in cosmology, must we and can we give up the Democritean philosophy and come back to Platonic or Aristotelian concepts? It would be extremely difficult to do that within the framework of modern scientific thought which has eliminated any theological and teleological reference and is very strongly bound to the classical concept of causality.

If it is yet possible, I think the Platonic or rather Augustinian way would be more promising than the Aristotelian which would not help to solve the difficulties mentioned. For, we found in Augustine's analysis of time something which would put the whole philosophy of time on a very different footing. He referred to that basic element of the experience of time, something familiar to everybody and yet completely ignored by Democritean philosophy and scientific thought: the permanent present *into* and *out of* which time flows. It is permanent indeed and eternally present, for no one ever certified that he was in the process of being born, nor, except in a famous short story of Edgar Allan Poe, that he was dead. I do not know what sort of metaphysics could now be built on that, but I am sure I should be unable to do it.

NOTES

1. Diels-Kranz, *Fragmente der Vorsokratiker*, 8th ed. 67 A 21 (II, p. 76); 68 A I (37) (II, p. 84); 68 A 40 (II, p. 94)

2. ibid. 68 A 82 (II, p. 104)

3. ibid. 68 A 66-67 (II, p. 101).

4. Phaedo 97 b-c.

5. Timaeus 29-31a.

6. ibid. 37 d.

7. ibid. 38

8. Metaphys. 1071b-1072a.

9. Metaphys. 1071b-1072a; de Caelo 279a 15-20.

10. Physics 278b 3.

11. Metaphys. 1072a.

12. ibid. 1072b

13. de Caelo 270b 14.

14. Book XI. xii 14

15. ibid. xiii 16

16. ibid. xiv 17, in fine.

17. ibid. xxiii 30, in fine.

18. *Commentary on the de Caelo* I, lect. 29.

19. On this, see F. C. Haber "The Cathedral Clock and the Cosmological Clock Metaphor," *The Study of Time II* (New York: Springer Verlag, 1975).

# The Past and the Future

D. Park

*Abstract*

*In the language of physics, which gives a reasonably exact and economical description of natural events, there exists no word or concept equivalent to "now." Most human cultures have such an idea, together with terms implying that "now" progresses from the future into the past. This paper attempts to identify aspects of the physical world which in contributing to the human experience of time give rise to metaphors of passage. Two facts are discussed in the language of physics: that our knowledge of the past is of a different kind from our knowledge of the future, and that while our acts have consequences for the future, there is nothing we can do to change the past. Both these facts are corollaries of the general increase in entropy asserted by the second law of thermodynamics, which in turn depends on the laws of physics and the overall history of the universe. To carry the analysis further and distinguish what depends on law from what depends on history seems impossible within the present disciplinary limits of science because to distinguish between scientific law and scientific fact requires that one can believe the fact could have been otherwise, and contemplation of the universe gives no grounds for such an opinion. Finally, it is suggested that the "passage of time" can be considered as a metaphorical expression of the pervasive consequences of the general increase in entropy required by the second law.*

In the early 1960's I met J. T. Fraser and became involved in helping to edit some of the contributions in a book he was then compiling, *The Voices of Time*.[1] In this process I became uncomfortably aware of a discrepancy between the way physicists use the concept of time in the physical description of nature and the way they talk about it in ordinary conversation. In brief, the equations of physics denote time by a letter $t$ which occurs in various formulas, but there is in these formulas no indication that one value of $t$ is in any way special: the value we denote as "now." And, lacking this, physics also lacks any way of expressing the ordinary intuition that the future is in some sense continually becoming now and turning into the past. At that time, I was not even curious as to whether anybody else had thought about this matter, since the first rule of the practice of physics is the old motto of the Royal Society, *Nullius in verba*, which means that if you want to understand anything you have to do the work yourself. In 1969 came the first conference of this Society at Oberwolfach. I talked about the question to several people, and finally Professor P. T. Landsberg said he did not think there is any problem; in physics, he said "now" simply refers to any given value of $t$. I could see that within the physical framework of ideas, which was what interested me at the time, this explained everything, but that it did not deal at all with our intuitive perception of time.

People interested in the exact laws of nature know that these laws consist of two logically unrelated components: mathematical formulas and the sentences which state in plain language what the symbols in the formulas have to do with our experience of nature. The history of physics since it became mathematical shows that the formula usually arrives first: it becomes apparent that nature is characterized by a mathematical relation of some kind, and only later does a very careful analysis show how to put meaning into the hollow phrase "is characterized by."

The only way to test the claim that "now is simply the numerical value attached to the letter $t$" is to see whether it is compatible with our experience of instants. I think that we are not conscious of instants but only of events (inside or outside our own heads) and that at any given instant of time, denoted by the letter $t$, it is our awareness of events, and of ourselves being aware of them, that makes our sense of "now." As Hugo Bergmann[2] summed it up many years ago, "'Now' is the temporal mode of the experiencing ego." The image of passing time in physics differs from that in ordinary speech: we normally speak as though we, with our "now," were somehow stationary in time while events pass through "now" from future to past, whereas physics expresses exactly the same relationship by saying that time, with its various values of "now," represents a fixed scale, against which are displayed events of all kinds, including those of human consciousness. These two formulations represent very different uses of language, so much so that it is difficult to maintain that they are merely two different ways of saying the same thing.

It seems that not every human culture represents the passage of time like the flow of a river. According to Whorf,[3] the Hopi Indians do not. Instead of dividing events into those in the past and those in the future, with the present as the boundary between them, the Hopi divide them into those already manifested and those evolving, with no sense of temporal progression, into manifested form. The distinction between them conceals temporal order under a much more general distinction between events we know about and events which affect us in other ways, and suggests time only in a secondary and derivative sense. The Hopi have no concept of a moving present.

Is Whorf exactly right? And are there other cultures that do not use the idea of temporal passage and express the corresponding facts of life in other ways? Let us suppose that ethnologists discover that this is indeed the case. It would still not be quite clear what we should conclude. I give two possible conclusions, both somewhat extreme: 1] The passage of time is a fact of nature or of human perception or both, overlooked only by a few backward cultures which limp along with inferior formulations. 2] It is a fad, arising in classical times because it enabled people to describe temporal relations, which are confusing, in terms of spatial relations, which are simple, without doing any of the hard thinking that is required if we are to develop clear concepts of time. Perhaps, as one says so often, the truth lies somewhere in between. I illustrate the wide range of possible views only to emphasize that my question is finally a question of fact, not opinion - that we ought to be able to find out whether there are human languages in which time does not pass and whether they serve their speakers well or badly. If it turns out that there are systematic and useful ways of talking about time that are different from our own, they will be of great value in allowing us to reach fact-based answers to old questions about being, becoming, and "the now."

To be sure, metaphorical language representing time as passage is very widespread. The words *past, passé, vergangen, praeteritus*, all contain the idea of motion, and a physicist attempting to understand time metaphors in terms of physical time must take account of their extremely persuasive character - so persuasive that for many people they are plainly and simply fact.

The metaphors of time are aspects of human consciousness, and so is physics, but it would be folly to assume that consciousness can be discussed in the language of physics. Take for example a much simpler question, that of understanding an electronic computer. Every part of it is physics, all the wires and transistors, but even a complete account of an operating computer expressed in such terms could not possibly explain what the computer is doing. For that you need the ideas and words of mathematics, which are unpredictable from those of physics, and if you wish to study why one kind of computer is used instead of another, or why the computer is there at all, still further extensions of ideas and words are needed, perhaps those of economics and business. The method of physical explanation is deductive: one shows that the observed phenomena can be understood if one assumes certain basic rules, but in no sense does mathematics follow from the rules of physics, or economics or business from either, so that the method breaks down when applied to the computer. I suspect that it breaks down, for the same reasons but more completely, when applied to the brain.

This does not mean, of course, that brain and mind cannot be related, but only that the mode of explanation belonging to this science cannot be deductive. We know something of the path to be followed. Somewhere along it occur sentences like "I know," "I believe," "I hope," perfectly good words which we all understand, but it is my understanding that nobody knows anything about the terms which will connect these words to the language of neurophysiology. At some point in that future argument there will occur for the first time the word "now," and it may be possible to understand why, for some minds at least, this "now" has a progressive character. What I hope to do in this paper is not to explain directly why we so often speak of time in terms of flow, but to show why certain temporal phenomena in physics make it very natural that we should do so.

PERCEIVED TIME

I am going to organize the distinguishing marks of perceived past and future around two facts:

1) We are surrounded by reminders of the past, including our own clear memories, pieces of evidence which have no counterpart with respect to the future. What we call knowledge, in so far as it refers to events at all, refers to past events.

2) The past cannot be undone. Whatever we may do affects only the future.

These sound like two separate statements, the one referring to our information and the other to our actions, but there is more to it than that, for it is in the nature of the human condition that they have much to do with each other. To the extent that our acts are not random sneezes and hiccups but instead are planned with regard to their future effects, they are conditioned by the information we have. Thus, information has the two aspects of knowledge on the one hand and organizing power on the other,[4] and it is this concept that forms the link between the two separate perceptions of time's directionality.

These remarks are very general, but they have been formulated in exact, quantitative language, notably by Costa de Beauregard,[5] through the use of information theory.

The purposes of our present acts are usually to impose a certain order on the future world. For this to be possible we must have, and use, an amount of information concerning the present which, according to a suitable measure, is at least as great as the measure of the order we wish to impose. If we wish to create only disorder we can do so by means which require very little information, perhaps by setting off an explosion. The assassin needs to study the daily habits of his victim, but bombers of airports and markets do not need to know anything at all. It is enough to have opinions, and intentions, and a bomb. A remarkable fact about time is that not knowledge, or techniques, or will are enough to enable us to foretell the future or change the past.

## KNOWING THE FUTURE

As Niels Bohr once remarked, "it is very hard to predict - especially the future." The ingredient in this fact that makes it of perpetual interest to physicists is that none of the fundamental atomic laws of physics that are relevant to prediction makes any distinction between past and future. That is, if the matter depended on them alone, prediction and retrodiction would be equally easy, or difficult.

Exactly how to explain the irreversibility of physical processes in terms of reversible physical laws is a century-old question whose answer has only gradually become clear, and I am able to use the word "clear" largely because P. C. W. Davies, in a critical work[6] of great penetration and subtlety, has at last made the distinctions that have to be made and given the explanation that fits our present understanding of the nature of the universe and the laws that govern it. My task is much easier: to give some qualitative impression of the size of the numbers involved, so that one can gain some estimate of *how much* more difficult it is to know the future than the past.

We live surrounded by very large numbers. Consider the weather. It is roughly uniform in a region 100 km on a side and 5 km in height. Appreciable variations begin on a larger scale than this. To predict the weather a week in advance it would be advisable, even if not strictly necessary, to take into account all the regions of the size just mentioned into which the Earth's atmosphere can be divided. There are about 15 million of them, and this number gives an estimate of the amount of information that would have to be added to all our other information about weather in general if a firm prediction were to be made. The amount of information that today's forecasters have available, or could handle, is much less than this. Similarly, I might estimate the number of human beings whose actions might be able to affect each of us in the next week, or the number of stored-up surprises which the earth and its cargo of rocks, trees, animals, insects, and bacteria may have prepared for us. Some people try more or less consciously to live in such a way that the amount of information they would need in order to predict their future is greatly reduced, but even in a monastery of the strictest kind, the amount remains very large.

If the world is so complex, how then do we know the past? How can we find out with certainty what the weather was here a week ago, or who was in this village? Of course, we cannot be completely certain about the past. We might be victims of a conspiracy to lie, or of other people's delusions, or of our own. But still, much less effort would be required to find out with almost perfect certainty who was here last week than to predict who will be here next week. There is a reason for this: the world was a much more orderly place last week than it is now or will be next week.

DISORDER

There is an obvious connection between concepts of order and information. Information is measured in terms of binary choices. If my hat can be in only one place in my house, then I need no special information in order to find it. If it can be in one of two places, one bit of information is required. If in one of four places, I specify the place by cutting the list in half twice: two bits. Any number from five to eight places: three bits. Thus in science as in daily life, disorder is defined in terms of missing information, and the unit of information, the bit, is defined as the amount of information required in order to choose correctly between two equally likely alternatives. The greater the disorder in my affairs, the harder it is to predict where my hat will be found; that is, the more information is required. Information is defined in terms of choices among possibilities, and when I speak of the rapidly increasing disorder of the world - that is, the rapidly increasing quantity of information required if deductions are to be made, I refer to the rapid expansion of possibilities.

Ideas like these are sometimes more manageable if one concentrates on trivially simple illustrations. Suppose that today 10,000 new schillings lie in the Vienna mint. Tomorrow they will be sent in equal lots to two banking centers, and each schilling is in one or the other. It then requires almost 10,000 bits of information, 9993 in fact, to specify where all the coins are. And at the end of the year, suppose that each coin is in some bag, box, or pocket, and that there are 100 million such hiding places in Austria. It will then require more than 265,000 bits of information to specify where they all are.

Perhaps there is an objection: I prejudiced the argument by choosing today as my base: a year ago the metal in the coins was widely dispersed over and under the earth, and consequently in much more disorder than today. I must ask you to accept on faith a universal theorem (a statement of the second law of thermodynamics) that order is only achieved at the expense of even more disorder, and if you do not believe me visit a mine and look at the waste and desolation around it.

Finally, I beg you to notice how limited a notion of the world's true complexity is given by the example of a few new coins. The scientific idea that makes precise the idea of disorder is entropy, and it involves thermal disorder, the entropy of energy that is dissipated as molecular motion into the atmosphere or outer space, as well as the disorder of objects. Here, because molecules are so small, the numbers are much larger. To pursue the matter of the coins down to the molecular scale, suppose I send agents to find them all, compensate their owners, and bring them together into one place again. The entropy of their spatial arrangement would again be zero bits, but the amount of entropy created by just one of the agents in eating and digesting his breakfast on the first day of the search would correspond to some $3 \times 10^{26}$ bits. The second law is not to be denied. I have never seen a numerical estimate of the combined daily entropy increase of the earth and its energy source, the sun, but in almost every part of the natural world where anything happens at all, the increase of this entropy is like a huge cataract, emptying into the sea. As the motive power of a waterfall is gravity, that of entropy is available energy. The energy of the universe originated in the process whereby the whole came into being, about 20 billion years ago, and after a series of transformations virtually all of what will ever be available for our use resides in the earth and the sun. The entropy flow will continue at its present rate until these resources begin to diminish. In the end, if it is the earth's destiny to die quietly, it will become easy to predict the future. Nothing will be happening; and as the landmarks and monuments preserving the record of the past are one by one by Time's fell hand defaced, past and future will become the same.

I think, then, that it is the rapid increase in the world's disorganization, arising from its rapid and complex transactions of energy, that makes the practical difference between the relative ease of finding out the past and of predicting the future.

CHANGING THE PAST

The relative ease with which we can know the future and the past is after all a quantitative matter: we are no more in total ignorance of the future than we are completely certain about the past, but there is another aspect of the difference between past and future which does not depend on quantitative arguments at all: it is not possible, by any act of will, to change the past in any way. Note that I must specify an act of will. If a stone dislodged by frost rolls down a mountain-side, the fact has various consequences that extend into the future and we assume in ordinary discourse that they do not extend into the past, but we have no way of knowing what the past would have been if the stone had not moved. What we do know, every day, is the futility of our own regrets.

At once, there is a very good reason for this futility which applies with equal force to past and future: we may not will impossibilities. We may not reasonably will either a past or a future that we know to be impossible given the present that contains us. I may not will that my mother was a man; that follows from the definitions of the words used and refers to a logical impossibility. But we may not even will that a river should flow uphill either in the future or in the past; logic does not forbid this but physics does, and we know why. Now it may be that in the view of a purely causal God the world as it is necessarily implies a single past and a single future, so that any wish to have them otherwise is unreasonable. Physics is at one with the human heart in not assuming such perfect determinism. Physicists know that the motion of an electron is not exactly, but only statistically determined by the forces acting on it. The question is how much difference this makes. In the ordinary processes of nature, very little. The indeterminacy principle states that one cannot simultaneously assign the position and motion of an object with perfect accuracy, and this has great influence in the theory of atomic structure, yet a spacecraft would orbit the earth for many thousands of years before this indeterminacy added an error of one atomic diameter to its predicted position. If mental processes depend on the motion of a very few electrons in the brain, then it is easy to conclude that our present thoughts are not determined by the past. But my physiologist friends tell me that nerve currents in the brain are not that small - they involve millions of electrons, and so the statistical uncertainties tend to cancel. If this were not so, we could easily find explanations for freedom of the will without having to do any careful thinking at all, but as it is, we have only our inner sense to tell us how free we really are. In particular, it is not clear how free we are to wish the past to be different from what it was, even though we may feel at liberty to do so. Our regrets over the past, and our desires that it should have been different, are shaped by past occurences. To say that we can will a different past requires us to believe that amid all this causality there is an area in which necessary causality does not operate. Having arrived at the door marked Freedom I shall not enter. The words and ideas or, if you like, the strategy of explanation that leads consecutively from the physics of the brain to the explanation of consciousness and freedom simply do not exist.[7] To finish the story will require imagination and hard work, and having shown as clearly as I can what is to be determined I make no effort to determine it, for it is not the only problem that confronts us if we are to understand why we cannot change the past. There remains the question of how it can be accomplished if we are free to will to make the attempt.

## THE PRACTICAL PROBLEM

If we are able to will the future and succeed, to some degree, in shaping it as we desire, it must be because our brains are, in some manner, parts of a great mechanism, the world, which evolves according to causal laws. Now we must think about the causal laws, and I use a specific example beloved of physicists, the disturbances in the surface of a pool of water. We know from laws of physics that these disturbances can be understood in terms of waves. There are simple waves that we can see very readily, or more complex disturbances which may be analyzed as the effect of a number of waves of different amplitude and wavelength crossing the surface at the same time. We know from the conservation of energy that waves neither come into existence nor disappear spontaneously; they receive their energy from moving matter and deliver it to moving matter. As an example, a wave reaching the edge of a swimming pool reflects back into the pool with scarcely any loss of energy, but waves on a pool in the woods, reaching an edge at which they can deliver their energy to floating leaves and grass, do not reflect at all.

Imagine that I sit beside such a natural pool, and that the water is flat. I throw in a stone. Waves spread outward from the splash, preserving for a moment the memory of the event, but until the stone actually touched the water the surface showed no premonition that the stone was on its way. Supposing that there were a premonition, it would have to take the form of a wave, starting at the edge of the pond and converging towards where the stone is about to hit. Such a wave must move inward; it cannot move outward because there is no energy source at the center. It would have to be produced by a concerted motion of leaves and grass at the edges of the pond, and these in turn would have to be produced by motion in the air around them. That is to say, it would be a case of very complex causes combining to produce a simple effect, of the world moving from a state in which much information is needed to specify it to one in which little is needed. As we have seen, the evolution of the universe decrees otherwise: the direction of time in which entropy increases is the same for all systems that interact in any way with each other and with the outside world.[8] The example of waves on a pond was chosen not because it is appropriate for contemplation at a summer conference, but rather because we are able to express and visualize our most profound understanding of the behavior of matter in terms of a theory of waves. Except for minor differences all waves are governed by a single mathematical theory, and the example of the pond may be taken as a model of very general considerations on the theory of interacting material objects. As the universe evolves, the overwhelming majority of individual processes progress from the simple towards the complex: waves move outward from a simple action at the center to manifold actions at the periphery.[6] If we were to act upon the past, we would have to reverse this motion and create the manifold actions at the periphery in order, earlier, to affect the center. But ordinary events increase the world's complexity at such an enormous rate that a reversal would involve the control of nature over a large region at a molecular level of detail. If all the magnitudes were different - if molecules were larger and fewer and the universe smaller, if our senses and fingers were more finely tuned, such an intervention could at least be thought about, and we would then have to think about the logical quandaries that would arise if I should decree that my father and mother had never met. I do not take this last difficulty as fatal. Logic, applied to events as we perceive them, is an experimental science like any other, and it is hard now to say what logical forms would be needed in such a case. There is a more profound difficulty, however: how much sense does it make to speculate what would happen if some of the numbers characterizing the universe and its contents were different from what they are?

STRUCTURE AND HISTORY

Science makes careful distinctions between general statements and particular statements. All atoms have mass but only some will combine with oxygen. The difference is one of chemical species. In nuclear fusion all deuterons have identical structure but some will react with tritons and some will not; it depends on the relative velocities. In the first case, the reaction depends on structure; in the second. on what has previously happened to accelerate the two particles. Suppose now that we notice that the universe has some property: the approximately equal number of protons and electrons, for example, or the huge preponderance (as far as we can see) of matter over antimatter, or the apparently universal tendency of entropy to increase. In what terms are we to explain it? In order to distinguish explanations based on past history from explanations based on structure, we find ourselves saying: Consider another universe, set moving in the same way but containing an entirely different amount of matter. Or even making arguments like this: Consider an ensemble consisting of a huge number of universes, in which a certain structural parameter varies at random: What is the probability that a universe chosen at random from this ensemble resembles our own?

It is possible, of course, to proceed blindly to answer such questions by mathematical arguments. One assumes that the laws of nature as we have derived them from our experience of a possibly tiny corner of space-time are valid universally and that there are no other laws; everything else is assumed to depend on the universe's initial state: how it was constituted and how it was set in motion. This procedure gives scientific results that are not absurd. It explains quite well, with hypotheses which we have grown used to even if they seemed wild to us at first, a number of observed facts about the universe. But at this point we are interested in the logic of explanation and it is not clear that a theory of this kind makes any logical sense at all. By what right do we distinguish between generic and specific properties of a thing, the Universe, of which there exists, by definition, only a single example? By what right do we assume that there could be a universe with any properties different from those we know, or that if there were such a thing, it would follow the same fundamental laws as our own? The usual methods of science are clearly not being followed here, and even if some day a consistent theory is developed which accounts for all the large-scale properties of the universe it will be open to the criticism: All you are saying, with great elaboration of detail, is that the universe is as it is because that is the way it is.

All of cosmology is infected with circular arguments, and I am afraid that this is the point at which we must leave the explanation of the enormous preponderance in the universe of processes leading to increased disorder. As Davies modestly says at the end of his book, "It seems that we have reached the limits at which *physics* can supply useful information regarding the *origin* of time asymmetry. The remaining problems in this respect appear to be philosophical rather than physical...." We have reached the limits of the usefulness of the language of physics and must stumble forward in the attempt to invent more general concepts which can neither be found, nor legitimated when they are found, by the methods of science as we know it. These questions will, as Davies says, "continue to keep the philosophers busy for a long time to come."

## CONCLUSION

The study of time is an unusually fertile area of imaginative thought. Most of the work that is done concerns strategies: the artist plotting to master time, social man trying to use it, philosophical man trying to fix it in categories of thought. The physicist is almost alone in trying, from his limited perspective, to explain it. But the word must be used with care, for time, in the physicist's sense, is an order we impose upon the world, or, if you wish, upon our experience of it, and so does not at first seem to merit any explanation beyond that which we give to our own artifacts. Yet the world is such that it allows, indeed seems to require some such concept if it is to be described at all, and here lies the challenge to achieve what clarity we can.

It is widely, though perhaps not universally,[3,9] agreed that there is something about our experience of time that demands metaphorical language of progress or flow in order to explain it. By taking the metaphor for literal truth one becomes involved in futile hypotheses and explanations that explain nothing, but even if it is recognized as a metaphor, we need some explanation why it is so pervasive. This I set out to do by considering two aspects of the human experience of time which seem to require the metaphor with special insistence: that we know the past but not the future, and that our willed acts affect the future but not the past. Both lend themselves to discussion in terms which represent life as a journey through time. In trying to understand them in terms which do not represent use of this metaphor[10] we arrive at familiar questions which lie ahead of modern science: the relation of consciousness to material substance and the structure and evolution of the universe as a whole. The intellectual problems encountered on the way to these two frontiers have not been too difficult, but what lies beyond the frontiers will be learned only slowly as we forge new intellectual tools which we have never needed before. So the subject is a living one, and even if by some miracle I have persuaded you of the truth of all I say, we are still far from a rational explanation of our experience of time's motion.

It is, surely, something that we experience - in our own minds as the accumulation of knowledge, in our bodies and the world about us as the processes of irreversible change. It exists. What is moving? In its fundamental sense, time is a dimension of our experience to which a scale can be attached that reads seconds or minutes or centuries. It is not the scale that moves; on the contrary, it is the fixed scale that allows us to define motion. Motion usually implies going from one place to another, and our intuition of "going forward in time" springs from an analogy with this kind of motion. But I remind you that in an older sense, the word was used to denote any kind of change, including increase and decrease. What forms of speech are available to describe in common language the feeling that everyone must know of holding on to life in a world which tends insistently towards disorder? In our culture the words refer to motion, to the flow of rivers, to departure. "...the houses, the streets, the avenues, are fugitive, alas, as are the years." These are metaphors which represent motion *in* time as motion *of* time. Motion in time is change, which can be fixed on a quantitative scale as a general increase in entropy, so vast and overwhelming in its speed and scope that at any moment of self-contemplation we may become conscious of it. It is motion in the sense of the old philosophy, before dynamical illustrations and explanations became so popular, and I believe it is this motion, perceived in the sweeping away of old landmarks and the gradual erosion of ourselves, which we attempt to fix into language by the metaphor of the motion of time.

NOTES

1. J. T. Fraser, ed., *The Voices of Time* (Braziller, N.Y., 1966).

2. H. Bergmann, *Der Kampf um das Kausalgesetz in der jüngsten Physik* (Braunschweig, 1929).

3. B. L. Whorf, "An American Indian Model of the Universe," in *Language, Thought, and Reality* (MIT Press, Cambridge, 1956).

4. "There are two ways of knowing: to possess knowledge (for as we say that one knows when he possesses knowledge); or to put the knowledge into practice." Aristotle, *Magna Moralia* 1201 b 12.

5. O. Costa de Beauregard, *Le second Principe de la science du temps* (Eds. du Seuil, Paris, 1963).

6. P. C. W. Davies, *The Physics of Time Asymmetry* (University of California Press, Berkeley, 1974, 1977).

7. J. T. Fraser suggests a strategy that uses a hierarchial scheme for classifying these levels in terms of the temporal concepts which must be introduced in order to explain them: *Time as Conflict: A scientific and humanistic study*. (Renouf USA, Brookfield, Vt., and Birkhäuser, Basel, 1978).

8. There could indeed exist a little world inside a box, even if we have no way to make it, in which events occur in such a way that inhabitants of the box assign the word past to our future and vice versa but only if the walls of the box isolate its contents from *all* interaction with the outside universe. See P. Morrison in A. de-Shalit, H. Feshbach, and L. Van Hove, eds., *Preludes in Theoretical Physics* (North Holland, Amsterdam, 1966).

9. H. Nakamura, "Time in Indian and Japanese Thought," in Ref. 1.

10. For detailed criticisms of the view which takes the metaphor as reality, see D. C. Williams, "The Myth of Passage," in *Principles of Empirical Realism* (Thomas, Springfield, 1966); A. Grünbaum, *Philosophical Problems of Space and Time* (Knopf, N.Y., 1963; Reidel, Dordrecht, 1973). For examples of how time can be discussed in plain language without the use of metaphors of passage, see M. Schlick, *The Philosophy of Nature* (tr. A. von Zeppelin, Philosophical Library, N.Y., 1949), especially Ch. 7; J. C. C. Smart, "Spatializing Time," *Mind 64,* 239 (1955); Ref. 5 above; and D. Park, "The Myth of the Passage of Time," in *The Study of Time*, v.1 (Springer, N.Y., 1972). The paper of S. Watanabe, "Creative Time," in the same volume illuminates with profound insight many of the points only touched on here.

## DISCUSSION AND COMMENT

*by Masano Toda*

Much of the argument given in Park's paper, which is both entertaining and stimulating, seems to depend upon the proposition that the past was more orderly than the future. The proposition itself is none but a commonly shared popular interpretation of the second law of thermodynamics. To me, however, this interpretation smells of naïveté. Except for this *interpretation* of the second law, there is no observable evidence for the proposition. Apparently, orderliness is a matter of definition. A housewife may complain that the orderliness in her house is so easily lost, she has to work always and hard to recover it. As a result of her work, however, the loss in the degree of orderliness in her house is only temporary; it merely oscillates. This is the orderliness from her own point of view. For her son the orderliness of the house will also oscillate, but does so out of phase from his mother's. After she put all his toys away, his orderliness will come to its nadir as he will be completely at a loss where to find his favorite toy.

Now, let me go a bit further. Imagine a universe in which the whole physical process is almost the complete reverse of what we are experiencing in this universe of ours. Note that this reverse world is governed by the same physical laws as ours except for the second law which is to be reversed, too. My question is "Are the physicists in this universe (antiphysicists who can make observations as photons are around even though they are absorbed by, rather than emitted from, stars) in more priviledged position than our physicists in predicting the future by virtue of the decreasing entropy?" As in Park's example, they may be able to predict from a slight atmospheric disturbances a concerted vibration of the molecules around the rim of a pond which will subsequently create concentric waves directing toward the center of the pond, where something will jump out when all the waves converged. But what is it that will come out, a stone, a frog or a bathing beauty?

In my conjecture, the work of antiphysicists will be just as tough as that of our physicists, More interestingly, they will find a different set of physical laws, a dual of ours, which, however, will lead to a drastically different *interpretation* of essentially the same laws. Consider, heat, for example. In a world where heat may at any moment *unpredictably* turn into work, they certainly cannot afford to entertain a notion corresponding to our heat. Instead of heat and entropy, they will have some entirely different principles. It would be a worthwhile project to identify them, even for a *normal* physicist.

# The Boundries of the Notion of Time*

M. Toda

ABSTRACT

*For the purpose of studying time, time as an existing entity is a rather untractable object as we are very poorly equipped--with only that clumsy instrument called the clock. Instead, therefore, I propose to study our notions of time, which are certainly richer in content than the homogeneous numerical time ticked off by a clock. On the one extreme end there is the spatialized version of physical time, to which the above mentioned clock-time actually belongs, and on the other end is the age-old intuitive notion of time, the richest in content and the hardest to formalize, the time that has the past, the present and the future, with all kinds of emotional overtones in relation to determinism, creation, free will, and so on.*

*The difficulty inherent in the content analysis of these notions of time is the absence of anything really similar to time so that the conventional strategy in content analysis of decomposing the object into familiar components does not work. The primary purpose of this paper is therefore to try out*

---

*Let me express my gratitude to Dr. Fraser without whose encouragement I would hardly have gotten into this fascinating dilemma of discussing the undiscussable. I also appreciate the freewheeling atmosphere of N.I.A.S., the Netherlands, where I was allowed to write the original version of this paper, only immersed in this atmosphere could the above dilemma have looked enticing.

*some unconventional research strategies. In the first section are discussed the intuitive notion of time as a notion coexisting with other notions in apparent harmony in the cognitive system, some hypotheses concerning the origin of the notion, and how the cognitive system has come to require the distinction between the past and the future. In the rest of the paper I attempted to accumulate evidence to define the border of the extent of the notion by testing the stretchability of one's imagination about time to which religious beliefs and science fiction yield many clues. The three major conclusions obtained are: 1) The notion of physical entropy, the honored resident of the kingdom of physical time, is probably a trespasser from the region of more human time. 2) The intuitive notion of space and that of time are very dissimilar; the former is much commoner compared to the latter, belonging, almost, to the class of sensory attributes. 3) The paradoxes in the fanciest imagination about time, time travel, are probably due to the fallacy introduced by the popular compromising image of time, that which may be called the spatialized intuitive, a modern version of the flowing river, represented by a moving point standing for "now" constantly turning the future part of the time-line into the past.*

## 1. THE INCONGRUENT NOTIONS OF TIME

Occasionally, my ignorance frustrates me, not only about time itself but also about what I really want to know of time. Obviously, it is a fool's errand to try to "define" time. Defining a notion is to find for it an equivalent ideational construct made of some other, usually more primitive, notions. The prerequisite for a successful definition, however, is that *every* aspect of the target notion is represented by some of the component notions used for the definition. Any attempt at defining time, therefore, is bound to be ridiculous, as there is nothing in this world that even remotely resembles time.

If one looks at analogies as poor and imcomplete defintions, however, the analogies of time such as the flying arrow and the flowing river, popular in many different cultures, seem to suggest a certain kinship of time, however tenuous, to "space" and "movement." The kinship, therefore, should provide a precious few clues to those who intend to study time, as clues are scarce, anyway.

Before taking up this issue, however, a grave question must be put about what we mean by the study of time, if time cannot be defined. Is it to understand time? But we do understand time at least on the intuitive level. Otherwise, how could we communicate with others about time, let alone discuss it, without a definition? Truly, someone (if there was one) who first got the rudimentary notion of time in a prehistoric era must have had a great difficulty in conveying the idea to others. But the notion should have been a great achievement, matched nicely with other notions in the (prehistoric) human cognitive system, so that some of his fellows, too, might have succeeded in developing the same notion for themselves with a minimum of hints from its originator.

This mode of learning notions as a process of self-development aided by culturally and personally provided hints applies to the acquisition, not only of the notion of time, but also of most of the *fundamental* primitive notions in our culture, those which cannot verbally be defined. Such a mode of learning would be possible, however, only when the notions are strongly in accord with the other components of our cognitive system so that they can emerge almost as a necessity. Everything suggests that our intuitive understanding of time is natural and *nearly* complete; virtually no misunderstanding nor miscomprehension occurs in our daily conversation about time--perhaps as long as one does not hear an esoteric argument about time given by a member of the International Society for the Study of Time. Nonetheless, it remains as a mystery why an argument about time almost never fails to stir up a considerable curiosity and excitement in the audience. Perhaps there is something, deep inside the smooth surface of our intuitive understanding of time, a feeling of insufficiency, calling for an explanation.

Come to think of it, however, this is not an exceptional situation. There are many things in the world of which one believes his understanding to be perfect; of his wife, for instance. But just one hint about Desdemona was enough for Othello to shatter his belief of perfect understanding, and would be for many others under similar situations. One suddenly feels how shallow his former understanding has been, which often results in an intensive quest for finding "truth." Why truth, which is most likely unpleasant? Perhaps he wants to recover security and possibly to regain the power of control--only with true knowledge can one plan with confidence and exert control.

Such a statement may sound like the bad habit of a psychologist, always eager to find a vulgar cause, such as the power of control, instead of believing in a noble search for information. This, however, is an unfair discrimination. As will be discussed later, information and control are twin notions, inseparably characterizing the basic human motivations. In any case, the issue of the controllability of time is an intriguing one, overtly or covertly tinging human interest in time. Is it not frustrating that, living in the era of great technological breakthroughs in controlling space, when people are hopping around the surface of the earth with tremendous speed, some having reached even as far as the moon, we are yet tied to a raft helplessly floating over the stream of time? With the aid of clocks we have learned how to adapt ourselves to time, but would it be not far better if we could navigate the stream of time up and down, if we could stay in the midstream for a while (to stay young, of course) by dropping a time-anchor?

Well, that will take care of the question why a news agency phoned me up with an excited voice as soon as they heard that I was studying time. In many cases, however, it seems to be the mysteriousness of time that attracts people's attention, rather than its controllability. But they are not really separate issues, and as issues they are not very traditional ones. The reason for this conjecture is that, if they really were old, there should have been worship of a diety who controlled time. Note that worship is an indirect way of control; the worshipper wants to influence the diety who has a mysterious power of controlling important entities. He is also known, or assumed, to be appeased by being worshipped; so a causal passage is open for the worshipper to exert an indirect control over the entity. Apparently, in ancient religions there were only dieties to represent time and control fate, but none to control time itself (Fraser, 1975). Instead, most of the gods just followed time as given, like six days for work and one day for rest, even though many of them exhibited a great power in neglecting spatial limitations under which mortals were, and still are, helpless. Combining these odds and bits of ancient beliefs, we may conclude that time was once thought as the uncontrollable, universal regulating agent which gods and men were equally to obey. When some entity is felt as absolutely uncontrollable, there is obviously no sense in worshipping it, and no feeling of mysteriousness would emerge either, as mystery presupposes the possibility that what is now mysterious could also be otherwise.

If there is some truth in such an argument, we may then suppose that time has become mysterious rather gradually, contingent upon, perhaps, the development of the second notion of time, the *spatialized time*. The notion of spatialized time, obviously owing much to the invention and refinement of clocks for its development, later culminated as the contemporary notion of physical time, particularly that in relativity theory. If this had been the only notion of time we had, there would not have been any mystery. But we have another, the much older notion of time as an indispensable component of our cognitive system, which, for the very reason, cannot just die out, even under great pressure from the other notion of time with all of its haloing glory of contemporary physics. The conflict between the two notions has become acute, cognitive tension is increased[1], and the sense of mystery magnified.

In order to clarify the nature of this conflict, we need to speculate a little about the nature of the non-physical, non-spatial, intuitive notion of time. The source of this ntoion should be found in the most basic class of animal behavior relevant to time, *i.e.*, *timing* behavior. Timing behavior is essential for survival. It is known to be facilitated in animals by various sorts of internal timing mechanisms such as circadian rythms. The basic motivation that led to the invention of clocks was a desire to improve the precision of timing; their use to tell time seems to have come later, as an afterthought.

Now, what is the essence of timing behavior? *Waiting* comes first. Then the temporarily frozen system, the brain and the muscles, must be kicked into activity at the right moment. The process taking place in the cognitive system for a timing behavior may be described in the following way. The primary cognitive components representing the person himself, the bow and the arrow held in his hands, must be kept still; while the ones representing his enemy, stalking behind a bush toward himself should be left to simulate the enemy's movement until the expected (or perceived) moment of attack. Then all the components in his cognitive system must be brought into full action.

As I have discussed in my previous paper (Toda, 1975), freezing the activities of the primary cognitive components is a difficult task, as it is against their nature of active simulation, and therefore the freezing and waiting with mounting tension will contribute a rather uncomfortable part of the direct temporal experience accompanying the timing behavior. On the other hand, the moment of activation and the complete removal of inhibition will carry an overtone of freedom and creation to the succeeding experience.

At any rate, if we assume that these freezing and activating cognitive operations are the source of our intuitive notion of time, there are further implications to consider. Note that when we *analyse* the content of our notions, the notions must be frozen. The best illustration for this proposition is the fact that when we analyse an operator notion represented by a verb, "run," say, the notion must temporarily be turned into a noun form such as "running," "to run" and the like. The standard use of a verb notion in the cognitive system is to apply it to an object notion such as "rabbit" and to let the latter really run for the purpose of simulating the real world process to see, *e.g.*, if a real rabbit is likely to run straight into the set trap. When such a notion is under cognitive analysis, however, its operational function must temporarily be suspended. It is therefore quite natural that the product of such cognitive analyses tends to be a static, timeless system. If the system requires time as a parameter, its sptialized version will do as a substitute. The very essence of our intuitive notion of time, "activate" as a verb, is then destined to be missing from our cognitive analytical products, as the frozen "activation" is no longer the same as "activate."

Another important aspect of intuitive time to be touched upon here is the distinction between the past and the future divided by the present, the distinction missing in the spatialized time of physics. I am interested particularly in why we tend to think as an established fact that the past is determined and the future is undetermined. Epistemologically speaking, the past and the future should not *exist* in the real world, as whatever that exists must be in the present. So what does one mean when he says that the past is determined and the future is undertermined?

It is only in the cognitive system that the distinction is meaningful, where some of the cognitive *events* are earmarked as "past" and some as "future." This is because the cognitive system has two functions, confirming by observation the events that are taking place now, the records of which are earmarked as "past," and extrapolating by simulation future events, the outcomes of which are earmarked as "future." Once they are recorded, they all belong to the memory of the cognitive system, but these two types of memorized events must be distinguished from each other as the cognitive system is apparently operating under a normative rule that the "future" events must be taken as modifiable but the "past" events should be taken as fixed. The only reason I can think of for this normative (and therefore not necessarily strictly observed) rule is the survival value it provides.

All these views of mine stated so far, concerning our intuitive notion of time, are wild speculations. We may believe, however, that this notion which recalcitrantly defies ordinary content analysis, perhaps for the wild reasons stated above, still hides some important clues to the nature of time, which may be uncovered only by unconventional analyses. As one such unorthodox but promising procedure, let me propose *imagination-stretching*. How far can one go to find the territorial border of the notion of time, to delineate time indirectly by eliminating non-time?

## 2. ENTROPY, AGAIN!

My natural first stop in this exploration is the disputed border between physical time and intuitive time, where the cognitive tension is the greatest. Tension attracts snoopers as honey attracts bees, for the clue to solving conflicts is most likely to be found there. The point of dispute is the claim by physical time over the conceptual region called the direction of time, to which ever-increasing entropy is the major, and in fact, the only supporting ground. A suspicion-ridden mind, however, would immediately find a certain amount of shakiness about this character, entropy. Why must physicists use so many human words in explaining entropy? Order and disorder. But Nature herself should have no "notion" of order and disorder. Work. But Nature does not work. And a heat engine, indeed, as if Nature should want to have one herself! Note that a heat engine alone is not enough to turn negentropy into work. An operator of the machine is needed to set it up *properly* within the thermal system, and he will need a proper Manual to refer to for the correct control of the machine.

So we have here the fundamental trio as the indispensable catalyst for the conversion of negentropy into work: the engine that symbolizes control, the knowhow that represents information and the man who is the link between information and control. So whenever I try to imagine the thermal death of the universe, I cannot help having an image of an old physics professor, emeritus perhaps, carrying a heat engine under his arm, finding himself entirely at a loss--and I am serious, as without him the picture of thermal death is incomplete.

Old professor or not, this indispensable operator of Carnot's heat engine always strikes me as the symbol of man--a creature who is under constant lookout for negative entropy. Whenever he finds it, he is there to install the machine. If he doesn't have a proper machine he tries to invent one with which to convert negentropy into work. Work for what? Perhaps for more work. One thing is certain. He is obsessed. He has accumulated conserved information, and thus far has tremendously increased his power to control. He is always working like mad. It is quite true that only the obsessed can really achieve something noteworthy in the end, like interferring with the processes of the universe. But I add to this conclusion the reminder that the majority of the obsessed ruined themselves.

Emerging from this brooding, let me emphasize that, if entropy needs a heat engine, it also needs man. So inside the abstract mathematical armor of the notion of entropy a man must be hidden, smuggled from beyond the border of physics, the agent who is responsible for the directionality of time.

When I arrived at this conclusion, another suspicion suddenly hit me. Is this operator of the heat engine the only alien agent in the kingdom of phyiscs? No. Suspicious figures called observers are now flitting around inside and outside of physical systems, creating new paradoxes while pretending to resolve some old ones. It could be that some bigger conspiracy is going on to undermine the supposedly non-human physics, within the scheme of which entropy may only be a minor accomplice. May there be a peace, but a good snooper must have a heart of stone.

## 3. SPACE VS. TIME

The obvious next stop of our exploration is the border between space and time. The relationship between these two notions appear peaceful enough, as space is always considered as a remote but still the closest kin of time, even though the territory of time has recently been encroached by space more and more often.

Why is space considered the closest kin of time? Aren't they dissimilar to each other? They certainly are. We have to admit, however, that they have similarities, too, and let me examine first the nature of their common blood. The first thing that comes to my mind is their shared attribute of continuity, not the continuity of themselves, but the continuous *relations* they hold with *objects*. (The continuity of time itself may very well be a garment of time borrowed from space.) Consider space first.

When an object moves within space, its spatial locus must, so we usually seem to believe, form a continuous line. The temporal version of this spatial continuity for the movement of objects is the temporal preservation of objects. If an object exists at one moment, then it should exist at the immediately succeeding moment. Of course, the observable attributes of the object may change, but not so much as to impair its identity. In particular, the identity preservation of one's own self is vital; for without it there would certainly be no time.

How strict is this rule of preservation? Evidently not so much as to allow no exception. It is quite true that we love preservation; we love physicists who provide us with preservation laws. Nowadays our trust upon them is so great that whatever odd things may happen in our universe from now on we expect them eventually to come up with some esoteric conservation laws with which everything in our universe is ultimately conserved, no matter what strange hide-and-seek matter and energy (and their higher derivatives) may play, popping in and out of some unobservable holes of space-time.

Nevertheless, we can occasionally give up preservation. Haven't we already given up the preservation of the soul? In the past we accepted a magical view of the world which was hardly scrupulous about preserving objects. The notion of time, therefore, certainly does not require the preservation of everything. On the contrary, in a world where nothing changes, including the observer himself, the notion of time will hardly make any sense. How about, then, the other extreme? What would you feel if your soul were snatched to another universe as a pure observer where your sensory data change so drastically and discontinuously that no identity of anything can really be kept? The reported LSD experiences may offer a crude approximation to this situation, and I may conclude that the identity perservation of at least some of the external objects is essential to keeping the sense of time. So my tentative conclusion is that for time to exist, at least some part of the world must preserve its identity while the attributes of the rest must undergo changes. What an untidy conclusion! But that is time. If someone claims to have obtained a clear-cut conclusion about time, we have a very good reason to reject it outright.

In comparison to time, space apparently presents disillusioningly little puzzle, though this plainness may very well be another illusion. Space, manifested in the spatial coordinates of objects, seems to be almost on a par with other attributes of objects, as demonstrated by Yuki when he aligned sensory attributes from the most space-like to the most space-unlike, on the basis of his experimental study of apparent movement (Yuki, 1965). From the results of his experiment Yuki concluded, in effect, that space is practically no different from the dimensions of sensory attributes while time is entirely something else.

This is about the spatial orientation of objects. Now let us consider the continuity of locomotions in space. It is needless to remind the reader that no other sensory attributes possess this property of strictly continuous change. True, we have never observed a discontinuous locomotion of objects in physical space, but the issue here is whether our intuitive notion of space allows the possibility of such a locomotion. The affirmative answer to this question is common in ancient religions, folklores and science fictions. Apparently, there were many gods, demons and magicians who had a power of showing up anywhere their whim led them, and the heroes in science fiction flit around the world by a special means called *teleportation* which allows them to show up at the destination of their trip without bothering spatially to fill in the intermediary points.

Note that the traded goods of science fiction writers are stretched imaginations, and they must trade with discretion. If the imaginations produced were too timid, they would fail to be interesting, and if they were too bold, few would be able to follow. Good imaginations therefore ought to settle in the borderline area of intuitive acceptability. So science fiction provides a very valuable source for my investigation as well as do myths and legends, and very often the basic repertory of ideas is the same in all these, meaning that the contents of our basic intuitive notions have remained mostly identical through the whole process of civilization, except for a few minor but significant additions. For example, the notion of time travel was created only after the spatialized time of physics became a common knowledge of people, to which topic I shall come back shortly.

Compared to time travel as a source of a host of paradoxes, teleportation is a triviality. It is just a nice way of traveling, well within the range of imaginability. So the rejection of continuous spatial locomotion as an unbreakable law hardly disrupts our intuitive notion of space, though it certainly does damage to the physicist's notion of space. Does it, really? Even though they would coolly reject the idea of teleportation today for the reason that it clashes with their model of the universe, they would not show the least scruple in writing a Nobel prize winning article about the structure of the continuous fourth dimension of space through which teleportation takes place, if someone, very likely one of them, happened to have invented it.

One may argue, however, that the idea of teleportation does not seriously interfere with our intuitive notion of space only because the happenings will be within the range of acceptable exceptions. Only certain people may teleport, but everything else will locomote continuously. This argument has a ground. It would be a madhouse if every object teleported. It is, however, hard to imagine this situation, as the identity of objects would then be lost, too, without which our understanding of the world would be impossible.

Before going into the topic of time travel, the temporal version of teleportation, let me remind the reader of the striking easiness of imagining the fourth dimension of space. If you have any doubt, just ask a young boy. With the risk of getting a contemptuous stare for your ignorance, you will learn all about the fourth dimension of space with lurid stories about its inhabitants, heroes and monsters. Such a fouth dimension is none but the four hundredth version of Never Never Land, but significance ought to be attached to the imagination-stirring characteristic of the fourth dimension. Even newspapers occasionally carry a headline like "ABDUCTION INTO THE FOURTH DIMENSION? AIRPLANES MISSING IN BERMUDA TRIANGLE AREA" with 90% mockery and 10% awe. In science fiction literature, we naturally find a tremendous variety of more-than-three dimensional spaces, strangely connected, warped, distorted, through which one can go, *e.g.* to The Greater Magellanic Cloud within--well, the time needed for the voyage varies widely from author to author.

This prolificacy is striking if we put it against the utter uncanny silence of science fiction authors concerning a second dimension of time. Of course, they have tried. They have invented some new times, deviating from the contemporary physical time, but only slightly. There are circular times, branching times, multiple times and so on, but they are all linear. In religion and philosophy, the situation is the same. Even in physics I have never heard of an idea of two-dimensional time. This is strange, as, *e.g.*, the two types of expansions of the equation describing the coordinates of an object traveling with the speed of light, $x_1^2 + x_2^2 + x_3^2 = c^2t^2$, into $x_1^2 + x_2^2 + x_3^2 + x_4^2 = k^2t^2$ and into $x_1^2 + x_2^2 + x_3^2 = k^2(t_1^2 + t_2^2)$ seem formally equally easy (or equally difficult). At least, again formally, there is nothing that should discriminate $t_2$ against $x_4$. Of course, there is the issue of how to define velocity with respect to two-dimensional time. But the difficulty is of a conceptual nature rather than a logical one. Note also that, when the cosmologists discuss the expanding universe, they *fix* their time by identifying it with the local time of some priviledged system of reference, while letting their *space* change (expand) freely. These things seem to indicate clearly that physicists, too, are strongly biased by their intuitive notions of space and time, which obviously place time in a far more privileged position than space.

## 4. TIME TRAVEL, PAST AND FUTURE

Now let us see how much we can stretch imagination within the range of linear time. The circular time and the multiple time actually do not present any new innovation concerning the notion of time. The former only states that the world process will eventually be repeated after some period of time, implying a sort of determinism. Concerning the multiple time, science fiction writers were left behind by physicsts who allowed each different system to have a different, though lawfully determined, local time. So perhaps out of desperation sciece fiction writers ascribed different *universes* to each stream of the multiple time flow, creating the so-called parallel universes representing the complete *un*determinism in such a way that a mere possibility in one universe is cold reality in another. Apparently, these two ideas borne by circular and multiple time reflect our notion of the past and the future, another integral part of our intuitive notion of time. So let us now proceed to the third version of extended linear time; branching time, or a temporal bypass through which we may time-travel.

As a matter of fact, time travel into the future is theoretically possible. An astronaut whose spaceship has undergone long and strong acceleration and deceleration will return to Earth preserving his physical youth only to find graves of his family, and, if lucky, may be greeted by his great-grand children. Physicists assure us that this is not a paradox. Granting it, let me show that a paradox can still be created out of this situation. Now consider a modern version of the flowing river analogy of time, a point moving on a line. The point represents one's "now," and by constantly moving it turns the region it has covered into the past leaving the region still uncovered as the future. Even though seldom recognized as a formal representation of time, this obvious compromise between spatialized and intuitive time is very popularly accepted, and many people use this picture, perhaps unconsciously, whenever the necessity arises to illustrate time. Now let me apply this model of individual time to the above situation: The astronaut lives the local time of his spaceship, and his travel will be represented by his now-point constantly moving on the time-line characteristic to the ship, while the now-point of the system Earth will proceed on its time-line according to its local rate. This is as if two boats leaving the port together are going into two different channels. Is there any guarantee that the boats will meet exactly at the spot where the channels join again? How can one be sure that, when the astronaut's now-point reached the temporal moment when the spaceship and Earth are scheduled to meet, the now-point of Earth, too, will exactly reach the corresponding temporal spot? If it does not, the astronaut meets the Earth where events have not yet happened, or the Earth where all the events have already happened. Apparently, complete determinism of the course of the universe is the easiest solution to resolve this paradox, though many would find themselves reluctant to accept such a solution.

Complete determinism will create another paradox if we allow the possibility of real time travel into the past. In order to get to the past one has to get on a time machine instead of a spaceship and spend some local "time" on the machine. The branching time stream that carries the machine will break into the main time stream in some temporal point in the past, where the passenger may meet his own younger self. The famous paradox of time travel begins when the time traveler commits an exotic suicide by killing his younger self. If the younger self is killed, however, his older self, the killer, cannot exit. Therefore, there will be no murder, which will resurrect the younger self, the older self, and the murder will again take place, and so on.

At least three types of solutions have been suggested to resolve the paradox: The first one is based on determinism; the existence of the older self is a good enough testimony that the murder did not take place in the past. So the time traveler *cannot* kill his younger self however hard he may try, and this implies that the *future* of the time traveler has been determined, too. In contrast to this solution the second idea is based on the indeterminism; even the past is not determined and the younger self may be killed. But as soon as the murder is committed, the world process that involves the returned time traveler goes into a parallel universe which is the *deus ex machina* to resolve the paradox. The third solution also allows the modification of the past. Whenever a modification like the murder takes place, its causal effect will propagate over the branching time system with a speed quicker than the normal, event-instigating time. So nothing will happen for a while after the murder, but when the propagated effect takes over the time traveler eventually, he simply disappears into thin air.

From these suggested solutions, one may draw the following conclusion: In order to resolve the paradoxes of time travel, an extra assumption is always needed which is extrinsic to the time *per se*, whether the assumption is complete determinism or an additional degree of freedom such as the parallel universe or the second time governing the propagation of the effects of a causal modification. This and the fact that the paradox seemingly disappears when we state "The astronaut will come back to see the old Earth much more aged then himself" are enough to make one suspicious that this additional element was smuggled into the picture by the now-point model itself. For the fear of dissipating the precious illusion of time travel entirely, however, I had better say no more.

## 5. UNTIMELY ENDING

The travelog for my tour of investigation around the boundaries of the notion of time should include a few more places of interest, but, dismayingly, the limitation of the *space* of this paper forces it to come to an untimely ending except for just a few cursory remarks. The topics all concern some logical paradoxes of time. The first is concerned with the well-known Bayes Theorem which states that under certain conditions one can infer *with certainly* what the cause is by observing its effects. The apparent paradox is brought forth by the fact that Bayes' Theorem is derived from probability axioms which contain no temporal statements. Therefore we must be able to reverse the direction of time contained in the argument to deduce, as another interpretation of Bayes' Theorem, the complete predictability of the future. In fact this is possible, but it does not create a paradox because Bayes' Theorem, in this reverse interpretation, describes the condition under which the complete control of a future event is obtained. (See (Toda, 1977) for more details.)

The second topic nagging my attention for a long time was related to Zeno's paradox concerning Achilles and the tortoise. The paradox, at its face value, is trivial as the statement consisting of infinite steps to describe a process that takes a finite time can hold its truth value also only for a finite time[2]. My question, however, asks if we can be sure that the end of a finite passage of time always becomes "now." Apparently, no logical difficulty is created if it doesn't. It is rather appalling to see it isn't even a matter of induction; if a finite interval of time does not meet its end, one cannot experience this happening so that experience is powerless in deciding this issue.

As an intriguing example, consider what would happen if time suddenly started to go backward, by which I mean that all the physical processes began to retrace their former paths. Of course, such a possibility is not included within the framework of contemporary physics, but that may simply be due to the fact that no physicist has ever experienced it. Actually, this last statement is the whole point of this argument; not only not physicists but no one at all can experience this reverse flow of time if it happened because, in this temporal phase, one does not perceive, does not memorize, does not learn, but *unperceive, unmemorize* and *unlearn*. (In this temporal phase, entropy decreases, but who cares? In this world, Carnot's heat engine will turn backward futilely to turn work into heat!) Suppose that time oscillates between two temporal moments A and B. When the time returned the earlier moment A, all of us will be brought back to the identical state we were once in at A, memory and all, and will begin to live the same life again, for the millionth time perhaps, without noticing it. The conclusion of this argument is that we shall never find it out if this oscillating time is indeed the real nature of the universe.

The exact duplication of the repeated processes, however, is a determinism. What if there is a quantum or two miserasure in someone's memory? That may create precognitions and prophesies. And precognitions and prophesies are, in contrast to the second dimension of time, well within the range of our stretched imagination of time, and therefore this oscillating time is also within the legitimate range of topics of this serious paper which should end here. I would like to thank the reader, for the millionth time, for his patience in reading the same paper a million times.

REFERENCES

Fraser, J. T. *Of Time, Passion and Knowledge* . New York: *George Braziller*, 1975.

Toda, M. Jikan tetsugeaku josetsu (Prolegomena to a philosophy of time). 1945, *Allzumenschliches*,No. 1, 10-44.

Toda, M. Time and the structure of human cognition. In J. T. Fraser & N. Lawrence (Eds.) *The Study of Time II*, New York: *Springer-Verlag*, 1975.

Toda, M. Causality, conditional probability and control. In C. Brumat (Ed.), *New Developments in the Applications of Bayesian Methods*, Amsterdam: *North-Holland*. (In press)

Yuki, K. "Undo to Kukan" (Movement and space), in *Collected Papers in Commemoration to the Retirement of Prof. Yuki*, Sapporo: Dept. Psychol., *Hokkaido Univ*. 1965.

FOOTNOTES

1. It is perhaps my predilection due to training that I prefer to interprete the ubiquitous process characterized by conflict, tension, its resolution in another level leading to a higher conflict, as something peculiarly human, rather than as something more metaphysical like Fraser's existential tension (Fraser, 1975), or Hegelian dialectic. Cognitive tension, however, is not the only conflict I am referring to. Social systems (as pointed out by Max Weber), engineering systems, or whatever, always go through the same cycle as long as man keeps working on them.

2. I just want to put it on record that essentially the same argument given here concerning the solution to Achilles and the tortoise paradox and the unprovable observability of the end of a finite passage of time which has not yet passed, was given in my earlier ( in fact, the earliest) article [Toda, 1945].

DISCUSSION AND COMMENTS

David Park

Professor Toda's brilliant paper should be read as a sequel to the one on "Time and the Structure of Human Cognition" published in Volume II of this series. I am sure I am not alone in awaiting future contributions in this series with the impatience of those who, in the old days, watched for the postman to bring them the latest chapter of *Great Expectations*. If in the following paragraphs I take issue with some of Toda's remarks it is not in a spirit of disagreement but in the hope of making some contribution to his argument, however slight.

Toda, if I understand correctly, starts with the undeniable fact that we live in an experienced but unexamined present . This is the first part of our life in time. The second part is what we experience when we pause to examine our thoughts or actions, on indeed any sequence of events, insofar as they form a connected sequence and are not considered as happening at random. Totally new categories are needed when we do that; among them are those of past, present, and future. (Present was there in the first part also, but a fish does not need a word for water).

It happens that there is a science called physics which concerns itself with laws of motion, and these can conveniently be explained as dynamical principles for connecting the future with the present and past. Perhaps they could also be read so as to tell about our experience in the only temporal mode in which experience can be had: the present. What is involved is not the equations of physics but the verbal commentary by which mathematical symbols are related to the perceived world. How we explain the world depends on how we think we perceive it, and that opens a very old and general question which far transcends physics in its scope and in its historical sources.

"Reality" is a good word, perhaps precisely because (as Toda suggests) we do not understand very well how it should be used. Some, like Heraclitus, have used it to refer to the flow of continual process; others, like Parmenides, use it to refer to our other mode of understanding: the history of the world's changes becomes part of the essence of the world and is included in its description. It is then nonsense to ask whether the world changes.

Outside the laboratory, the tools of physics are linguistic just as much as they are mathematical, and physicists are obliged to use the language of the culture around them. They are allowed to invent new words but not new syntax. Perhaps there are cultures in the world whose syntax is adapted to communicating in terms of Bergson's *duree* the instant which we experience when we let ourselves live, but the languages I am familiar with, structured as they are with an apparatus of verbs relating to past, present, and future, seem to have evolved, as Toda suggests, in response to a need to simulate events in causal sequence. It may not be a coincidence that physics, and especially dynamics, arose among speakers of such languages.

One should not underestimate the importance of communication, or, if one wishes, meaning in physics. Toda speaks of a "supposedly nonhuman physics" and insists on putting a little man into it. But there must always be a little man, for all of physics refers implicitly to human senses, human assumptions about reality, and human desire to know. Physical concepts are meant for use. If one is engaging in entropy arguments for purposes of power engineering, then the little man *ought* to carry a steam-engine. For other purposes he carries phase space on his shoulders. For still other purposes one can formulate entropy with reference to information, this amounts to putting the little man somewhere else.

What is the right way to formulate physical law remains unknown to us; I suspect that it depends on language and culture. But if physics has been even partly successful in its program it is because it has been formulated in so many different ways: solemnly, with linear vector spaces; ironically, with little men.

# VI. SOCIETY

## Temporal Inventories and Time Structuring in Large Organizations

P. Clark

*This paper examines the conceptions of time utilised by two groups of scientists who have an interest in the design of large scale organizations. Both groups claim that large organizations are important because they embrace and shape the work-milieus for large sectors of the populations of modern industrial societies. Both groups also take a distinctive view of the role of time in the study of organizational phenomena. Each group faces particular, yet different problems which arise from their usage of time as a construct.*

*First the management scientists typically adopt a conception of time derived from seventeenth century science and the analogy of the clock. Time is treated as a homogenised and a readily calculable facet of organizational life. The standardised units used by the management scientist treat the organization as a temporal inventory which can be spent in a limited number of ways. An important and recent development within this paradigm has been the creation of a variety of techniques which show how sequences of activities can be scheduled. It is important to acknowledge that management science does recognise that time is an important construct. The major limitation is that much of the time reckoning in large organizations is done in terms of heterogenous time reckoning systems.*

*Second, organizational scientists typically have, in the past two decades, attempted to research the social structure of organizations. They have based their researches on a sharp dichotomy between structure and process and a sole preoccupation with research designs which are single-shot and cross sectional. Consequently, the time dimension has been treated casually. Recent self-examinations by organizational scientists have pointed to the problematic status of the time dimension.*

*This paper argues that the management and organizational scientist both need to re-examine their conception of time. Both groups claim that their activities contribute to the design of the structure of large scale organizations. It is shown that this objective requires an explication of both homogeneous and heterogeneous time reckoning systems. Particular attention is given to the ways in which time structuring in large organizations is undertaken by the members of these organizations.*

*The objectives of this paper are two-fold. First, to show that the efforts of management scientists and of organizational scientists to produce diagnostic frameworks facilitating the design of organizations are vitiated by the inadequate treatment of time. Second, to present an approach to time-structuring which examines large organizations as systems containing a plurality of time reckoning systems. This approach is summarised in the theory of structural activation.*

## 1. MANAGEMENT SCIENCES AND HOMOGENEOUS TIME RECKONING

The management sciences are to be recognised by their concern to develop theories which explain frequently occurring practical problems in all sectors of administration. These theories should be based on extensive research. From this research the management scientist extracts those established relationships between variables which form a causal network around key objectives like productivity. The management scientist is also heavily involved in the modelling of existing ways of working and comparing the performance of these with an array of alternative models.

The management scientist should follow the broad problem solving approach of operations research in which even undefined-problems are examined by interdisciplinary groups. Their first output is a definition of the problem. Subsequently they would produce suggestions which would be both technically feasible and compatible with the requirements of the social system. However, it is widely accepted that the management sciences have been shifted from broadly defined problems to problems which are more narrowly defined. Typically these problems will be ones in which it is possible to construct a hierarchy of preferences from alternative values and to work from known cause-effect relationships. These problems now constitute the core of teaching in the management sciences as is evident from student texts and from the articles which are published in a key journal, Management Science.

The management sciences have a close interest in time, but because there is a preference for applying computational strategies, the notion of time which has been adopted is that of *homogeneous time reckoning*. Time is therefore based on the analogy with the clock. Time can be subdivided into many equally sized units which can precisely be measured. Each unit is directly comparable with other time units. The units can be cumulated, divided and so on.

Historically the management sciences are intimately involved in the application of the clocktime to work and discipline (Thompson, 1967). Before the industrial revolution the majority of the working populations worked in agriculture and lived in rural milieus. A prime characteristic of work was its irregularity. That is to say, there were periods of intense working followed by other periods of relaxation. Within the week there was, according to the ballads of the time, a strong tendancy for Monday to be a casual day like Saturday and Sunday, and for most of the work to be done in the middle of the week. Then the length of the working day was largely determined by the time of the year. In those days the practice of dividing the day into equal parts was in its infancy.

In the industrial revolution work was shifted from the fields into factories and into urban milieus. The factory owners were part of a commercial network within which the calculation of interest rates against time had become an established practice. These entrepreneurs had a very different conception of time from the farmer. They wanted their employees to work for defined periods each day and each week. Further, they wanted equal amounts of work produced in each time period. Clocks were placed on the walls of factories. Wages were calculated against the clock. Also clandestine timing of work commenced.

According to the myths of scientific management (Wrege and Perruni, 1975) F. W. Taylor is credited with transforming these clandestine timings of work people into "time study" and "work measurement" (Curie, 1970). In these later methods a trained practitioner observes the actual time taken to do particular pieces of work. He assesses two things: first, whether what he sees includes any unnecessary actions by the observed worker; second, he assesses the speed of working along a scale. This second part is known as rating. In rating the observer compares the observed time against a continuum which has two anchored points, one for the unmotivated worker and another for the motivated worker. Each point is given a numerical figure in the ratio of 1:1:33. That is a motivated worker is one third more productive than the unmotivated. The rating is applied to the raw observed time and various additions are made to allow for relaxation periods and for interruptions.

The total time for the job is now given. This total can be used for a variety of purposes. For example, we can assume that a factory with a hundred motivated workers can produce in each hour the equivalent of one hundred thirty three hours work. Then if we know that each product requires one hour's work we can calculate the rate of output. The same statistic can be used for standard costing and production scheduling.

Today the methods of time study have become more sophisticated, especially with the development of standardised time systems for every human movement.

The principle which underlies all these systems is that of homogeneous time and the concept of the organization is that of the "temporal inventory" (Moore, 1963) which can be spent in various ways. According to Thompson the modern concept and experience of time-discipline for the worker is that of evenness in the passage of time. He suggests that this transformation has been significantly achieved through the experience of time in schools. For example, early education gives great emphasis to punctuality and to the breaking down of time into equal periods regulated by the bell.

In the post-1945 period the management sciences have found another use for homogeneous time reckoning. This is in the forward planning of activities through longish periods. It is assumed that any activity involves both a sequence of different stages and that some stages must be done before others whilst some stages can be done in parallel. The method used here is that of critical path networks in which every identifiable stage of an activity is mapped onto a network and a plot is made of which stages can be done in parallel, and which, in strict sequence. The time of each stage is calculated. From this the shortest time route can be constructed. Clearly this approach has a strong appeal to those experts facing the problem of planning large construction projects.

The management sciences operate with a homogeneous time reckoning system. This has two important attributes. First, the management scientist works with a particular concept of *duration*. Second, he deals with *sequences*.

According to Miller and Rice (1967) and Clark (1972) the models and proposals of management scientist for the layout of equipment and for the flow of raw material and of information embody assumptions about the spatial and temporal characteristics of the structure of relationships between people. We may therefore enquire whether these assumptions are made explicit and whether their appropriateness is assessed. A recent review of organizational design concluded that the role of heterogeneous time reckoning systems was badly neglected by the management sciences (Clark, 1975). Clark argues that the management sciences need to revise their conception of time in organizations away from "temporal inventories" to "time structuring".

In defence of the management sciences it may be argued that they have made two very important contributions which can be incorporated into the approach to time which this paper recommends. First, they have well developed techniques for the study of the spatio-temporal aspects of the deployment of people and the flows of raw materials. These could be modified to incorporate the anthropological approaches to the spatio-temporal aspects of social systems (as Mauss, 1904; Evans Pritchard, 1940; Gearing, 1958; Clark, 1976a). Second, the approach of Forrester to the study of system dynamics represents a valuable way of understanding certain key organizational processes and their temporal patterning. These assumptions about time are open to possible revision along the lines suggested later.

## 2. THE TIME-FREE CHARACTER OF THE ORGANIZATIONAL SCIENCES

The organizational sciences have been defined by Lammers (1974) to embrace the researches and theory-building of an interdisciplinary collection of scientists whose major concern is to advance our understanding of the structures and processes in organizations. These people claim that organizations are major definers of the work experience of large sectors of the populations and therefore require specialised study.

The organizational sciences to have several key journals from which the direction of their studies can be discerned (e.g. Administrative Science Quarterly). Unlike the management sciences there is no established group of practitioners who own particular problem territories in organizations. The possibilities for professional practice are only just being recognised.

Given that the organizational sciences include a high proportion of social scientists it might be expected that they would be concerned to explicate the heterogeneous conception of time. In fact they have typically taken a very different approach. They have tended to ignore the sequential, durational and spatio-temporal aspects of organizational structures and to concentrate upon "structures" (Clark, 1976a; Hage, 1976).

The emphasis upon structures and the rejection of studies of processes can be best understood by reference to the implicit manifesto of one of the most prestigious research groups within the organizational sciences, the so called Aston School (see Pugh, 1976). In an early and important statement they argued that the organizational sciences should proceed by using strict operationalizations of concepts into arrays of scaled items which could be factor-analysed to produce dimensions which are grounded in the previously collected measurements. These new dimensions could then -- at a later stage -- constitute the framework for study of processes (Pugh, 1976). In this manifesto the whipping boy was the case study of processes. The Aston School argued that case studies could not produce a lawlike analysis because the concepts used were too gross and global to facilitate comparisons.

The work of the Aston School is based on a number of key assumptions. First, that the study of structures should take precedence over the study of processes. In that assumption they directly oppose the suggestions of the systems theorists in sociology like Parsons (1951). Second, the concept of structure is operationalised by reference to observable items like organizational charts, job titles, documents and by reference to the judgements of a small number of key informants who supply specific details about organizational relationships. This approach encourages the use of a simplified interview schedules by research assistants on short visits to a large number of sites. This minimises the inconvenience to the management and does not require access to more than one major elite within the organization. It may be objected that the Aston School have not published data on the degree of consistency between the interviews when recording in the same firm. Third, it seems unlikely that concept of structure is as unambiguous as commentators like Hall (1972) have claimed. Fourth, the approach treats the organization as an homogeneous entity through levels, functions and over time. This is not necessarily a limitation for achieving the immediate objectives, but the cross sectional design does not allow causal statements. This is explicitly recognised by Pugh (1968) and is consistent with the decision to leave the study of processes, and of structural variables like flexibility, until a later study. Replication studies (e.g. Inkson et al) indicate that the structural features are stable over periods like four years, and perhaps, rather longer.

The approach of the Aston School is representative of the organizational sciences. It is essentially time free. In a recent overview of the first fifteen years of researches Pugh and Hickson observe:

> "longitudinal studies struggle to describe change against a calendar, without knowing if the variations described are major, or are misleading within longer cycles of larger trends which cannot be seen...*the problem of chronological time is known but 'organizational time' is not*", (1976 p.1)[1]

Notwithstanding this limitation the respecification of structure and the identification of key contextual predictor variables is a major achievement with important consequences for joint projects between management scientists and organizational scientists.

However, Clark (1971; 1975; 1976a) has demonstrated that design work does require the treatment of processual aspects. It is claimed that this cannot be undertaken until the problem of organizational time is unravelled.

## 3. EXHIBIT: HETEROGENEOUS TIME RECKONING

In this section the focus is upon presenting an analysis of a time reckoning system within one large organization, Acorn Hosiery Company. The time reckoning system combines elements of the homogeneous system of the calendar with event-based heterogeneous components. It is an example which makes for interesting comparisons with heterogeneous systems already reported from studies of non-industrial societies. The exhibit is from the marketing department and it represents a case of strategic time reckoning with implications for the overall structure of the firm.

The eight managers in the marketing department included amongst their various responsibilities the provision of advice based on an analysis of environmental trends in customer behaviour. The analysis was directed towards assessments of three areas: the anticipated level for sales in the next season, the anticipated level for the season following that, the anticipated levels for the same period of the next year. The outputs of the analysis were delivered to two interested parties, the strata of executives just below board level and the heads of the production departments. The final decision reflected the confidence which these latter parties had in the original projections. There were some product areas which all three set of managers considered were highly predictable and joint-decision making was straight-forward. Other areas were considered to be especially problematic, particularly customer behaviour in purchasing outerwear.

The original study of the marketing men was undertaken as part of a larger study of the areas of discretionary decision making possessed by management. This was carried out within the framework of the theory of the "time span of discretion" elaborated by Jaques (1951) in which the analyst has to identify the areas of discretion and then to discover these decisions which cover the longest period of calendar time before they are evaluated by superordinates. It was necessary to study these managers over a period of several months.[2] One of the major areas of discretion was the advice given about the future state of the market. These decisions could not be prescribed.

The final decision of the marketing department was only made after considerable discussion, but its content can be simplified as a choice between three major alternatives. The three choices were: first, to state that the incoming season was to be one of high sales; second, to state that the incoming season was to be characterised by low sales; third, to anticipate a major shift in customer preferences affecting the manufacture and marketing of the product.

The outputs of the discretionary decision making had very considerable financial implications. For example, a correct anticipation of either high or low levels meant that the firm would either be prevented from wasting money on stock for which there was no effective demand, or, alternatively that the firm could have full warehouses ready for a high effective demand.

When the marketing men anticipated low levels of sales this was the general signal for a sequence of actions in production departments including the cutting of overtime work, the introduction of cost saving schemes and waste programs, also a slowing down of recruitment and a general spurt of housekeeping activities to clean up the work areas. Conversely the anticipation of high sales was the signal for overtime, the offering of inducements for high output, a reduction in concern with housekeeping activities and less concern about the wastage of the raw materials. The third possibility, the anticipation of a change in customer preferences was the signal for a change in the role of the design and development sections. They would be reformed from the previously dispersed components in various departments and given a sharply increased budget to assist in the production of new styles. The production departments would know that the routine of medium-length production runs would be constantly interrupted by the appearance of special samples requiring new combinations of old skills for their manufacture.

Probably because the Acorn Hosiery was a long established firm with many long-stay employees there was a high proportion of the employees who were very used to the different ways in which the seasons might unfold. They had grown to expect good and bad seasons, and short bursts of innovation. The manager organized these expectations into typologies. The typologies contained a number of items among which one was of particular interest. This was the belief that the shape of a future season could be detected by reference to a particular sequence or trajectory of identifiable events part of whose patterning could be inferred from the intervals between the events.

Observation of the daily management meetings showed that these began in a similar fashion. They started when the statistics for the previous days sales were made available. These statistics were collated by type of product (e.g. footwear) and by the total and value of sales for the previous day. Alongside that statistic was the figure for the same day in the previous year. At first the figures would be examined rather closely, but soon it became apparent that the figures were merely a convenient point of focus for the daily update on the likely market trajectory affecting the next season. Consequently a whole range of factors would be introducted to explain the figures. These would include: the state of the economy, the recent weather, a fluctuating belief about the market credibility of the next season's colour shades, the styles being offered by rivals...and so on.

A mass of additional information would be brought into account from a whole variety of sources including recent gossip from raw material suppliers, the dyeing activities of the general dyers, impressions from overseas visitors. All these pieces of information would be utilised in an attempt to demonstrate that a particular trajectory was either quite obvious, or, would have to be rejected in favour of an alternative trajectory.

In effect these managers were matching up sequences of events, including the sales figures, against their own mental store of event sequences. Sometimes they made decisions which turned out to be quite inaccurate. For example, in one season the men originally observed and correctly anticipated a major change in customer preferences which heralded a change in the weight and texture of outerwear garments as well as in the mix of colours. However, another marketing group in a branch factory of the same firm missed some of the signs used by the first group and wrongly concluded that the next season would be an isolated case of a season characterized by very low sales.

There are some relevant comparisons which may be made between the actions of those marketing men and the way in which some of the members of non-industrial societies seek to anticipate the onset and termination of regular changes in the climate as reported by anthropologists. For example, the Nuer elders consult on a daily basis to discuss changes in could formation and flora in order to establish the end of the dry season (Evans Pritchard, 1940). There is, however, at least one important difference between the Nuer and the marketing men. This is the way in which the latter use the calendar as an adjunct to their calculations.

The marketing men were utilising a time reckoning system which was both heterogeneous and strategic. It was heterogeneous because the units utilised to establish the benchmarks and time intervals within the betwixt them were *not* even in pace, or, equally divisible, nor could they be readily cumulated. Further, the time reckoning was quite local and could only be understood by a few persons. It was strategic because its usage affected all sectors of the firm.

The next task is to construct a brief definition of heterogeneous time and to outline the social functions of time reckoning.

## 4. TOWARDS A DEFINITION OF HETEROGENEOUS TIME RECKONING SYSTEMS

The objective of this section is to provide a working definition of heterogeneous time reckoning. We shall not aim to review the extensive literature, but rather to outline the major features and to point to some contrasts between heterogeneous systems and hemogeneous systems like the modern clock.

A review of the sociological literature revealed many implicit definitions and examples (Clark, 1977a). The many examples of different time reckoning systems supported the contention that all societies utilize pluralities of systems. But these various usages possessed two common features. First, they referred to some identifiable sequence of events. Second, the intervals were given a durational interpretation. It is therefore proposed that a heterogeneous time reckoning system is defined as:

shared sets of rules in which indentifiable sequences of anticipated events are constituted into socially prescribed blocks which are given a durational interpretation.

It is now feasible to make some broad comparisons between the homogeneous system of management science and heterogeneous system discovered amongst the marketing men.

Homogeneous systems are characterized by many factors: a uniformity of pace; the divisibility into equal sized units; the possibility of cumulating units; the fact that large populations who are geographically spread will recognise the units of the system; the openness of the length of units to unlimited extension; the absence of contingency;the absence of evaluations of time; and the lack of concern for either the past, the present or the future. Heterogeneous systems are at the opposite pole of each of these dimensions.

The definition of heterogeneous time reckoning can now be utilised to respecify the analysis by H. A. Turner and colleagues of the incidence of strikes in the British motor industry (1967: 124f). Turner argues that the data suggests that there is a periodicity to strikes which can be correlated with the time of the year as measured on the calendar. It follows from the definition and the earlier analysis of the marketing men in Acorn Hosiery that some revisions of the time scale are required. First, it is important to construct scales of event sequences and to plot strikes against events. Second, it will probably be necessary to have more than one event-scale because in some years the trajectory may differ from previous years. Using these definitions of time it is now possible to make a more precise analysis of the data and test of the implicit hypothesis.

The example of the marketing department and the claim that their time reckoning system is both heterogeneous and also strategic raises the important issue of the functions of time reckoning systems and of their hierarchical organization. Several social functions are suggested by the analysis of Durkheim, Mauss, Sorokin and Gurvitch. First, time reckoning systems constitute part of the framework of concepts which provide the solid frame within which social activity and thought takes place. They are part of the world which is taken for granted. Second, they play a central role in the coordination of intra and inter group relations. For example the expansion of the scope of economic trading from small geographical areas to a world wide system implies an array of time reckoning systems to coordinate such activities as the making of accounts, the calculation of penalty clauses, the scheduling of transportation and so on. Third, time reckoning systems are an integral part of control systems. This is clearly evidenced in E. P. Thompson's analysis of the changes in time discipline accompanying the industrial revolution. Also it is evident that the usage of homogeneous time in the management science is intimately tied in with the use of particular controls and their content. Part of that usage is in the way in which time reckoning in the aggregated form is the basis of commercial exercises (see Nowotony, 1976) and of detailed planning. Fourth, heterogeneous systems are an integral part of the collective memory. One only has to think of the role played by particular events like "the birth of Christ", or, "the Great War".

These social functions exemplify the role of time reckoning in the continuity and persistance of social organizations of all kinds including large organizations. Therefore, changes in the sequences or durations which constitute these systems have considerable implications for adapting to change. The notion of future shock is based on the contention that sequences have remained the same, but the intervals have been speeded up, yet peoples' expectations are anchored in the durational expectancies established much earlier.

A series of time reckoning systems exist in any social organization. It is possible to consider whether the repertoire is adequate for the anticipated exigencies which might arise. For example, Jahoda's study of the unemployed men in Marienthal strongly suggested that their existing repertoire was quite inadequate for coping with unemployment.

In this section a general definition of heterogeneous time has been presented in which it is stressed that all systems contain sequences and durations. Further it has been emphasised that large organizations will contain a variety of time reckoning systems which may, or may not, be hierarchically organised. These systems vary in their heterogeneity. They share similar social functions. The next task is to examine how the notion of time reckoning can become incorporated into a concept of structure. That is to say, a concept of structure which will be equally useful to the management scientists and the organizational scientist.

## 5. TIME AND STRUCTURE

In this section I have outlined three problems affecting the establishment of a theoretical connection between time and structure. These problems are:

(a) assessing the extent, direction, and relevant period of time in studies of structural change;

(b) assessing the role of structural flexibility as defined by the Aston School;

(c) assessing whether structural flexibility is a gradual transformation along certain dimensions or whether it is a relatively sharp change from one configuration to another

Each of these problems is examined and proposals made for their explication by utilizing the concept of time proposed in the previous sections.

First, many studies of the structure of organizations claim to have studied structures over time. Clark and Ford (1970) observe that these studies do not typically specify the antecedent conditions. Consequently it is not possible to assess whether these are studies of change *of* the structure, or, change *within* the repertoire of structures possessed by the organization. For example, Simmel reports that nineteenth century London tailors were organised quite differently in wartime from in peacetime. In wartime the tailors were tightly bound to particular inns and all the inns elected representatives to a central coordinating agency. These structural characteristics disappeared in peacetime. It could be misleading to carry out a study of the structure of the tailors in wartime, then in peacetime, and claim that the structure had changed. The misleading aspect would be in the failure to discover the basic structural repertoire and the appropriate time period. The claim to study organizations over time is quite empty of scientifically generalisable statements. For this reason many case studies of organizational processes must be rejected. Similarly it may be noted that although case studies often are conducted over a period of several months it is only in extremely rare cases that the social definitions of time reckoning utilised by the members of the organization have been investigated.

Second, what should be role of structural flexibility as defined by Pugh (1963) and members of the Aston School. This variable was initially one of six structural variables, but was omitted from the empirical study because it was a processual variable. The remaining five variables were used to define the underlying structural dimensions of large sclae organizations and to identify the main contextual predictor variables. That study uncovered four structural dimensions: the degree to which activities were structured, the extent to which authority was centralised, whether the control system was located with supervision or in an impersonal system, and the size of the administrative support component. It was also discovered that the position of these could be predicted from three contextual variables: size, technology and interdependence (Pugh et al, 1968; 1969). Flexibility of structure can now be respecified as movements along the four structural dimensions. Flexibility *implies* the presence or absence of a capability for making transformations along these structural dimensions as in the case of the London tailors. It will be recalled that the Aston Group decided to leave flexibility of structure until a later study (see Pugh, 1976). Clearly it will be necessary to disentangle "change of" and "changes within" the structure.

Third, the cross sectional studies of the Aston School have made a very useful contribution by specifying the key structural dimensions, but their methodology does not allow an examination of the extent to which structures vary rhythmically. Etzioni suggests that all large organizations are typified by periods of intense activity in which the structure is quite different that operating in other periods (1961:283). There are very few empirical studies of this phenomena. A fruitful exemplar for such studies is provided by Mauss (1904). He demonstrated that both the spatio - temporal arrangements and the intensity of eskimo social life covaried with the seasons of summer and winter. Mauss further claimed that *all* modern industrial societies possess similar rhythms at the level of large organizations as well as the society as a whole (e.g. the August vacation in France). This claim is strongly supported by Kuznets's (1933) analysis of seasonal phenomena in American firms. The claim by Mauss also receives theoretical support from the phase hypothesis of the systems theorists, Parsons, Shils and Bales (1951). A recent longitudinal study by Clark (1977b) documents the claim with respect to retail organizations and many industrial organizations. These pointers suggest that in large organizations we might expect to find that there are several structural arrangements in the repertoire and that each is intended to be matched with particular situations. This conclusion would give theoretical import to the case material of the marketing men in the hosiery factory, but it raises a new conceptual problem: what is the appropriate concept for analysing structural flexibility *within* the structural repertoire?

## 6. TIME-STRUCTURING AND STRUCTURAL POSE STRATEGIES

The problem of formulating an analytic unit appropirate for explicating the durational and sequential aspects of large organizations in a manner which facilitates the activity of organizational design touches on a familiar problematic in the social sciences. In this section it is argued that the concept of the *structural pose strategy* is an appropriate analytic unit. The concept has been developed and utilised by Clark in a study of structural change in supermarkets, canmaking factories and sugar beet plants (Clark 1977c).

The rhythmic variability of structures through time has been noted by economists (e.g. Kuznets) and by sociologists (e.g. Sorokin). However, apart from vague references to the notion of process there are only two major attempts to develop an analytic unit which might be utilised to undertake a deeper study of time-structuring. First, March and Simon (1958) claim that a great deal of organizational behaviour is structured into "performance programs". These are sequences of behaving which are evoked by pre-selected cues in the environment. For example, in a prison the alarm bell evokes a sequence prescribing the behaviour of the warders. March and Simon state that structures are summations of the "mosaic of performance programs". Although they suggest that performance programs can be investigated by interview, by observation and by examining records they have only extended this concept in a very restrictive manner. Second, in a virtually uncited article the anthropologist Gearing (1958) suggests the concept of structural pose. The structural pose consists of the rules which categorise frequently occurring situations and specify which members of a social organization should be involved and what should be their manner or arrangement. He observes that the eighteenth century Cherokee Indian village typically possessed some four structural poses, each of which had one primary function, but also a series of additional functions. For example, a red flag was the cue evoking the structural pose for conducting warfare against another village. When this was raised the village became organised on a clan basis under the council of elders. The roles of various sex and age groups was prescribed. This same structural pose could also be used for other occasions, including the playing of friendly games of ball with other villages.

The value of the concept of performance program is in drawing attention to the way in which behavious in large organizations is organised into sequences and showing how the evoking of these is of central importance. There are some disadvantages. March and Simon exaggerate the ease of investigating and identifying performance programs and they fail to distinguish between intention and actual behavious. Further, they fail to suggest that an organization may have a repertoire of alternatives whose evoking, or, activation, may be precarious as in the case of the marketing men in Acorn Hosiery. Another serious defect is in failing to explicate the durational aspects.

This concept of the structural pose has the particular relevance of implying that similar sequences can fit several occasions. This makes sense of the way in which intended behaviour is approached in large organizations. For example, recently a number of British organizations approached the problem of rehearsing for bomb scares by utilising the arrangements which already existed for fire drills. One can extend Gearing's analysis by arguing that in large scale organizations there will be a *repertoire* of structural poses. A further advantage of the structural pose is that it explicitly covers the spatio-temporal distribution of individuals and groups. This is an important dimension for organizational design. One difficulty with the treatment by Gearing is that he does not consider the activation process in detail, nor, does he consider the availability of several poses and therefore the dilemma of choice. Similarly, the durational aspects not examined.

Clark (1975;1976) proposes the concept of *structural pose strategy* and argues that large organizations will possess repertoires of structural poses which are activated by strategically located timekeepers. A structural pose strategy is a model shared by the members of the organization. The model specifies categories of frequently occurring situations or anticipated problems of importance (e.g. fires). It further specifies some of the cues by which the *anticipation* of particular situations can be recognised. These cues possess a sequential pattern containing specific bench mark events and intervals between the benchmarks which can be reckoned by reference to both clock/calendar time and to other more heterogeneous items like the occurrence of sunshine to ripen the crops. In addition to specifying the situations and problems it also prescribes the *appropriate* response in terms of expectations and actions. This will include the defining of which statusses and roles are involved and their spatial patterning through time.

As a matter of convenience the repertoire of structural poses possessed by large organizations can be grouped into three major types:

(a) the structural pose strategies for coping with total round-of-events which the organization may face. For example, the Acorn Hosier Company had an annual period containing several seasons. From the earlier discussion it is apparent that Acorn possessed several pose strategies for each season;

(b) the pose strategies for detecting the requirement for innovation and for specifying the innovation procedure;

(c) the pose strategies for dealing with situations which can be anticipated, but whose occurrence cannot be readily predicted (e.g. fires, bomb scares, earthquakes.)

The emphasis upon a repertoire implies that there are choices. It further implies that there can be changes in the repertoire arising from the addition of new structural poses, or, the loss of existing ones through non-use, or, the turnover of organizational members.

This treatment of structure as a repertoire of structural poses places a heavy emphasis upon recursiveness in large organizations. This might seem to be rather a restrictive contention, but from the example of the marketing men in Acorn it may be noted that there is often a dilemma about the activation of specific structural pose strategies.

Also, in some occasions the wrong poses are activated, and in other occasions the organization does not possess an appropriate pose strategy because a new situation is unfolding.[4]

This structuring is central to the way in which the members of huge organizations will constitute the models which make up the repertoire of structural poses. Time structuring is involved in the evoking, or, activation state, as well as in the subsequent unfolding of the selected structural pose.

## 7. IMPLICATIONS

How can the concepts of time reckoning systems and structural pose strategies be connected to the particular problems of the concept of time which arise for the management science, and for the organizational sciences, when these sciences become involved in organizational design?

The management sciences require an insight into both the behavioural consequences of their proposed schemes and into the diagnosis of ongoing social systems (as Boothroyd, 1974). It has been argued that time reckoning by heterogeneous systems is central to the development of the management sciences. Further, the concept of structural pose strategy is an analytic unit which is the right level of generality for diagnosis and for planning. The management scientist should, therefore, specify the repertoire of structural poses. This includes *some* mapping of existing time reckoning systems. Management scientists should then consider the necessary congruence between what exists, what might be readily learnt, and their own proposals. In each part the focus on time structuring is a mindhold to a significant slice of the coordination and control mechanisms within the client system.

The organizational sciences require an explication of organizational time so that structural change can be investigated and also so that the time dimension can be investigated and also so that the time dimension can be takled in longitudinal research designs (see Galtung, 1970). The problem of time can be explicated by discovering the systems utilised by the strategic time keepers and by adopting a theory of structures rather than structure. With respect to longitudinal research designs Galtung's time dimension can be replaced by several event-based dimensions to reflect the various time and structure possibilities which typically may be found in organizations. These suggestions require some revision in the theory of structure which the organizational sciences have utilised. Fortunately that requirement coincides with a recent resurgence in the concern for theorizing.

## 8. SUMMARY

It has been argued that the problem of time-and-structure arises when the management and organizational sciences become involved in organizational design. This problem can be explicated by mapping the time reckoning systems utilised by strategic time keepers and by identifying the repertoire of structural pose strategies possessed by large organizations. These should form the basis for all designs of future organizations.

ACKNOWLEDGEMENTS

I am indebeted to the Fellows of the Netherlands Institute for Advanced Studies in the Humanities and Social Sciences at Wassenaar for their guidance and suggestions during 1972-73 and to my colleagues at Bradford University, particularly David Hickson, Stweard Clegg and Andrew Patrick. I am indebted to the members of this Society for help with improving the final draft, especially Helga Nowotony who assisted in clarifying the distinction between her treatment and my own. The responsibility for interpreting these ideas is, of course, mine.

NOTES

1. Italic added.

2. The observations were undertaken in two phases separated by two years. They suggest that although the managers only spent about forty minutes per day in the scheduled meeting that there was considerable continuity between the content of the meetings. Cf. the conclusions of Mintzberg, 1973.

3. See the summary in Clark, 1977a.

4. The survival of disappearance of organizations may be examined within the socio-evolutionary perspective elaborated by Weick, 1969.

REFERENCES

Boothroyd, H., 1974. *On the theory of operational research.* Mimeo: 64 pps. Centre for Industiral Economic and Business Research, Paper No. 51, University of Warwick, England.

Clark, P. A. and J. R. Ford, 1970. "Theoretical and methodological problems in the study of planned organizational change," *Sociological Review* , 18. I. 29-52.

Clark, P. A., 1971. "Organizational cycles." Mimeo: 26 pp. Management Centre, Bradford University.

Clark, P. A., 1972a. *Organizational design: theory and practice*, Tavistock.

Clark, P. A., 1975. "Organizational design: a review of key problems." *Administration and Society*, August, 213-256.

Clark, P. A., 1976. "Some analytic requirements for an applied organizational science." In Pondy L et al, *Managing organizational design*, Elseviers.

Clark, P. A., 1977a. "The plurality of time reckoning systems in modern industrial organizations." In Stoffle R, *Human aspects of industrialization*, Van Gorcum.

Clark, P. A., 1977b. *Time and Structure in Organizations* , in preparation.

Clark, P. A., 1977c. *Time in the management and social sciences*, in preparation.

Currie, R., 1970. *Work Study*. Pitman.

Durkheim, E., 1915. *The elementary forms of the religious life,* Allen and Unwin.

Etzioni, A., 1961. *Complex organizations: a comparative analysis*. Free Press.

Evans, Pritchard, E. E., 1940. *The Nuer*. Oxford.

Galtung, J., 1970. "Diachronic correlation, process analysis and causal analysis: the quest for a diachronic, nomothetic social science." *Quantity and Quality*, IV, 55-94.

Gearing, F., 1958. "The structural poses of the 18th century Cherokee villages. *American Anthropologist*, 60, 1148-1157.

Gurvitch, G., 1964. *The spectrum of social time*, Reidel.

Hall, R. H., 1972. *Organizations: structure and process*. Prentice Hall.

Inkson, J. H. K. et al, 1970. "Organization context and structure: an abbreviated replication." *Administrative Science Quarterly*, 15.

Jahoda, M., Lazarsfeld, P. E., and Zeisel, H., 1972. "Marienthal: the sociography of an unemployed community." Travistock.

Jaques, E., 1957. *The measurement of responsibility*. Tavistock.

Kuznets, S., 1933. *Seasonal variations in industry and trade*. National Bureau of Economic Research.

Lammers, C. J., 1974. "The state of organizational sociology in the United States." *Administrative Science Quarterly*, 19. 3. 422-430.

March, J. G. and H. A. Simon, 1958. *Organizations*. Wiley

Mauss, M., 1904. "Essai sur les variations saisonniers des societies Eskimaux." *L'Annee Sociologique*, IX.

Miller, E. J., and A. K. Rice, 1967. *Systems of organization*. Tavistock.

Mintzberg, H., 1973. *The nature of managerial work*. Harper Row.

Moore, W. E., 1963. *Man, time and society* . Wiley.

Nowotny, H., 1976. "Time Structuring and Time Measurement: On the Interrelation between Timekeepers and Social Time," in *The Study of Time II*. Edited by J. T. Fraser. N. Lawrence. Springer-Verlag.

Parsons, T., R. F. Bales and E. A. Shils, 1953. *Working papers in the theory of action*. Free Press.

Pugh, D. S., D. J. Hickson, C. R. Hinings, and C. Turner, 1968. "Dimensions of Organization Structure," *Administrative Science Quarterly* , 13, pp. 65-91.

Pugh, D.S., D. J. Hickson, C. R. Hinings, and C. Turner, 1969. "The Context of Organization Structures," *Administrative Science Quarterly,* 14-1, pp. 91-113.

Pugh, D.S. and D. J. Hickson, 1976. *Organizational structure in its context*. The Aston Programme I. Saxon House.

Simmel, G., 1950. *The sociology of Georg Simmel,* Free Press.

Sorokin, P. A., 1937. *Social and cultural dynamics*.

Sorokin, P. A., 1943. *Sociocultural causality, space and time*. Duke.

Sorokin, P. A., 1966. *Sociology Today,* Free Press.

Thompson, E. P., 1967. "Time, work-discipline and industrial capitalism." *Past and Present*, 38, 56-97.

Turner, H. A. et al, 1967. *Labour relations in the motor industry.* Allen and Unwin.

Weick, K., 1969. *The social psychology of organizing.* Addison Wesley.

Wrege, C. D. and A. G. Perroni, 1974. "Taylor's Pig-tale: A Historical Analysis of F. W. Taylor's Pig Iron Experiments." *Work Study and Management Services*, November. pp. 564-570.

Discussion and Comment

Helga Nowotny

With Peter Clark's contribution we have moved into the realm of social time. Socially structured time, as I have called it before (1), consists of imposing temporal order on human activities, of creating beginnings and endings, of producing different rates of change, shorter or longer units. All of this is socially meaningful, based on a shared system of rules that underly human interaction and vary widely from one social setting to another.

Peter Clark has chosen to focus on organizational time, i.e. social time as it is experienced in today's prevalent work setting. It is about how men organize their own work, and how men organize the work of others (especially in the hierarchical sense of management organizing worker's time). He has given us examples of a plurality of time reckoning systems, all of which are outgrowths of the process of structuring time. However, some essential ingredients basic to this process, have hardly been touched upon. Modern men, factory workers, executives or scientists, are selling their labour *in* time and this brings us to the relation of time to economics. The basic temporal units in any modern organization can be expressed in man/years or productivity figures; they allow for accumulation and for conversion into monetary units.

It is within this overall time reckoning system - standard economic time - that we have to locate the plurality of organisation time reckoning systems that Clark has described. The interface between them and the dominant temporal system frequently leads to *conflict* which may find its temporal manifestation in *crises*, marking clashes of different ideologies of time as well as relations of dominance and subordination which do not go unchallenged. For time in organizations as in economic life, is characterized by fundamental *inequalities:*

- there is inequality between time reckoning systems: the official time reckoning system - company time - dominates the organization's members' time;

- more generally, there is inequality of how time is spent: what a factory worker or manager does within the same unit - one hour - is differently valued by society;

- there is, as a consequence, cheaper and more expensive time (e.g. I can relegate certain tasks, regarded as more menial or more disliked by me, to my secretary, because her time is cheaper than mine);

- in a fundamental sense, there is also unequal access in a society to certain central goods and services, indicating that any social structure embodies temporal inequalities as well.

Social time, we may conclude, is therefore also about power. Its many faces have a temporal dimension as well.

Clark also mentions the concept of strategic time keeping. To what extent, we may ask, have modern economic production methods, intent on reducing uncertainty, succeeded in creating a predictable temporal environment: abolishing seasons or creating new ones, fit for the simultaneous sales of winter and summer holiday wear or of imposing on us consumption patterns which contain prescriptions of what we are to consume , when and how? Or, to go one step further, to what extent has strategic time keeping entered into careers, into life planning, into forecasting trends in order to make us anticipate by certain responses? This brings us back to questions of power in social relations. Who tells us how to spend our time, when to do what, how long a working life is to last, when to live and when to die?

---

(1) Nowotny, H. "Time Structuring and Time Measurement: On the Interelation Between Time and Timekeepers" in J. T. Fraser & N. Lawrence (Eds.) *The Study of Time, Vol. II*. New York & Heidelberg, Springer-Verlag. 1976

# The Individual and Society

J.T. Fraser

*During the period of history just preceding our epoch, much ingenuity was expanded on divising a means of checks and balances whereby the often opposing interests of the individual and society could be continuously reconciled. This mode of reconciliation is now under attack by doctrines which define the individual entirely in terms of its position within the collective. As a result, we are witnessing a crisis in the dialectic between the individual and the collective identities of man.*

*An attempt is made to understand this unstable, world-wide condition in terms of a class of principles which have recently been proposed under the name "time as conflict."*

*The paper begins with a brief outline of the working concepts of that theory, it proceeds to examine those of its teachings which are relevant to our inquiry, and concludes by applying the findings to an interpretation of the complex predicament of contemporary man.*

This paper deals with the dynamics of the struggle between the individual and collective identities of man in general, and with the crisis in this struggle as I see it develop in our own epoch, in particular. My analysis is based on the principles of the theory of time as conflict, a theory of time proposed and discussed in other publications.[1]

We shall approach our task in three steps. First I will give a brief outline of the working concepts of the theory; then we shall examine those of its teachings that are most relevant to our inquiry; finally, we shall apply our findings to an interpretation of the complex predicament of contemporary man.

## 1. THE TIME AND TIMES OF MATTER, ANIMALS, AND MAN

The theory of time as conflict sees the basic matrix of the world as an open ended hierarchy of integrative levels, each with its peculiar temporality, causation, language, and unresolvable conflicts. This section is a truncated as well as abbreviated synopsis of that theory, and is intended only as an introduction for the handling of our subject in a depth appropriate for this paper.

• It was over half a century ago that the German biologist Jakob von Uexkull outlined his *Umweltlehre* or, in free translation, his principle of species-specific universes. He noted that an animal's receptors determine its world of possible stimuli, his effectors its world of possible actions, hence for each animal the world as perceived, together with the world as it might be acted upon, is delimited by the possible functions of its effectors and receptors. He called this world, carved out of the totality of the animal's environment (as that is perceived by us) the animal's Umwelt. What is not within an animal's Umwelt must be understood as not existing in its world.

For several reasons I retained the use of this German word but I enlarged its meaning substantially. The idea of Umwelts may be easily formulated for specific sensory systems, then extended to the instruments of experimental science and eventually to the principles and equations of theoretical science. If, after thorough inquiry, a domain of nature is revealed to us consistently and exclusively only through a certain type of formalism, and if the appropriate abstract languages cannot accommodate certain features of the world which we ordinarily take for granted (or else, make familiar features appear in strange guise) then that domain of nature to which the formalism applies must be regarded as a distinct Umwelt.

- There is a particular division of nature which I found very useful. It consists of the recognition of certain semi-autonomous integrative levels, that is, of certain groups of things and processes which display a great degree of unity, or wholeness, on some suitably selected scale. In this scheme the basic substratum of the world is the integrative level of massless particles (photons, gravitons, and neutrinos) which all travel at the speed of light; the model of this world is a pure relativistic gas. Above this level I perceive the world of elementary particles with finite non-zero mass; the model of this world is a pure monatomic non-relativistic gas made up of countable but otherwise indistinguishable particles. Above this we find the astronomical universe of matter bunched into heavy masses that form stars, star clusters, galaxies, and clusters of galaxies.

On a spherical object near one of the stars there evolved the integrative level of life; out of the many forms of life came human life characterized by a particular control that I shall call noetic. The highest integrative level known is that of civilizations and cultures; I shall call it the societal level.

Each of these integrative levels may be usefully described as a distinct Umwelt; each has its own peculiar temporality.

- The world of massless particles is *atemporal*. By this is meant that there are no ways whereby the hallmarks of time (future-past-present, before-after) may be recognized, if this world is judged entirely from within. The primitive time of the particulate Umwelt I called prototemporal for "proto-" the first or lowest of a series. Here distinction can be made between temporal and spatial features even though our ideas of "here" vs. "there" and "now" vs. "then" are only loosely applicable. Causation is probabilistic, events can be described only statistically.

| Stable Integrative Levels of Nature | Temporalities and their Descriptions | Paradigms and Other Examples |
|---|---|---|
| First signals | ATEMPORAL. No before/after, no future/past/present. | Paradigm: the umwelt of particles with zero restmass.<br>Other examples: physical, physiological, and perceptual chronons. |
| Particulate matter | PROTOTEMPORAL. Temporal and spatial positions of events ill-defined. Events and things sometimes interchangeable. Causation is probabilistic. | Paradigm: the umwelt of indistinguishable particles, such as all electrons.<br>Other examples: all universes whose elements are countable but not orderable by numbers, such as all workers in a factory, all voters above 18 years of age, all lightbulbs. Also the domain of time perception above the perceptual chronon but below the order threshold. |
| Ponderable matter | EOTEMPORAL. Pure succession: not everything happens at once yet time does not have an arrow; endings cannot be distinguished from beginnings; connections are by deterministic causation. | Paradigm: the umwelt of the Newtonian world of heavy, gravitating bodies.<br>Other examples: all universes whose elements are orderable by number but do not constitute autonomous systems that would demand internal coordination. Repetitive sequences of dance; periodic motion of the planets; the domain of time perception above the order threshold but below the threshold of conscious action; dream imagery that contains future, past and present yet unwinds "in time." |
| Life | BIOTEMPORAL. Nowness may be defined; future may be distinguished from past, endings from beginnings. Connectivities may be those of final causation. | Paradigm: the umwelt of living organisms.<br>Other examples: the moods of those literary and artistic creations that suggest the emergence of presentness. |
| Mind | NOOTEMPORAL. Future and past may be sharply distinguished; nowness is that of the mental present; connectivities include human freedom. | Paradigm: the umwelt of the human mind.<br>Other examples: none known, but in principle all universes that comprise the symbolic transformation of experience. |
| Society | SOCIOTEMPORAL. The possible features of this temporality and the reasons why it is difficult to delineate them are argued in this paper | Paradigm and only example: the (potential) global society of man. |

TABLE I. *The Hierarchy of Temporalities*

The Newtonian universe of massive, astronomical bodies is *eotemporal*, implying the dawn of time (for Eos, the Goddess of dawn). There is nothing in this world that could help us distinguish happenings that "flow" from past to future from those that "flow" from future to past, and as in the atemporal and prototemporal worlds, nothing can correspond to our ideas of a "now." In this world causation is deterministic.

Living matter has its own Umwelt, the *biotemporal*. It is only here that presentness becomes definable (in terms of the coordination necessary to maintain the autonomy of a living organism). We observe a series of "presents" as we progress from the primitive and cyclic to the complex and aging orders of life. Futurity and pastness become increasingly polarized and final causation can be given a meaning.

The Umwelt of the mind I called *nootemporal*. This is the world of personal identity, and of human symbols. There is a sharp distinction between pastness and futurity; here the biotemporal present of animals opens up to the mental present of man with its continuously changing boundaries. Causality is enlarged to include human freedom.

The Umwelt of the global collective may be called *sociotemporal*. Since the existence of an integrative level that would correspond to the total family of man is only a potentiality, it is difficult to discern the hallmarks of this temporality. We shall go only as far as inquiring into problems that are likely to be associated with a transition from the nootemporal to the sociotemporal Umwelt.

For a summary description of temporalities see Table I. To the content of that Table I wish to add that just as every integrative level subsumes those underneath it, so each temporality is taken to subsume the temporalities beneath it.

• In the theory of time as conflict each major integrative level is identified with certain *unresolvable conflicts*. By "unresolvable" is meant that through functions available within that Umwelt, the conflict may only be maintained or else eliminated by collapse into a lower integrative level. But, since the integrative level lasts only as long as the conflicts last, the collapse of the conflicts does not truly constitute their resolution. However, the unresolvable conflicts of a level can and do provide the motive forces for the emergence of a new integrative level. This new Umwelt, from its very inception, may again be identified with certain unresolvable conflicts of its own.

In prior works I dealt mainly with the integrative levels themselves, though I did note that there are classes of phenomena which do not seem to belong in the major stable integrative levels, but fall in between adjacent Umwelts. One sympathetic and knowledgeable critic found this feature important enough to remark that "nature does not make jumps, they used to say, but if you look at the hierarchy of complexity she seems not to linger at intermediate stages." I believe that the position of man in our epoch is at such an intermediate stage between the integrative level that corresponds to his individuality and one that corresponds to that of the family of man wherein individuals are significant only by virture of their role in the communal enterprise. Let us, therefore, turn now to a discussion of the interfaces in general.

## 2. POLICIES COMMON TO THE INTERFACES

Throughout nature we may observe many examples of the unpredictably new arising entirely from within a stable integrative level. Thus, new elements were created during the formative years of the universe from primordial elements; innumerable life forms have arisen from the biotemporal integrative level; an impressive store of ideas has been created by individuals, working more or less alone. It is not necessary to hypothesize interfaces just to discuss inorganic or organic evolution, or the proliferation of human thought. However, it is only from conditions and functions that I shall class as belonging to the interfaces that new temporalities seem to arise. The emergence of new temporalities may be described as time's rites of passage.

Let me,therefore, state without detailed arguments what I regard as the distinguishing features of interfaces taken as a group. Following each bullet I shall state briefly one of the "policies" of interfaces, then point to examples, progressing from the atemporal/prototemporal interface to the prototemporal/eotemporal one, then to the eotemporal/biotemporal, and finally to the biotemporal/nootemporal region.

• Structures and processes that comprise the interfaces assume ambiguous positions between two adjacent Umwelts: sometimes they seem to be appropriate for a particular integrative level, sometimes for the level beneath it. They are, so to say, "unpopular," or disowned by their stable neighbors. By a term borrowed from chemistry, I shall describe such conditions of ambiguity as those of *metastability*.

Upon close argument a case for metastability may be made for the "unpopularity" of atomic states which would separate the massless particles from those with finite masses and thus the atemporal from the prototemporal level; and again, for aggregate states that would be neither prototemporal nor eotemporal. Between the eotemporal and the biotemporal Umwelts the region of biogenesis is certainly metastable; between the biotemporal and the nootemporal worlds we recognize a region of our functions which are too biological for the mind, as it were, and too tenuous and alien to the body: these are the unconscious manifestations of our minds.

• Evolution has shown great ingenuity in finding *new uses for the functions and structures* of an integrative level, and through this policy it succeeded in determining the features of more advanced Umwelts.

Biogenesis is a rich example of this policy. All the elements that are necessary for primitive life must be assumed to have existed when life was born, but it is the new uses of already existing elements and compounds which is one of life's distinguishing features.* Equally rich in examples is the interface between the biotemporal and the nootemporal. For instance, the nervous system, which is employed by animals mainly for

* Including the evolution of machinery to manufacture complex molecules which cannot be found in non-living matter.

the control of locomotion and communication, evolved into the human brain with functions of a much more complex nature. The auditory loop which, in animals, assists the survival of the species by such means as the blending of individual sensitivity to friend, foe, and food into collective sensitivities evolved, in man, into the means that makes language possible.

- The forms of matter that inhabit a new integrative level, and the principles that characterize the functions of this matter usually evolve from a few forms and principles, chosen by natural selection, from a large variety of forms and principles available on the lower integrative level. Let us call this the *natural selection of forms,* and consider it a special case of the more general phenomenon of morphogenesis.

The manifestations of this policy along the physical interfaces are much less striking than they are along the higher ones, though examples can nevertheless be found. Leaving the eotemporal world for the biotemporal one, we note that the percentage composition by elements of living substance does not correspond either to that of the universe at large, or to that of the earth. Carbon, nitrogen, oxygen, hydrogen carry the great bulk of organic behaviour, with a dozen or so other elements crucially but only minimally present. Going from life to man, we find that of the million and a half named species, and innumerable other species that died out, it is only a very few, perhaps only a single one that came to evolve the brain whose functions determine the nootemporal Umwelt.

- Let us mean by the "language" of an integrative level classes of signals and symbols in which the laws and regularities of nature must be expressed so as to satisfy the critical and practical intelligence of man, the formulator and tester of those laws. When so understood, we note *changes in language* as we cross the interfaces. In this view, languages are Umwelt-specific, with each language incorporating those beneath it while adding some of its own peculiarities. Thus, the interfaces may be said to be semi-permeable to the languages of the integrative levels which they separate: information from below may be passed upward, but level-specific information from above cannot ordinarily penetrate to below. This is a non-reductionist stance, one that is essential to the theory of time as conflict, but it is a principle which cannot be rigorously proved; rather it can only be made increasingly plausible.

When the hierarchical asymmetry of languages is examined in detail, a good case can be made for distinguishing three different types of communications. Explanation given in a language appropriate for an Umwelt can be usefully described as "intelligible" for the purposes of that Umwelt. Signs and symbols appropriate to a higher Umwelt may be described as "unintelligible" in terms of the lower language, while those appropriate for a lower integrative level are "obvious." For instance, the processes of natural selection working on the phenotype are intelligible in biotemporal language; the laws and regularities of molecules that make up the genes are intelligible in prototemporal and eotemporal language and obvious in biotemporal language. The symbolism of dreams is intelligible in nootemporal language but unintelligible in prototemporal language.

• In the theory of time as conflict the unresolvability of certain conflicts, indigenous to an Umwelt, are seen as the motive forces for the emergence of the next higher integrative level. The dynamics of this process may be discussed under the name of *conflicts and their resolutions*. When the specifics of the emergence of new Umwelts are examined, it can be shown that it is along the interfaces (that is, among functions and structures that are metastable, that separate languages of integrative levels, etc.) where the complete failure, the fiasco of prior modes of conflict resolution become evident and the leading edge of the new integrative level is first manifest.

The essence of the physical conflicts may be implied by pointing to the opposition between the entropy increasing trends in inanimate nature expressed in the famous Second Law of Thermodynamics, and those specific laws of physics and chemistry which minimize that entropy increase. But, passive physical systems cannot be more efficient in opposing entropy increase than to make it minimal or even zero; in this condition I see the inadequacy of the physical mode of conflict resolution.

The limitation was overcome through the appearance of life, that is, through stable systems which decrease entropy locally (even if the total entropy increase of closed systems containing open systems will more than compensate for the local decrease). Life lasts only as long as the conflict lasts between the entropy increasing and decreasing trends; if and when this conflict vanishes living matter returns to its inanimate form. Conflict is thus seen to be immanent in life and unresolvable by means available within the biotemporal Umwelt. Life itself ought then to be understood not as a one-way thrust of some kind but as a conflict between growth and decay.

But organic evolution is limited in the rate at which it can provide adaptation. In the plant world the rate of adaptation has been increasing throughout the evolution of the plant kingdom by such means, for instance, as the descendency of trees in general and the ascendency of shorter-lived plants; these latter can adapt most readily, hence faster, to available environmental niches.[2] In the history of the evolution of the most advanced animal species the limitation of the rate at which evolutionary diversification can take place became a crucial issue, especially since the environment to which advanced life forms were to adapt became increasingly more complex because of the very success of organic evolution.

The limitations just implied were overcome through the capacity of the human mind to create symbolic transformations of experience. The mind can construct a symbolic continuity known as the "self." With the assistance of this symbol, and of all other symbols of our "inner landscape," it became possible to effect evolutionary changes without the need of going through the organic selection process.

However, the mind also has its own unresolvable conflicts: those between the expected and the encountered. A tension, or a difference between the expected and the encountered must be maintained if the identity of the self is to be retained. Should such conflict vanish for any length of time, the mind would begin to manufacture new goals and desires. If it is impossible to reestablish and maintain the conflict, the self collapses and nootemporality vanishes: a person becomes senile or insane.

But the functioning of the individual mind leads to a dead-end whenever its expectations get too far away from the conditions encountered. This conflict gives rise to yet a new integrative level, that of the sophisticated machinery of the societal Umwelt.

3. INDIVIDUAL VS. COLLECTIVE IDENTITIES

Let us turn now to the theme of our main concern: what might be the likely features of the interface between the integrative level that corresponds to the individual mind and that which might correspond to a single human society on earth. By "society" I mean a collective of humans that has existed and is likely to continue existing for a sustained period of time, bound together by common interests, including those of survival and reproduction. I am aware of some of the problems that sociologists face when they try to give a satisfactory definition of what they mean by "society." It is fortunate that for our purposes many of their problems are absent. For, although I will use "society" in the sense just defined, by the societal integrative level I shall mean the potential, common Umwelt of all people on earth. The reasons for so doing relate to an observation, an opinion, and as assumption.

The observation is that the mutual interdependence among individuals and nations in the world community has been increasing at a rapid rate. This increase is encouraged by a call for universal industrial civilization which, eventually, will not be able to function within areas smaller than the total surface of the earth. It would demand a multiple, communicative interconnectedness and organization that will surely cement its members into a functioning, single whole.

The opinion is that such a world society, if it should come about, would in fact constitute a new integrative level of nature. I have argued recently that when the brain, in its evolution, reached a certain degree of complexity it gave rise to the integrative level of the mind, which is capable of producing other minds of equal or superior sophistication via its network of signs and symbols. Likewise, I believe that when this network of signs and symbols reaches a certain complexity, we may look for the emergence of a new integrative level, the societal.

The assumption is that the interface between the individual mind (the noetic Umwelt) and the societal Umwelt would, in fact, follow the policies that the lower interfaces do.

I shall now take up the five policy features identified in the prior section.

(a) New Uses for Old Functions

The nervous system of man, including his brain, became so well adapted to its role as the coordinator of the functions of an individual that it has not yet stopped expanding its executive domain. It tends to extend the limits of its boundaries by coordinating groups of individuals into society. I believe that since the brain is already of such complexity as is possible to produce by biological means, what we have been doing during the evolution of historic man is learning how to put this complexity to better use.[3] The societal extension of the functions of the mind is part of that learning process. By "mind" I understand the process description of the brain; "behavior" may then be interpreted as the acting out of certain brain states.

The internal happenings that correspond to behavior would be the signals carried in the brain by appropriate neural codes, with the brain itself the immediate environment of the mind. The most direct and richest representation of the internal codes of the brain is, surely, the spoken and written tongue: it enables the individual to formulate and establish his identity and tie this symbolic continuity to the symbolic continuities that we know as "other selves." This method of establishing identity is projected into the world of the collectives of man where it assists in the creation and perpetuation of that new symbolic continuity which we call mankind. Just as the brain may be said to be the environment of the mind, so collectives of individual minds form the environment of the societal Umwelt. It is individuals that generate, provide for the transmission, and exchange the signs and symbols appropriate to the new integrative level of society. The network of these symbols is the ancient and modern means of communication. By sound and light modulation, by electric and mechanical signals communication does for society what the neural network does for the individual. The use of societal symbols and signs in the establishment of the collective identity is then one example of a new use for already existing functions.

In the model of the mind which I developed some time ago, it was useful to postulate the workings of two imaginary actors: the Observer and the Agent.[4] These two actors represented, respectively, the evolutionarily older, eotemporal function of the brain (that was the Observer) and its newer, nootemporal functions (that was the Agent). They were found to bear a hierarchical relation to one another and were said to be "distrustful" of each other's opinions. The tension and the communication between the two were found to display certain features which, taken together, suggested conscious experience and free will.

In the societal integrative level I discern a perennial struggle between these two actors, in the ancient role of the "Prophet" and the "Statesman." The Prophet is rather like the Observer: he claims to be in command of knowledge concerning both future and past; hence surveys the affairs of man in terms of unchanging criteria. "Alone he saw the field of time, past and to come" said Homer of Mastorides, the Forecaster. The Prophet's memories and expectations are certain and resemble the deterministic Umwelt of eotemporality. The Statesman is rather like the Agent. His time is asymmetrical because his future contains certain irreducible uncertainties with which he must deal in a crucial present. Just as with the Agent and Observer for the individual mind, so with Statesman and Prophet, it is their interaction, dialogues, enmities, trusts and mistrusts that set the fate of the societal body of which they are part; except that in the societal setting the two individuals need not be and usually are not the same person.

The separation of a single mind into two imaginary actors is, of course, an analytical trick; it is only the underlying existential tension that can be given ontic status. But that some of the functions of the individual mind, when projected across the interface break up into components which then materialize as two distinct persons, is an example of the evolutionary division of labor, a policy of evolution well known in the development of complex organisms.

There are many other examples for new uses of old functions and structures, carried across the interface between man and society by division of labor. Technology, for instance, is a communal enterprise that extends the bodily functions of man in certain ways that no individual if working alone, could possible match. Science, as distinct from technology, is yet another example. It is a collective enterprise in a search for knowledge which communal judgment holds to be true, that is, unchanging through time. Science engages the capacities of the individual minds but directs them into domains which are unthinkable in a world of independent individual selves, no matter how ingenious each individual might be. Even ethics may be interpreted as a collective experimentation with the imagery of the individual mind, an enterprise which is quite meaningless except in a communal framework.

It seems, then, that political, scientific, and ethical practices, though originating in the mind of the individual, form a language which is that of the societal and not of the noetic integrative level.

(b) Natural Selection of Forms

Let us first consider some characteristics of the lower interfaces. For instance, the chemical composition of living matter is quite different from the natural abundance of elements of inanimate matter in the crust of the earth, even though life did arise from the earth; or, the human mind is quite uncharacteristic of living forms in general, even though man evolved from among all other living creatures. Out of what elements should we expect the leading forms of the societal integrative level to be selected? Out of symbolic continuities ordinarily referred to as "ideas." I do not mean disembodied ghosts, but rather the actual world of signals that communicates ideas among men. They determine an Umwelt as distinct from that of the individual mind, as the nootemporal Umwelt of the mind is distinct from the biotemporal one of the brain.

Without detailed deliberation one cannot even guess which specific ideas might comprise the major form of the societal world, but it is possible to make two observations.

One concerns the symbolic continuity of the private self: that curious construct which is believed to operate in the world external to its body, yet without a completely identifiable external referent. Group identity is an analogous construct. It is defined and continuously refined by conflict, and by comparison with the collective identities of other groups. "One nation, indivisible, under God" is thinkable only in the company of other nations, equally indivisible. For the societal Umwelt, that is, for the family of man, this process of definition, by comparison, is not available, because there are no other humanities against which the identity of a global society could be defined. It is very likely, therefore, that the selection of the major forms which are to constitute the societal Umwelt will run up against problems that have no parallel among the lower interfaces.

The other observation is that in all lower Umwelts, for the selection process to work, it was necessary to have a large store of different elements upon which to operate. Although only a relatively few forms were then carried on into the initial structures of the next higher integrative level, the continued existence of other elements remained a necessity. It may thus be speculatively inferred that if a societal Umwelt were to emerge around a few central ideas, it will be able to retain viability only if it remains submerged in a sufficiently large store of ideas other than those upon which the identity of the family of man might be built.

(c) Change of Language

Methods of communication that are useful among individuals, such as the spoken, written and - in a more general sense - the acted-out languages, draw upon the biological and mental capacities of the individual; these are the languages appropriate for families, tribes and nations. Would the same languages be appropriate for the societal integrative level which I envision as arising from the noetic world? I do not believe so. But I am not thinking of such trivialities as, for instance, the diplomatic language used among heads of state, but rather of the fact that individuals prefer to communicate with individuals. Franz Kafka's <u>K</u> had great difficulties in crossing the communication boundaries between himself and the different languages spoken by the Castle.

I characterized the asymmetry about low interfaces as "obvious," when looking down, as "intelligible" when looking around, and as "unintelligible" or "mystical" when looking upward. Let us consider a few examples from the relationships between the individual and society.

Certainly, the replacement of individual values by collective values is often unintelligible. Again, I do not mean such easily identifiable practices as the willful beclouding of issues by certain governments. Rather, I am thinking of the replacement of individual reality by collective reality, such as in interpreting the actions of man as an historical beast. The story of man is filled with more examples of senseless horror than, prorated per capita, we would admit as likely. Theories that propose to account for the bloody discontents of civilizations in terms of the drives and pains of the individual might well reach the sources of such discontents but, precisely because they consider the individual alone and not society as a whole, they cannot account for the qualitative change, something more than the simple amplification of individual behavior, displayed in the historic actions of the masses. One contention of this paper is that the regularities of mass behavior are those of the societal and not of the noetic Umwelt.

These and similar issues have been discussed in philosophy under the rubric of holism vs. individualism. In sociology, certain related matters are known under the heading of "unintended results." Rather crassly, this is the problem of the soldier looking at his comrades: "If neither you not I really want to be here, and if the people across the trench do not want to be here either, then why are we here?"

What we have learned so far suggests that the sources of unintelligibility, and of possible feelings of mysteriousness, are to be sought in the epistemological asymmetry of the languages that surround the noetic/societal interface. That is, explanations of the regularities indigenous to the societal Umwelt cannot be given in a totally satisfactory way in languages appropriate only to the Umwelt of the individual mind.

Consider the unfolding affairs of the world and witness the growing multitudes of people, increasingly joined by certain proposed uniform solutions of their common needs. The impression is unavoidable that the messages that carry their ideas have some functions of their own and possess a degree of freedom over and above those of the individual mind.

The asymmetry of languages is encountered not only while looking up, but also when looking downward, and there are many examples of such "downward" looks. Claims for the inferiority and insignificance of the individual as compared with the collective self have probably been made ever since man appeared, but it is only with the explosive growth of communication and the beckoning development of a single human community that the awesome ramifications of this lopsided relationship comes into full view. Surely, whatever is beneficial to world-wide society does not necessarily benefit the individual and vice versa. This asymmetry has often been noted, bemoaned, or praised in languages appropriate for the individual, for it is to him that such comments have traditionally been addressed. It is quite conceivable, however, and specifically suggested by the theory of time as conflict that if, and as, the world enters the state I called the sociotemporal Umwelt, languages in which the plight of the individuals might be expressed will retain no more relative significance than the complaint of a lost egg or unused sperm has for its donor. The family of man may have no language left in which to bemoan the erosion of unique personality traits or express the suffering that goes with the loss of life.

(d) Metastability

Things and processes that constitute the interfaces might be described as "unpopular" in that they do not properly belong to any of the stable integrative levels. But as we rise along the hierarchy of Umwelts, they become more evident. That is, although as a class they are all metastable, as the complexity of their neighboring Umwelts increase so does the identifiability of metastable processes. I would like to discuss now some evidence that suggests that as a family of man we are entering a metastable integrative state. My examples are drawn from thoughts on ethics.

Throughout the known history of man, instructions for praiseworth conduct seem to have been around, regardless of the size of groups. That such instructions were apparently always needed suggests that conflicts between the interests of communities and those of individuals accompanied the social history of man. In the social life of animals we can also find rules but, as far as one can tell, collective demands either do not elicit conflicts within the individual, or if they do, the conflicts do not have the potentiality of becoming creative forces; altruism, a currently popular term, is not to be confused with compassion. The reason for this profound difference between animal and human communities is the absence in animals of individual selves which could find themselves opposed to the collective self. The interest of the group and the interest of the individual usually coincide: the struggle of the individual against the identity of the species is either nonexistent or insignificant. In stark contrast, one way to interpret the history of man is in terms of the perennial struggle between individual and communal destinies.

As in the matter of language asymmetry and of the natural selection of form, the issues of the individual/societal interface come into sharp focus only with the changes that prepare the possible emergence of a world community. In traditional societies it was ordinarily much easier to be a rugged individual living in the Norse woods, *or* an essentially nameless member of a human anthill (small or large), than to be both, simultaneously. It is not easy to give to the King what is the King's and to the individual what is the individual's, for they are often mutually exclusive. Much thought and energy has been expended in modern times in the socially advanced portions of the world toward the establishment of a working order where individual and collective interests may be harmoniously reconciled. In terms of our prior findings, such a reconciliation, if achieved would imply conditions that might prevail within, rather than below or above the noetic/societal interface. If the policies of lower order interfaces are useful guides, a balance between the individual and the societal selves, when assumed to apply to a world-wide society, is at best a precarious and metastable condition; the prognosis for the duration of this developmental state as a world-wide condition is one of radical brevity. As were the first living things which did not survive at all, and as is the buffer zone between body and mind that survived as our unconscious, the balanced condition that must characterize the nootemporal/sociotemporal interface may only be very short lived developmentally, even if its remnant would survive among the structures and functions of the new integrative level.

4. BETWEEN TWO WORLDS

It is appropriate now to return explicitly to questions of time's current rite of passage. Consider first that because the language of the nootemporal Umwelt subsumes all lower languages, we should be expected to be able to make authoritative statements about temporalities below the noetic. I believe that we can do so. Certainly, our formal sentences about the physical world carry great authority, even if it is impossible for us to experience atemporality, proto-, or eotemporality, other than in terms of moods. We can also explore biotemporality with confidence, though our understanding of the temporal world of organisms is not as well grounded as is our understanding of lower temporalities. In spite of the difficulties of regressive sharing, however, we can at least approach in our own experience the temporal Umwelts of higher animals. When it comes to nootemporality, our knowledge seems to be almost entirely that of feeling rather than understanding. A degree of unintelligibility has been one of the hallmarks of questions pertaining to "the time of man."

It is one thing to talk about the end of a particular physical process, or the end of the life of a flea, or a rabbit, or someone else: it is quite another thing to contemplate the end in time of the self. It is, again, one thing for me to talk about the beginning of a chemical change, or the birth of a child, and something quite different to contemplate the past that preceded my conscious experience. It is fascinating to reflect upon the time of the prototemporal, just barely distinguishable from the spatial; or upon the pure asymmetry of the eotemporal, or upon the aging of frogs, flowers, and human males in general: but whence derives in my own mind that emphatically asymmetrical attitude toward post-mortem and prepartum existence?

There are also other issues. For instance, the atemporal is understandable. The probabilistic causation of the prototemporal, once understood as a primitive connectivity, can be accomodated in our scheme of thought. The deterministic causation of the eotemporal is convincing and convenient, as are the multiple and final causations of the biotemporal. Causation in human life is intuitively given, but it is immensely difficult to comprehend it discursively. How can I accommodate that paradoxical feeling which informs me that some of my actions can be, and have been, freely taken in a world of processes that function according to law?

Consider next the thrust of man's history. The past could not honestly be called unintelligible, yet neither is it truly intelligible. As far back as one can see, our species has been driven by aspirations whose goals it cannot hope to reach, yet cannot accept as unreachable, such as ethical needs for justice and demands for consummate beauty.

The hierarchical structure of the world contemplated in the theory of time as conflict, suggests that answers to questions such as these may be had only after they have been formulated in the language of the integrative level above that of the mind, that is, in the language of the sociotemporal Umwelt. I am not imaging that citizens of a "brave new world" would be more perceptive than we are, or even better informed; the opposite is more likely to be the case. What I am saying is that in the language appropriate to the societal Umwelt some aspects of such issues that pertain to birth and death control, to free will and destiny, to the role of the individual vs. the collective self, which now elude even the keenest of minds, may be so stated as to become answerable by the collective.

In a very disturbing way, since the features of new temporal Umwelts arise from regions left unrecognized by the epistemology of a lower level, working within the confines of nootemporal language it is not even possible to delineate which issues fall into this category. That is, it is not possible to identify which of our unanswered questions may be answerable "from above," as it were, and which shall, or at least may, find satisfactory explication within the world of the individual mind.

Let us recall the unresolvable conflicts of the mind: those between the expected and the encountered, between passion and knowledge. Shakespeare put it this way in *Troilus and Cressida:*

> ...that the will is infinite, and the execution confined; that the desire is boundless and the act slave to limit.

This conflict may be resolved by collapse: a man may become senile or lose his mind; the nootemporal then returns to the biotemporal. Or the conflict may be maintained. Doing so without self-destruction is usually regarded as a sign of the maturity of the ego. But, in our epoch something is happening in the nootemporal Umwelt that resembles the condition of life's cul-de-sac which gave rise to the emergence of the mind. This time it is the individual mind which cannot function rapidly and efficiently enough; it cannot adapt to an environment which changes by the very deeds of the collectives of the individual minds. This, then, is the fiasco of the capacity of the individual self to deal with its own unresolvable conflict. The theory of time as conflict would identify such conditions as suggestive for the emergence of a new integrative level which, in some sense, would resolve the conflicts of the lower level.

There are many observations one can make that reinforce the suspicion that the family of man is indeed entering into a developmental state that belongs in the class of Umwelts which I have described as interfaces.

Let the sensitivity of playwrights be our guide. The change in modern self, as we learned at the first conference of this society, is reflected in the change of prevailing dramatic forms: in our epoch tragedy has come to be replaced by comedy, or, at best, by something of an "applied pathos," resembling uncomfortably closely the "passion surrogate" of the *Brave New World.* In *Romeo and Juliet* society is reprimanded for its assumption of preeminence over the individual; whereas in the plays of Beckett the individuals are punished for assuming preeminence over society.

During the period of history just preceding our epoch, much ingenuity was expended on devising means whereby the often opposing interests of the individual and of society might be reconciled. A foremost representative of these efforts is the American Constitution, drafted and ratified 189 years ago, putting forth certain principles based on a particular evaluation of state and man. For a number of reasons, among which we may list the remarkable skill and wisdom of the drafters of that constitution, the governmental structure that derived from the power of this document may be described as one whose primary task is to maintain the continuous reconciliation between individual and collective interests and among segments of government. John Adams spoke of this system as one of "checks and balances." By chance and historical good luck, and by the surviving genius of skillful compromise, the government so constituted succeeded for a while in permitting and encouraging a condition of permanent revolution, one that was able to maintain and contain within boundaries the unresolvable conflicts between the nootemporal and the sociotemporal worlds. But this mode of checks and balances is now under challenge from doctrines which define the individual entirely in terms of its position within the social collective.

The division of labor advocated by these doctrines demands the interchangability of people within occupations, thereby forcing the mind of man to operate in the world resembling the prototemporal Umwelt of indistinguishable particles. Human anthills are in the making: some drab, some grey, some many-colored, but anthills just the same. Kafka's Castle is being exported from its natural habitat to the new and even newer world, distributed and promoted by the unholy alliance of opportunistic ideologies, international terrorism, and multi-national corporations. As in the gastrulation of embryos, so also different groups of man are shifting around in search for, or anticipating their final position, in the family of man. The traditional bonds of solidarity are dissolved under the pressure of industrial ethics which, ironically, has its sources in Christian soteriology, intended for the salvation of the individual.

"Now it is time that we were going," said Socrates, "I to die and you to live, but which of us has the happier prospect is unknown to anyone by God." The Socratic puzzle has not been answered but by-passed; its unresolvable conflict is on its way to resolution though the interchangeability of individuals. It has been prophesied that there will be one fold and one shepherd, but the mental image that used to go with this prophecy has changed.

The theory of time as conflict can say absolutely nothing about the actual future development in the relationship between the individual and society. It may only assert that the type of balance in which we find ourselves today is metastable. The theory does point, however, to two possible paths suggested by what we have learned about the lower order interfaces. The unresolvable conflicts of the mind may be resolved by the emergence of a new integrative level, that of the societal Umwelt; or else, resolved by regression to the noetic Umwelt of the individual minds grouped in tribes and families; or else, even by regression to the biotemporal, leaving the earth for the beasts that crawl, fly and swim.

What I have described as the metastability of the noetic/societal interface is not to be identified with any of the classical ideas of revolution. For it is not the revolt of the hungry against the well fed, or that of one race against another or one nation against another, and not even one ideology against another, although it would include all of these. Rather, it is a revolt against the unresolvable conflicts of the mind.

Hence, the march is not to the tune of Dies Irae, or to the Marseillaise, not even to that of the Communist Internationale, but to something much more elemental. We are in a metamorphosis wherein, as Kazantzakis put it "life has grown more savage, and the gods grown more powerful."

If all this sounds ominous, and it does, we might take the advice of Justice Oliver Wendell Holmes, a man who was profoundly dedicated to the permanent revolution as a societal way of existence. "Have faith," he wrote, "and pursue the unknown end."

## NOTES AND REFERENCES

1. J. T. Fraser, *Time as Conflict: a Scientific and Humanistic Study* (Basel: Birkhäuser Verlag and Brookfield, Vt.: Renouf U.S.A., 1978). Also *Of Time, Passion, and Knowledge* (New York: Braziller, 1975).

2. Cf. the paper by Professor Hans Kalmus in this volume.

3. "Complexity, as here understood, is not a measure of the number of component units of a system, but of the number of ways in which the members of that system are, or may be, interconnected." Fraser (1978), *op. cit.* p. 113

4. I am using the figures of Observer and Agent as they are employed in attribution theory. Their functions are not to be confused with the separation of theoretical and practical knowledge as suggested by Kant.

## Discussion and Comment

Frederick Turner

The paper constitutes an extension of the theory of time as a hierarchy of unresolvable conflicts; my comments question not the theory but some details of its extension.

The picture of the superhuman collectivity Fraser paints at the end of his paper seems a pessimistic conclusion to that burgeoning creative process he has described so vividly at work in the universe. Are we indeed doomed to a Hegelian-Marxian-Durkheimian Brave New World, in which Society has become a merciless and inhuman God? I wish to question whether the sociotemporal umwelt is higher than, and emergent subsequently to, our own. Creatures lower in the evolutionary scale than humans do experience thoroughgoingly social modes of existence. The ethologists have demonstrated that highly complex animal societies can exist without conceptual thought and its attendant nootemporal umwelt. The most recent work on the ancestry of Man seems to indicate that the precursors of human society and culture existed before the genus Homo acquired his full neural cortical endowment. Human society evolved the human mind, rather than the reverse: one major selective pressure on early forms of Man was that of his own society. By this argument nootemporality would succeed sociotemporality rather than vice-versa.

Let us thus organize the human umwelts, in ascending order: sociotemporal, nootemporal, theotemporal. I choose this term, theotemporal, without any ulterior ideological motives; the very emptiness of the idea of God in modern terms makes it useful as a label for what we, who exist in the nootemporal umwelt, cannot understand or find language to express. What might we infer about the theotemporal umwelt? If mind is more intensely alive than life, and life more intensely material than matter (life is matter that can record itself, conferring a new category of characteristics upon matter by sensing it)--then the theotemporal must be more mindlike--more free, intelligent, playful, conscious, creative--than mind.

# City Rhythms *

M. Melbin

*ABSTRACT*

*The large city is active at all times of day and night, and the city's population displays rhythms in its moods and social behavior around the clock. In the city of Boston, self-afflicting problems, threats to others, fights, and noisy disorder, show 24-hour cycles. Each of these patterns leads the next by several hours. They were discerned by analysis of emergency calls to the telephone company and to the police department. The rhythms may be due in part to a selective distribution of types of people throughout the 24 hours of activity. The findings prompt ideas about how the city functions, and suggest that a multi-city activity-time census would have theoretical and practical value.*

Consider the possibility that social behavior and human feelings are rhythmic around the clock. My initial premises are that there are noticeable cycles for social conduct over the 24-hour day, and that these may be interpreted both for what they reveal about the way a city works and about individuals living there.

Urban life is rhythmic. For most of us there is a periodic repetition of work, play, and rest, day after day. We are conscious of our daily affairs pulled into orbit by

*I gratefully acknowledge grant #MH-22763 from the Center for Studies of Metropolitan Problems, National Institute of Mental Health (U.S.A.) through which the research and the preparation of this essay was supported.

the commitment to work beginning shortly after daybreak. Tides of people surge to and from the town center. Eating, commuting, and shopping have their places in the cadence. The tempo follows regular speedups and slowdowns.

Since people are synchronized in these events their social behavior and their emotions may be rhythmic as well. I wish to address the question of what is implied by cycles of human feelings, and what these reveal about the urban milieu and persons living there. However this must be preceded by a description of what is going on. Till now, much of the attention to urban rhythms has focused on traffic movement, on the demand for electric power, and on the task of scheduling employees to work the day, evening, and night shifts. It is more difficult to tally social acts than to measure traffic and energy use. But there are two regular sources of information about the conduct and feelings of city dwellers. One is the police department. Police officers make records of the events they are called upon to investigate at all hours. The other is the telephone company, whose telephone operators keep records of emergency calls to which they must respond. These sources do not provide a full picture of what is going on in the city. The records mainly tell of troubles that beset people there. Although these do not even give the whole story of urgent problems, it is information about what emergencies are happening to large portions of the population, and the entries have the merit of being made as a matter of course. So the analysis of police and telephone operators' records is an economical way of learning about certain types of events. Accordingly I collected this information while engaged in a larger program of research on 24-hour activities in the city of Boston (see footnote, page 000).

In the main part of this essay I will not describe the methods of data collection in detail or discuss the technical aspects of analysis. Instead I have provided a description of the samples and an outline of research procedures in an appendix.

Having gathered information on the timing of specific events for forty-nine days during 1974, I plotted their frequencies throughout the 24-hour period on a graph. The examination of several such graphs became the starting point for the analysis: First to check whether there were noticeable fluctuations in the occurrence of these events around the clock. Next to identify what time of day or night the peak frequencies were reached. Third to learn whether some patterns keep in step with one another or, conversely, are always out-of-phase. Fourth to reflect on their possible significance.

## SOME SOCIAL AND EMOTIONAL RHYTHMS IN THE CITY OF BOSTON

Let us first review three types of police activity: investigations of sick persons, drunkeness, and violations of public order. The curve shown in Figure 1 for *violations of public order* (or briefly, disorder) combines four specific categories used by police -- disorderly conduct, noisy party, gathering causing annoyance, and 'other minor disturbance'. Drunkeness, one might imagine, is a fifth category belonging with these. Our culture views drunkeness as a problem of public order. In Boston, as in many parts of the United States, public drunkeness is a minor crime. This is reflected in assigning it to police jurisdiction, and police deal with public drunkards as with others behaving in a disorderly way.

Yet in comparing the curves in Figure 1 it is clear that the timing of drunkeness coincides more with the rhythm of people being sick than with people being disorderly, at least as much as these events are called to the attention of the police. Indeed the time series correlation between sick and drunk is .51 whereas between drunk and disorder it is only .14. There is a chance that drunkeness and violations of public order are alternative outcomes of the same causes, merely expressed at different times of the day. This idea would be supported if they are consistently out of phase. I checked two other possible rhythms, one in which drunkeness leads disorder by eleven hours (5 intervals, see Appendix C) around the clock and the other in which drunkeness follows it by two hours (one interval). The correlation coefficients are .41 and .35 respectively. These are not as high as the relationship found being drunk and being sick.

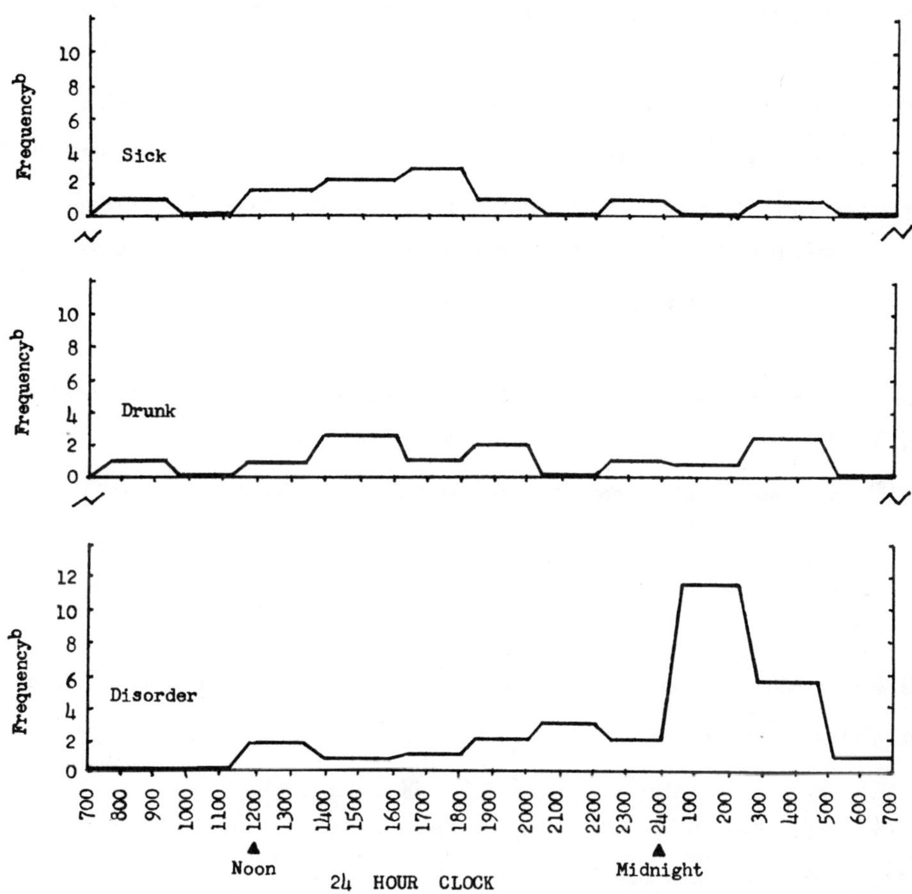


*Figure 1. Police investigations into persons being sick, drunkeness, and violations of public order.*[a]

a. *Averaged for a residential street, a shopping street, and a transportation hub.*
b. *All are 49-day frequencies and are adjusted for 24-hour sampling variations (see Appendix C).*

Shall a rhythm be known by the company it keeps? If so it suggests that drunkeness is like a sickness. I will return to this possibility after introducing more information. It is appropriate to wonder whether other forms of individual suffering also show daily rhythms.

Four kinds of emergency calls to Boston telephone operators are charted in Figure 2. *Suicide* refers to threats of and attempted suicide. Successful instances are not included, for unless actually witnessed those cases are first reported as deaths and only labeled suicide after an inquiry. *Mental ill* includes events in which people are reported to be acting strangely, for example an elderly person observed walking naked in the street. *Stress* refers to persons very upset, screaming, or saying they are frightened. The *drugs* category refers mostly to persons having taken an overdose of sleeping pills and the like, but also includes individuals on LSD "trips".

Of these four telltales of personal suffering, drunkeness is closest to drugs. Drinking can be viewed as a form of drugging oneself, and indeed the extreme consequences -- "DT's" and "bum trips" -- have much in common. This idea is supported by a correlation of .66 between the rhythm of drunk (Figure 1) and the rhythm of drugs (Figure 2). A hospital bed rather than a jail cell would seem to be called for in severe cases. This finding confirms a trend to use a medical strategy in dealing with alcoholics even though they embarrass others as well as themselves in public places. (Later I will raise the possibility of another interpretation of the drunk rhythm.)

There is another finding worth noting in Figure 2. All the categories testify to individual suffering. All the categories show a main surge of appeals for help in mid-afternoon. Taken separately, each cycle has modest amplitude. But if we interpret them as varieties of a basically similar condition and combine the frequencies into one curve, we see a sharp peak of occurrence in one phase of the 24-hour day -- the afternoon.

The higher the peak at one point during a fluctuating, rhythmic pattern, the more suggestive it is of a potent force operating then to accomplish that effect. These individual predicaments occur most often at the very time that most people are up and about. What happens to people throughout the city at that time of day?

It will help to bring more evidence to bear. One difference between being sick and violating public order is who suffers when the event occurs. Sickness or stress are

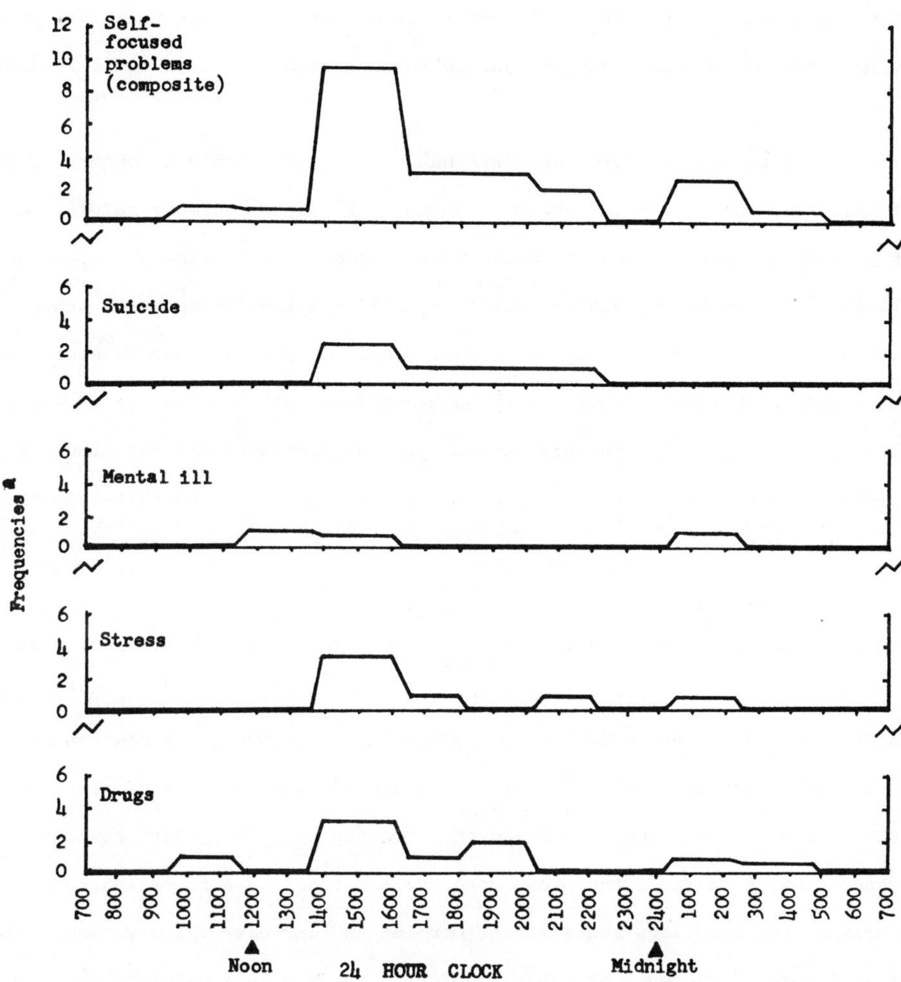


*Figure 2. Various self-focused problems reported in emergency calls to telephone operators in the city of Boston.*

*a. All are 49-day frequencies and are adjusted for 24-hour sampling variations (see Appendix C).*

self-affecting problems, although of course others may become worried that someone is in such a state. By definition, sick persons are suffering themselves. A drunkard may bother others but there is often evidence of personal suffering as well. On the other hand, persons at noisy parties or creating a minor disturbance may actually be enjoying themselves while they inflict discomfort on others. Do events that inflict suffering on others also show a rhythm, and do they occur at the same times of day?

Threats and fights are two forms of disturbance bringing trouble to others. The timing of telephone calls reporting them is shown in Figure 3. *Threats* refer to one person putting another into danger deliberately, such as promising physical hurt, persons with guns or knives acting as if they will use these weapons on others, intruders, and persons reported trying to kill others. *Fights* include persons being beaten, physical arguments ranging from barehanded assault and the use of weapons, to riots. The chart shows that threats tend to precede fights around the clock. The correlation is .94 between threats in one phase and fights in the next (about two hours later).

We have often thought that menacing gestures come before battles, for the same parties. That is, the threatener at one stage becomes the fighter in the next. The curves in Figure 3 suggest more. The linked pattern is citywide. Since the emergency calls come from throughout the city area they are not simply pairs of messages referring to threats and fights involving the same parties. It appears to be a population phenomenon, a trait of the urban species. And there is a circadian rhythm to these brawls. The rumblings begin in the morning and increase all day long, culminating in a blowoff of violence at about midnight. The city is a volcano.

Do the social rhythms interweave? We can review the *set* of patterns: self-afflicting problems (Figure 2), threats, fights (Figure 3), and violations of public order (Figure 1). All these connote tension being managed or released. Each is a cycle. Each has a dominant peak in a different phase of the 24-hour day. And each *leads* the next by several hours. Taking this leading time into account the correlation between the composite self-focused problems and threats (about six hours later) is .62, the correlation between threats and fights (about two hours later) is .94, and the correlation between fights and public disorder (about two hours later) is .69. We do not know how many fights also involved inebriation, for the fights are most frequent about the time the bars close; but here we are looking at the pattern of emergencies as announced and not -- in this respect -- delving into the matter of causes.

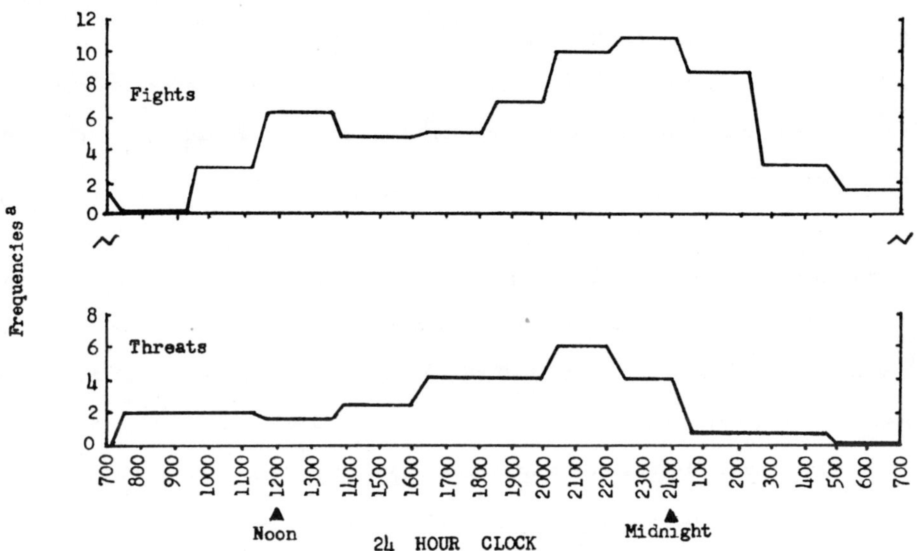


*Figure 3. Threats and fights reported in emergency calls to telephone operators in the city of Boston.*

*a. All are 49-day frequencies and are adjusted for 24-hour sampling variations (see Appendix C).*

CITY RHYTHMS AND THE SYSTEM

Here is an example of how communication and transportation technology alter the human use of space and time and become part of the change from the simpler community to the more complex city. Imagine the sequence of a person screaming, being overheard by a dweller in the next apartment, who reports it to the telephone operator, who in turn contacts the police, who -- upon investigation -- then summon medical assistance. The isolated individuals in trouble do not realize the process set in motion by their conduct. Most are neither aware nor concerned about the impact their actions have upon the city functioning as a whole. But their problems, originating in scattered places, are *centralized* by the telephone appeals. What is happening to people everywhere becomes known in one place. As appeals of certain types accumulate, they become a field of force acting upon the city to introduce specialized units -- a suicide prevention center, a riot squad, a drug hot line. The police are called upon often, even to help the sick (see Figure 1), because they are always available, they can deal with emergencies, and they are mobile. The result is more interdependece and more reliance on standardized agencies rather than on the kinfolk equivalents in earlier communities.

These incidents reflect a cyclical mood for the city as an entity. To be sure there is self-selection in reporting, and the information may be weighted toward people less enmeshed in personal networks. But this would reflect a problem of representativeness for the population, and not necessarily for the *timing* of the events. I have no evidence nor reason to suspect that those who do not report such emergencies have a consistently different temporal pattern for the same problems. And even if parts of the cycles were contributed by different subgroups, this would still be a valid portrayal of the whole, in the same way that the gross economic product of the Tyrol is a composite of tourism, timber and other ventures. Moreover, the rhythms discovered are system-wide. *Communicated events* affect the overall functioning of the city. Decisions for human services are based on such information. Other emergencies, not reported, do not enter as vigorously into urban dynamics.

There is also a practical implication of uncovering the city's cyclic temperament. The rhythms to these events invoke the same planning and administrative task as we have for physical energy demand. We draw graphs of electricity usage and they show a peak at a certain time of day. Because of it we build our generating plants for a certain capacity and prepare to deliver the power at that hour. Now that we are able to plot human needs for help that also show peaks, we face the imperative of providing services able to meet those levels of demand at those times.

With their periodicities revealed, it should be easier to do something about these problems even though we still do not understand how they are generated. This immediate utility of the findings carries with it the familiar risk of coping with symptoms rather than with causes. Consider our belief that stable rhythms in body physiology are vital to individual health. Even the regular voiding of poisonous waste is healthy. In the same way the stable cycles of stress, aggression, and public disorder may imply something for city health. If humans must grapple with problems in the urban milieu, then the daily discharge of some tensions in these forms relieves the system. It is not a reason to encourage such emergencies, but it is worth being aware of their possible function. We should act to ameliorate the causes and not merely concentrate on quelling the expressions of problems. Or else we may next confront even more troubling forms.

## QUESTIONS OF CAUSE AND OF COMPARISON

There still remain the haunting questions of why there are city-wide rhythms to these events. What conditions promote such timing of self-focused problems, attacks on others, and letting off steam? Why do certain forms have consistent leading relationships to other forms? There are a number of plausible explanations. Probably all of them should be combined in some way to account for what is revealed. I will review three possible factors.

One is the situational influence upon *reporting* some events (rather than what causes them to occur). In broad daylight people see drunkeness and in the dark people hear noisy parties. Drunks at night are hidden from view and noisy parties at midday are merged in the general din. Such conditions, that result in reporting the events, thereby contribute to the discernible rhythms. To the extent that the drunkeness pattern reflects its visibility rather than its causes, its linkage to sickness and drugs would be spurious. This discussion does not detract from the cycles of suicide, stress and drugs that peak in mid-afternoon.

Biological rhythms may have an influence. We know that bodily functions fluctuate round the clock and that behavior is related to these circadian processes. People show irritability when blood sugar is low, it begins to get low in the late afternoon, and the liver has used up much of its glycogen by the time midnight passes. (Luce, 1970, p. 48). Yet we also know that biorhythms -- though probably innate in disposition -- are readily influenced by outside stimuli including the activity patterns of individuals. We know too that the body's clock resets itself to accommodate to shift work and then operates according to those schedules. From other research I learned that 70% of the total work force in Boston is on the day shift, 21.2% on the evening shift, and 8.8% on the night shift. But the peaks of the cycles are not in a 70-21-9 ratio to one another to suggest that the problems parallel the distribution of the work force around the clock. With large portions of the population out of phase with one another, it seems that biorhythms are not as dominant as other factors in establishing the patterns. These are cycles for the city.

A large city is active at all time of the day and night. People and their pursuits have spread out over the twenty-four hours. If different groups of people were dispersed differently around the clock, their social backgrounds and characteristics could be behind the different conduct manifest at different hours of the day. There is *a time territoriality* at work that *selectively disperses* members of the population among the twenty-four hours and affects the cultural atmosphere of different times. The daytime, especially the afternoon, is the well established *settlement,* the center of society. The population up and about then has larger proportions of females and older persons. It is a time-neighborhood in which surveillance by other persons is plentiful, and formal and informal controls are widespread. These conditions weigh so heavily that they stifle the outward expression of tension. There is a good deal of personal adjustment by bending one's raw edges inward. The inner-focused, depressive forms of tension management show up at those times.

As city life moves on into evening and the dark hours it is traveling toward its time *frontier*. The region is populated by younger people, more of whom are males. Some males step out of bars at closing time as they stepped out of saloons in the Wild West. At the frontier it was customary to deal with problems by taking matters into one's own hands rather than relying on the law, and social life was more violent there. Beyond that time the deep night is an uncolonized region, a *wilderness* that knows almost no restraint except that which those who venture into it bring with them. In those population-sparse hours, when there are few others to observe one's conduct, and anonymity is conferred by the darkness, there is more uninhibited venting of tensions.

Additional research is called for on these matters. At this point my findings are based on modest sample sizes, small enough to warrant concern about sampling error. The sources used may not give information on the total set of emergencies happening in a city. The hypotheses are speculative and lack direct supporting evidence. There should be more inquiry into the causes of these emergencies. The rhythms already discerned make more extensive study -- with larger sample sizes -- seem promizing.

The limitation of culture-bound information is another sampling issue. These are patterns found in the city of Boston. Do they occur in other cities too? The research should encompass cities in different cultures, in different time zones, in different latitudes, to generate simultaneous comparative data in order to develop a general theory of urban rhythmic behavior. A check on such cycles in rural areas would help decide whether these are universal patterns or peculiar to metropolitan settings.

Variations in phasing from city to city could also be sorted out. The starting time of day for Boston is earlier than for some cities and later than others. This circumstance varies among cities of the world, even for those in the same longitudes. It is important to recognize that they are not all in phase with one another, as universal time zones would imply. Whereas the early afternoon is the most thickly active period for cities in the temperate zone, the opposite is true nearer the equator. Noel Coward observed that in the tropics only "mad dogs and Englishmen go out in the noonday sun".

In plotting events around the clock I find that some are in phase with one another. They share the same time of occurrence. If they are in phase and have similar content it is suggestive to interpret them as the same type of behavior, probably stemming from the same causes or having the same functions for the system. For example, suicide, mentally ill conduct, stress, and drug-taking were all classed together as self-focused problems on that basis. So time series analysis along with 24-hour chartings may deliver insight into the nature of some conduct.

Looking at other chartings I find patterns that are out-of-phase with one another. In some of these cases they form a chained relationship, one cycle consistently leading another in time. Depending on their content, these out-of-phase linkages may be evolving situations or actions that are alternatives to one another. For example the rhythmic coupling of threats and fights appear to be an evolving circumstance. The rhythmic coupling of self-focused problems with fights and threats appear to reflect alternative ways of coping with problems, perhaps characteristic of different subgroups in the population.

If we could learn what rhythms there are it may be valuable in understanding urban life. Charting the timing of the events would permit dealing with problems on an actuarial basis, as well as helping to work out ways to avert such emergencies. It may prove so useful that in addition to our spatial population census, a city *activity-time census* should be carried out each decade.

# APPENDIX

## Notes on Methods of Studying Urban Behavior Cycles

### A. The task in general.

A direct, wholesale research program for the purpose of studying the city as a system in time would be difficult and very expensive. But it is possible to conduct studies using information already compiled by other organizations. Even if one approaches the matter with a wholistic attitude, one will collect details of specific patterns and seek to imagine what the system is like from them. A picture of urban life around the clock would then be achieved by the merging of several data files. The risk here is that different methods of data collection were used, different forms of recording, and different categorizations suited to the purposes for which the information was originally collected. I used single categories here, I aim to use multiple coding where possible from now on, but this will not be possible consistently when relying on others' data.

It is best to establish specific categories rather than global ones in coding events. Such categories may be merged later into more inclusive classes based on analysis, as was done here for the four categories subsumed under self-focused problems (see Figure 2). The scarcity of direct information about some events will make it necessary to measure those variables by proxy, counting their presumed correlates rather than the events themselves.

### B. Definitions.

A *cycle* is any pattern of event showing recurrent fluctuation. A *period* is the time span over which a cycle completes itself and begins again. In this research the maximum period is twenty-four hours. A *rhythm* is a cycle that occurs repeatedly at a uniform time period. In this research, for a cycle to be rhythmic, its peak and trough of frequency would have to occur at the same times day after day. An *interval* is the portion into which the twenty-four hour daily period was divided for purposes of sampling. As explained in section C below, the intervals I used here were two hours or somewhat longer in length. A *phase* is an identifiable segment of a cycle, located with reference to some other cyclic variable; usually this other variable is intervals of clock time. In this study I pay attention to the peak of a cycle. When the peaks of two cycles occur in the same interval, they are *in phase*.

C. Boundaries of the sampling intervals.

All frequencies plotted on the graphs in Figures 1, 2, and 3 have been adjusted to compensate for the somewhat uneven time lengths of the sampling intervals. The reason for uneven sampling intervals is explained in this section.

Assuming that fluctuations in the rate of events occur around the clock, the sampling intervals should be established close enough to discriminate among peaks and troughs and to discern the gradients of change. (Since there is risk that randomly occurring events will obscure cycles, ample and spaced sampling is also desirable, for it would allow a stable pattern -- if present -- to ultimately emerge. For this reason my sample covered three seasons of the year, Summer, Autumn, and Winter, as described in section D.)

The time structure of daily life can be marked by certain boundary points. Clock hours are the most obvious of these, and the 24-hour clock is the fundamental set of points used in this study. It is pleasant, in social science, to be able to use such a clear set of markers as times of day in one's research. Yet there is a useful distinction between clock intervals and cultural units of time. How shall the day be partitioned to reflect humanly meaningful phases? The community acknowledges some of these junctures by tolling the hours on tower bells, sirens go off at noon, and factory whistles announce the start and end of work shifts. People apply labels to pertinent phases, including "rush hours", "open hours of business", "lunch hour", "closing time", "happy hour", "dinner time", "curfew", and "sleep time",

The answer depends in part on settling when a day begins. A chronographer chooses midnight as the transition point between two days. But the urban day does not end then in the psychology of inhabitants. People who come out of a theatre and then go to a restaurant from which they depart at 2 a.m. do not feel they have traversed a two-day period. Sleep is usually taken as the terminating phase of the day. Waking from sleep becomes the qualitative boundary separating that day from the next. "...in most cultures...[there is] the idea that to waken from sleep is to begin afresh, to start a new segment of activity with the past partially cancelled." (Aubert and White, P. 52)

The findings reported here are part of a larger research program* which had a dominant sample design worked out for *street* observations in the city of Boston. Since those studies focused on publicly accessible events, I relied on street population density -- both of pedestrians and of vehicles -- as an aid to establish the junction from one day to the next. In Boston the morning rush hour begins and ends sometime between 0700 and 1000. In his study of Washington, D.C., Chapin reported that the local journey to work started at about 7 a.m. and peaked at 8 a.m..(1974, p. 107) In our study the sharpest discontinuity in the trend of increasing amounts of pedestrian and of vehicle traffic occurred between 0645 and 0745, and I set the beginning of the day for Boston at 0730.

I used intervals of about two hours long in partitioning the 24 hours. Along with the choice of 0730 as the beginning of the day, this interval length permitted me to align

*The overall research program is based on the fact that more and more people are up and about, engaged in increasingly varied activities, at all hours of the day and night. I address myself to two broad questions: 1. What are the conditions under which this expansion of time is fostered? 2. What social patterns are occurring at various hours of the daily cycle and how do they relate to one another? Program title: "The City as a System in 24-Hour Time." supported by a grant from the Center for Studies of Metropolitan Problems, National Institute of Mental Health, HEW-U.S.A.

some of the sampling units with socially significant phases of the day. A two-hour interval from 0730 to 0929 would span the morning rush hour nicely. The two-hour span was also suitable for the evening rush hour, which I established as occurring from 1615 to 1814. These became the starting points for plotting intervals for the remainder of the cycle. The beginning of the day could have been set earlier, since people are up and about in their homes before they embark on the journey to work. But to do so would mean that some of the boundaries of two-hour intervals would cut into socially recognized spans. For example, set the day to start at 0700 and the first interval would end at 0900, which cuts off the tail of the rush hour. Set the day beginning earlier, and the rush hour would be split even more.

Having aligned some intervals in this way, it was impossible to fit the remaining sampling units in place neatly. To insert twelve two-hour intervals into the period would force some of the spans to be out-of-phase with familiar time boundaries in Boston. Therefore *eleven intervals were established for the 24-hour period*, some of them -- scattered around the clock -- being longer than two hours to absorb the remaining two hours' worth of minutes.

The eleven-interval decision is a first try at an appropriate sampling design. Because most of the information gathered is recorded to the minute, the data analysis and charting need not be constrained within these particular boundaries. However, the use of eleven intervals for the day allows flexibility and some shuffling of the boundaries to suit different cultural patterns among cities, and so makes comparisons easier. For another discussion of the problem of intervals and of time-related notations, see Parkes and Thrift (1975).

The frequencies for any set of unequal intervals may be adjusted readily by appropriate weightings.

D. The samples used.

The samples of data in this study are for seven full weeks (49 days) over 24 hours for each day. This research was aligned with the sample for the street observations (see C above), and the weeks occurred in 1974, two in June, two in September, and three in December of that year.

Figures 2 and 3 are based on records of emergency calls to telephone operators from all over the city, while the data for Figure 1 comes from police files for selected precincts only (see below).

1 - Telephone operators sample: This is the entire set of records of emergency calls (other than those having to do with telephone service problems) for the main part of Boston (with Brighton, Hyde Park, and West Roxbury -- the outlying areas -- ommitted).

The telephone company is the major hot line of a city, and its operators have come to be used as a general resource in emergencies of all kinds. They receive calls of distress not only from the sufferers themselves but also from others who observe people in trouble. The telephone operators keep records of such calls as a matter of course, noting the time of the call and the nature of the problem reported. A skilled telephone operator read the records to me, without disclosing identities or the originating telephone numbers. Information as to date, time of day, to what party the caller was connected by the operator [e.g., to the police, Alcoholics Anonymous, the gas company, etc.], and the content of the call, was read out. A total of 1089 such calls were recorded and used in this analysis.

Since the calls came in from all over the city, at all hours of day and night, in three different seasons of the year, it is very likely that these events involve different individuals in almost all instances of every type of emergency, rather than the same individuals being repeatedly involved. In this respect I believe that it is a representative sample of that portion of the Boston population who use this means of reporting emergencies both for themselves and for others.

There are other hot lines in Boston, organizations that respond to telephone calls about emergencies. Several of them are staffed around the clock. Two limitations to research in such agencies is that each taps a selective segment of the spectrum of difficulties that arise in the metropolitan area, and some of the agencies do not keep records of their calls. But although the rate of emergency appeals through telephone operators is probably higher than for all other agencies combined, further research in this sphere would do well to include other hot lines, to check whether their data show offsetting patterns to the ones reported here.

2 - Police sample: Drawn from the Boston Police Department's computerized files, for the 24-hour periods of the seven weeks mentioned above. This sample more precisely matches the sample used in the larger study of street observations, covering only certain parts of the center city: a residential street (.53 mile, including 3 intersections), a shopping street (.5 mile, including 4 intersections), and a transportation hub (.5 mile in longest diameter, including 6 intersections). The events recorded are those for which police traveled to the scene of the emergency, and are of all forms -- from traffic control to investigation of suspicious persons, to assaults, to people having heart attacks.

A total of 300 such events were recorded. Since the frequencies in some categories are small, sampling error may be large.

E. Data analysis.

Are telephone and police calls reliable indicators of emergencies in urban settings? The two samples are dissimilar in the demographic areas they represent, which makes a reliability check more uncertain. The three sites used for the police data are not altogether typical of the city as a whole. For example, there are only a handful of transportation hubs of the importance of the one included here. Another difference between the sets of records made by telephone operators and by police is that the operators record the information about the problem *before* there is responsive action while the police record the event *after* arriving on the scene and taking action. Thus the telephone operator records may be more accurate about the time of the onset of the difficulty, and its peak. The police records may be more accurate as the the nature of the event -- since the officers make their entries after investigation, while the telephone operators' notes are based on what the caller says.

I compared reports of similar events in both sets of data, for three categories in my initial data codes that appeared to be almost identical. Anticipating that police records would lag behind telephone records, in each case I paired telephone operators' data from one phase with police entries for the next phase and found the following correlations:

| Telephone data | Police data | Correlation coefficient |
|---|---|---|
| Drunk | Drunkeness | .45 |
| Fights | Assault | .48 |
| Holdup | Rob store, taxi, person | .37 |

The correlations are modest, but consistently positive. Given that the police data is only from several precincts while the telephone data is citywide, the use of the same areas of the city and reliance on larger samples would be major improvements for these tests. Even so the evidence lends some support to the possibility that the rhythms are reliable.

Absolute levels of occurrence cannot be emphasized in the analysis. The rates of reporting may differ for aggression (fights, threats) than for self-focused problems. And the frequencies for any category may be lower than actual at those times of day when *other* human service agencies are available and receiving appeals for help.

Some problems of cycle analysis recede because the 24-hour day is imposed as the constant period in which the information will be assessed. Thus the maximum length of the cycle is 24 hours. There is still the question whether around-the-clock fluctuations in the frequencies of events are other than random, that is, whether a cycle exists. A significant rhythm may be obscured by random perturbations. Some categories of events may assume wavelike forms by chance. A cycle may have more than one peak. Massive sampling is a valuable first step toward answering a number of such questions. Such sample sizes are not difficult to collect if the data is computerized or otherwise stored and adequately indexed. Large enough samples, say of one full year running, afford the opportunity to discern hidden periodicities, to reject spurious periodicities, and to establish the reliability of a multi-modal pattern. Analyses might use the curve-fitting and harmonics of Fourier and spectral analysis. Luce (1970, ch. 7) provides a general review of the approach, while Halberg (1965, 1967) and Sollberger (1969, 1970) offer more detailed discussions of pertinent issues and techniques.

In this study, pairs of values were available for the same number of intervals in the same-length periods for any two types of events. Therefore I was able to calculate a linear correlation coefficient to ascertain the strength of phase relationships between their rhythms.

Issues of causal analysis may be initially tackled by using longer sampling spans and then making more refined correlations with illumination, season, day of week, neighborhoods (since certain patterns, discernible for the whole, may vanish when part of the system is focused on), etc., and by cross-cultural studies of cities.

REFERENCES

Aubert, V. and White, H. (1960) "Sleep: A Sociological Interpretation. I.", pp. 46-54 in *Acta Sociologica* vol. 4, no. 2.

Chapin, F. S., Jr. (1974) *Human Activity Patterns in the City: Things People Do in Time and Space* NY: Wiley.

Halberg. F., Engeli, J., Hamburger, C. and Hillman, D., (1965) "Spectral Resolution of low-frequency, small-amplitude rhythms in excreted ketosteroid; probable androgen-induced circaseptan desynchronization," PP. 1-54 in *Acta Endocrinologica Supplement* no. 103.

Halberg, F., Tong, Y. L., and Johnson, E. A., (1967) "Circadian System Phase: An Aspect of Temporal Morphology, Procedures and Illustrative Examples,: pp. 20-48 in Mayersbach, H. von (ed) *The Cellular Aspects of Biorhythms* 8th International Congress of Anatomy. Berlin: Springer-Verlag.

Luce, G. G., (1970) *Biological Rhythms in Psychiatry and Medicine* Chevy Chase, Maryland: National Institute of Mental Health (PHSP #2088).

Parkes, D. and Thrift, N. (1975) "Timing Space and Spacing Time", pp. 651-670 in *Environment and Planning. A* vol. 7.

Sollberger, Arne "How are biological time series related to the normal values concept?", pp. 602-625 in *Annals of the New York Academy of Sciences* vol. 161, no. 2, 1969.

Sollberger, A. (1970) "Problems in the Statistical Analysis of Short Periodic Time Series," pp. 49-88 in *Journal of Interdisciplinary Cycle Research* vol. 1, no. 1, May.

DISCUSSION AND COMMENT
*By Gisela Trommsdorff*

Daily rhythms in human emotions and behavior are well known in biology, neurophysiology, psychology (e.g. body temperature, heartbeat, activity, perception, working behavior). Melbin's study on city rhythms represents an interesting and important contribution to the question of rhythmic processes of human behavior in an urban setting. Melbin asks how a city works and acts on its inhabitants, and whether city life can be analysed in terms of systematic variation of behavior over a 24 hour period of time.

Melbin aims to (a) detect rhythms of emergencies in order to (b) diagnose problems of urban living and (c) suggest means of ameliorating the symptoms and causes. To achieve these goals, first one has to select reliable and valid indicators for emergencies in urban settings. Melbin uses the entire set of records of emergency calls to the telephone company and investigations by the police department of Boston for seven weeks. These data do not necessarily give reliable information on the total population of emergencies in a city: they are second-hand reports, possibly distorted by subjective interpretation. Though we do not have a complete picture of what is really going on in the city, we can study the timing of communication emergencies in a metropolitan area. Can the data point out the causes of urban problems?

Melbin assumes that the reported emergencies are a result of tensions; these tensions are related to urban problems. Tension release (emergencies), in turn, produces further problems.

Thus, the theoretical and methodological problem is to investigate causes of tensions and cyclical tension release in urban living.

The communicated emergencies are classified into categories such as suicide, drunkenness, drug-taking, threats, fighting, and other disturbances of public order. According to Melbin these incidents represent two patterns of tension release, "self-focused" problems and "events that inflict suffering on others". Thus, it is assumed that communicated emergencies really represent only one dimension of urban problems, that is "tension release".

However, neither the unidimensionality nor the validity of these indicators for tension release is discussed. Desirably, the choice of such indicators would be guided by a theory of tension release and its social conditions in an urban setting.

Melbin's results show (a) trends of cyclical patterns of emergencies, and (b) positive correlations between the timing of various emergencies. These results support the assumption that some indices of urban violence do indeed represent the concept of tension release (e.g. "self-focused" problems such as stress, suicide, drug-taking, mentally ill conduct).

However, it seems highly questionable to view emergencies which consistently do *not* occur together (nonsignificant correlation of timing) as alternatives to one another. Such an explanation of "out-of-phase" occurrences implies that these incidents are caused by the same variable and fulfil the same functions. Possibly, tension may be the underlying cause, and certain urban conditions channel tension release in such a way that systematic sequences of emergencies occur.

Melbin explains the rhythmic occurrence of self-focused problems in the afternoon and other-directed emergencies at night by a "time territoriality" which implies differences in the strength of social control. Since informal and formal social control is strong during daytime and weakens at night, *external violence* occurs less frequently during daytime and rises at night. This phenomenon is well known from the literature on urban living (cf. Jacobs, 1961). However, can the concept of social control also explain the peak of *self-inflicted violence* like suicide in the afternoon? It seems questionable to treat suicide and other self-focused emergencies as equivalent to actions that inflict suffering on others. The psychological quality of tension which is relieved by such acts may be different. If the social function of these acts is assumed to be equivalent, the kind of social function should be defined. If these different kinds of emergencies represent only one dimension (of urban problems) the following conditions would have to be fulfilled:

(a) Inhabitants of a city do suffer under tensions; (b) these tensions are so strong that they demand tension release; (c) tension releases may be self- or other-directed suffering; (d) if public control is weak, tension is released as other-directed violence; (e) if public control is strong, tension release cannot produce other-directed violence, instead, it is self-directed.

In order to test these assumptions it should be determined (a) who suffers under tension and why; (b) what kind of tension calls for what kind of release; (c) under what conditions tension is more readily released when public control is weak (e.g. why suicide attempts do not have their peak at night contrary to fights); and why some tensions are more readily released when public control is strong (like suicide). This should underline the question whether suicide and fights are equivalent or different expressions of tension release and whether both incidents are linearly related to public control. Or: Do people who suffer from tension look for release either in terms of fights or in terms of suicide?

The critical factor determining the kind of tension release would then be the time of day which, in turn, indicates whether public control is weak or strong.

Obviously, the indicators of internally directed violence (suicide) and the indicators of externally directed violence (public disorder and fights) do not represent various degrees of one single dimension.

Probably, different kinds of tensions are resolved under different circumstances (by different people) differently. Conditions which induce people to commit suicide do not necessarily induce them to engage in fighting.

As we know from studies on the causes of suicide, certain personality variables have to be related to certain situational conditions in order to increase the probability of suicide (cf. Seligman, 1975). Furthermore, the strengthening of public control may be a release for suicide attempts and may be a suppressor of fights, while the weakening of public control may not effect suicide attempts but induce externally directed violence. That is to say that public control does not necessarily induce the expression of one specific kind of tension release, but may encourage and inhibit different expressions of tension release and violence in different samples.

One may conclude that Melbin's data support the thesis that interaction density produces some public control and protects people from externally directed violence; this protective effect is highest in the early afternoon and lowest at night.

However, it remains to be explained why interaction density (or time of the day) works against violence between people but does not discourage self-induced violence. The theoretical questions remain: What are the determinants of emergencies? Are emergencies the product of tension and more or less violent tension release? What are the causes for such tensions and the factors inducing tension release? Future research on violence should work on these questions in a clearly defined theoretical framework which helps to construct valid instruments (Trommsdorff, 1978). In order to achieve the goal of curing problems of urban life, future research should, furthermore, work out adequate rules for transforming theoretical knowledge into programs of social action and change.

Melbin's study is an important step in this direction by giving empirical evidence for the cyclical occurrence of emergencies in an urban city. This phenomenon needs theoretical explanation.

## REFERENCES

Jacobs, J. *The death and life of great American cities*. New York: Vintage, 1961.

Seligman, M. E. P. *Helplessness. On depression, development, and death*. San Francisco, Calif.: Freeman, 1975.

Trommsdorff, G. Probleme und Möglichkeiten des Kulturvergleichs am Beispiel einer Aggressionsstudie. Kölner Zectschrift für Soziologie und Sozialpsychologie, in press

# The Study of Time in Poland, Czechoslovakia, and the Soviet Union*

W. Voisé, J. Zeman, J.B. Molchanov, I.A. Akchurin

*Three reports were presented to the Conference from Eastern Europe and the Soviet Union. Professor Waldemar Voisé, of the History of Science Section, Polish Academy of Sciences, personally delivered his report on work done in Poland. Also received were the reports of Dr Jiri Zeman, Philosophy Section, the Czechoslovak Academy of Sciences, and by Professors J. B. Molchanov and I. A. Akchurin of the Soviet Academy of Sciences. Professors Voisé and Zeman assisted me in translating Polish and Czech bibliographical information. For the translation and transliteration of Russian titles, and for checking the accuracy of the English rendering of Russian names, I wish to express my gratitude to my colleague, Professor Alex E. Alexander. The numbered references refer to the alphabetical bibliography at the end of each of these three essays.*

*Charles M. Sherover*

## POLISH CONSIDERATIONS OF TIME

*Waldemar Voisé*

Anyone interested in chronosophical studies in the old Russia should refer to the works of Professor M. Vilnitskij of Kiev and particularly to his book, published in 1955, *The History of the Concepts of Space and Time in Classical Physics.*[13] In that book, he draws particular attention to the studies of time carried on in the 18th and 19th centuries by such Russian scholars as Lomonossov, Lobachevsky and Umov, and by the Ukrainian mathematician, Osipovskij, who was critical of Leibniz and Kant.

-----

*The Editors of this volume wish to express their appreciation to Professor Charles Sherover for editing this complex contribution.

The interdisciplinary approach evident in some recent books on time published in the United States, England and France is also to be found in a new Russian collection of essays, *Rhythm, Space and Time and Art*.[7] The editors and authors participating in that volume are well aware of the current importance of the subject as well as of the difficulties it presents. Their immediate interest arises from the modern pre-occupation with the passing of time: our growing need to look for 'time reserves' in the life of modern man, and our increasing concern with the technical, social and cultural demands that are made upon our time. The difficulties involved in writing the essays contained in that book stem primarily from its aim - to arive at as comprehensive as possible a solution of the very complicated problems which arise out of their interdisciplinary nature. For the problem of cooperation between the arts and modern science has been of passionate interest to artists and art theorists as well as to scientists.

In contrast to those traditionalists who have maintained that rhythm, space and time do not respond to interrelated treatment because they are separate 'categories', B. S. Meylakh, in his editorial preface, makes it clear that the purpose of this book is to correlate these three separate areas of investigation. Participating in the book is a group of authors from the Leningrad branch of the Soviet Academy of Sciences; continuing the research on artistic creativity which was begun in Leningrad in 1963, they have studied three groups of problems: (a) the general problems of rhythm, space and time; (b) the place of these problems in literature, the theater, architecture, music and the cinema; and (c) aspects of these problems as they pertain to studies in mathematics and the natural sciences.

The book proposes twenty-one theses. Each one can be taken as a starting point for generalization provided that the reader has some knowledge of the particular discipline involved. Helpful, of course, especially regarding methodological themes would be a reference to books by the particular authors.

One of the most original of these books is Danil Granin's *This Strange Life*,[3] which concerns the problem of time in our lives. It is in the form of a biography of a biologist who also invents special strategies to study the human attitude toward time. One short passage illustrates the author's style and the nature of his mind:

> Man has always been hostile to time. He somehow succeeded in mastering space, that is matter. But time still remains something tremendously elemental. And now, when Man has taken a peep into the distant universe and heard the ticking of the clocks out in space, counting out milliards of years, he has seen the galaxies disintegrating, time is still more terrifying to him.
>
> I am amazed by the boldness with which Man has dealt with the substance of time. He has learned how to get the feel of it, how to master the pulsating, slippery 'here and now'. He was not afraid to measure out in days and hours the disappearing remainder of his life. Man cautiously stretched time, squeezed it, trying to save it so as not to miss even a tiny bit of it. He esteemed time as he esteemed his daily bread. It would never enter his head to do something to 'kill time'. Every moment was regarded as something precious. For each moment represents the time to create, the time to discover things, the time to enjoy life. Man worshipped time. It turned out that life was not at all as short as it had seemed.

But let me focus on time-studies in Poland. The history of Polish chronosophy goes quite far back. Forty years ago Professor Zawirski published *Evolution of the Concept of Time* in French;[17] although it is somewhat out of date by now, it has been cited many times. Unfortunately, there has been no second edition. But a book of reflections on time in human experience, music and literature by the late Roman Ingarden (1893-1970) is still in print, (as are some of his other works).[4]

A new generation of philosophers and physicists has been working on many chronosophical questions. Most of these physicists are in Cracow in Jagiellonian University's Institute of Theoretical Physics; its head, Professor Z. Augustynek has, within the last few years, published two books on many of the essential properties of physical time.[1] In the first he analyses two kinds of properties which are assumed in modern physics to be attached to time: the topological and the symmetrical; his aim is two-fold: to define these properties precisely and to investigate the present state of crucial questions concerning what is presupposed in time. His second book deals with the nature of time; the question, 'What is time?' is considered as involving the definition of physical time. Insofar as physical theories use a particular notion of time without defining it, he postulates, in his final chapter, a new definition fulfilling conditions of non-locality and of correspondence. In the end he is clear concerning difficulties concerning whether or not the proposed notion of quasi-time is of theoretical value in physics; but as this idea is yet only a rudimentary one, it is not speculative. The author suggests that the notion of quasi-time may be of some general philosophical importance, namely in trying to solve questions concerning the nature of time - of course in terms of the present level of contemporary physics.

Both books have extensive summaries in English - so the interested investigator may examine them for himself.

Another author, Dr S. Zalewski, discusses methodological and philosophical aspects of the classical idea of time in his book, *Time and Being*.[16] He begins by showing the ways in which the concept of time was handled in the philosophies of nature inspired by Aristotle and St Thomas Aquinas. He then proceeds to try to draw a connection between the concept of time and the existential conception of being. Out of his study, he draws three conclusions: (a) that the concept of time is closely dependent upon epistemology and philosophy generally; (b) that diverse variants of modern Thomism entail different concepts of time; and (c) that a study of the existentialist concept of 'being' suggests that the philosophical conception of time stresses above all the problem that *esse* (being) comes after that of *non-esse* (non-being).

Two authors have written interesting essays on historical time. Professor J. Topolski[12] discusses the problem of time indication in historical narration; the English summary shows that the author is concerned with time as an element of historical narration and leaves aside any ontological understanding of time. Date indication is regarded as the most characteristic of time indications for historical narration. Various types of dated time indication are discussed. Annalistic time is used in cases where the range of time of the historical sequence covers the range of time of the event described. The time of the chronicler is applied to historical descriptions which provide information concerning antecedents of the described event. When historical description considers future time, in relation to a described event, two different kinds of indication are employed: (a) prospective time or (b) prospective-and-retrospective. However, historical narration which aims at the reconstruction of certain frequently repeated events commonly uses a kind of time indication that presents the general period of time in which the events are repeated, that is, the notion of durational time, and this may be handled in a variety of ways.

Historical narration is indeed a 'mosaic' of sentences applying various kinds of time indicators. The predilection for specific types is connected with specific programs for the writing of history. Accordingly, idiographic historical writing uses the annalistic indicator of the chronicler. Structural historiography makes a greater use of time indicators which imply durational time. The introduction of theoretical elements into historical narration leads to a use of non-specific time indicators and the general abandonment of time indicators such as dates.

In his article concerning semantics of temporal relations, Professor S. Pickarczyk[8] carries out a functional analysis of temporal events and the phenomena resulting from the common use of expressions for 'simultaneous', 'precedence', and 'sequence' in sentences of the aTb type - where 'T' is a facultative temporal relation and 'a' and 'b' variables concern the group of events or processes being discussed. These terms are generally used with but little precision. This is seen in bringing together a number of common relations of 'simultaneous', 'precedence', and 'sequence' into several groupings. One would contain only relations fulfilling certain conditions concerning mutual relations of lengths of time periods, intervals between the beginning and termination of particular events in terms of temporal 'points'. A number of terms for temporal relations are used in colloquial language which preserve their separate linguistic forms while denoting phenomena which are ontologically identical. Use of a specification lacking precision to denote the length of particular intervals does not permit us to establish the simultaneity of events preceding or following other events. For some temporal relations that are grouped in this manner are transitory relations.

The paper also discusses the application of the principle of the excluded middle and the law of contradiction for variables in temporal relations set forth in different sentences. The author ought to be able to make the historian sensitive to the exactness of terms for temporal relations which he uses while revealing the complexity of the temporal orientations of contemporary man. His use of language continues use of remnants of those orientations which are to be found in periods of history when time was not yet treated as a rational quantity.

A book by Dr Z. Lewicki,[6] discusses time as it appears in the early stream-of-consciousness novels of Joyce and Faulkner. The final section concerns itself with general theoretical problems connected with the significance of time for such fiction. Such novels, he points out, have a very complex problem with which to deal for they not only must develop the individual time of a character whose consciousness is being portrayed; they must also relate that temporal stream to time more generally understood. This double temporality invades the functions of the narrator, the plot, the action and the way in which they are related to each other. His argument is complicated because only one of the books he discusses, *As I Lay Dying*, is written completely in terms of a stream-of-consciousness technique. Consequently one has to be careful in avoiding misinterpretations such as those which Sartre, among others, has drawn. But Lewicki's time analysis enables us to denote some conspicuous differences between traditional fiction and the three novels discussed; the handling of questions of time is thus established as a differentiating factor for the generic classification of stream-of-consciousness fiction.

In Poland, literature and music have long been the domain for studies of time. For many years Professor Z. Lissa has been publishing work on the topic of time in music; Professor K. Wyka, who died only recently, wrote a fascinating paper[10] reinterpreting the chronosophical viewpoint of Reymon's novel *The Peasants* which brought him the Nobel Prize in 1924.[14]

This is obviously not a full account of the books by Polish chronosophers but serves to illustrate what is being done in the field. I should, however, summarize some of the other work being done and regret that I cannot here include in this summary a survey of the numerous papers being written by Poles, in both Polish and other journals, such as Dr Irena Szumilewicz's paper on the direction of time and entropy or the reflections on the concepts of time in both old and modern physics by Dr M. Heller and Dr B. Kuchowicz.

Much has been written in various languages about sun dials by Professor T. Przypkowski who is the former owner and presently the director of a museum containing one of the most extensive collections of sun dials. Dr.L. Zajdler has published a book, *The History of Clocks*, in 1956,[15] and a second edition is about to appear. Horology is represented by a multi-volume series by a Franciscan monk, Father Podwapinski; the first volume appeared in 1948 and the last one, *Electric Time Pieces* appeared in 1974.[10] Many questions concerning students of time appear in books and articles on futurology. One author in particular, Dr W. Rolbiecki, has recently published an important article on interdisciplinary studies of time as they bear on horological concerns.[11]

Poets, of course, continue to write about time. The poet, M. Jastrim, discussed the significance of time in older as well as contemporary literature in a series of invited lectures at the University of Warsaw, published under the title *The Battle for Words*.[5] A recently published poem, "Time, My Hired Assassin,"[9] by M. Pilichowski, is of interest here and I should like to quote a passage from it:

My time
Stands in a jar on top of the cupboard...
And I, although I'm not bottled up in the jar,
Feel as if I were in prison.
My time is everywhere.
It even sleeps with me,
Which some people might even not approve of,
For we're the same sex.
I hired time only
So that it could kill me.
By myself I wouldn't be able to do it.
And in any case who would be able to do it as well
as Time.
For after all time is my assassin.

The fact that I bring this paper to an end with a quotation from a poet seems not only apt but imperative. For it demonstrates once more that in Poland time is the subject of generally philosophic and not only of scientific study and concern. Time is a subject that intrigues painters as well as poets; the Cracow painter, Mrs. Ewa Kierska, recently painted a picture called "Man and Time" as an illustration of one of Pascal's *Pensées*.

Leaving art aside, we have seen that 'chronosophy' covers a wide range. This is so partly because the Polish word for 'science' (*nauka*) does not only refer to the exact sciences but, like the German *Wissenschaft*, has a wider reference encompassing the whole range of man's intellectual activities. But the primary reason is that those who write on the subject regard questions concerning time to be a problem too important to be confined only to the exact sciences. Philosophy must come into such discussions as well as it deals with questions that are as old as human thinking. Metaphysics, particularly, must face questions of time, metaphysics as it was understood by Aristotle as reflection about being and about truth.

REFERENCES


1. Augustynek, Z., *Wlasnosci czasu* [*The Properties of Time*], Warsaw: PWN, 1970.

2. _____, *Natura czasu* [*The Nature of Time*], Warsaw: PWN, 1975.

3. Granin, Danil, *Eta strannaia* [*This Strange Life*], Moskva: 1974.

4. Ingarden, Roman, *Works*, Warsaw, PWN, 1966. See esp. *Utwor muzyczny i sprawa jego tozsamosci* [*Musical Composition and its Identity*], Cracov: PWM, 1973; *Ksiazeczka o czlowieku* [*Booklet on Man*], Cracov: Wydawnictwo Literackie, 1973; also in English: *Roman Ingarden and Contemporary Polish Aesthetics*, Warsaw: PWN, 1975, and *Time and Modes of Being*, trans. Michejda, Springfield, Ill.: Charles C Thomas Publisher, 1964.

5. Jastrim, M., *Walka o slovo* [*The Battle of Words*], Warsaw: Czytelnik, 1973.

6. Lewicki, Z., *Czas w prozie strumienia swiadomości* [*Time in the Stream-of-consciousness Novel*], Warsaw: PWN, 1975.

7. Meklakh, B. S., et al (eds.), *Ritm, prostranstvo i vremia v litieraturie i iskustvie* [*Rhythm, Space and Time and Art*], Leningrad: Nauka, 1974.

8. Piekarczyk, S., "Z problemow topologii czasu" ["Some Problems of the Topology of Time",] *Methodological Studies*, No. 8, Poznan: 1971.

9. Pilichowski, M. in *Literatura*. 3 April 1975.

10. Podwapinski, Fr., *Zegarmistrzowstwo* [*Horology*], Warsaw: Libra, 1948-1974.

11. Rolbiecki, W., in *Zagadnienia naukoznawstwa* [*The Problems of Science*], No. 4, Warsaw: 1968.

12. Topolski, J., "Czas w narracji historycznej" ["Time Indication in Historical Narration"], in *Studia Metogologiczne*, No. 10, Poznan: 1971.

13. Vilnitskij, M., *K istorii razwitia predstavlenii o prostranstvie i vremeni v klassiceskoi fizikie* [*On the History of the Concepts of Space and Time in Classical Physics*], Kiev: Nauka, 1955.

14. Wyka, K., "Proba nowego odczytania Chlopow" ["The Trial of the New Interpretation of 'The Peasants'"], *Pamietnik Literacki* [*The Diary of Literature*], Warsaw: 1968.

15. Zajdler, L. *Dzieje zegara* [*The History of Clocks*], Warsaw: Wiedza Powszechna, 1956.

16. Zalewski, S. *Czas i istnienie* [*Time and Being*], Warsaw: PAX, 1971.

17. Zawirski, *L'évikytuib de ka bituib dy tenos*, Cracov: Gebethner & Wolff, 1936.

# THE STUDY OF TIME IN CZECHOSLOVAKIA

*Jiri Zeman*

The study of time in Czechoslovakia is not yet systematically developed. I here summarize highlights of what is being done in the natural sciences, sociology and philosophy.

## 1. NATURAL SCIENCES

Questions concerning time are dealt with in some books and paper by workers in the fields of astronomy and physics, biology and biochemistry, neurophysiology and psychology.

The book by the astronomer, Y. Grygar[5] is a survey of questions of modern astronomy and cosmology. The problems of time are studied in the chapter concerning relativity theory, anti-matter, gravitational collapse, red shift, and other considerations concerning the structure and evolution of the universe. These problems are also studied in works of the astronomer, P. Andcrle.

In the field of physical time is the voluminous book by V. Votruba.[15] Studied from perspectives in mathematics and physics are such questions as simultaneity, time dilatation, and Minkowski space-time. These problems are also examined in work by I. Úlehla and J. Pachner among others.

Biological problems of time have been studied particularly by the biophysicist, F. Herčík in three books;[6-8] he has particularly studied the problem of condensation and the rarity of biological time in the processes of the evolution of living organisms. Questions of time and evolution from the perspective of biochemistry have been followed by the biochemist, J. Koštíř.[10] J. Holubář has studied the problem of the sense of time from the perspective of psychology, discussing it in connection with the conditioned reflex, biorhythms, brain rhythms and related concerns.[9] Works by M. Morávek on consciousness and J. Bureš on memory also touch upon some questions of time.

2. SOCIOLOGY

Sociological aspects of time are studied by P. Maydl in the European Center for Leisure and Education (UNESCO) and in its section devoted to the study of various life-styles. J. Filipec and B. Filipcová have given careful study to different aspects of styles of life and questions of human needs in contemporary socialist society and have examined ways in which contemporary man uses his leisure as well as the ways in which work is related to leisure.[4]

Sociology is particularly oriented to the study of changes in the time structure of different social groups and to the study of leisure. In this regard, attention is directed to the works of B. Filipcová[2,3] and that of J. Vítečková and J. Linhart.[14]

3. PHILOSOPHY

A survey of the Marxist conception of time is given in the book by V. Tlustý.[13] M. Skyba has dealt with the problem of time in connection with the Marxist conception of evolution in two books.[11,12] One recent book on modern aspects of time and the Marxist conception of time was written by J. Dubinčka.[1] J. Zeman has studied the question of time in connection with problems of epistemology and information theory.[16-21] Participating in two internationally authored volumes in English, he has contributed two papers: in one volume,[18] his essay "Concept of Gradient Channel in Ontology and Epistemology and the Problem of Time," examines the application of the concept of the information channel to the question of time flow; in the second volume,[20] his paper "Information, Knowledge and Time," studies the application of the theory of the information channel to epistemological process and cosmical flow and seeks to show the possible connection between relativity theory and information theory in terms of time and redundancy.

Philosophical problems of time are being studied in Czechoslovakia by a new group of Czech and Slovak philosophers and scientists who have started to work together.

## REFERENCES


1. Dubnička, J., *Kategória cäsu z hlodiska marxistickej filozofie.* [*Category of Time from the Viewpoint of Marxist Philosophy*], Bratislava: 1976.

2. Filipcová, B. *Člověk, práce, volný čas* [*Man, Labor, Leisure*], Praha: 1966.

3. Filipcová, B., a kol., *Volný čas a kultura v průmyslovém městě* [*Leisure and Culture in the Industrial City*], Praha: 1974.

4. Filipec, J. and Filipcová, B., *Různoběžky života* [*Different Lines of Life*], Praha: 1975.

5. Grygar, Y., *Vesmír je náš svět* [*Universe is Our World*], Praha: 1970.

6. Herčík, F., *Život na ruby* [*Life Inverted*], Praha: 1945.

7. _____, *Život cloveka* [*The Life of Man*], Praha: 1947.

8. _____, *Úvod do kvantové biologie* [*Introduction to Quantum Biology*], Praha: 1949.

9. Holubář, J., *Časový smysl* [*The Sense for Time*], Praha: 1951.

10. Koštíř, J., *Chemický a biochemický vývoj vesmíru a země* [*The Chemical and Biochemical Evolution of the Universe and of the Earth*], Praha: 1964.

11. Skyba, M., *O věčnosti vesmíru* [*On the Eternity of the Universe*], Praha: 1960.

12. _____, *Matérie-determinismus-vývoj* [*Matter-Determinism-Evolution*], Praha: 1967.

13. Tlustý, V., *Prostor a čas* [*Space and Time*], Praha: 1958.

14. Vítečková, J. and Linhart, J., "The Development of Work Time and Non-Work Time and Leisure in Socialist Czechoslovakia," *Society and Leisure*, 1975, No. 1.

15. Votruba, V., *Základy speciální teorie relativity* [*Basis of the Special Relativity Theory*], Praha: 1969.

16. Zeman, J., *Poznání a informace* [*Knowledge and Information*], Praha: 1962.

17. _____, "Problém času ve filosofii [The Problem of Time in Philosophy]," *Filosofický časopis*, 1967, No. 3.

18. _____ (Ed.), *Time in Science and Philosophy*, Praha-Amsterdam: 1971.

19. _____, "Čas a informace," *Filosofický časopis*, 1974, No. 3.

20. _____ (Ed.), *Entropy and Information in Science and Philosophy*, Praha-Amsterdam: 1975.

21. _____, *Teorie odrazu a kybernetika* [*Theory of Reflection and Cybernetics*], Praha: 1976.

# THE PROBLEM OF TIME IN THE SOVIET NATURAL PHILOSOPHY LITERATURE

*J. B. Molchanov, I. A. Akchurin*

It is only recently that the problem of time has been considered separately in the Soviet literature concerned with natural philosophy. It used to be regarded earlier as belonging either to the theory of relativity or being part of the more general problem, that of the philosophical categories of space and time.

In tracing the history of the studies of time that have been conducted in this country mention should be made above all of the works by A. I. Fersman,[50] V. I. Vernadsky,[62] and A. M. Deborin.[16] They dealt with the notion of time - its origin, objectivity and significance for science.

At the initial stage of philosophical discussions on the problems of the theory of relativity (in the years 1920-30) the question of time was not considered very often. It was L. I. Mandelshtam who first dealt with this problem at length in his lectures on the physical foundations of the theory of relativity. He delivered them in 1933-34, but they were only published in 1950.[33]

Since 1958 the theoretical discussions of the theory of relativity have been intensified. As a result Soviet philosophers and physicists succeeded in working out a new interpretation of time relationships which form the basis of the theory of relativity. In their investigations they have been particularly concerned with the evolution of the notion of time in physics, and, above all, with the dialectic of the understanding of time in classical and modern physics; see work done by A. D. Alexandrov, G. I. Naan,[45] M. E. Omeljanovskij[47] and V. A. Fok[20,21] among others.

Many interesting problems of time have been also discussed by W. I. Svidersky,[56,57] R. A. Aronov,[8] R. Y. Shteinman,[54] though these writers worked within their general studies of time and space, with special attention being paid to the notion of space.

The problem of time as a separate field of study has been discussed only in the works of Y. F. Askin[9-12] and in those of Y. A. Urmanzev[61] and Y. P. Trusov. The book by Y. F. Askin,[11] was the first book in the Soviet literature on that subject. Additionally important questions connected with the notions of time and space were investigated by L. B. Bazhenov,[14] and A. N. Vjalzev.[63] The growing interest in the problems of time and in the studies conducted in this field led to the issuing in this country of the translations of books by H. Reichenbach,[52] G. J. Whitrov,[64] A. Grünbaum,[23] as well as a collection of articles by some French writers,[51] studying these questions.

The problem of time contains a complex of fundamental issues: the nature of time and its relation to matter; the objective value of time; the passing of time and the objective value of becoming; the direction of time and its irreversibility; the universality of time and of its dimensions; continuity and discontinuity, finiteness and infinity. All these questions have been discussed more or less completely in the Soviet philosophical literature.

While agreeing on the objectivity of time - attributing real objectivity to time relations - the Soviet philosophers have differed about the nature of time, its relation to movement and the interaction of material systems. This in turn has led to the realization that two conceptions of time can be advanced regarding the relation of time to matter or substance. One of these conceptions considers time to be an independent entity, ruled by special laws and unaffected by movement and the interaction of material systems. The second conception regards time as a feature or relation of any interaction of material systems outside of which there is simply no time. The first of these conceptions, treating time as an absolute entity, appears in Newtonian physics, the second in relativistic physics.

These two different conceptions have been given various names, both in our own and foreign literature. So for instance, Y. B. Molchanov called them respectively the "classical" and "relativistic" conceptions of time.[34-36] Y. A. Askin described them as a "substantial" one and "a form of being of matter".[11] P. S. Dyshlevy was inclined to accept A. Grünbaum's terminology which calls these two conceptions "absolutistic" and "relativistic". In our view the most fitting is L. B. Bazhenov's suggestion to call them the "substantial" and "relational" conceptions. A critical discussion of these questions can be found in the works of L. B. Bazhenov[14] and Y. B. Molchanov.[37,38,39]

The substantial and relational conceptions of time differ in their approaches to simultaneity which, when the philosophical implications of the theory of relativity used to be discussed, led to long and sharp polemics on the relativity of simultaneity.

It is generally assumed that the problem of simultaneity and the ways of its determination or fixation was first advanced in A. Einstein's fundamental work[19] in which he formulated the thesis on the relativity of simultaneity; however A. A. Tjapkin[58,59] drew attention recently to the great significance of an earlier article by H. Poincaré, entitled "The Dimension of Time."

In our literature the problem of simultaneity has been most extensively discussed in the works of L. I. Mandelshtam,[33] V. A. Fok,[20,21] A. D. Alexandrov,[2] M. E. Omeljanovskij[47] and M. V. Mostapanienko.[44] While pointing out all the differences between these two conceptions, Y. V. Molchanov subjected the notion of simultaneity as used by both of them to a detailed analysis.[34,35,36]

Molchanov's point of view is basically similar to that of H. Reichenbach and A. Grünbaum, though he also considers that these writers did not attach enough importance to the fact that a pair of simultaneous events, established by A. Einstein "by definition", has been chosen from a collection of objectively simultaneous (in the relativistic approach to time) events. Apart from that, Molchanov maintains that the two simultaneities, the "topological" and "metrical" one advanced by A. Grünbaum, do not reflect sufficiently the complex character of this relationship, which should be expressed by two correlative notions, namely: the relativity and absoluteness of simultaneity as a unique relation on the one hand, and as a universal relation on the other.

This approach has been criticized by A. A. Tjapkin who is inclined to admit a greater freedom in the definition of simultaneity and so also allow Galileo's transformation in the theory of relativity.[59] P. G. Kard, too, has been critical towards that approach, since he considers that, just the contrary, Einstein's definition is by no means merely conventional, having a quite objective basis.[29]

The third important aspect of the problem of time is the relation between time and happening, being, material systems. This is connected with the question of the objectivity of "becoming" and "the passing of time". Different interpretations of this relationship gave rise to two conceptions of time: the static and dynamic.

According to the static conception of time there is no difference, as far as real being is concerned, between the events of the past, present and future. All of them are real and exist, to put it like that, "simultaneously".

According to the second, dynamic conception of time, only present events exist. Past events have no longer any reality. The whole collection of events and material systems of which the universe is made up has been moving on in time from the past, through the present, to the future, assuming reality, appearing and vanishing, being transformed into other events and systems of matter.

All these problems are discussed, both in the foreign and the Soviet literature, mostly at the level of logical and linguistic statements which allow of various points of view on the reality of becoming. This is apparently no coincidence. The present state of these considerations accords with Lenin's view, expressed in "The Philosophical Notebooks",[32] on the attempts to verify visually Zeno's paradox: "The question is not whether movement does exist, but how it should be expressed in the logic of concepts." So what is discussed is not whether there is a passing of time or of becoming, but how this should be expressed in the logic of concepts. In our literature this aspect of the problem has been dealt with in the works of A. A. Zinoviev[67,68] and A. A. Ivin.[25,26]

And yet, apart from the linguistic and logical arguments, one could advance many philosophical and physical reasons strengthening one or the other conception. They have been reviewed by Y. V. Molchanov[37,38] who indicates how important for the solution of these questions is a clear distinction between such basic notions as 'now', 'the present' and the 'simultaneity'.[39]

The problem of becoming and the passing of time has been also studied by A. M. Mostapanienko[42] who, while supporting the dynamic, or as he called it the "kinetic" conception, stated that both these conceptions deal with two closely linked aspects of real time, though none of them is an extensive one.

However, it is the problem of the direction of time that is currently attracting mostly the scientists' attention. It would be no exaggeration to say that the major part of all the publications on time, being issued now in the world, deals with its direction. In this country an interest in this field of study was stimulated by the well-known work of H. Reichenbach *The Direction of Time*, both before the appearance of its Russian translation[52] and afterwards. The works by G. Whitrov[64] and A. Grünbaum[23] have also played some part in it.

The purpose of all the discussions in this field has been to find objective physical criteria which would make it possible to determine the direction of time and its irrevocable nature. Indeed, the papers published by Soviet writers over the last years have contributed considerably to the elucidation of that problem. Mention should be made in this connection of the works by Y. B. Zeldovich and A. D. Novikov,[65] Y. A. Askin,[11,12] V. P. Kazaryan,[31] G. G. Suchkova and A. Tursunov,[55] Z. G. Alibekov,[4] V. S. Jaroshenko[27] and A. Tursunov.[60]

A common feature of all these works on the direction and irreversibility of time, which have appeared in our literature, is a contention that it may be useless to seek at any cost a unique law determining the direction of time. This idea seems to be confirmed by the numerous irreversible processes and phenomena which cannot be reduced to each other. But it would be equally unwarranted to reject in advance the possibility that all these astonishingly disconcordant processes and phenomena, belonging to different areas of reality, are simply various manifestations of one fundamental law.

In recent years many researchers have also been investigating the dimensions of time. There have been two reasons for this study: first, a search for an objective physical proof of time's one-dimensional nature which is one of its main topological features, and second, the frequent advancement of a thesis that time may be two- or even multi-dimensional, a contention by means of which an explanation of various unexplored phenomena of the human psyche (such as: imagination, dreams, hallucinations, foreseeing the future) is offered.

In our philosophical literature the one-dimensionality of time has been postulated as a rule, without being however subjected to a theoretical analysis. It was A. M. Mostapanienko[41] who was the first to undertake a theoretical study of time's one-dimensionality. Having considered the empirical proofs of time's one dimension he quoted also some arguments in favor of its two- and even multi-dimensionality - and formulated the thesis that although one dimension of time is an obvious physical fact on the macroscopic level, we nevertheless cannot exclude the possibility that, on the microscopic level, time has other topological features and can appear as being two or even multi-dimensional. This question of time's dimensions has also been studied by Y. F. Askin[11] and A. M. Zharov.[24]

In I. A. Akchurin's book[6] the problem of time's topological features has been studied in the light of the new over-lapping topologies of Grothendieck. As a matter of fact, the operational methods of topology had been so far "automatically" applied to time, whereas they can only have sense in relation to bigger macroscopic objects whose any part may be cut out by means of a physical procedure of "cutting". In time relations however, especially in regard to its distant past or future sections, such operational topological methods are devoid of sense - any "bits" of any sections of time in the distant past or future are determined through their "residual vestiges" left in the material objects of our environment or in various processes (the motion of hands in a mechanical clock, radiation of electromagnetic waves, historical chronicles, fragments of life, etc.). So from the very beginning, in fact, "bits" of any sections of time are not determined by the classical topologies of "cutting out" but rather by the new Grothendieck topologies - the topologies of reflection. This poses a number of major questions in relation to time such as those of the possibility of it being represented by collections, the then necessary cyclic nature of its group features, the possibility of an interpretation in terms of time and space of organized objects by means of a system of the so-called in-built primary ideals, and the nature of time topology in biology.

The Soviet researchers have been also probing into the problem of the continuity and discontinuity of time. Many articles and a number of monographs have been devoted to this subject. Among them mention should be made first of all of the works by I. Shapiro,[53] R. A. Aronov,[8] V. G. Kadyshevsky,[28] A. N. Vjalzev,[63] E. P. Andreyev,[7] I. A. Akchurin,[6] B. S. Gott,[22] M. D. Akhundov,[5] A. I. Panchenko.[49]

The problem of the universality of time, that is, whether time relations are of a microscopic character, whether they are valid both in the micro- and macro-worlds, has been discussed by A. M. Mostapanienko,[42] I. S. Alexeyev,[3] P. S. Dyshlevy and W. S. Lukyanec,[17] V. S. Barashenkov[13] and others.

Also very prominent in the Soviet philosophical literature is the problem of the finiteness and infinity of time, considered as part of the broader question of the universe's finiteness and infinity - in the light of the contemporary cosmology and the general theory of relativity. Attention should be drawn in this respect to the works by G. I. Naan,[46] A. L. Zelmanov,[66] or E. M. Chudinov,[15] L. B. Bazhenov,[14] A. S. Karmin[30] and others.

Thus the problem of time, as it has already been said, constitutes a whole group of various problems. But alas, with the exception of time's objectivity, none of these problems has been solved unequivocally and definitely. All of them are still being discussed and studied, while remaining at the center of broadly conducted researches in the field of natural philosophy. These are indeed extremely profound and topical problems since answers to them must be included in the formation of a contemporary, scientific outlook on life. And that is why so much attention has been paid to them in the work of scientific research.

REFERENCES

1. Alexandrov, A. D., "Filosofskoie sodierzhaniie i znacheniie tieroii otmositie z'nosti," *Filosofskiie problemy sovriemiennogo iestiestvoznanija* [ "The Philosophical Content and Meaning of the Theory of Relativity," in *Philosophical Problems of Contemporary Natural Science*] , Moskva, 1959.

2. _____, "Tieorija otnositiel'nosti kak tieoriia absolutnogo prostranstra i vriemieni," *Filosofskiie voprosy sovriemiennoj fiziki* [ "The Theory of Relativity as the Theory of Absolute Space and Time" in *Philosophical Questions of Contemporary Physics*] , Moskva, 1969.

3. Alexevey, J. A., "O gipotiezie makroskopichieskoj prirody prostranstvienno - vriemiennych priedstavlenii," *Filosofskiie problemy tieorii tjagotienija Ejnshtiejna - Einsteina - i riejlativitskoj kosmologii. Tezisy dokladov i soobshchienij na Vtorom Vsiesojuznom simposjamie* [ "On the Hypothesis of the Macroscopical Nature of the Space-Time Concept," in *The Philosophical Problems of Einstein's Theories of Gravity and the Relativity of Cosmology. Theses of Lectures and Communications at the Second Nationwide Symposium*] , Kiev, 1966, p. 75.

4. Alibekov, Z. G., "Prostranstwo i vriemija" [ "Space and Time"] , *Filosofskiie Nauki*, 1975. No. 5.

5. Akhundov, M. D., *Probliema prieryvnosti i nieprieryvnosti prostransiva i vriemieni* [ *The Problem of Intermittance and Continuity of Space and Time*] , Moskva, 1974.

6. Akchurin, I. A., *Jedinstvo iestiestviennonauchnogo znanija* [*The Unity of Science*], Moskva, 1974.

7. Andreyev, E. P., *Prostranstvo mikromimira* [*Space of the Microworld*], Moskva, 1969.

8. Aronov, R. A., "O gipotiezie prieryvnosti prostranstva i vriemieni,""[ "On the Hypothesis of the Intermittance of Space and Time"], *Voprosy Filosofii*, 1957, No. 3.

9. Askin, J. F., "Vriemja i viechnost," [ "Time and Eternity"], *Voprosy Filosofii*, 1963, No. 6.

10. _____, "Probliema nieobratimosti vriemieni" [ "The Problem of the Irreversibility of Time"], *Voprosy Filosofii*, 1966, No. 5.

11. _____, *Probliema vriemieni: Ieie Filosoksoie istolkovaniie* [*The Problem of Time: Its Philosophical Interpretation*], Moskva, 1966.

12. _____, "Napravlieniie vriemieni i vriemiennaja struktura procesov," *Prostranstvo, vriemja, dvizhenie* [ "The Direction of Time and the Temporal Structure of Processes," in *Space, Time, Movement*], Moskva, 1971.

13. Barashenkov, B. S., Fizicheskiie priediely prostranstvienno-vriemiennogo opisanija" [ "Physical Boundaries of Space-Time Descriptions"], *Voprosy Filosofii*, 1973, No. 11.

14. Bazhenov, L. B., "Probliema prostranstva i vriemieni," *Filosofija iestiestvoznanija*, vol. I, [ "The Problem of Space-Time" in *The Philosophy of Natural Science*], Moskva. 1966.

15. Chudinov, E. M., *Tieorija otnositiel'nosti i filosofija* [*The Theory of Relativity and Philosophy*], Moskva, 1974.

16. Deborin, A. M., "Probliema vriemieni v osvieshchienii akad. Virnadskogo" ["The Problem of Time in the Interpretation of Acad. Vernadsky"], *Izvestija A.N.USSR.Otdielieniie matiematichieskikh i iestiestviennykh nauk*, vol. 4, 1932.

17. Dyshlevy, P. S., and Lukyanec, V. S., "Probliema statusa prostranstvienno-vriemiennykh koncepcij v tieorietichieskoj fizikie," ["The Problem of Status of Space-Time Concepts in Theoretical Physics"], *Voprosy Filosofii*, 1970, No. 10.

18. Dyshlevy, P. S., *Materialisticheskaja dialectika i fizichesskij rieljativizm* [*Materialistic Dialectics and Physical Relativism*], Kiev, 1972.

19. Einstein, A. "Electrodynamics of Moving Bodies," Russian translation in *Sobraniie Nauchnykh Trudov*, Vol. I, Moskva, 1965.

20. Fok, V. A., "Sovriemiennaja tieorija prostranstva i vriemiani," ["The Contemporary Theory of Space and Time"], *Priroda*, 1952, no. 12.

21. _____, *Tieorija prostranstva, vriemieni i tjagotienija* [*The Theory of Space, Time, and Gravity*], Moskva, 1961.

22. Gott, W. S., *Prostranstvo i vriemija mikromira* [*Space and Time of the Microworld*], Moskva, 1967.

23. Grünbaum, A., *Filosofskiie probliemy prostranstva i vriemieni*, [*Philosophical Problems of Space and Time*], Moskva, 1969.

24. Zharov, A. M., "Ob empirichieskom i tieorietichieskom obosnovanii odnomiernosti vriemieni" ["On the Empirical and Theoretical Basis of Time's One-dimensionality, *Voprosy Filosofii*, 1968, No. 7.

25. Ivin, A. A., "Logichieskiie tieorii vriemieni" ["Logical Theories of Time"], *Voprosy Filosofii*, 1969, No. 3.

26. _____, "Logika vriemieni," *Nieklassichieskaja logika* ["The Logic of Time" in *Nonclassical Logic*], Moskva, 1970.

27. Jaroshenko, V. S., "K filozowskoj ocenkie sovriemiennykh fizi cheskikh priedstavlienij o nieobratismosti vriemieni" ["Toward the Philosophical Evaluation of Contemporary Physical Ideas on the Irreversibility of Time"], *Filosofskije Nauki*, 1975, No. 3.

28. Kadyshevsky, V. G., "K tieorii diskrietnogo prostranstva-vriemieni" ["Toward the Theory of Discrete Space-Time"], *Doklady AN SSR*, 1961, No. 136.

29. Kard, P. G., "Rieljativistskaja odnovriemiennost'," *Metod modielirovanija i niekotoryie filosofskiie probliemy istorii i mietodologii iestiestvoznanija* ["Relative Simultaneity" in *Method of Modeling and Some Philosophical Problems of History and the Methodology of Natural Science*], Tallin, 1975.

30. Karmin, A. S., "K postanovkie probliemy bieskoniechnosti v sovriemiennoj naukie" ["Toward the Organization of the Problem of Infinity in Contemporary Science"], *Voprosy Filosofii*, 1955, No. 2.

31. Kazaryan, V. P., "Otnositiel'no priedstavlienij ob obratnom tiechienii vriemieni" ["Concerning the Ideas of the Backward Flow of Time"], *Voprosy Filosofii*, 1970, No. 8.

32. Lenin, V. I., "Filosofskiie tietradi," *Polnoie sobraniie sochinienij*, v. 29 ["*Philosophical Notebooks*" in *Complete Collection of Essays*, v. 29].

33. Mandelshtam, L. I., "Liekcii po fizicheskim osnovam tieorii otnositiel'nosti," *Polnoie sobraniie trudov* [Lectures on the Physical Basis of the Theory of

Relativity," in *Complete Collection of Works*], Leningrad, 1950.

34. Molchanov, J. B., "Ponjatiie odnoviremiennosti i iego evoljucija" ["The Concept of Simultaneity and Its Evolution"], *Voprosy Filosofii*, 1964, No. 9.

35. _____, "O razlichnykh smyslakh otnoshenija odnovriemiennosti (k istorii voprosa)" ["On Various Meaning of the Treatment of Simultaneity (Toward the History of the Question)"], *Einshtiejnovskij sbornik*, Moscow, 1968.

36. _____, *Viremja v klassicheskoj i rieljativistskoj fizikie* [*Time in Classical and Relativity Physics*], Moskva, 1967.

37. _____, "Probliema sintieza pazlichnykh konciepcij vriemieni," *Sintez sovriemiennogo nauchnogo znanija*, ["The Problem of Synthesis of Various Concepts of Time" in *Synthesis in Contemporary Natural Science*], Moskva, 1973.

38. _____, "Dialiektika i probliema vriemieni" ["Dialectics and the Problem of Time"], *Voprosy Filosofii*, 1975, No. 8.

39. _____, "The Notions 'Now', 'Present' and 'Simultaneous' in *Different Conceptions of Time: Proceedings of International Congress of Logic, Methodology and Philosophy of Science*, London, Ont., 1975, vol. VII, pp. 39-40.

40. Mostapanienko, A. M., "K probliemie razmiernosti vriemiene" ["Toward the Problem of Measurement of Time"], *Voprosy Filosofii*, 1965, No. 7.

41. Mostapanienko, A. M. and Mostapanienko, M. V., *Chetyrykhmiernost' prostranstva i vriemieni* [*The Four Dimensions of Space and Time*], Moskva-Leningrad, 1966.

42. Mostapanienko, A. M., *Prostranstvo i vriemja v makro-mega- i mikromirie* [*Space and Time in the Macro-, Mega- and Micro-World*], Moskva, 1974.

43. _____, *Probliema univiersal'nosti osnovnykh svoistv prostranstva i vriemieni* [*The Problem of the Universality of Basic Characteristics of Space and Time*], Leningrad, 1969.

44. Mostapanienko, M. B., *Matierialisticheskaja sushchnost' tieorii i otnositiel'nosti Eijnshtiejna* [*The Materialistic Essence of Einstein's Theory of Relativity*], Moskva, 1962.

45. Naan, G. I., "K voprosu o principie otnositiel'nosti v sovriemiennoj fizikie," ["Toward the Question of the Principle of Relativity in Contemporary Physics"], *Voprosy Filosofii*, 1951, No. 2.

46. _____, "O bieskoniechnositi Vsieliennoj," ["On the Infinity of the Universe"], *Voprosy Filosofii*, 1961, No. 6.

47. Omeljanovskij, M. E., *Lenin i fizika XX vieka* [*Lenin and the Physics of the 20th Century*], Moskva, 1947.

48. _____, *Dialiektika v sovriemiennoj Fizike* [*Dialectics in Contemporary Physics*], Moskva, 1973.

49. Panchenko, A. I., *Kontinuum i fizika* [*Continuum and Physics*], Moskva, 1975.

50. Fersman, A. I., *Vriemja* [*Time*], Pietrograd, 1922.

51. Rigal, J. L. (ed.), *Les temps et la pensée physique contemporaine*, Russian translation, Moskva, 1970.

52. Reichenbach, H., *The Direction of Time*, Russian translation, Moskva, 1962.

53. Shapiro, I. S., "O kvantovanii prostranstva i vriemieni v tieorii eliemientarynykh chastiej" ["On the Quantitavity of Space and Time and Theories of

Elementary Particles"], *Voprosy Filosofii*, 1962, No. 8.

54. Shteinman, R. J., *Prostranstvo i vriemija* [*Space and Time*], Moskva, 1962.

55. Suchkova, G. G. and Tursunov, A., "Probliema anizotropii vriemieni i kosmologii" ["The Problem of Anisotropy of Time and Cosmology"], *Voprosy Filosofii*, 1971, No. 12.

56. Svidersky, V. J., *Filosofskoie znachieniie prostransvienno-vriemiennykh priedstavlienij v fizikie* [*The Philosophical Meaning of Space-Time Ideas in Physics*], Leningrad, 1956.

57. _____, *Prostranstvo i vriemja* [*Space and Time*], Moskva, 1958.

58. Tjapkin, A. A., "Konviencional'nie opriedielienija i obiekti-vnyie invarianty" ["Conventional Definitions and Objective Invariant"], *Voprosy Filosofii*, 1970, No. 7.

59. _____, "Vyrazhieniie obshchikh svoistv fizichieskikh processov i prostranstvienno-vriemiennoj specialnoj teorii otnos-itiel'nosti" ["Expressions of General Properties of Physical Process and the Space-Time metzic of the special Theory of Relativity"], *Uspiekhy Fizicheskikh Nauk*, vol. 106, No. 4, 1972.

60. Tursunov, A., "Napravlieniie vriemieni:novyie aspiekty staroj probliemy" ["The Direction of Time: New Aspects of an Old Problem"], *Voprosy Filosofii*, 1975, No. 3.

61. Urmanzev, Y. A. and Tzusov, Y. P., "O svojstvakh vriemieni" ["On the Characteristics of Time"], *Voprosy Filosofii*, 1961, No. 5.

62. Vernadsky, V. I., "Probliema vriemieni v sovriemiennoj naukie," ["The Problem of Time in Contemporary Science"], *Izvistija AN SSR Otdielieniie matiemati-*

*chieskikh i iestiestviennych nauk,* vol. 1, 1932.

63. Vjalzev, A. N., *Diskrietnoie prostranstvo-vriemija* [*Discrete Space-Time*], Moskva, 1965.

64. Whitrow, G. I., *The Natural Philosophy of Time,* Russian translation, Moskva, 1964.

65. Zeldovich, J. B. and Novikov, I. D., *Rieljativistskaia astrofizika* [*Relativistic Astrophysics*], Moskva, 1967.

66. Zelmanov, A. L., "*Mnogoobrazie* matierial'nogo mira i probliema bieskoniechnosti vsieliennoj in *v. Bieskoniechnost' i vsieliennaja* [ "The Diversity of the Material World and the Infinity of the Universe" in *v. Infinity and the Universe*], Moskva, 1969.

67. Zinoviev, A. A., "O prostranstvienno-vriemiennoj tierminologii," [ "On Space-Time Terminology"], *Voprosy Filosofii,* 1969, No. 5.

68. _____, *Logichieskaja fizika* [*Logical Physics*], Moskva, 1972.

# VII. LITERATURE AND THE ARTS

## Fiction: The Language of Time— Thomas Mann and James Joyce

M. Church

*ABSTRACT*

*Techniques found in Thomas Mann's* Magic Mountain *and James Joyce's* Ulysses *seem to illustrate similar views about human time. Repetition of events, as described by Mann and Joyce, in which theme and motif occur and recur, suggests that on this earth the influence of each person continues only as part of the huge gathering snowball he has helped to form, and that death is the still center, apart from process, wherein individuality is lost. Mann and Joyce see the circular pattern of lived time as the ultimate reality. They both use the circle to describe process, although process itself may be variously interpreted by them. It is this observation, made with the help of fiction, of a circular reality basic to various points of view that substantiates, in my opinion, the validity of the philosophical position on time as* circle, spiral, cycle, *or as simply* round, *like, perhaps, space.*

It is commonly held by casual readers of Thomas Mann's *Magic Mountain* either that Naphta was right and time is an illusion, its flow the result of functions or the senses, and that the real existence of things is an abiding present; or that Settembrini was right and things and people have an objective existence, apart from our perception of them, and the flow of time is no illusion, but experience itself. Organic reality, however, according to Mann, rests on the principle of repetition and recreation, on the circle and the spiral. Hans Castorp's conclusions, like Mann's, differ from either Settembrini's or Naphta's, as we may see from a crucial image in the "Fullness of Harmony" chapter: the needle on the gramophone record describes a spiral pattern, progressing inward to the vortex, to the still center - thus combining the principles of Castorp's two mentors. In this opening part of my paper I shall use the gramophone record as objective correlative of time, so as to show that the cycle which the needle describes on its surface is like the cycle of time: it combines both essence and existence, both eastern and western philosophies. It is fiction itself which makes the point.

To repeat, we are working with a spiral, one that converges toward the center pole, the still point. We are thus involved with a process of circular reality whereby the needle continually returns to essentially the same place, but a point removed, by a fraction of an inch, in its course toward the still center. Literature may give us proof of the thesis that through both motion and stillness we may describe process.

The structure of Thomas Mann's *Magic Mountain* supports Mann's primary belief about the progression of time. Everything in the book moves in circles. Up and down, to and fro, have no real significance since, as parts of circles, they are easily confused or reversed. Everything returns to its starting point in one way or another. But it is not the closed circle of repetition, Nietzsche's "ewige Wiederkehr," that Mann celebrates here (despite his earlier admiration for Nietzsche), for now the closed circle is the equivalent of what Mann sees as "measureless monotony"[1] or routine. We must break out of circular into spiral time. The hands of the watch, the routine of the Berghof, the needle of the compass - all describe closed circles, but true human activity is described in spiral form. Thus the early dualism established by the rudimentary conflict between Clavdia and Settembrini, between body and mind, in Hans' consciousness, gives way, in Chapter VI, to the more complex dualism between Settembrini and Naphta, between this world and the next. It is subsumed in the elaborate figure of Mynheer Peeperkorn, who represents both Christ and Dionysius, in effect all of Hans' previous positions wrapped in one. It is shortly after Peeperkorn's death that the image of the gramophone record is introduced. In essence, what we have in the chapter called

"The Fullness of Harmony" are five different records, each representing a previous portion of the novel, each spiraling around to its conclusion, a segment of the larger spiral culminating in Schubert's "Der Lindenbaum." Mann describes the circling disk in this way: "Its motion was not only circular, but also a peculiar, sidling undulation, which communicated itself to the arm that bore the needle, and gave this too an elastic oscillation, almost like breathing, which must have contributed greatly to the *vibrato* and *portamento* of the stringed instruments and voices."[2] The sidling motion of the arm created by the spiral form is the life-giving force of the whole process for Mann, contributing the *vibrato* and the *portamento* - that is, emotional intensity and passage from one tone to the next.

To see time as Naphta does, as an illusion of the senses, is to ignore the music itself, is to traffic with death. The present moment is not for Mann a single still frame in a succession of frames that our brain is manufacturing and projecting so fast that we do not perceive their essential stillness. Rather, for this author, the present is a point in a series of points that make up the spiral form of life, so that we return as Clavdia does to the Berghof, as Joachim returns from the military life, as Hans returns to the sanatorium in the guise of Uncle James Tienappel, as Hans returns to the flatland - the same position varied only by its slight difference in distance from the center. It will be noted that Mann's image is fulfilled logically, in that the circles of content become progressively smaller as the book runs on. The largest circle is that of Settembrini and Clavdia, covering the first five chapters of the book. Next, Naphta and Settembrini are accorded a full chapter, Chapter VI. Peeperkorn receives half a chapter; the gramophone itself, twenty pages.

The still center, then, is the conclusion of process. In *The Magic Mountain* it is "The Thunderbolt" which concludes the book, not the mock and highly questionable séance scene. At the still center for Mann - as we have learned in the Schubert song - stand the linden tree "am Brunnen vor dem Tore," the spring before the gate, representing life and opportunity. The hero rejects the delusion of peace and rest offered by the tree's sheltering branches. Instead he elects the tensions of life, the wind blowing straight in his face, death as a part of the life process, for life feeds on life. It is this tension of movement which the still pole or peg at the center of the disk supports. Form and civilization develop, Mann writes, "always in silent recognition of the blood-sacrifice."[3] Thus the culminating image of the gramophone record enables Mann to make his point, a point which lays emphasis on the here and the now as of intrinsic worth, not illusory stages in the progress of man toward eternity.

During the years (1912-1924) when Mann was working on *The Magic Mountain*, James Joyce published *Dubliners* (1914), *A Portrait of the Artist as a Young Man* (1916), and *Ulysses* (1922), all based on a sense of historical circularity. In fact, the comparison between Mann and Joyce is a fascinating one, for both authors use the thunderbolt as conclusion to process, as the inductor to the still center. And like Mann, Joyce puts the emphasis on process itself, not on the attainment of stillness. Joyce's interpretation of the eighteenth-century Italian philosopher Vico lies at the heart of his work, and through Vico, we may trace in *Ulysses*, my exemplar here, a spiral process somewhat similar to Mann's as elaborated in *The Magic Mountain*. The difference lies in that Joyce's pattern rests on Vico's notion of the rise and fall of empires - a pattern visible throughout human history, whereas Mann's spiraling reality rests more upon a Jungian concept of the collective unconscious, of the repetition inherent in myth and, before that, in nature itself.

It is not only in the minutiae, sentences and words, but in the larger structure of *Ulysses* that Vico may be seen. Joyce wrote in a letter to Harriet Weaver that the circumstances of his own life were what forced him to accept the theories of Vico.[4] Furthermore, we know from many sources that Joyce was "passionately interested"[5] in the work of Vico, as attested, for example, by Joyce's pupil, Paolo Cuzzi, who took English lessons from him in Trieste (where, incidentally, one of the chief piazzas is the Piazza Vico). More than a historical theory, Joyce sees in Vico a psychological progression, the circumstances of human lives. As Richard Ellmann points out, Joyce sees Vico's divisions not as chronological divisions of ideal history, but as psychological ingredients which combine and recombine. "I use his cycles as a trellis," Joyce said.[6] As such, Vico's influence does not lead to an abstract pattern, but is closely connected with character development, the vine that grows on the trellis.

*Finnegan's Wake* is crowded with references to Vico, establishing beyond doubt the influence of Vico's cycles on this novel. But it is my contention that Joyce began using Viconian trellises as early as *Dubliners*, as I show in "*Dubliners* and Vico"[7] and in "*A Portrait of the Artist as a Young Man* and Giambattista Vico: A Source Study."[8] Vico's three ages, the age of the gods, the age of the heroes, then the age of men was a cycle of decline, as outlined in his book *The New Science* (1725). To them Vico added the *ricorso*, a recycling stage whereby a new age of the gods was instituted. Joyce's names for the three ages varied slightly from Vico's to underline his own special interpretation of them. Joyce called them: Age of the Fathers, Age of the Sons, and Age of the People, stressing their psychological and social rather than their chronological significance. But for both Vico and Joyce, spiral succeeded spiral in the development of process, and for both the emphasis lay on the spiraling pattern itself rather than on a realm beyond it at the end of process.

In *Ulysses*, the spiraling ages outlined above may be clearly seen in the structure of the book. The first three parts of *Ulysses*, often called the *Telemachia*, may represent the completion of a cycle begun in the last chapter of *A Portrait of the Artist as a Young Man* where the "gods" (faculty) of the university become Stephen's new parents, after he has cast off his early life at home. The first episode in the *Telemachia* would represent, then, the Age of the Sons, the second - the Nestor episode - the Age of the People, and the third (Proteus), the *ricorso*. Critics have long argued about how to explain this final chapter of *A Portrait*, which seems to stand alone and disconnected in the earlier book. It would be logical to see *Ulysses* as continuing the story of Stephen at the point where it is broken off in *A Portrait*, following Stephen as he continues on this second cycle of his life (the first cycle having been described in the first four chapters of *A Portrait*). The Age of the Sons, the heroes, unfolds in his stay at the Martello Tower with Buck Mulligan and Haines; the Age of the People (men, women, and children), in his experiences at Mr. Deasy's school; the *ricorso* in the circulation and recirculation represented symbolically in the swirling waters and, metaphysically, in Stephen's swirling thoughts in the Proteus episode (Proteus being a sea god of shifting forms).

The middle section of *Ulysses* (Episodes 4-15) replaces Stephen as central character with the figure of Leopold Bloom because, I believe, Joyce saw that Stephen himself was incapable of relating to others, of ever assuming a real role in the complex social milieu of the book. In this central section of *Ulysses,* we find further evidence of the cyclical and spiraling development of the novel. It is necessary, at the beginning, to note Joyce's preoccupation with the consubstantiality of Father and Son, suggesting that the ages, as I will outline them here, are actually not so neatly distinguishable as they will often appear to be.

Nevertheless, in the opening episode, Calypso, Bloom is seen initially as husband and father, a kind of mock *pater familias,* in his home on 7 Eccles Street, as he feeds the cat and prepares Molly's breakfast. We see him next in the Lotus Eaters episode, the Age of the Sons, as Mr. Henry Flower, engaged in narcissistic and titillating adolescent behavior in his secret correspondence with Martha Clifford, and later in his scented bath as he views his own navel. In Hades, the Age of the People, we find Bloom relating to the community, both to the *Umwelt* and the *Mitwelt,* as he and his friends proceed through the streets of Dublin in the funeral cortege of Paddy Dignam. And finally in the *ricorso* to this first cycle, Bloom appears in the newspaper offices where Aeolus (the printing press) disperses, separates, and destroys lives and where circulation and recirculation run rampant. Although Vico's cycles, as I have already maintained, were cycles of decline, the character of Joyce's cycles was more ambiguous. Whereas Leopold Bloom may appear outwardly less heroic than his prototype, Ulysses, he has at the same time inner qualities of compassion, of understanding, and of forebearance which give him stature in a moral sense. Joyce continually mocks his hero, as in the newspaper office where Bloom's only invitation is to kiss the editor's arse, but Bloom's self-restraint, his patience in the face of persistent frustrations he meets in every encounter during his day, raise him ethically above his archetype, the wily and brawny Ulysses. Joyce seems to say, therefore, that the cycles may spiral either upwards or downwards depending on one's perspective. Arbitration, understanding, concern for others, even one's enemies, characterize the modern hero, Leopold Bloom.

The next four episodes trace still another Viconian cycle. We find Bloom first, in the Lestrygonian episode, as provider, feeding the gulls, as in Calypso he had fed the cat and Molly, but the theme of this section centers around brutish father figures. The Lestrygonians were cannibals, and their descendants in Burton's restaurant, where Bloom first goes for his luncheon, do not, like Bloom, feed others, but concentrate on "swilling, wolfing goblets of sloppy food, their eyes bulging." As he leaves, Bloom remarks: "Eat or be eaten."[9] Fleeing to Davy Byrne's pub, Bloom joins still other fathers, Nosey Flynn, Paddy Leonard, Bantam Lyons, and Tom Rocheford, in this Age of the Fathers. In the Age of the Sons that follows, we turn from Bloom to Stephen, as he holds forth in the library on another famous son, Hamlet. The Lestrygonians have been replaced by stone and whirlpool, Scylla and Charybdis, the latter a spiral within the larger spiral movement. Next in the Age of the People, the Wandering Rocks, we follow persons and groups of persons, the populace of Dublin, as they circulate and recirculate through the streets.[10] And finally in the *ricorso* at the Ormond restaurant, the reader is besieged with clacks, taps, pops, crackling, and the breaking of wind, suggesting that the world of this second cycle is falling apart. One of the last images is that of the tram, a favorite Joycean device to suggest circularity, for the progress of the tram describes a circle, ending where it began. Often the tram was turned at the end of the line by a *round* table for its journey back along the streets.

The third group of episodes in this middle section of *Ulysses* opens with Cyclops, a cannibalistic giant, like the Lestrygonians in the Age of the Fathers in cycle two. It is clear that Cyclops and the Citizen are one, an ironic comment on the character of Dublin fathers in general. By contrast we see Bloom in this episode as he turns the other cheek to the Citizen's wrath and to the hostility of the group of bar flies at Barney Kiernan's tavern. Nausicaa describes a new Age of the Sons (or Daughters, in this episode), developing once again, as in the Lotus Eaters, adolescent patterns (i.e., voyeurism and masturbation). Linking the two episodes is Bloom's letter to Martha Clifford, which he remembers as he watches Gerty. The Age of the People follows at the lying-in hospital where we see that all men are connected by means of the umbilical cord and where we join, instead of Mina Purefoy, a party of medical students and their friends, "all off for a buster, armstrong, hollering down the street."[11] The grand *ricorso* is, of course, the Circe episode, a potpourri of all previous sections, concluding with its thunderclap, the shattering of the chandelier, and the celebration of Black Mass. One great concussion here replaces the slighter but more numerous sound effects of the *ricorso* of the Sirens episode and that of Aeolus. As the thunderclap had caused Hans to change his direction in *The Magic Mountain,* so in *Ulysses,* the thunderclap will cause Stephen and Bloom to seek new cycles of development.

One of these is begun in the Nostos of *Ulysses,* composed of the final three sections of the book. Here we start again with a new Age of the Fathers as we read about Bloom in Eumaeus, as father to a new son, as protector and guide for Stephen. In keeping with Joyce's theme of consubstantiality, the next section, Ithaca, portrays father and son as equal and interchangeable, Blephen and Stoom, predecessors of Shem and Shaun. Both are sons and lovers of Molly, who in the final section, the Age of the People, becomes the earth goddess, Gaea Tellus, where all men meet. Bloom through his relation to Molly is seen in this Age of the People in his relation to all men, as he himself says in Ithaca: "neither first nor last nor only nor alone in a series originating in and repeated to infinity."[12] "Riverrun" and Anna Livia derive from Molly who circulates and recirculates, leading to the giant *ricorso* (*Finnegan's Wake*) that Joyce provides for the cycle begun in the Nostos of *Ulysses.*

Let us examine briefly, the different emphases placed on cyclical return by Mann and by Joyce. With Joyce (despite his concern with the historical theories of Vico) the stress is ultimately on individual development, whereas Mann stresses the collective experience of mankind. Mann himself often worried about the individuality of his characters, fearing that they were more archetypes than persons.[13] At the same time, Vico's philosophy of the recurrence of the three ages suggested to Joyce (born in Catholic Ireland) a new social resurrection, a view of history, reborn phoenix-like, from the ashes of the past, a Lazarus risen, although it was used to outline the individual development of his hero, Leopold Bloom. The spiraling reality, the repetition of event, provided a rich source of imagery for Joyce. Thus Bloom's own gentle fathering of others could be contrasted to advantage with the cannibalism of the Cyclops and Lestrygonians, with tyrants and with dragons of earlier Ages of the Fathers. In the Age of the Sons, Bloom's adolescent preoccupations seem relatively harmless when contrasted with delusions and stupor of Homer's lotus eaters. And Scylla and Charybdis offer far more danger to life and limb than Stephen, as he holds forth in the library. The earlier Ages of the People, as symbolized by Hades, the Wandering Rocks, and Oxen of the Sun, are fraught with danger by comparison with life in Dublin.

On another level, we see the world of Leopold Bloom as a diminished and impoverished world when compared with the world of the golden court of Menelaus, the splendid horses of Nestor, or the enchanted isle of Calypso. But the heroic age of the epic gives way finally in *Ulysses* to the Age of the People and yields honor at the end to Leopold Bloom for his wisdom and ethical maturity. Bloom, rather than the wily Ulysses, is a compassionate father, as well as consubstantial, a compassionate Christ. Thus the emphasis turns inward from the outward glory of things past to the inner triumphs of Joyce's twentieth-century hero. As Hans Castorp sheds Settembrini and Naphta, the gods of his early stay at the sanatorium, so Bloom sheds the problems and preoccupations of the earlier part of his day as he reaches a calm resolution in Ithaca. Both Joyce and Mann see, in other words, that development of civilization moves from stress on outer worlds to stress on inner worlds. (As Berdyaev suggests, Renaissance man, having discovered that the earth was not the center of the universe and that the universe extended apparently to infinity, that the earth was not even the center of its own planetary system, turned from scrutiny of impossible space to scrutiny of self.[14] In Ancient Greece, Psyche was the last of the gods to be created.)

Joyce's use of Viconian cycles, then, is in the interests of depicting the psychological maturity of his hero, Bloom. Rather than slaughtering the suitors to Penelope's hand, Bloom becomes reconciled at the end to the fact of mathematical sequence. Rather than hurling insults back at Cyclops (a cycle himself), Bloom departs from the Citizen's wrath without retaliation as "ben Bloom Elijah," "having rainment as of the sun."[15] Finally, instead of encouraging Stephen to take the place of his lost son, Rudy, Bloom gives Stephen freedom.

The spiral development is given form in *Ulysses* by the *ricorso,* whereby one cycle collapses or explodes only to be reformed and recycled at a different level. We recall that it is through the thunderbolt, which gives its title to Mann's final chapter in *The Magic Mountain,* that Hans Castorp is freed from his life-denying enchantment - the thunderbolt which is seen as a hellhound, "a huge explosive shell, a disgusting sugar-loaf from the infernal regions."[16] Neither Joyce nor Mann sees fulfillment in the still center. Death is the enemy come from the infernal region. Death is part of process, but not in itself fulfilling for the individual. Joyce and Mann may be seen, then, to complement one another (Joyce more Freudian, Mann more Jungian), to fulfill the same ultimate aim, essentially humanistic and Greek in character.

These extended analyses of two major contemporary novels show that circular reality is in them ultimately the most valid description of the process of time. Even in mystical works, we can find the same circular emphasis. For example, in D. H. Lawrence's "The Rocking Horse Winner," psychical insights are achieved by the circular process of rocking, and circular race tracks act as objective correlatives for the tediousness of the life cycle as seen in the boy's home. And in another genre, in T. S. Eliot's *Four Quartets,* we see that it is through physical circularity (the course of the earth) that the still center is attained: "At the still point of the turning world."[17]

Furthermore all metafiction, from *Don Quixote* down to its numerous descendants, rests on a view of fiction which is basically concentric in character, incorporating books within books in an infinite regress. Cervantes himself employs a far more complex circular reality than Mann's relatively simple progression of cycles and Joyce's slightly more complicated one. It is a circular reality particularly well suited to mirroring the meshing of countless wheels which, in the view of Cervantes, characterizes life. Behind the appearance of linear progression, in this understanding of life, lies repetition; no line is straight except in the abstract, for there is always a perspective to prove it curved.

It is an observation of a circular reality, made with the help of fiction and basic to many points of view, which, in my opinion, strengthens and substantiates the philosophical metaphors of time as *circular, spiral, cyclic,* or simply *round,* not unlike clocks, sundials, and perhaps even space itself.

NOTES

1. Thomas Mann: *The Magic Mountain* (New York: Alfred A. Knopf 1960), p. 547.

2. *Ibid.*, pp. 640-1.

3. *Ibid.*, p. 496.

4. Stuart Gilbert (ed.): *Letters of James Joyce* (New York: The Viking Press 1957), p. 241.

5. Richard Ellmann: *James Joyce* (New York: Oxford University Press 1959), p. 351.

6. *Ibid.*, p. 565.

7. *James Joyce Quarterly*, Vol. 5, No. 1, Winter 1968, pp. 150-6.

8. In Thomas F. Staley and Bernard Benstock (eds.): *Approaches to Joyce's "Portrait"* (Pittsburgh, Pennsylvania: University of Pittsburgh Press, 1976), pp. 77-89.

9. James Joyce: *Ulysses* (New York: The Modern Library, 1934), p. 168.

10. The eighteen episodes in Wandering Rocks form a kind of *Ulysses* in miniature, redivided into Viconian cycles, like the subdivisions of Aeolus, Cyclops, and Oxen of the Sun. Joyce amused himself by superimposing cycles upon cycles and inserting cycles within cycles.

11. Joyce, p. 417.

12. *Ibid.*, p. 716.

13. See Harry Slochower: *Thomas Mann's Joseph Story* (New York: Alfred A. Knopf 1938), p. 13. Slochower discusses Mann's concern for balancing the individual and the typical in his novels.

14. Nicholas Berdyaev: *Dostoevsky* (London: Sheed and Ward 1934), pp. 44-50, pp. 95-101.

15. Joyce, p. 339.

16. Mann, p. 715.

17. T. S. Eliot: *The Complete Poems and Plays* (New York: Harcourt, Brace and Company 1952), pp. 119-121.

# The Eternal Moment: D.H. Lawrence's *The Rainbow* and *Women in Love*

G.H. Ford

*How time is viewed in D. H. Lawrence's novels has been diversely interpreted. Some critics see his writings as past-oriented and cyclic. Others argue that he "never looked back at the past," and that his writings are future-oriented. A resolution of these contrary readings can be effected by a close study of his two major novels,* The Rainbow *and* Women in Love. *What becomes evident is that his fictional world sings "of what is past, or passing, or to come," and that the two novels embody all three of these experiences of time.*

The Rainbow *can be seen as an historical novel, yet the past of mankind drawn upon is predominantly mythic rather than historic, providing "a renewal of the past in the present." Time present appears in two versions in these novels. Many of the characters live a day-to-day existence, unconcerned with past or future. More distinctive is the special kind of experience of present moments, in which the intensification of the experience effects a suspension of clock-time, what Browning called the "Eternal Moment." Some of Lawrence's characters, however, are committed to moving beyond the present experience and forward into a future when a utopian society will be realized. Ursula Brangwen's characteristic yearning is towards what she calls the "unrisen dawns," rather than for her present experience or for nostalgic recollections of past experiences.*

*In one of his late essays, Lawrence exclaimed: "What next? That's what interests me. What now is no fun anymore." In his best novels, his treatment of time is never so simple as this. Instead, "What next?" is combined into a complex and fascinating fictional world which includes "What was?" and, surely his most memorable vein, "What now?"*

I.

In his pioneering study of 1952, *Time and the Novel*, A. A. Mendilow demonstrates how a preoccupation with time has dominated the novels of the twentieth century, in particular the novels of Joyce, Woolf, Conrad, James, Gide, Proust, and Mann. And some ten years later Margaret Church's *Time and Reality: Studies in Contemporary Fiction* added to this list by discussions of such novelists as Kafka and Sartre and Faulkner.

Interestingly enough, neither book deals with the novels of D. H. Lawrence, and there are good reasons for such omission. In many ways, Lawrence was one of the wildest experimenters in twentieth-century fiction. As Walter Allen said some years ago, Lawrence and Joyce are still so way out that contemporary novelists have not yet caught up with them.[1] Yet although Lawrence certainly merits the title of a bull in the novel-shop,[2] in his treatment of time this bullish quality is curiously subdued. When contrasted with the chronological manipulations in the fiction of Conrad or Malcolm Lowry or Nabokov, Lawrence's novels seem merely conventional. Despite this seeming conventionality, Lawrence's treatment of time merits a closer look, especially as it can provide useful insights into an understanding of his two large-scaled masterpieces, *The Rainbow* and *Women in Love*.

In an essay of 1919 called "Poetry of the Present" Lawrence contrasts three different ways of viewing time as illustrated in the work of three poets. As an example of a past-oriented writer he cites Keats and his "Ode to a Nightingale," a poem in which "we hear the pause and the rich, piercing rhythm of recollection, the perfected past." As an example of the future-oriented writer he cites Shelley and his "To a Sky-Lark." "It seems when we hear a skylark singing as if sound were running forward into the future, running so fast and utterly without consideration, straight on into futurity." And finally, as an example of a writer who is present-oriented, he cites Whitman. Here no particular poem is specified, but Whitman's lines about the mockingbird, "Out of the Cradle," would serve to round out the sequence. Lawrence explains:

> But there is another kind of poetry: the poetry of that which is at hand: the poetry of the immediate present. . . . .It is not of the nature of reminiscence. It is not the past which we treasure in its perfection between our hands. Neither is it the crystal of the perfect future, into which we gaze. Its tide is neither the full, yearning flow of aspiration, nor the sweet, poignant ebb of remembrance and regret. . . . In [Whitman's] free verse we look for the insurgent naked throb of the instant moment. . . .Such is the rare new poetry. One realm we have never conquered: the pure present. One great mystery of time is terra incognita to us: the instant.

Obviously it is Whitman's view of time that happens to be favored in this particular essay, but I cite the passage here not for its praise of Whitman but because it can lead us on to consider the question of where Lawrence himself belongs in these three categories. The answers to this question are indeed various. For example, according to an article by Edward Alexander, "Lawrence's fictional spokesmen...are always celebrating the vital past at the expense of the decadent, sterile present."[3] Laurence Lerner makes a similar observation that Lawrence "is very fond of harking back to a happy past," and, in his view, "some of the sloppiest and most superficial writing" in the novels occurs when Lawrence celebrates a Golden Age of the past:

> The Golden Age is a lady of easy virtue: she will lie down with any author who enjoys denouncing the present, and her price in truthfulness is never high. Like any easy lay, she corrupts those who use her.[4]

And in a more gently censorious vein, the eminent critic, Father Ong, likewise argues that Lawrence's view of time is past-oriented, which to him is a somewhat deplorable lapse. According to Father Ong, urbanization eliminates the four seasons and the traditional round of day and night, and hence our writers ought to abandon the "old" cyclic sense of time. Our writers should abandon, that is, brooding over the past and recording the recurrences of man's experience--with loss of Eden and all our woe. Instead they should provide for us, he says, an awareness that "we live in an evolving universe";[5] our writers, in short, should be future-oriented.

For present purposes I do not want to quarrel with Father Ong's lively essay; I wish merely to note how he has classified Lawrence as a writer wedded to a sense of the past and devoid of a sense of future progress. If Lawrence is to be pinned down, like Prufrock, in a formulated phrase, it is odd that other critics have had the opposite impression of his treatment of time. Virginia Woolf, for example, says in her airy fashion: Lawrence "never looked back at the past." To her Lawrence was obsessed with a prophetic view of man's future. Joyce Carol Oates likewise comments: "it was that past, the pastness of the past, the burden of history and tradition that infuriated him." Lawrence's characters, according to Scott Sanders, "live almost exclusively in the present, because instincts are not subject to history."[6]

To speak loftily on one side or the other of this disputed area is a foolish exercise in righteousness for it is not difficult to pile up evidence from Lawrence's writings that seem to substantiate either side. This is because in his representations of past, present, and future, he draws on different assumptions about time. His handling of these three phases of experience accounts for one source of our difficulties in understanding *Women in Love* and *The Rainbow*; it resides in his gallantly ambitious attempt to portray the values of all three phases of time. His fictional world is one which sings, like Yeats's golden bird, "of what is past, or passing, or to come."

As J. T. Fraser notes in *The Voices of Time* (citing N. O. Brown): "Mankind's destiny, for Freud, as for St. Augustine, is 'a departure from and an effort to regain, paradise; but in between these two terms man is at war with himself.'"[7] Although Fraser makes no reference here to Lawrence, his statement is an apt description of the fictional world of that novelist.

II.

Let us begin with Time past.

What, in general, is the sense of time past that we get in a Lawrence novel? Does he agree with Carl Sandburg that the past is a bucket of ashes? Among several critics John Raleigh may be cited: "Joyce stands for history, Lawrence for futurity,"[8] and hence (according to Raleigh) Lawrence has little or no concern for the past. This is the kind of general statement that could be used as a final examination question on a novel course, but as a blanket in which to wrap up the present topic it is too full of holes as to be of use. Actually Lawrence was fascinated with history; indeed he was the author of an Oxford Press textbook: *Movements in European History*, (1921). In his novels he is constantly reminding us of past civilizations so that the actions of one generation can be highlighted by the experiences of earlier generations. Ursula, in *The Rainbow*, as a little girl, listens to the stories her grandmother Lydia tells of the old days, stories that became for her, Lawrence says a "sort of Bible":

> She clung to her grandmother. Here was peace and security. Here, from her grandmother's peaceful room, the door opened on to the greater space, the past, which was so big, that all it contained seemed tiny, loves and births and deaths

> . . .within a vast horizon. That was a great relief, to know the tiny importance of the individual, within the great past.

This "great past" (as Ursula calls it) can be viewed in both of Lawrence's novels as public time as well as private time (terms used by Jerome Buckley in his book *The Triumph of Time*, 1966). Public time involves us in history and myth; private time is the sense of time experienced by the individual characters such as memories of happenings in their earlier lives.

The issue of history and public time leads to the question of whether *The Rainbow* and *Women in Love* are historical novels. The ingredients are there, certainly for *The Rainbow* at least, and to read this novel as a contribution to an understanding of nineteenth-century social and economic history provides one perfectly legitimate framework for discussing it. We can concentrate, if we like, on Lawrence's impressive account of the shift in three generations from the traditional rhythms of farm life to the frenzied tempo of the modern industrial economy, with its mines, canals, railways, and even, at the end, its automobiles. In the opening chapter there are vivid accounts of this historical shift. The age-old rhythms of man's rural life, so gloriously described in the opening paragraphs-

> They felt the rush of the sap in spring, they knew the wave which cannot halt, but every year throws forward the seed to begetting, and falling back, leaves the young-born on the earth--

these traditional rhythms are juxtaposed with the new noises and smells of a progressively industrialized society, the coal mines and railways proliferating on the other side of the canal, and later in the industrial town called Wiggiston, a town that makes Dickens' Coketown seem almost idyllic by comparison.

Of this kind of social and economic history there are many reminders in *The Rainbow*, and the historic dimension is, of course, enhanced by the time-span covered. Sixty-five years of history, from 1840 to 1905, are there, with allusions to the Sudan or to the war in South Africa. Yet after having said this, one must nevertheless admit that history is of subordinate importance in *The Rainbow*. When we learn that Baron Skrebensky was appointed to his post as a clergyman by Mr. Gladstone we are apt to be brought up short. The historical fact is accurate enough, but somehow we had not thought of the Brangwens and Skrebenskys as inhabiting the same world as a Victorian Prime Minister, especially, perhaps, Mr. Gladstone.

The sense of the past provided by *The Rainbow* is something more than history--history as Lord Raglan defines it: "the recital in chronological sequence of events that are known to have occurred."[9] Man's past is of great significance in *The Rainbow*, but it is the past of legend or myth that is constantly being drawn upon and which affects our reading profoundly: stories of the Garden of Eden and the Fortunate Fall, stories of the Sleeping Beauty, stores of Noah and his ark, or of the powers of Pan or of a moon goddess, stories of a search for a Promised Land. The historic narrative of nineteenth-century life, with its precise clock-time and "chronological recital" is there in *The Rainbow*, but interwoven with it, and immeasurably enriching the texture, is the Once Upon a Time world of other pasts of mankind, a world that offers the reassurance of continuity through recurrence. Myths, in Thomas Mann's words, are "a renewal of the past in the present"[10] and, as such, can provide what Father Ong wittily calls a "time-shelter" in the modern world of threatening change.

So much for *The Rainbow* in this vein. What of *Women in Love* and time past, public time past that is?

The span of time in this later novel is, of course, drastically shrunk. The story of this quartet of lovers covers less than a year from the opening scenes of spring and summer in England to the winter scenes in the Tyrol, culminating in the icy death of Gerald Critch. And it is not only the short time span that reduces the historical elements; even more reductive is Lawrence's deliberate effort, as he indicates in his

Foreword for the novel, to eliminate historical references. One Prime Minister (Lloyd George) is mentioned in passing, and there is also one reference to the Kaiser, but in general Lawrence achieves his aim: "I should wish the time to remain unfixed," he says.

In my book on Lawrence the paradoxical argument is made that although the 1914-18 War is never mentioned in *Women in Love*, the novel is nevertheless one of the greatest war novels in our literature. What *Women in Love* embodies is an awesome record of the state of mind of wartime, its hates and loathings and despairings, a record of these rather than a history of trench warfare or zeppelin bomb raids.[11]

The impact of the 1914-18 War affects not only the treatment of history in *Women in Love* but also the treatment of myth and earlier histories. Most of the myths in this novel, unlike those in *The Rainbow*, are not time shelters to console us with reassuring recurrences. In this novel they are usually not time shelters but rather time bombs, ominously ticking away like Gudrun's clock, to remind us of doom in store for the modern equivalents of Sodom and Gomorrah, or the Greece of Thycydides, or the elegant cultures of ancient Africa. Reassurances from the past are still there in *Women in Love*--the happy union of lovers takes place first in Sherwood Forest, with all the associations that locale implies--yet the principal role of myth in this novel is apocalyptic, a point to which we can return later.

With regard to private time past, if we try to discover how the characters in these two novels view their own pasts, it is once again evident that there are marked differences between *The Rainbow* and *Women in Love*. I must remark here that I was startled, in preparing this essay, by how this topic makes one aware of these differences. Lawrence once proposed to his publisher that the two novels be brought out together as a single unit. Obviously his proposal had merit; the two novels have much in common and do make up a sequence. Yet when we consider how time is treated, one realizes that *The Rainbow* (1915) is predominantly a work of the prewar period whereas *Women in Love* (written in 1916, published in 1920) is infused with the bitter spirit of the war years.

One of the chief ingredients contributing to the bitter flavor of the later novel derives from the treatment of private time past. In this novel the characters are cut off from their own past or they themselves have elected to cut themselves off from it. About Birkin's past life, before *Women in Love* opens,we know almost nothing. Lawrence comments about him: "He moved about a great deal, his life seemed uncertain, without any definite rhythm, any organic meaning." And with Ursula in this novel it is not that her past is unknown but that she is resolved to repudiate it. "I'm sick of the beloved past" she exclaims when Birkin admires an antique chair of the age of Jane Austen, and her repudiation takes in the whole of her previous life. In one of the most bitter scenes in this bitter novel the Brangwen sisters return for a final visit to the vacant house in which they had lived as a family--the "little grey home in the west" as they sarcastically call it. Birkin arrives and asks them: "Are you both weeping over the past?" And Ursula replies yes that they are weeping, but "not weeping that it's gone, but weeping that it ever *was*." Later she prays that all memory of her past twenty-six years could be blotted out. "She felt that memory was a dirty trick played upon her. . . .What had she to do with parents and antecedents?" Ursula's repudiation may strike a familiar note in many households today, so familiar, in fact, that we may miss how symptomatic it is of the sick society portrayed in *Women in Love*.

*The Rainbow* is different in its representation of private time past and is more typical of Lawrence's usual practice. Here is a sentence from that novel which may give us a lead. It sets up a contrast between Ursula and her fellow-schoolteacher friend, Maggie Schofield:

> She [Ursula] was staunch for joy, for happiness, and permanency, in contrast with Maggie who was for sadness, and the inevitable passing-away of things.

What I shall try to work towards is to show that Ursula's kind of time sense (or time-senses) is the dominant one in this novel. Nevertheless Lawrence is aware of what

Maggie Schofield stands for. Much of the power of such novels as *Sons and Lovers* is generated by his view of his own past, and his poem *Piano* with its nostalgic tears for a lost childhood is in the vein of Dickens or Tennyson. What he called "the lovely accomplished past" of prewar England was also a lifetime reference point for him.

In *The Rainbow* there were several occasions when one of the characters is led to review the family's past or his or her own past. Such reviews usually occur at a moment of crisis, as for example, when Ursula is setting out to begin teaching school in the Ilkeston blackboard jungle:

> As she waited at the tram-terminus she reverted swiftly to her childhood; her teasing grandfather, with his fair beard and blue eyes, and his big monumental body . . . her grandmother, whom Ursula would sometimes say she had loved more than anyone else. . . .With a passion she clung to the past.

Ursula's creator himself had behaved similarly when war broke out in 1914; his letters of that period are full of evocations of the English past. Confronting disaster, one calls on one's predecessors for the reassurance of a sense of continuity. *The Rainbow,* with its story of three generations, provides many occasions for the novelist to remind us of recurring human situations, or variations on previous events. Especially moving is the scene in the barn when Tom Brangwen goes out on a rainy night and sees his daughter Anna with her young lover, Will Brangwen, in her arms, and he thinks back to "the child he had carried out at night into the barn, whilst his wife was in labour. . ." (one of the great scenes of this novel, one of the great scenes in fiction I think). Less poignant, but also memorable, is the scene of Anna's wedding, which is seen through her father's eyes. At forty-five Tom Brangwen cannot believe that he is participating in his daughter's wedding; he has a blurred sense of time, not all attributable to brandy, that gives him the illusion he is himself getting married again:

> He felt himself tiny, a little upright figure on a plain circled round with the immense, roaring sky: he and his wife, two little, upright figures walking across this plain. . . .When did it come to an end? Did one never get old, never die?

And knitting all three generations, there is the scene of Ursula's first kiss when she is walking back from the Marsh Farm to the Brangwen cottage with Skrebensky, and the author reminds us that the young lovers are walking under the same ash trees where her grandfather Tom had walked the night in March when he made his proposal to Lydia Lensky, with a bunch of daffodils clutched in his hand, and where her mother, Anna, had likewise gone with her young husband, Will Brangwen, "walking close upon him as Ursula was now walking upon Skrebensky."

This kind of knitting or counterpointing is a memorable ingredient of *The Rainbow*.[12] A sense of the past is an essential element in this novel. But to round out this problem of time past another passage needs to be cited, one which will lead on to something else.

When Tom Brangwen, the Noah-like patriarch, is drowned in a flood his body is brought to the cottage of his daughter, Anna, and Lawrence describes her response at this moment of crisis:

> When Anna Brangwen heard the news, she pressed back her head and rolled her eyes, as if something were reaching forward to bite at her throat. . . .Since she had married and become a mother, the girl she had been was forgotten. Now, the shock threatened to break in upon her and sweep away all her intervening life, make her a girl of eighteen again, loving her father. So she pressed back, away from the shock, she clung to her present life.

The passage is full of insights, but I do not want to pause over these. What is significant for our purposes here is the final sentence: "she clung to her present life." This is indeed what most of Lawrence's characters typically do. His *characters*, let me emphasize the word, cling to the present life. For them time past is important and they are shaped by it, but time present is more important, and also, for some of them as we shall see, time future is more important. The nostalgic experiences that are crucial in the lives of the characters in such retrospective novelists as Thackeray, Dickens, Proust, Faulkner, or Evelyn Waugh are less drawn upon by Lawrence.

To clinch this point a couple of lines from T. S. Eliot's *Four Quartets* can be cited, a poem that teems with reflections about the nature of time. In *East Coker* , the expatriate poet visits the village in England from which his ancestors had emigrated to America, and he speaks of how such an experience makes "the pattern" of dead and living a more complicated one:

> There is a time for evening under starlight,
> A time for evening under lamplight
> (The evening with the photograph album).

The evening under starlight connotes the intense experience of the present moment, the moment of love, the moment in the rose garden. The evening under lamplight connotes recollection. And in Eliot's terms, the characters in Lawrence's novels spend more of their evenings under the starlight, undergoing present experiences of love or hate, than they spend under the lamplight reviewing their pasts via the photograph album. The past is vitally essential in *The Rainbow*, but it is a public past experienced by the reader more than a private past experienced by the characters.

III.

About time-present, some philosophers of time remind us of the paradox that there is perhaps no such thing--that we are always in a state of flux between past and future.

The problem is a fascinating one but must be left dangling for now. For our purposes, a character who lives relatively heedless of the past and unconcerned about the future--who responds more or less contentedly to immediate day-to-day experience--is present-oriented. This kind of consciousness is characteristic of the generations of Brangwen farmers so vividly described in the memorable opening pages of *The Rainbow*. We encounter it again in Anna Brangwen when she settles down to breeding her big family of eight children.[13] Anna, Lawrence reminds us, was at this stage "for the immediate life of to-day." Her husband too, although his case is a more complex one, lives most of his life with a similar sense of time. There is at one point an interesting account of his going to London and his being led to reflect momentarily on past and future. Like Marlow in Conrad's *Heart of Darkness* Will Brangwen thinks back to a time when what is now London was a land of savages, and he reflects on how civilization has developed. But he realizes finally he has no vital concern for man's future status; reality for him is confined to the daily round of domestic life, his contacts with his wife and children. As Lawrence says: "It was as if now he existed in Eternity, let Time be what it might." In reality, of course, Will Brangwen is aging in time like all of us, but his instinct is to assume that he can stay in Eden, the timeless garden (and also the "thornless" garden as Tennyson calls it in *Maud*).

This, of course, he cannot achieve, nor can anyone inside or outside Lawrence's books. What can be achieved, however (and the two novels are full of this kind of experience), is the experience of moments when, in effect, time stands still.

Perhaps I am muddying the waters by introducing this crucially important experience under the heading of time-present, but I'll venture it. The ordinary heedless response to successive sensations in the present can, under special circumstances, be expanded to a point of intensity in which the present becomes, as we say, timeless. This, in Lawrence, is the Eternal Moment,[14] an experience analagous to what Robert Brumbaugh calls in an essay in this volume the Present Eternal.

And, as in Dickens, such moments are celebrated with a special kind of prose. Instead of the jabbing staccato style of many of Lawrence's pages, these moments call from him a lushly elaborated style, insistently rhythmical and glowing with color.

What is more noteworthy, however, are the differences from Dickens. Dickens and his contemporaries usually celebrate such moments as they occurred in the past.[15] What we get from the Victorians is, if not emotion recollected in tranquility, at least emotion recollected. Lawrence's moment is a present moment. Here is his account of Will and Anna on their honeymoon at Cossethay. Outside their bedroom, as the chapter continues to remind us, there is a clock on the church tower whose chimes sound the hours, but in the timeless present of the lovers, the sounds do not register:

> Inside the room was a great steadiness, a core of living eternity. Only far outside, at the rim, went on the noise and the destruction. Here at the centre the great wheel was motionless, centered upon itself. Here was a poised, unflawed stillness that was beyond time, because it remained the same, inexhaustible, unchanging, unexhausted. As they lay close together, complete and beyond the touch of time or change, it was as if they were at the very centre of all the slow wheeling of space and the rapid agitation of life, deep, deep inside them all, at the centre where there is utter radiance, and eternal being, and the silence absorbed in praise: the steady core of all movements, the unawakened sleep of all wakefulness. They found themselves there, and they lay still, in each other's arms; for their moment they were at the heart of eternity, whilst time roared far off, for ever far off, towards the rim.

And again: "It was even irritating the way the church clock kept on chiming: there seemed no space between the hours, just a moment, golden and still, whilst she traced his features with her finger-tips, utterly careless and happy, and he loved her to do it."

The Eternal Moment, when the clocks stand momentarily still, is induced by different clusters of experiences in Lawrence's novels. Most commonly it is induced by the physical contacts of lovers--the preliminary stage of the kiss or by the act of consummation itself. The courtship of Anna's parents in which Tom Brangwen literally passes into oblivion after his first kiss with Lydia, would illustrate this experience, as likewise would some of the scenes between the third generation of lovers, scenes in which, as Lawrence says, the partners let themselves "go from past and future" and enter "the eternal, changeless place into which they had leapt together."

In *Women in Love* the tender love scenes in which Birkin and Ursula are transfigured by an embrace have a similar effect, although there are fewer references to the timeless quality of the experience. What *Women in Love* does to reinforce for us the quality of the Eternal Moment is to provide scenes portraying what is, in effect, the opposite experience, when the clocks do not stand still but, instead, impose their incessant presence upon the consciousness of a character. The result, in its most intense form, is the obverse of a transfiguration; it is a kind of nightmare. And this is appropriate for the world of *Women in Love*.

The economic historian Carlo Cipolla, in his book on clocks, notes that although man has always lived in time and had devices to measure it, the clock is a relatively modern invention, and its widespread availability for precise measurement obviously has had a profound effect on our consciousness.[16] Availability of clocks and watches imposes city time everywhere, replacing rural time with its changing rhythms of seasons and sunsets. J. B. Priestley in his book on time comments with amusement how businessmen in America like to take vacations in the wilderness, roughing it round a campfire where they are achieving a purge of modernity by living like our ancestors, but what spoils the whole experiment are the watches they carry on their wrists.[17] In some utopias such as Rabelais' abbey or Butler's Erewhon, clocks are forbidden, but *Women in Love* is very distinctly not a utopia, and clocks are very much in evidence. They are associated, in particular, with Gudrun Brangwen,[18] that fascinating and luscious decadent whom Lawrence portrays as the embodiment of modern consciousness.

I cited earlier the honeymoon scene in *The Rainbow* in which the lovers blot out from their bedroom the sound of the nearby church clock. In *Women in Love* the first bedroom encounter between Gudrun and Gerald Critch also features the sounds of a nearby clock but with a marked difference. After their first coming together Gerald falls asleep, sleeping "as if time were one moment, unchanging, unmoving." But Gudrun remains wide awake, listening to the clock striking, and acutely conscious of being relentlessly carried forward in time. In later scenes she once more is obsessed with clocks. In her cottage in England Gudrun has a clock with one of those painted faces that "wagged with the most ridiculous ogle when the clock ticked and back again with the same absurd glad-eye at the next tick." The clock affects her with a "maddened disgust." But it is at the end of the novel that Gudrun's clock-madness is fully portrayed. Hating life as she does, the thought of time passing drives her to a frenzy so intense that she imagines her hair will have turned white by the following morning. This scene of her soliloquy has been praised, and rightly praised, by F. R. Leavis:[19]

> The thought of the mechanical succession of day following day, day following day, *ad infinitum*, was one of the things that made her heart palpitate with a real approach of madness. The terrible bondage of this tick-tack of time, this twitching of the hands of the clock, this eternal repetition of hours and days--oh God, it was too awful to contemplate. And there was no escape from it, no escape . . . .
> Oh, how she suffered, lying there alone, confronted by the terrible clock, with its eternal tick-tack. All life, all life resolved itself into this: tick-tack, tick-tack, tick-tack; then the striking of the hour; then the tick-tack, tick-tack, and the twitching of the clock fingers. . . . There she was, placed before the clock-face of life. And if she turned round as in a railway station, to look at the book-stall, still she could see, with her very spine, she could see the clock, always the great white clock-face. In

> vain she fluttered the leaves of books . . . . She knew she was not *really* reading. . . .She was watching the fingers twitch across the eternal, mechanical, monotonous clock-face of time.[20]

But let us return from Gudrun's chamber of horrors to the more positive experiences of the Eternal Moment. In addition to the experiences of love there is a second cluster of experiences which induce an almost identical sense of timeless present moment, a "transfiguration." This is associated with religion, or, more specifically, with religious buildings and art. A character's response to a cathedral may resemble a kind of sexual consummation, a linking that may shock some readers but one that is crucial to our understanding of the baffling cathedral scene in *The Rainbow*. The account of the interior of Lincoln Cathedral, as seen by Will Brangwen, is almost identical with the passage describing the bedroom at Cossethay, already cited:

> Here the very first dawn was breaking, the very last sunset sinking, and the immemorial darkness, whereof life's day would blossom and fall away again, re-echoed peace and profound immemorial silence.
>
> Away from time, always outside of time! Between east and west, between dawn and sunset, the church lay like a seed in silence, dark before germination, silenced after death. Containing birth and death, potential with all the noise and transition of life, the cathedral remained hushed, a great involved seed, whereof the flower would be radiant life inconceivable, but whose beginning and whose end were the circle of silence.

In addition to love and religious experiences, there is a third set of circumstances which also induce the timeless moment. These involve a sort of resurrection rather than a transfiguration, a painful experience of shedding, a dying into life, as in the opening section of Lawrence's late story *The Man Who Died* with its account of Christ's awakening in the tomb. Ursula's soul-shattering encounter with the horses, near the end of *The Rainbow*, includes this analysis:

> As she sat there, spent, *time and flux of change* passed away from her, she lay as if unconscious upon the bed of the stream, like a stone, unconscious, unchanging, unchangeable, whilst everything *rolled by* in transience, leaving her there, a stone at rest. (Italics mine)

First of all to be noted here is a fascinating bit of counterpointing, for the adjectives used to describe Ursula's state of timeless obliteration ("unconscious, unchanging, unchangeable") are virtually identical with the adjectives used to describe the timeless state experienced by her parents during their honeymoon--a passage previously cited--"inexhaustible, unchanging, unexhausted." Noteworthy, also, is the image of the stone in the midst of the river of time, which may remind us of James Joyce's Anna Livia--an effective figure for a complicated experience, but an experience here made more complicated when the stone is metamorphosed into an acorn, an acorn which will put forth shoots and revert to the world of time and organic growth, the world of time-future, that is.

Finally, so far as time-present is concerned, the obliteration of the clock can sometimes be induced by an intense response to a scene of natural beauty--a hillside of wild-flowers in the spring, or a sunset, moments which are celebrated by some of the most effective and characteristic passages in Lawrence's writings.

For example, here is a seascape scene, and one that provides a convenient bridge from the topic of time-present to time-future. It occurs near the end of *The Rainbow* when Ursula, in her early twenties, is on a summer holiday with her family and is moved to tears by the sight of the ocean:

> She stood and looked out over the shining sea. It was very beautiful to her. The tears rose hot in her heart. Out of the far, far space there drifted slowly in to her a passionate, unborn yearning. "There are so many dawns that have not yet risen." It seemed as if, from over the edge of the sea, all the unrisen dawns were appealing to her, all her unborn soul was crying for the unrisen dawns. As she sat looking out at the tender sea, with its lovely swift glimmer, the sob rose in her breast, till she caught her lip suddenly under her teeth, and the tears were forcing themselves from her. And in her very sob, she laughed. Why did she cry? She did not want to cry. It was so beautiful that she laughed. It was so beautiful that she cried.

It is fascinating to contrast this passage with the celebrated lyric, "Tears, Idle Tears," as sung in Tennyson's poem *The Princess*, by the nostalgic Maggie-Schofield-kind-of girl (whose name is Violet).

> Tears, idle tears, I know not what they mean.
> Tears from the depths of some divine despair
> Rise to the heart, and gather to the eyes
> In looking on the happy autumn fields
> And thinking of the days that are no more.
> Fresh as the first beam glittering on a sail,
> That brings our friends up from the underworld,
> Sad as the last which reddens over one
> That sinks with all we love below the verge;
> So sad, so fresh, the days that are no more.

In both passages, a beautiful scene prompts seemingly inexplicable tears to rise in a girl's eyes, but the difference remains a striking one. In Tennyson, the tears derive from a yearning for past experiences--the risen dawns now lost (the days that are no more). In Lawrence they derive from a yearning for future experiences--"the unrisen dawns."

Much of the complexity and difficulty of *The Rainbow* and *Women in Love* is attributable, I think, to Lawrence's having endowed his heroine with this strong sense of unrisen dawns, of time-future, a sense that is in conflict with his celebration of time-present and time-past. As a prophet and reformer of society, he must show his leading characters moving out of the present-oriented Eden into the world of flux, pilgrims who will lead mankind to a future Promised Land as symbolized by the rainbow arch of the final chapter of that novel.

It should be noted that in this prophetic vein, Lawrence's pictures of time-future are of two strikingly contrasting varieties. In *Women in Love*, with some qualifications to be noted in a moment, time-future is generally represented apocalyptically; we are confronted with an awesome vision of the coming doom of mankind. In its predecessor, *The Rainbow*, the vision of the future, towards which Ursula yearns, is, contrariwise, utopian rather than apocalyptic. The goal may be vaguely identified, but the urge toward it, as represented by Ursula in the final scenes of the book, is powerful and driving. This is what Lawrence meant, I think, when he said in a letter of 1917 (after his novel was written but not yet published), that *Women in Love* is "purely destructive, not like *The Rainbow*, destructive-consummating." Thus in the earlier novel, Ursula moves from the still center at the hub of the wheel out to the rim in which time revolves. After her encounter with the horses, she laboriously climbs a hill and decides what her role must be; it is: "to create a new knowledge of Eternity in the flux of time."

I must say quite humbly that I am not sure what Ursula means or what Lawrence meant, but I am sure that whatever it is, it is prophetic. And the prophetic future-oriented note persists into *Women in Love* as well, although here it is considerably muted. Birkin sees our century as the end of some "world-cycle" but adds: "There is now to come the new day, when we are beings each of us, fulfilled in difference." The older

Ursula, too, remains future-oriented.[21] For her, Lawrence, notes, "the sense of an unrealised world ahead triumphed over everything"--a sense opposite to her sister's gloomy view of the future. Thus when Birkin, himself, in a gloomy mood, predicts the end for present mankind as a final one, Ursula will not buy it. Like T. S. Eliot in the *Quartets*, Birkin plays on the famous saying of Mary Queen of Scots: "If we are the end," he says, "we are not the beginning." Ursula disagrees: "Yes we are," she said. "The beginning comes out of the end."

This prophetic and future-oriented vein in Lawrence's writings has been much admired,[22] and as I have tried to show in passing, it is responsible for much of the dramatic tensions of his best novels. These dramatic tensions are also evident in his letters as well as in his novels. As David Cavitch's *D. H. Lawrence and the New World* (1969) has stressed, at the time Lawrence wrote these two novels he was passionately concerned with the possibility of founding a Utopian colony in Florida which might serve as a model for the future of a war-torn and sick mankind. There is a letter of 1915 which illustrated Cavitch's point as well as mine. The letter was written to Koteliansky after Lawrence had made a Christmas visit to his family of relatives in Derbyshire:

> We are here with all my people--very nice: but it is painful to go back so into the past. One's people are the past, pure without mitigation. And it is so hard to get to the future: one must create the future. That is why we go to Florida: a new life, a new beginning: the inception of a new epoch.[23]

This letter is, of course, in the same vein as the final sections of *The Rainbow*, which call for a "new dawn" of a "new day"--a Shelley-like future-oriented prophecy which some of his readers find not only strident but incongruous.

We encounter it again in his lively essay, "Surgery for the Novel--or a Bomb" where he loudly proclaims his preference for time-future.

"*What next?* That's what interests me. *What now* is no fun anymore." However much fun the prophetic strain may be, and however admirable and functional it is, I'd nevertheless contend that his most effective writing was not inspired by this dipping into the future far as human eye can see, but by his celebration of present moments, a celebration that may feature a suspension of time. Curiously enough, these celebrations--these epiphanies (to use Joyce's overworked term)--in which clock-time is suspended, derive their force from this novelist's uncomplaining awareness of the passing of time. From early boyhood, Lawrence lived, like Keats, with a sense that he would die young (that he lasted to 45 would have astonished his mother had she herself lived).[24] The effect of this awareness on his appreciation of present moments can be epitomized in two lines from one of his favorite hymns, which he learned as a child. Addressing God, he prays:

> Teach me to live each day
> As 'twere my last.

NOTES

1. See Walter Allen, *The English Novel* (New York, 1957, p. 439, and in *New York Times Book Review* (September 5, 1965), pp. 4, 25.

2. George H. Ford, *Dickens and his Readers* (Princeton, 1955), p. 254.

3. Edward Alexander, "Thomas Carlyle and D. H. Lawrence." *University of Toronto Quarterly* (April, 1968), p. 256.

4. Laurence Lerner, *The Truthtellers*(London, 1967), p. 193.

5. Walter J. Ong, "Evolution, Myth, and Poetic Vision." *Comparative Literature Studies* (1966), 1-20. Ong's distinction is essentially between writers who believe in progress (he cites Tennyson, not altogether aptly, as an example), who view time as "linear," and those writers who believe that the past repeats itself in the present, that there is no true progress, and who view time hence as "cyclic." As examples of the latter attitudes he cites Yeats, Lawrence, and Joyce. Yeats's view of time, Ong says, is "spectacularly and desperately anti-evolutionary." --On the historical background of these two concepts of time, see G. J. Whitrow's observation that in the mediaeval period "the linear concept was fostered by the mercantile class and the rise of a money economy." "The cyclic", on the other hand, was reinforced by "ownership of land," for to the landowner "time was felt to be plentiful and associated with the unchanging cycle of the soil. With the circulation of money, however, the emphasis was on mobility." --Whitrow, "Reflections on the History of the Concept of Time." *The Study of Time*,ed. J. T. Fraser, *et. al.*, (Berlin, 1972), p. 7.

6. Scott Sanders, *D. H. Lawrence* (London, 1973), p. 101. See also Oates, *New Heaven and Earth* (New York, 1974), p. 39.

7. J. T. Fraser, *The Voices of Time* (New York, 1966), p. 254.

8. John Raleigh, in *Partisan Review* (1958), p. 260.

9. Lord Raglan, *The Hero* (New York, 1956), p. 4 -- cited by Claire Rosenfield, *Paradise of Snakes* (Chicago, 1967), p. 31.

10. See Rosenfield, p. 31

11. See G. H. Ford, *Double Measure: A Study of the Novels and Stories of D. H. Lawrence* (New York, 1965), ch. 8.

12. In *Women in Love* there are occasionally scenes of the same sort, most memorably when the lovers visit the inn at Southwell Minister: "Father came here with mother," Ursula remarks (ch. 23).

13. For a useful analysis of how Lawrence employs the present tense in *The Rainbow* see Roger Sale's article in Colin Clarke's Casebook, *The Rainbow and Women in Love* (London, 1969), 104-08.

14. For a discussion of the phrase as used by Lawrence, see Oates, pp. 50-51. Browning's poetry, of course, may also be cited, as when the speaker in "The Last Ride Together" reflects: "What if we still rode on, we two/ With life forever old yet new, / Changed not in kind but in degree, / The instant made eternity." --See also "The Experience of Timelessness," a discussion of ecstacy in the dance, the forest, and the bower, by J. T. Fraser in his *Of Time, Passion and Knowledge* (New York, 1975), 305-11. Fraser's account of the dance could be effectively illustrated by Lawrence's fine essay, "The Dance of the Sprouting Corn" in *Mornings in Mexico* (1927), and also by the sheaves-gathering scene in *The Rainbow* (ch. 4).

15. See G. H. Ford, "Dickens and the Voices of Time," *Dickens Centennial Essays*, ed. Ada Nisbet and Blake Nevius (Berkeley, 1971), 46-66.

16. Carlo M. Cipolla, *Clocks and Culture: 1300-1700* (London, 1967), p. 105.

17. See J. B. Priestley, *Man and Time* (New York, 1968), p. 20.

18. Ursula also suffers sometimes from a despair that her life has been pointless (chapter 15), but the experience, for her, is transient.

19. F. R. Leavis, *D. H. Lawrence: Novelist* (London, 1955), pp. 173-174.

20. On the general effects of tick-tock, see Frank Kermode, *The Sense of an Ending* (New York, 1967), 44-46.

21. Cf. Gudrun and Loerke who "never talked of the future." (Ch. 30).

22. See James R. Baker, "Lawrence as Prophetic Poet." *Journal of Modern Literature* (July, 1974), 1219-38.

23. *The Quest for Rananim*, ed. George J. Zytaruk (Montreal, 1970), p. 61. --For a useful discussion of prophetic writing, *Heilsgeschichte* (salvation history), see J. T. Fraser, *Of Time, Passion, and Knowledge*, pp. 21-11; 368-78.

24. See Ford, *Double Measure*, p. 97.

*DISCUSSION AND COMMENT*

A. A. Mendilow

In his sensitive and highly perceptive paper, Professor Ford analyses Lawrence's artistic exploitation of time, and shows how he applied in *practice* the multiple aspects of some of the three tenses; in particular, Ford dwells on the timeless quality of one form of the present--the "Eternal Moment". I would like to complement this approach by taking up Lawrence's *theory* of the multiple aspects of the present. During the period of the First World War which, he believed, foretold a major shift in the culture patterns of the Western world, he worked not only on his saga of the Brangwens but concurrently on his "theory of being" or "metaphysic". The connection of the two is clear: the novels give body to the doctrine, and the doctrine illuminates the characters, their relationships, and the discussions on religion, art, sex and society which abound in the novels, themes which he saw as different facets of a single *Weltanschauung*. Briefly, the metaphysic resolves itself into a dialectical tension between two universal forces which promotes the eternal process of creation; these he calls "male" and "female". The two forces confront each other, are momentarily reconciled and interfuse, and then separate back into distinctiveness. To each he attributes specific characteristics, images and symbols. The female force is represented by God the Father, the male by God the Son, and the "Reconciler" of the two by the Holy Ghost. The instant of fusion, if and when it comes, is the impregnating moment of "mystic conjunction", and it constitutes "the immediate present, the Now". It is "the moment of perfect being", "the eternal moment of Truth". Much of the "theory of being" is devoted to the exploration of the nature and function of the present, of which five broad types may be distinguished: two experiential--one empty and one filled; two mystical or timeless--one empty and one filled; and the fifth--the timeless present of art which is the revelation and communication of "the living moment".

1) The empty, quantifiable "tick-tack" present. It is unprogressive, convention-ridden, and backward-looking. Those who live in this kind of present are "servants of

necessity, repeating old experience". They are like "regulation cabbages" and are "rotting at the core for lack of power to run into blossom".

2) The value-filled present which allows "the full achievement of the self"; "we lean on the sill of all the unknown" "at the extreme tip of life", prepared for "the fall into the future".

3) The timeless present of "excess" which is "the thing itself at its maximum of being". This is the supreme moment of consummation and creativity, when the female force "starting from her stable eternality" of the past meets and fuses with the male force of "movement and time and change" thrusting toward a millenial future. The two eternalities of past and future are equally "partial" and "relative", however, but the moment of "permanent union in opposition" is "absolute, timeless, beyond time or eternity, beyond space or infinity". It constitutes "the Timelessness into which are assumed the two Eternities". But the mystic moment cannot last, and "we, who are temporal and eternal, at moments only we cease from our temporality".

4) The empty timeless present, when the separation that must follow the moment of fusion is denied and the two protagonists seek artifically "to prolong the moment of consummation". The result is "only the geometric abstraction of the moment of consummation, a moment made timeless. And this conception of a long, clinched timeless embrace, this overwhelming conception of timeless consummation, has arrested the Italian race for three centuries." The corollary is that "whenever art or any expression becomes perfect, it becomes a lie. For it is only perfect by reason of abstraction from the context by which and in which it exists as truth." The sin is, therefore, to try "to tie a knot in Time...The error of errors is to try to keep heaven fixed and rocking like a boat within the flux of time"; all it creates is a "stony nullity", and "its very aspect of timelessness is a fraud."

5) Only through art can we hold on to the moment of creative ecstasy and gain the illusion of timelessness. Art is expressed through a concrete medium which has existence in time; but "matter is a very slow flux, the waves ebbing slowly apart. So we engrave the beloved image on the slow, slow wave...This is art,

> this transferring to a slow flux the form that was attained at the maximum of confluence between the two quick waves. This is art, the revelation of a pure, an absolute relation between the two eternities." Its function is to be like the Holy Spirit, the Reconciler of the two opposing forces of the past and the future in "the living moment".

A few days before his death, Lawrence wrote of Eric Gill, in an unfinished review, that he was not "a born thinker, in the reasoning and argumentative sense of the word". Neither was Lawrence himself. But the structure of his thinking is clear; it affords a comprehensive, if at times not easily comprehensible or coherent, picture of his universe. His "metaphysic" may not be that of a philosopher, but as Keats insisted: "Axioms in philosophy are not axioms until they are proved upon our pulses." Lawrence proclaimed they could be proved on the plexus and the ganglia. But his real proof is in his writing. In the Preface to his *New Poems* (1920), describing his "poetry of the sheer present", he referred to "the pure present" as "the great mystery of time". In his "metaphysic" he tried to solve the mystery, and in his novels to apply his solutions.

NOTES

All the quotations are from the doctrinal essays, the *Study of Thomas Hardy* (1914), *The Crown* (1915), *Love* (1917), and *The Two Principles* (1919).

# The Changing Iconography of Father Time

S. Macey

*ABSTRACT*

*Though Saturn-Cronus, as Panofsky suggested in 1939, is the single most important influence on the Father Time of the Western World, the two have been very differently represented. They seem to have little more than age in common, and this impression is strengthened when we consider their natures. The accretions and metamorphoses -- as benevolence, nudity, forelock, wings, hourglass, and scythe -- which gave to Saturn the symbols that we have come to associate with Father Time are traced through a number of works including the illustrators of Petrarch, the emblem books, and Hogarth.*

*The change that we are tracing is from a Saturn who had castrated his father and devoured his own children -- the saturnine and even malevolent patron of cripples and criminals -- to a Father Time who by the sixteenth century was frequently depicted as the benevolent father of Truth. Among other developments, Father Time, who had earlier taken over the symbols of Death, stands back aghast from him by the time of Quarles' Hieroglyphikes (1638). In Hogarth's last work Tailpiece, or the Bathos (1764), Time -- now more sinned against than sinning --* expires *surrounded by his broken symbols.*

*Though Father Time did not die (Cupid and he are the only characters from the old emblem books that survive), he is today a very different figure from that depicted in the earlier illustrations. The main purpose of my essay has been to delineate the changing iconography of Father Time, while a subsidiary purpose has been to relate this to important developments in technology and society.*

## 1. INTRODUCTION: FATHER TIME'S ASSOCIATION WITH THE MALEVOLENT SATURN-CRONUS

There have been remarkable changes in the iconography of Father Time during the past millennium. My purpose is to examine these changes and to suggest some explanations for them. Though, as Panofsky indicated in 1939,[1] Saturn-Cronus is the single most important influence on the Father Time of the Western World, Saturn-Cronus and Father Time have been very differently represented. An examination of those differences will help us to understand important recent changes in our attitudes to life and time.

For me, the most memorable figure of Time in the modern period is Hogarth's *Tail-piece, or the Bathos* (1764) as depicted in Fig. 7. Like Pope's *Dunciad*, it is Hogarth's farewell to his times. Both are works in which Time ceases to exist -- a modern Armageddon in which the forces of evil have prevailed. They lack even the modified optimism of Dryden's *Secular Masque* (1700) when his Janus and Chronos respectively closed with the lines: "'T is well an old age is out: / And time to begin a new." In Hogarth's engraving, a dying Father Time -- his scythe and hourglass broken -- exhales his last breath, reclining naked against a broken pillar. If we take by comparison a first-century Saturn to be found on a Pompeian mural (Fig. 1), we shall quickly see how much has changed. It is not merely that Saturn's primitive sickle has become Hogarth's two handed scythe. Saturn is a malevolent-looking figure with a good crop of hair and clothed in a toga, whereas Hogarth's Time is a naked, unhappy, winged, dying creature, with a single forelock that is symbolic of the "Opportunity" mankind seems never to have been capable of grasping.

It appears at first that Saturn and the modern Father Time have little more than age in common, and this impression is increased when we consider their natures. Saturn,

*Figure 1. Saturn. Pompeian mural, after 63 A.D. Museo Nationale, Naples.*

until at least the fifteenth century, was the patron of cripples and criminals, a god who had castrated his father and who, Panofsky thinks, often walked on crutches by way of implying similar wounds that he had received from Jupiter.[2] Worse still, Saturn-Cronus was the devourer of his own offspring.[3] Father Time, too, was occasionally represented both on crutches and as a child-eater during the course of his iconographic development from the illustrators of Petrarch's *Triumph of Time* through to the early seventeenth century (Fig. 2 is a late example). Indeed Hogarth himself, in a conscious return to historic iconography, produced a horrifying picture of Time in his *Emblematical Print on the South Sea Bubble* (1721).[4] Most of us, of course, know Goya's even more monstrous painting *Cronus Devouring his Children*. But it is symptomatic of the change which had taken place that Goya's audience would not readily identify so malevolent a Cronus with the new iconography of Father Time.

## 2. THE SYMBOLS ASSOCIATED WITH FATHER TIME

Before we can consider the early iconography of Father Time himself -- as he appears in the many illustrations to Petrarch's *Triumph of Time* -- let us review briefly those accretions and metamorphoses which gave to Saturn the symbols that we now associate with Father Time. We shall look first at the sickle of Saturn-Cronus. This was an agricultural implement, but one which Hesiod tells us that Gaia frist made from steel (or adamant) and with which her son Cronus "harvested his father's genitals."[5] It seems very likely that the symbolic parallel between harvesting and death was made in classical times. We know further that, despite the etymological difference, Cronus, the father of gods, was identified with Chronos, the personification of time, by Plutarch if not earlier.[6]

The change from sickle to scythe reflects a development in technology. Singer suggests that the sickle is the earliest known agricultural implement. It was used at least 8,000 years ago by the Mesolithic Natufians of Palestine, of whom it is uncertain whether they sowed seed to supplement the wild grasses which they gleaned with their sickles.[7] The development of the scythe came later. Michael Partridge says that

*Figure 2. Fr Perrier, Time the Destroyer, 1638.*

"the Romans used a one-handed instrument with the blade set at right angles to the handle. This was probably the earliest form of scythe. By the Middle Ages...hay was mown with an instrument very similar to the modern scythe in that it consisted of a long, slightly curved iron blade attached to the end of a pole that stood nearly as high as the user."[8] (In medieval times hay was a common allegory for worldly values.) The technological change to which Partridge alludes is reflected in the changing size and design of the scythe used by Saturn, Death, and Time.[9] Partridge's statement that "in many areas the scythe totally replaced the sickle during the nineteenth century" also reflects a technological development which resulted eventually in the sickles of Saturn and Death being almost entirely replaced by scythes.

Like the scythe, Time's hourglass provides a symbol that is directly related to technological change. But in this case the symbol would seem to be radically new. Panofsky notes that the image of Time produced by the illustrators of Petrarch's *Triumphs* "was frequently emphasized by an hourglass, which seems to make its first appearance in this new cycle of illustrations."[10] What seems not to have been noted is that sand-glasses probably did not appear earlier because they did not exist earlier. Drover's article in *Antiquarian Horology* (1960) demonstrates that there is no definite proof of sand-glasses having existed before the fourteenth century.[11]

It would appear that the hourglass -- like all the other attributes of Father Time with which we have been thus far concerned -- was first associated with other allegorical and historical figures. The earliest known example of a sand-glass (it is illustrated in Drover's article) would seem to be the one held by Temperance in a fresco at Siena (1338) by Ambrosio Lorenzetti. Later, some of the first illustrations of clocks are shown in the hands of Temperance,[12] and she seems also to be carrying an hourglass in the "Temperance" of *The Virtues* by Cornelis Massys (1509-1584). Other early allegorical figures carrying the hourglass are Death, to whom we shall be referring later; the *Melancholia* of Dürer (1514) and of H. S. Beham (1539); the later *Truth with the Attributes of Time* of Daniel Meisner (1637); and the three identical emblems of Occasio (or Opportunity) used with different verses by Friedrichs (1617),

Oraeus (1619), and Meisch (1661).[13] Significantly, Occasio (unlike Time) had already appeared in the first emblem book. This work by Alciati -- which went into ninety editions in the sixteenth century alone after being first published in 1531 -- also contains two Deaths and several blind Cupids, but the early editions seem to have neither Father Time nor hourglasses.[14]

From Occasio, who became conflated with Fortune,[15] Father Time seems to have taken the forelock, just as he took the wings on the back and feet from Kairos, the classical figure who signified the turning point in existence through scales balanced on a knife edge.[16]

It would seem that the new characteristics that Father Time assumed did not carry the sort of opprobrium that might be associated with the less attractive side of Saturn-Cronus. Indeed early engravings of the hourglass show it not only with the Virtues, but with historical figures of undoubted propriety. Among these we may mention Dürer's two *St Jeromes* (1511 and 1514), Signorelli's *St Augustine* (1519, National Gallery, London, *Predella panel*), and Fabrian's particularly fine *St Jerome in his Study* (Baltimore, Walters Art Gallery, signed and dated 1451).

Unlike the scythe, the hourglass, the forelock, and the wings, not all the attributes with which Father Time was associated have remained a part of his iconography. Inevitably, as the clock became more popular, it was occasionally incorporated into the iconography of Time. In a woodcut of *Time* from Stephen Hawes' *Pastime of Pleasure* (1509), he is carrying a foliot clock and what seems to be the sword of Justice. (G. A. Gilio also shows *Time with the Scourge of Justice;* she was, as we shall see, one of the three sisters of Time's daughter Truth.)[17] Father Time is surely also standing on the foliot of a clock in Sellaio's *Triumph of Time*, though Panofsky takes it to be a sundial.[18] Time wears a clock in his head, rather like a mitre, in *Time turning Fortune's Wheel* (before 1454), the earliest known Spanish copper-plate.[19] In Corrozet's emblem book *Hecaton-graphie* (1543), a winged Time with wings and wheels on his feet, as well as a balance in his hand, is reminiscent of Kairos.[20] Like Saturn[21] or Aion[22] before him, Father Time was also sometimes associated with the dragon or snake with its tail in its mouth, symbolizing eternity or a cyclic concept of time.[23] But neither the older snake with the tail in its mouth nor the newer clocks developed into the standard iconography of Father Time.

Perhaps the hourglass came to supplement the scythe so well in the iconography of time because in a secularizing world -- a world which was to witness Hogarth's death of Time -- man began to visualize his existence less and less in terms of eternity. Unlike the snake with its tail in its mouth (or the clock whose spring could not be seen to run down), the hourglass offered a very dramatic symbol of time coming to an end insofar as the individual mortal was concerned. Vaughan questions those who ignore eternal values as symbolized by the ring in "I saw eternity the other night" (1650), but the essential difference between the emblem of Time and the emblem of Eternity is set out much more simply in Bunyan's *Book for Boys and Girls* (1686), at the close of the two great centuries of emblem books and the allegorical modes of throught that emblems imply:

UPON TIME AND ETERNITY

Eternity is like unto a Ring.
Time, like to Measure, doth it self extend;
Measure commences, is a finite thing.
The Ring has no beginning, middle, end.

## 3. FATHER TIME'S EARLY RELATIONSHIP WITH THE ICONOGRAPHY OF DEATH

For the Christian -- particularly the Christian during the Medieval and Renaissance periods -- death was the gateway to eternal life. During that period, the iconography of Death and the memento mori message in which he was involved overlapped to a very considerable extent with the iconography of Time. Moreover, Death seems to have been the figure that one met by far the more frequently of the two. Unlike Time, Death, with his sickle, had a relatively respectable background in Christian allegory.

Revelation 14. 13-20 provides just such an image of Death "having on his head a golden crown, and in his hand a sharp sickle...and he...thrust in his sickle on the earth; and the earth was reaped."

Gertrud Schiller in her book on the *Iconography of Christian Art* says that not until the eleventh century were personifications of life and death sporadically included among the symbols used to interpret Christ's death on the Cross. The symbols were used to illustrate Christ's defeat of death. In the example that she gives of a manuscript illumination from the first quarter of the eleventh century, Life and a fully-clothed Death are at the foot of the cross; the lance of Death has snapped, and the broken sickle slips from his hand.[24]

After the middle of the fourteenth century, Christian representations of Death were no longer sporadic; they had become legion. By the process known in rhetoric as synecdoche -- a representative part standing for the whole -- Death at the foot of the cross is represented again and again by a skull.[25] As with Saturn, Death's sickle seems to be transformed into an increasingly modern scythe. In the *Death on Horseback* of Giovanni de Paolo (documented 1326-1360), Death, apart from the fact that he has no horns, looks remarkably like the black and hairy devil in Paolo's *Detail from the Last Judgement*.[26] In an *Expulsion from Paradise* (1485), Death with his scythe has become virtually a skeleton.[27]

Rosenfeld, in *Der mittelalterliche Totentanz*, sees the Papal Bull of 1336 as influencing the introduction of the Dance of Death, because it debased the meaning of Judgement Day and made way for individual redemption.[28] Whatever the reason, the Totentanz became a widespread phenomenon north of the Alps, whose pictorial evolution reached its culminating point with Hans Holbein's celebrated drawings published at Lyons in 1538. In the Totentanz, Death is frequently shown with the hourglass.[29]

Transi tombs (in which a horrifying sculpture of the body in the course of physical disintegration was often placed beneath a body idealized in all its worldly pomp) appeared in Northern Europe during the same period, beginning in the latter part of the fourteenth century. Kathleen Cohen feels that the calm faces and ideal beauty of most thirteenth- and fourteenth-century European tomb figures clearly expressed confidence in God's mercy and salvation, whereas the later transi tombs reflect tensions and fears caused by the Black Death, contemporary memento mori imagery, the accumulation of great wealth, and the attempt to humiliate the body in order to gain salvation.[30] Because of its relevance to the period when Death will become less gruesomely displayed, and when Father Time will tend to separate and stand back aghast from him, it is worth noting the statistics regarding the transi tombs that Cohen documents. She found only 5 from the fourteenth century, 75 from the fifteenth, no less that 155 from the sixteenth, a mere 29 by the seventeenth, and by the eighteenth century transi tombs as such had essentially disappeared.[31] Such gruesome depictions would undoubtedly be hard to reconcile with an increasing secularism, with the growth of eighteenth-century sentiment, and with eighteenth-century optimism in the best of all possible worlds.

In Bernini's Tomb of Alexander VII at St Peter's in Rome (1671-1678), Death, his head hidden by a coverlet, shakes his hourglass in the direction of Truth, the beautiful daughter of Time. Her naked beauty had provided an even more strikingly idealized contrast before Innocent XI caused her to be covered by a metal garment painted white. While this is not a transi timb, the imagery demonstrates how closely interwoven are the developments thus far discussed which related to Time and Death.[32]

Behind Bernini's figure of Death shaking his hourglass at the allegorical figure of Truth lies a long tradition of Death appearing unexpectedly with his hourglass to surprise people in the middle of living. This goes back at least to Dürer's *Death and the Lansquenet* (1510) and is given deeper meaning in his *Knight, Death and Devil* (1513). The last four of Aldegrever's eight plates on the *Power of Death* (1541) show Death shaking his hourglass at a Pope, a Cardinal, a Bishop, and an Abbot respectively. What seems to be lacking in such people, with the possible exception of Dürer's Knight, is a readiness to overcome Death by being prepared for a Christian salvation.[33]

Just as Death at the foot of the Cross became reduced to a skull by the process of synecdoche, so did Death with the hourglass become the skull with the hourglass. B. Beham's *Child with Three Skulls* (1529) is a good example.[34] Though the early editions of Alciati's *Emblematum Liber* (1531) do not seem to have included an hourglass at all, the hourglass (like the skull) quickly became one of the favourite images of the emblem writers during the rest of the sixteenth and seventeenth centuries.[35]

When Death met his victims, his grinning skull suggested the pleasure of victory. But there were exceptions. For the most part -- as in Donne's "Death be not proud" (*Holy Sonnets*) -- the counterforce is provided by Religion's promise of eternal life. Baltens and de Oude both have paintings of *Religion Triumphing over Death*; in Cecill's *The Christian Knight* (1628), Truth, Faith, and the Spirit are clearly putting Death with his scythe and hourglass out of countenance. A somewhat more secular conquest of Death is provided by Fame when the blast from her trumpet almost makes him drop his scythe in a French sixteenth-century miniature.[36] Death is conquered by History (often a substitute for Time) in Elstrack's "Triumph of History over Death and Oblivion" that provides the title page for Raleigh's *History of the World* (1614).

In summarizing what has been discussed so far, we can say that until the seventeenth century Time and Death often shared very similar allegorical functions, that Time was less often represented than Death, and that neither the scythe nor the hourglass was exclusively associated with Time

## 4. PETRARCH'S TRIUMPH OF TIME: THE SEPARATION FROM DEATH

It is really not until the fifteenth century and the beginning of the widespread illustrations for Petrarch's *Triumphs* that the modern Father Time began to have a recognizable iconographic existence which could be separated from Death. In the series of six Triumphs, Love is conquered by Chastity, Chastity by Death, Death by Fame, Fame by Time, and Time by Eternity. No theme, outside the cycles of Old and New Testament story, gave more frequent employment to artists and craftsmen. About the

*Figure 3. The Triumph of Time, ca. 1470-75, possibly by Filippo Lippi.*

second quarter of the fifteenth century the scheme and character of such designs became curiously fixed and uniform, within certain narrow limits of variation.[37] In two very fine engravings, possibly by Filippo Lippi about 1470-75, Death carries the scythe and drives his or her buffaloes over human bodies, while Father Time (See Fig. 3) is a winged old man on crutches flanked by two hourglasses, and pulled along by two stags.[38] These look for all the world like reindeer taking him and his accompanying multitude over a desolate waste-land. Similarly, in each of the four different Triumphs shown by Panofsky as well as the one shown by Iwasaki, the triumphal chariot of Time is drawn across a desolate wintry landscape by two stags. But Father Time is not yet ready to be conflated with Father Christmas. Valgrisi's *Triumph* (1560) still shows Father Time eating a child, and the illustrations of Petrarch's *Triumph* emphasize Time's saturnine appearance corresponding to the poet's verbal description of Time's "despotic reign" and "malignant hands."

Peter Breughel's *Triumph of Time* (1574), reproduced on the opening page of J. T. Fraser's *The Voices of Time* (see Fig. 4), clearly relates to this tradition. Although Breughel is also making a statement of his own, Father Time is still a malevolent

*Figure 4. Pieter Breughel, The Triumph of Time, 1574.*

child-eating Saturn. He carries the sign of eternity in his hands, unaware perhaps of the contradiction between this symbol and that of finite time represented by the enormous hourglass on which he sits and the clock above his head. When one considers the powerful malevolence in this image of Saturn-Cronus, it is hard to believe that in less than two hundred years Hogarth's Father Time will be a passive and sad old man expiring among his broken symbols. Indeed, the second state of Breughel's *Triumph of Time*, published in the same year, emphasizes the power of Time through the added message: "Tempus Omnia et Singula Consumens."[39] In Breughel's work, Time or Saturn is followed by a very bedraggled-looking Death with the scythe, over whose head Fame blasts away on the trumpet.

## 5. TIME AS THE FATHER OF TRUTH: A MORE POSITIVE CONNOTATION IN THE SIXTEENTH CENTURY

The modern Father Time, like the classical Saturn, reflected the paradox that time both consumes and brings to fruition. During the sixteenth century, just when Time was being portrayed as the most malevolent of creatures in paintings like Breughel's, he was also developing a quite different reputation as the father of Truth. Samuel Chew, in *The Virtues Reconciled*, has shown that from the eleventh century there developed an important allegory in which Truth and Justice, Peace and Mercy were widely represented as the daughters of God.[40] F. Saxl, in his essay "Veritas Filia Temporis," had earlier demonstrated that Time too had a claim to the paternity of Truth,[41] who, according to Democritus, lay at the bottom of a deep well. Despite the implied sacrilege in the conflicting claims to Truth's paternity,[42] Time's claim held good; this was probably because it was so useful an allegory in the conflict between Protestant and Catholic. As Samuel Chew points out, though Protestants during the reign of Edward VI declared that papists had locked truth in a cage, "no sooner had Mary Tudor come to the throne than she took *Veritas Filia Temporis* for her motto. Again, on the accession of Queen Elizabeth the Time-Truth allegory was promptly turned to the services of Protestant propaganda, and it remained in that service."[43]

As early as 1535, *Truth the Daughter of Time* appeared in William Marshall's *Goodly Prymer in Englyshe* (Fig. 5). In this simple woodcut, a winged and naked Time actually

Math. x.
Nothyng is couered, that shall not be discouered.
And nothyng is hydde, that shall not be reueled.

*Figure 5. Truth, the daughter of Time.*
*Woodcut in W. Marshall, Goodly Prymer, 1535.*

smiles as he draws his naked daughter out of a cave or well, while Hypocrisy tries in vain to interfere.[44] One of the mottoes reads: "Tyme reveleth all thynges." Time is here depicted iconographically only by his age, beard, and wings on back and heels. In the woodcut *Veritas Filia Temporis* (Venice, 1536),[45] a similarly benevolent and naked Time -- on this occasion with wings and hourglass -- draws up Truth with Calumnia trying to prevent him. In 1539 (only eight years after Alciati's first emblem book), La Perrière has an emblem in which Democritus shows a naked and winged Time with a scythe where his daughter Truth is hidden in a well.[46] The *Emblemata* (1565) of Junius has a naked and winged Time with a scythe drawing his daughter Truth out of a well to the consternation of Envy, Strife, and Slander. The same emblem was used by Whitney in his *Choice of Emblemes* (1586), the first English emblem book. Here, too, Time appears as a benevolent and protective father of Truth as he does in Bronzino's *Vindication of Innocence* and his *Exposure of Luxury* (1546).[47] What Father Time is exposing in the latter work is Cupid in a rather questionable pose with his mother, Venus. Only Time and Cupid were effectively to survive the reaction against allegory that took place in the third quarter of the seventeenth century. The reaction against allegory can in part be ascribed both to the scientific revolution and to neoclassicism. There is, however, the irony that the scientific revolution was related to ideas of progress and militated against the former conviction that there existed an absolute truth.

There can be little doubt that in the sixteenth century Time's role as a revealer of truth did much to enhance his image. We still find him working in this capacity during the seventeenth century in England. In the title page to *Truth Brought to Light* (1651), dealing with the reign of James I, Time and Truth each draw aside a curtain that reveals the dead king. While his daughter tramples on Error, Time -- with scythe in hand and clock on chest -- smiles as he tramples on Death.[48] In the broadside *A Cloak for Knavery*, a Puritan Father Time -- with forelock, wings, and hourglass -- whips off the cloak of Religion from a gentleman whose multifarious crimes include dissimulation and fornication. Truth no longer needs to be present or even named. She is implicit in the rubric: "Religion worn out, under which was hid much iniquity now in time is discovered."[49] By 1589, Horozco, in his *Emblemas Morales*, could show such a transformed Father Time arranging a marriage of his child with the child of the virtue Moderation or Temperance.[50]

## 6. TIME'S RELATIONSHIP WITH TECHNOLOGICAL CHANGE IN THE SEVENTEENTH CENTURY

It is difficult to give any precise reason why Time should have become iconographically transformed in this way, but there may well be some connection with the concurrent interest in horology spurred on by the needs of astronomy and navigation. We have now arrived at the period of Galileo and the Cartesian mechanistic philosophy, which was to lead directly into the British horological revolution of Restoration England. Then God himself became a watchmaker, and one of the most celebrated debates revolved around the question of whether his universe was a Newtonian or Leibnizian clock.

There would seem to be a direct relationship between technological change and references to time in literature. In Shakespeare and the metaphysical poets, there are extensive references to time as well as numerous horological images. Quinones points out that "in the early 1590's a spate of English works appeared with time as a vital concern,"[51] and this may be related to the statement in Britten's *Old Clocks and Watches* that "No English watch is known of a date before 1580 and only a short time before this is there any record of an English watchmaker."[52]

In the case of the hourglass and the scythe it was technology that seems to have changed the iconography of Father Time. The change in his personality is not as easily explained, but the coincidence of Time's relationship with Truth in the sixteenth century seems to have contributed to a radical change of the manner in which he was depicted. This is by no means to imply that Father Time had altogether become a jovial Father Christmas. But by the early seventeenth century, we do at least find him prominently displayed on title pages with no obviously pejorative connotations.[53] Men, of course, continued to worry about the effects of time. In the title page to

Francis Bacon's *History of Life and Death with Observations...for the prolonging of Life* (1638), the iconography demonstrates that Art can slow Time's decay. As previously with Death, a synecdoche frequently takes place in the iconography, and a winged clock or hourglass represents Father Time (just as a skull or a skull and hourglass represent Death).[54]

## 7. THE INCREASING ESTIMATION OF TIME IN SIXTEENTH AND SEVENTEENTH CENTURY EMBLEM BOOKS

While both Time and Death tend to become less harshly represented during the seventeenth century, Time is the milder of the two figures. We see this when Time takes over the duties of Death. Typical examples occur in *Age, guided by Time, leaves behind the treasures of the world* -- a woodcut that appears in the *Emblemata* of Sambucus (1564) and Whitney's *Choice of Emblemes* (1586) -- or in the *Woman Sleeping, trying to hold Time back, who is fleeing from her* by de Oude (1565-1637). The extent to which Time is taking over the role previously assigned to Death is demonstrated by Otto Van Veen's *Horati Flacci Emblemata* (1607). Of van Veen's 101 emblems, eleven deal with the dangers of impending death. That two employ images of Death and six employ images of Time to convey the message suggests the increasing use of Time for this important allegory. It is perhaps in part because they did not start publishing until 1586 that the English emblem writers demonstrate significant developments in the treatment of Time.

At first, three leading English emblem writers -- Whitney, Wither, and Quarles -- used the printing blocks of the continental authors and engravers. Whitney's *Choice of Emblemes* (Leyden 1586) is a selection of continental emblems for an audience many of whom were already familiar with the genre. Whitney shows no skeletons and the only skull is in his penultimate emblem. Perhaps more to our purpose, he uses the fewest emblems of Time among the leading English emblem writers. On page 4, he gives *Veritas Temporis Filia* (from Junius 1565), and on Page 199, he shows *Age guided by Time leaving behind the treasures of the world* (from Sambucus 1564) with the advice that people "use their goodes whilst that they may, for time apace doth speede." For the last emblem he has chosen a setting sun with the rubric "Tempus omnia terminat."[55] In addition to the two emblems of Time with his scythe, Whitney shows only one hourglass with the injunction: "spende no idle hower..../For losse of time, all other loss exceedes" (p. 172).

George Wither's *Emblemes* (1635) reflect a greater attention to Time. Wither uses the de Passe engravings from Rollenhagen (1611-1613). Not only do eight of the two hundred emblems contain hourglasses, but each of the four title pages repeats the same emblem of a winged skull over a scythe crossed with a bone. Above this is an hourglass surmounted by what looks like the foliot of a clock. The four title-page emblems suggest that time is a central theme of the work, and indeed at least twelve of the emblems refer directly to the subject of time.

The question of attention to Time in Quarles' *Emblemes* (1635) is more complex. Quarles' volume is divided into five books of fifteen emblems each. The last three books employ the emblems of Hugo's *Pia Desideria* (1624), of which no less than forty-two Latin editions had been published by 1757. *Pia Desideria* evolved from erotic emblem books concerning the adventures of Cupid. Amor and Anima now became a boy and a girl whose adventures suggest a religious-erotic relationship between the winged child Jesus and the human soul. The continental Amor and Anima books had been produced essentially for a Catholic audience,[56] but Quarles composed quite different verses for Bolswert's particularly attractive engravings. His book was by far the most popular emblem book in England, and numerous editions with new engravings were published until late in the nineteenth century. Bolswert's engravings in the 1635 edition misleadingly suggest that Quarles was far less interested in Time that was Wither in the same year. Father time, with scythe and hourglass, appears in two emblems, I.ix, and III.xv. The only other iconographic reference to time is the sundial to which Anima points (III.xiii) and says to Amor: "Are not my dayes few?...let me...bewayle me a little." Though one is naturally aware of death (in fact Anima seems more and more to welcome it as the book progresses), its iconography is far less gruesome than in the preceding centuries. The only skeleton provides a memorable portrayal of poor Anima imprisoned inside the left portion of its thorax (V.viii).

I have collated with the 1635 edition of Quarles an edition of 1885 which has a completely different set of highly ornate Victorian engravings dated 1860. Quarles' original text is of course retained. The Victorian illustrator nowhere depicts Father Time, but only his symbols.[57] There are, however, far more allusions to time than in Bolswert's engravings, and these make the reader more sensitive to the importance of that topic in Quarles' original text. I.i illustrates, for example, the story of the Serpent and Eve, using a winged hourlgass ingeniously constructed of two bones and a pair of skulls placed chin to chin. In I.ix, Father Time has been replaced by a scythe and a winged hourglass. The white wing represents day and the black wing represents night. In II.v, a watch carried in the hand provides a topical representation of Vanitas. For the new engraving of III.xiii, the artist has done his best to illustrate such mixed horological metaphors as: "my glass is half unspent," "The secret wheels of hurrying time," and my "Total's but from eight to four." He provides respectively a winged hourglass, a clock at five minutes past noon, and a sundial showing 4 p.m.[58] The Victorian illustrator replaces the Father Time of III.xv by a winged hourglass composed of two worlds. The hourglass has, instead of posts, sticks surmounted by fool's-caps. A second hourglass lies below on its side with one end broken, reflecting Anima's desire to "dissolve/These fleshy fetters." The new emblem at IV.viii depicts a butterfly (Anima) with the hours of a clock marked around the edge of its opened wings; the rear edge of each wing points respectively to IV and VIII o'clock. The last two stanzas of the related verses -- though they do not have the quality of Shakespeare or the Metaphysical poets -- demonstrate that Quarles (1592-1644) was their contemporary in his use of the clock as a metaphor:[59]

My soul's a clock, whose wheels (for want of use
And winding up, being subject to th' abuse
  of eating rust,) want vigour to fulfill
  Her Twelve hours' task, and show her Maker's skill,
But idly sleeps unmov'd, and standeth vainly still.

Great GOD, it is thy work, and therefore good,
If thou be pleased to cleanse it with thy blood,
  And wind it up with thy soul-moving keys,
  Her busy wheels shall serve thee all her days;
Her hand shall point thy pow'r, her hammer strike thy praise.

The epigram that follows continues in the same vein:

Look not, my watch, being once repair'd, to stand
Expecting motion from thy Maker's hand.
He's wound thee up, and cleans'd thy clogs with blood:
If now thy wheels stand still, thou are not good.

Quarles followed the success of the *Emblemes* (1635) with a shorter work of only fifteen emblems on a theme unified around the candle which appears in each engraving. *Hieroglyphikes* (1638)[60] was later normally published as the sixth book of Quarles' *Emblemes*. There is no known source for the plates of *Hieroglyphikes*, and even the poetry is less obviously derivative. It is therefore significant that this work deals even more directly with Time. Moreover, it juxtaposes Time and Death in a manner which makes Time appear the more benevolent of the two.

Quarles' Hierogliph VI (sic) shows Time -- with wings, forelock, and glass -- standing beneath a sundial (Fig. 6). His right arm is holding back the arm of Death who is carrying his traditional dart and is about to snuff out the candle. In the text, Death says to Time: "Surcease thy pleading, and enlarge my hand." Time replies: "Great Prince of darkness..../What needst thou snatch at noone, what will be thine at night?" There is a great deal more in this vein, and we learn that though Death has the executive power it is Time who can "bid, When." But Time's benevolence towards man is surely further underlined by the fact that though he says it is noon, the sundial in the emblem seems to be pointing to 4 p.m. The epigram advises the reader: "Wouldst thou live long? Keepe *Time* in high esteeme." Hierogliph IX plays with a clock metaphor

Figure 6. Francis Quarles, "Hieroglyph VI," Hieroglyphikes, 1638.

on the theme of "Our life's a Clocke." In fact, Hierogliphs IX-XV represent the seven ages of man. The candle burns down one seventh in each succeeding hierogliph as "The swift-foot Post of Time" runs through a further stage of life.

Though Descartes was the first major thinker to incorporate the clock analogy into a complete philosophical system, in the later seventeenth and earlier eighteenth century, this metaphor was used by virtually every major philosopher and a host of major and minor writers in every field.[61] Father Time's star was therefore in the ascendancy, but emblem literature certainly was not. Rosemary Freeman, in *English Emblem Books*, relates this to the decline of allegory as a mode of thought, adding that by the time of the Restoration was it dismissed altogether as a needless obscurity.[62] Ironically -- as R. F. Jones brilliantly demonstrated in the 1930s -- during the third quarter of the seventeenth century, the very science which was contributing to Father Time's ascendancy made its greatest onslaught on all unnecessary figures of speech.[63] In any event, only Father Time and Cupid seem fully to have survived the attack on allegorical figures.

## 8. FATHER TIME IN THE EIGHTEENTH CENTURY: A PATHETIC GOD

Two passages in Swift can be readily adduced as evidence that Time still remained an emblem in the consciousness of Englishmen. In *Tale of a Tub* (1704), Swift says that "the Writers of and for GRUB-STREET, have in these latter Ages...nobly triumph'd over *Time*; have clipt his Wings, pared his Nails, filed his Teeth, turn'd back his Hour-Glass, blunted his Scythe, and drawn the Hob-Nails out of his Shoes." Twenty years later, when he was writing his *Gulliver's Travels*, Swift's birthday verses to Stella say "That *Time* sits with his Scythe to mow/Where erst sate *Cupid* with his Bow." It is unlikely that even in fun he would have spoken in this vein to Stella about a Time who retained the pejorative attributes of the Saturn-Cronus about whom we spoke earlier.

If one were to choose three works of Pope that represent his philosophy regarding man and society, they would I think be the *Moral Essays*, the *Essay on Man*, and Book Four of *The Dunciad*. In each of the three, an image of time is used to illustrate Pope's crucial concept. In the *Moral Essays* (as in the *Essay on Man*), Pope feels that the key to understanding both men and women involves an insight into each person's Ruling Passion. He says in *Moral Essay* I: "Time that on all things lays his lenient hand/Yet tames not this [the Ruling Passion]; it sticks to our last sand." (The adjective "lenient" for Time's hand is worth noting.) In *Essay on Man* II (lines 52-80), Pope takes as his image the escapement in a mechanical clock. He tells us that "Two Principles in human nature reign;/Self-love, to urge, and Reason, to restrain"; and he compares self-love to the "spring of motion" in a watch, and Reason to the "comparing balance" in the escapement.

*Dunciad* IV (1742-43) is Pope's final work. It is a work of overwhelming pessimism in which the greatest poet of his time describes a social Armageddon with frightening immediacy. In a secularly oriented age, Pope considers the end of his world to be the result of a contagion started by Grub Street writers,[64] but now spreading to all levels of society. He envisages nothing less than the end to Time through a reversal of the image in the opening passage of Genesis. What we have said earlier about Truth as the daughter of Time highlights the emblem which he shares with his readers:

> *Art* after *Art* goes out, and all is Night.
> See skulking *Truth* to her old cavern fled,
> Mountains of Casuistry heaped o'er her head!
> ........................................
> Thy hand, great Anarch! Lets the curtain fall;
> And universal Darkness buries All.

It is no coincidence that twenty years later Hogarth left a similar final statement. In *Tailpiece, or the Bathos* (Fig. 7), Father Time, more sinned against than sinning, dies surrounded by the broken artifacts that have represented his iconography through the ages. The sub-title *The Bathos or Manner of Sinking in Sublime Paintings* links this with Pope's *Peri Bathous: or the Art of Sinking in Poetry*, a work of Pope that

*Figure 7. William Hogarth, Tailpiece, or the Bathos, 1764.*

is directly related to *The Dunciad*. A further link is that in 1727 (a year before the publication of *Peri Bathous*), Hogarth had himself published *Masquerade Ticket* (Fig. 8), which was already interpreted in the eighteenth century as involving "a metaphorical view of a Prelate killing time [Father Time on the far left] at a masquerade."[65]

*Figure 8. William Hogarth, The Masquerade Ticket, 1727.*

The Augustan age was the age in which men tended to be involved with social rather than metaphysical values. In practice if not always in theory, they were more openly concerned with how one used a finite number of years upon earth for their own sake. Since Father Time appeared somewhat more secular than Death even during the dark days of the Renaissance it seems a little hard that the greatest poet and the greatest painter of the age should have felt the need to bury him even metaphorically during the so-called period of the Enlightenment. Both men, and Pope in particular, killed Time because they were disgusted with the values of their age. The Augustan reaction against poor taste in art and poor ethics in life was an aristocratic reaction against what Dryden called "the dregs of a democracy," against the very modernism of which we are the direct heirs.

## 9. CONCLUSION: NEW ROLES FOR A MORE BENEVOLENT FATHER TIME

But Father Time did not die. He never thrived more than in the years that followed. Suitably packaged -- with his nails pared and his scythe blunted -- he has become one of the standard adjuncts of modernism. To this day, not only does Father Time continue to appear in New Year celebrations and New Year cards (as Cupid does on Valentine cards), but terms like "sic transit gloria mundi" or "tempus fugit" are to be found ubiquitously on clocks or elsewhere with or without an emblem of the old gentleman. (Fig. 9 shows us what a kindly fellow Father Time could be in the Victorian era.) An even more widespread manifestation of Father Time, though it is beyond the scope of this paper, is the conflation between Saturn and St Nicholas which has given us Christmas and New Year in the sense that we now understand them.[66]

Changing funeral customs seem to have eliminated Father Time from churchyard memorials, and may soon eliminate gravestones altogether. Burgess -- dealing with an earlier age in *English Churchyard Memorials* -- has documented the direct relationship between the emblem books (particularly Quarles' *Hieroglyphikes*) and a long tradition of churchyard imagery related to Father Time that continued right into the nineteenth century. He notes in particular those allegorical figures in which "Time sprung aghast from Death."[67]

*Figure 9. Cruickshank's illustrations for a Victorian edition of Quarles: Johann Abricht [Jonathan Birch], Devine Emblems, London, 1838.*

In conclusion, I have demonstrated the remarkable change in the iconography of Time, and perhaps particularly in the relationship between Time and Death. One can, of course, only speculate on the various reasons for this change, which are by their nature closely interconnected. I have already referred to Time's relationship with Truth in the sixteenth century and with advances in clockmaking in the seventeenth century. Other reasons for the change in the iconography of Father Time may include the lengthening of life expectancy both for ourselves and for the world as we know it, and also the changes in religious emphases, which are themselves related to technological change.

Whittick, in *Symbols, Signs and their Meanings*, says of the hourglass that "It was a common symbol in the eighteenth century and was frequently introduced on tablets and gravestones, but it is rarely seen on stones after the early years of the nineteenth century." Like the scythe and the skull, he thinks that "It is inappropriate on the Christian memorial as, beyond ignoring the fundamental Christian consideration of a future life, it implies that life ends with its material manifestation."[68]

Implicit in Whittick's view is surely the fact that the memento mori no longer operates as it did in the Renaissance and Medieval periods. Most of us are not using our finite years on earth in order to prepare for an infinite life hereafter. The emblem of Father Time is still a potent one, but over the centuries it seems to have undergone a subtle metamorphosis. Today, Father Time still warns us that time flies, that our glass will run out, and that our harvest will be cut down. But though we may protest to the contrary the lesson that we are most likely to infer is that we should make the best possible use of our time on earth, precisely because we do not know what will come hereafter.

NOTES

1. Erwin Panofsky, *Studies in Iconology* (New York: Harper & Row, 1962), pp. 73f. I am particularly grateful to Professor Adam Mendelow for a number of helpful suggestions related to this paper.

2. Ibid., pp. 78, and 79n. See also Jean de Meun, *The Romance of the Rose*, trans. Charles Dahlberg (Princeton, N.J.: Princeton University Press, 1971), p. 113 (lines 5534ff.).

3. For children of Saturn who were cripples and criminals see Soji Iwasaki's *The Sword and the Word: Shakespeare's Tragic Sense of Time* (Tokyo: Shinozaki Shorin Press, 1973), Figs. 3 and 27, or Panofsky, Fig. 48; for Saturn as a castrator see Vasari's *Mutilation of Uranus by Cronus* (Palazzo Vecchio, Florence); for Saturn as a child-eater see Iwasaki, Fig. 5, or Panofsky, Figs. 46 and 47.

4. Panofsky, Figs. 56, 57, and 60. For the "Emblematical Print," see Rev. John Trusler's *Works of Hogarth* (London: E. T. Brain, n.d.), facing p. 173. In 1766 Trusler was employed by Hogarth's wife, Jane, to write explanations of the prints. For the much less pejorative ways in which Hogarth (and his father-in-law Thornhill) normally portrayed Time, see Ronald Paulson, *Hogarth: His Life, Art and Times* (New Haven and London: Yale University Press, 1971), Plates 33, 35, 58, 151b, 178, 230a, 274, 287, 313a and 313b.

5. Hesiod, *Theogeny*, trans. Dorothea Wender (Harmondsworth: Penguin, 1973), pp. 28-29; *Theogony* 147-208.

6. For the early identification of Chronos with Cronus see under "Chronos" in W. H. Roscher, *Ausführliches Lexikon der Griechischen und Römischen Mythologie* (Leipzig: Teubner, 1884-1890), Vol. I.

7. Charles Singer and others, ed., *A History of Technology* (New York and London: Oxford University Press, 1954), I. 501-503, 513-514, and 520.

8. Michael Partridge, *Farm Tools Through the Ages* (Reading, Berkshire: Osprey, 1973), pp. 134-135.

9. Compare Panofsky, Fig. 13 (Saturn); Giovanni di Paolo (documented 1326-1360), *Miniature: Death on Horseback* in Bernard Berenson, *Italian Pictures of the Renaissance* (London and New York: Phaidon, 1968), II, Fig. 613; and any modern depiction of the scythe used by Father Time.

10. Panofsky, pp. 80 and 73.

11. C. B. Drover, "Sand-Glass 'Sand,'" *Antiquarian Horology*, 3 (June 1960), 62-67. Under "Sand-Uhr," Zedler's *Grosses Vollständiges Universal-Lexikon* (Leipzig, 1742) says: "Die Alten haben an statt des Sandes Wasser gebraucht...and das Wasser hierzu aus einem besondern Fluss schöpfen, weil es keiner Fäulniss oder Veränderung unterworffen." I have not found this supported by later historians, but Junius in Emblem No. 5 of *Emblemata* (1565) refers to an hourglass as a "clepsydra" or water clock.

12. Drover, p. 67. See also F.A.B. Ward, *Time Measurement* (London: H. M. Stationary Office, 1966), pp. 7-8 (Item 21).

13. Gottfried Kirchner, *Fortuna in Dichtung und Emblematik des Barock* (Stuttgart: Metzlersche Verlagsbuchhandlung, 1970), pp. 25-27; Abbildungen 6-8.

14. I have examined a French edition of 1536, and facsimiles of the Augsburg (1531), Paris (1534), and Venice (1546) editions. Death appears first in the Paris edition of 1534 (pp. 69 and 70).

15. Kirchner, pp. 25-33.

16. Panofsky, pp. 71-72; and Roscher, "Kairos."

17. Panofsky, Fig. 51; Samuel C. Chew, *The Virtues Reconciled* (Toronto: University of Toronto Press, 1947), Fig. 13. Justice was a daughter of Zeus (see Roscher under "Dike"). After the eleventh century, Truth, Justice, Peace, and Mercy were widely represented as the four daughters of God (Chew, pp. 35-37).

18. Panofsky, pp. 80-81, and Fig. 55.

19. Iwasaki, Fig. 12.

20. Roscher, "Kairos."

21. Panofsky, Fig. 13.

22. Roscher, "Aion."

23. Panofsky, Fig. 60.

24. Gertrud Schiller, *Iconography of Christian Art*, trans. Janet Seligman (London: Lund Humphries, 1972), II, 114-115, and Fig. 385.

25. *Christ on the Cross* (1510) by Lucas van Leyden is a typical example.

26. Berenson, II, Figs. 613, and 612.

27. Iwasaki, Fig. 26.

28. Hellmut Rosenfeld, *Der Mittelalterliche Totentanz*, 2nd edn. (Cologne: Böhlau, 1968), pp. 44-45.

29. See Holbein's "The Child," "The Queen," or "The Emperor," in Holbein's *Dance of Death* (1538); "The Dance of Death," Woodcut in John Lydgate, *The Daunce of Machabree* (London, 1554); or Claesz', *Death Dance* (7 plates, 1562) in F. W. H. Hollstein, *Dutch and Flemish Etchings Engravings and Woodcuts ca. 1450-1700* (Amsterdam: Menno Hertzberger, n.d.).

30. Kathleen Cohen, *Metamorphosis of a Death Symbol: The Transi Tomb in the Late Middle Ages and the Renaissance* (Berkeley: University of California Press, 1973), pp. 1 and 4.

31. Cohen, p. 194.

32. Ibid., p. 185, and Fig. 121; Erwin Panofsky, *Tomb Sculpture* (New York: Abrams, n.d.), p. 95. For an interesting comment of Truth, naked and clothed, see Adam A. Mendilow, "Tennyson's World-Picture and 'The Riddling of the Bards,'" *Scripta Hierosolymitana*, XXV (1973), 145-146.

33. F. W. H. Holstein, *German Engravings Etchings and Woodcuts ca. 1400-1700* (Amsterdam: Menno Hertzberger, n.d.); see also the paintings of de Gheyn and de Oude in which Death stands behind an old man and an old woman respectively presenting money to young people (Hollstein's *Dutch Engravings*). As far as I know, De Gheyn's *Two Misers Surprised by Death* is the only case where a clock is used in this situation.

34. Hollstein, *German Engravings*.

35. Arthur Henkel and Albrecht Schöne, ed., *Emblemata: Handbuch zur Sinnbildkunst des XVI. und XVII. Jahrhunderts* (Stuttgart: Metzlersche Verlagsbuchhandlung, 1967), pp. 997-1000.

36. Hollstein, *Dutch Engravings;* Iwasaki, Figs. 34 and 29.

37. Francesco Petrarch, *The Triumphs* (London: John Murray, 1906), Mr. Colvin's Notes upon the Engravings.

38. Ibid. For a discussion of Death as a woman in Petrarch and elsewhere see Adolphe Napoleon Didron, *Christian Iconography*, trans. E. J. Millington (New York: Ungar, 1965), II, 156ff.

39. Hollstein, *Dutch Engravings*.

40. Chew, pp. 35-37.

41. F. Saxl, "Veritas Filia Temporis," *Philosophy and History: Essays Presented to Ernst Cassirer* ed. R. Klibansky and H. J. Paton (New York: Harper & Row, [1963]), pp. 197-222; see also Donald Gordon, "Veritas Filia Temporis," *Journal of the Warburg and Courtauld Institutes*, 3 (1939-40), 228-240.

42. Chew, pp. 54 and 69.

43. Ibid., pp. 69-70.

44. Edward Hodnett, *English Woodcuts 1480-1535* (Oxford: The University Press, 1973), John Byddell, No. 2013.

45. Iwasaki, Fig. 46.

46. Guillaume de la Perrière, *Le Théatre des bons engins* (1539), No. 48.

47. Panofsky, *Iconology*, Figs. 61 and 66, also pp. 83-84 and notes; Iwasaki, Figs. 48 and 51, also p. 180.

48. Margery Corbett and Michael Norton, *Engraving in England in the Sixteenth and Seventeenth Centuries* (Cambridge: The University Press, 1955), II, Plate 214.

49. Ibid., III, Plate 210. (Vol. III was published in 1964).

50. Horozco, *Emblemas Morales* (1589), No. 40.

51. Ricardo J. Quinones, *The Renaissance Discovery of Time* (Cambridge, Mass.: Harvard University Press, 1972), p. 297.

52. Cecil Clutton and others, *Britten's Old Clocks and Watches and their Makers*, 8th edn. (New York: Dutton, 1973), p. 43.

53. Corbett and Norton, *Engraving in England*, II, Plates 118 and 162; III, Plate 44.

54. La Perrière, No. 71; Covarrubias Orozco, *Emblemas Morales* (1610), No. 42.

55. Geffrey Whitney, *A Choice of Emblemes and other Devises* (1586; rpt. Amsterdam: Da Capo Press, 1969); see also pp. 50, 181 and 227.

56. Herman Hugo, *Pia Desideria* (1624; rpt. Menston: Scolar Press, 1971), I am indebted to the introductory note by Hester M. Black. It is ironic that the "Catholic" Amor and Anima derived from Emblem No. 45 in *Emblemes...Chrestiennes* (1571) of the Huguenot, Georgette de Montenay; see Mario Praz, "Profane and Sacred Love," *Studies in Seventeenth-Century Imagery*, 2nd edn. (Rome: Edizioni di Storia e Letteratura, 1964).

57. Not all the illustrators, of course, emphasized the same qualities. Mario Praz complains that Cruikshank's illustrations for an edition of Quarles in 1838 turned Anima into a bumptious little woman like a portrait of Queen Victoria as a child, but we are more concerned with the kindly expression on the face of Father Time, Praz, pp. 166-168 and Figs. 65 and 66.

58. Minute hands were not common until the pendulum in clocks (1657) and the balance spring in watches (c. 1674). None of the other clocks to which allusion has thus

far been made, show two hands. This was to be a useful element in the horological iconography of Hogarth. See Samuel L. Macey, "Hogarth and the Iconography of Time," *Studies in Eighteenth-Century Culture*, Vol. V, ed. Ronald C. Rosbottom (Madison, Wis.: University of Wisconsin Press, 1975), pp. 41-53.

59. See my forthcoming article on "Time and Clocks in Shakespeare," in *Shakespeare Quarterly*.

60. The term is related to the fact that Egyptian hieroglyphics were considered to provide a pedigree for emblems.

61. Samuel L. Macey, "The Impact of Horology on Literature 1660-1760," *Expression, Communication and Experience in Literature and Language*, ed. Ronald G. Popperwell (London: Modern Humanities Research Association, 1973), pp. 209-212.

62. Rosemary Freeman, *English Emblem Books* (London: Chatto and Windus, 1948), p. 31.

63. R. F. Jones, "Science and English Prose Style in the Third Quarter of the Seventeenth Century," *PMLA* (1930), 977-1009; R. F. Jones, "Science and Language in England of the Mid-Seventeenth Century," *JEGP*, 31 (1932), 315-331; and R. F. Jones, "The Attack on Pulpit Eloquence in the Restoration: An Episode in the Development of the Neo-classical Standard for Prose," *JEGP*, 30 (1931), 188-217.

64. Among the Grub-Street writers, he included both Quarles and Wither. See, for example, *Dunciad I*, lines 140 and 296.

65. Trusler, pp. 271-272; Paulson, I, 172-174.

66. For the relationship between Saturnalia and Christmas see W. F. Dawson, *Christmas: Its Origin and Associations* (London: Elliot Stock, 1902), pp. 13, 15, 29, 168-171, and 191; A. R. Wright, *British Calendar Customs* (London: The Folk-Lore Society,

1940), III, 193-194; William S. Walsh, *The Story of Santa Klaus* (Detroit: Gale, 1970), pp. 69-76, 158-159, 166, and 210; and William Muir Auld, *Christmas Traditions* (New York: MacMillan, 1931), pp. 35-43. For the Time with three faces that is "in effect a Janus," see Didron, II, 24-25, and Iwasaki, Fig. 13, or Panofsky, Fig. 50. The early iconographers of Father Time concentrated on the saturnine rather than the saturnalian aspect of Saturn.

67. Frederick Burgess, *English Churchyard Memorials* (London: Lutterworth, 1963), pp. 113, 168-171, Plates 16, 20-22; and Katherine A. Esdaile, *English Monumental Sculpture since the Renaissance* (London: Society for Promoting Christian Knowledge, 1927), pp. 30-31, 119, and Plate II.

68. Arnold Whittick, *Symbols, Signs and their Meaning* (London: Leonard Hill, 1960), pp. 200-201, 252, 254, and 261.

## DISCUSSION AND COMMENT

by Francis C. Haber

Professor Macey has presented an interesting and illuminating study on the iconography of Father Time that carries the subject well beyond the 17th century where the pioneering studies of Erwin Panofsky and Fritz Saxl left it. He has incorporated subsequent relevant scholarship with his own research and made a persuasive case that the iconography of Father Time continued to reflect changing attitudes toward time, changes that do not end the interest in eternity, cyclical time, or the dualism between mortality and immortality, but increasingly overshadow them by the interest in the time of worldly affairs.

It would not be possible in a paper of this scope to present both the iconography and an analysis of the causes of the shifts in the culture itself. I have reservations about some of the few passing remarks pertaining to the cultural changes. Certainly the growth of science and technology were among the important cultural changes that fostered the kind of secularization Macey sees affecting the images of Father Time. Improvements in horology were part of the growth of science and technology, but I fail to see how these improvements would affect the meaning of an icon directly once the mechanical clock had been added to the iconography, any more than the substitution of a scythe for a sickle changes the meaning of reaping. This is not to deny that seeing technological innovations reflected in iconography is interesting, but merely to suggest that refinements in technology may not have a developmental effect on the meaning of what a timekeeper, or a reaper, conveys in a metaphor.

I would cavil at the statement that Descartes was the first major thinker to incorporate the clock analogy into a philosophical system. St Thomas Aquinas and Nicholas of Cusa were major thinkers and both incorporated the clock analogy into their philosophical systems[*]. More seriously, however important the idea of clockwork was in

* See my article in *The Study of Time I*, pp. 389-91. 39-91.

the thinking of Descartes, I wonder if the most important aspect of his thought on Father Time was not his general influence on the growth of rationalism and secularism which made the whole emblematic approach seem trivial in the Enlightenment. Also, we have seen how *Veritas Filia Temporis* was used for dogmatic purposes in the 16th century, but under this banner there was a growing historical knowledge that fostered criticism of the past. By the end of the 18th century, the daughter was not only liberating herself, but her Father as well. In conclusion, my remarks have more to do with judgments about the context than with the iconography itself and are not intended to detract from Professor Macey's positive achievement.

# Time in the Musical Consciousness of Old High Civilizations—East and West*

L. Rowell

*ABSTRACT*

*This study of time organization in the musics of ancient Greece, India, and China, based on the speculative literature (the theory) of music, explores attitudes toward time and its role in music, showing that man's rhythmic experience reflects certain cultural preferences for such things as linearity, circularity, and continuity. The paper excludes tribal, folk, and "popular" musics as well as musics bound to the rhythm of the spoken word, "logogenic."*

*The functions of a rhythmic system are examined, and it is proposed that a system of musical rhythm is also a cosmological statement, with music constructed on the model of time. The evidence of language is considered, and a number of rhetorical devices are suggested as paradigms for the generation of musical structure.*

*Time organization in ancient China -- a macro-calendric time that is manifested in music as a steady quadruple meter -- is dealt with*

---

*In 1975-76 the author was the holder of a Senior Research Fellowship from the American Institute of Indian Studies for research in India while on sabbatical leave from the University of Hawaii.

*summarily, rejecting the evidence for "irregular rhythms" and accepting Granet's view (in* La Pensée Chinoise, *1934) that time in Chinese thought is essentially discontinuous and compartmentalized. Time in Chinese music is neither a creative nor a casual time -- it is a time to be kept.*

*The paper proceeds with comparisons and contrasts between the rhythmic system of classical Greece, as described by Aristoxenus and Aristides Quintilianus, and the Indian* tāla *system, as set forth by Bharata, Dattila, and Abhinavagupta. The topics of these systems are briefly defined, and the principal terms are analyzed for their etymological and semantic development. Both systems reveal a characteristic world outlook in their terminology: the Greeks saw music as a geometry, a network of lines and points; Indian authors related musical time to the threefold world process of creation, preservation, and dissolution.*

*The paper concludes with a set of short comparative discussions on time, gesture, and energy; time-keeping and percussion; continuity; complexity; part and whole; cyclical time; time and perception.*

## I. INTRODUCTION

Music is not only an art that employs or occupies time; I suggest that music is also a model of time and that the rhythm of music gradually comes to reflect cultural ideas on the nature of time. In this paper I will present evidence of what a few ancient cultures thought and felt about time and its role in their music. A topic for another occasion, but of compelling importance, is the process through which these ideas and feelings became part of the subsequent development of various world musics.

Although music theorists have long recognized time as one of music's major dimensions, their exploration of this dimension has been less than systematic. Studies have tended to focus instead upon problems of pitch, the tonal dimension of music, and the infrequent contributions to the theory of temporality reveal an obsession with the microtemporal elements of rhythm and meter, treating larger time structures in music almost as spatial forms. As a result our process descriptions are primitive, and the visual aspects of traditional notation can easily lead one to assume that music is more a state than a process -- more being than becoming.

The music of the so-called "old high cultures" of Later Antiquity, such as Greece, India, and China, is known to us chiefly through a body of musical speculation, a few extant fragments of musical notation upon papyri, marble pillars, rock inscriptions and the like, and what we can deduce from surviving musical practice. Virtually no such documentation exists for earlier Mediterranean or West Asian civilizations. If one cannot examine the prior development of musical time concepts, how hopeless it is for us to speculate profitably on the origins of music -- a favorite topic for past generations of musicologists. My attention is engaged at the point where ideas of musical time are formally stated in terms of a rhythmic system: a hierarchically-organized set of interdependent temporal concepts set forth in explanation of a then-living repertoire of music.

Current studies of ancient music generally fall into one of two categories: (1) textual studies that relate the speculative literature (the theory) of music to the history of ideas, the category to which this paper belongs, and (2) the ethnomusicological study of living musical traditions. The former appears to be more appropriate to high art cultures, the latter more fruitful for "undeveloped" or "primitive" musical societies. I firmly believe that ideas *do* influence music, and that cultural preferences for such things as linearity, circularity, continuity, etc. gradually seep into -- or perhaps emerge from -- man's rhythmic experience and enter into the systems he constructs to represent and explain this experience. In the musical thought of ancient high cultures we find many of these preferences embedded in the rhythmic systems and provided with a rationale for their existence.

Among the cultures of Later Antiquity from which some documentation of the music and musical speculation has survived, I find three great rhythmic systems: the Chinese, Indian, and Greek. Their dating is roughly parallel: the basis for each system of musical time was fully operative between the fifth and second centuries B.C., highly codified and conventionalized by the second century A.D., and still viable at the end of the first millennium, although the underlying fabric of ideas had become highly refined by the great commentators such as Augustine and Abhinavagupta.

Each of these systems has left its mark on the world map of musical rhythm: the steady quadruple meter of ancient China has dominated virtually all of East Asia (with the notable exception of Korea); the rhythms of India have spread in one form or another throughout West Asia, South Asia, and both continental and insular Southeast Asia; and the Greek rhythmico-metric scheme of time organization undoubtedly reigned supreme in European art music until the Later Middle Ages. Both in concept and in practice Hellenic rhythm spread throughout the Mediterranean Basin, and many of its most characteristic and colorful patterns still persist in Balkan and Anatolian folk-music.

Common sense tells us that there are certain rhythmic experiences that are common to all people; but at the same time we must admit that the rhythmic structure of music presents these experiences in a rich diversity of contexts, modified under the pressure of specific cultural traditions and ideas. This paper contains little that pertains directly to the time structures of tribal, folk, or "popular" musics, which are at times simpler and at times more complicated than the time structures of art musics. Also, most of the discussion will not apply to a very large body of the world's music -- that music which is bound to the rhythm of the spoken word or *logogenic*, "word-born." Musical speculation has left this repertoire largely untouched, and it remains primarily an oral tradition of chanting the ancient scriptures or reciting the traditional epics. Its proper time is the time of elevated speech.

## II. THE FUNCTIONS OF A RHYTHMIC SYSTEM

What purposes does a rhythmic system serve? A few come readily to mind: preservation, pedagogy, mnemonics, and the insurance of accurate ritual performance. And I suggest some other functions that may not be so obvious:

1. to make objective, clarifying to the mind the intangible and mysterious experience of sound.

2. to obtain precise divisions and measurements of the dimension of time.

3. to regulate and control the interaction of music, verse, and dance, demonstrating a practical concern for performance.

4. to provide an explanation for the creative, causal force in music.

5. to furnish sheer intellectual gratification and delight in the exuberant play of ideas.

6. to embody visual and aural patterns of cultural significance, analogous to those found in the visual arts and literature.

7. to stimulate physical response and mental imagery.

8. to provide a great variety of patterns within a larger controlling unity.

9. to furnish an explicit generative basis for large-scale musical structure, thus enabling the composer/performer to command large expanses of time.

10. to construct as complete a model of the prevailing cosmology as possible, in a sensuous medium: in the history of ideas, pitch is often represented as the vertical element in music and is symbolized by the world mountain, tree, cosmic serpent, planetary relationships, etc.; I suggest that duration represents the horizontal orientation to the cardinal directions, the seasons of the year, the stages of life, and their presiding deities. This is a strand in the history of ideas that deserves vigorous exploration: a musical system is, at the same time, a cosmology.

## III. THE EVIDENCE OF LANGUAGE

It is tempting to believe that the temporal patterns of language, specifically those of poetry, can be used to deduce the temporal patterns of music. But despite what is known of various ancient languages, it is clearly impossible to reconstruct the rhythmic system of a music on purely linguistic evidence. The rhythmic structure of music has both constraints and formal possibilities well beyond the scope of spoken and written language.

However, in the musical thought of Antiquity, speech patterns were frequently cited as the basis for short rhythmic patterns. And an even stronger case can be made for rhetorical devices as paradigms for larger musical structure. I will list some features of language -- especially Indo-European languages -- that seem to have become embodied or at least paralleled in the organization of music:

1. rhyme
2. meter
3. event length, as limited by breath
4. hierarchical structure, using the complex [syllable/word/phrase/period/stanza] as a model for construction

5. accents: tonal (pitch), stress (amplitude), and agogic (duration)

6. tension, in the conflict between the ideal and the actual

7. regulating devices such as catalexis and "indifference", designed to fit surface irregularities into larger regular patterns

8. deviation, arising between the successive levels of structure, composition, and performance

9. composition by formulae, typical of pre-literate phases of both literature and music

10. parallel construction, balance, and antithesis

11. the concept of tempo, conventional pace, or *tempo giusto*

12. the "laws" of (a) alternation (of strong and weak sounds)
    (b) recurring accent
    (c) climax (increasing durations or momentum)
    (d) end rigidity/beginning license

These principles suggest productive approaches to the study of temporality in music, although they fall far short of a comprehensive system of rhythmic organization. Traditional scholarship frequently became ensnared in the old arguments over rhythm and meter, into which I refuse to be drawn. I view metrics as the science of temporal norms -- the *ideal* to which rhythm serves as the *actual*. In music rhythm is the experience, and meter is the matrix by which we measure that experience.

## IV. TIME ORGANIZATION IN ANCIENT CHINA

The Chinese concept of musical time, although it occupies quite a subordinate role in this paper, deserves mention if only for its antiquity, persistence, and wide dispersal throughout East Asia. Since I claim no expertise in Chinese music and culture, I was mildly surprised to discover the lack of respect or interest that many leading Sinologists display for the temporal aspects of their musical tradition. With them I must admit that there is nothing inherently interesting in the system of incessant "four-square" rhythm that Curt Sachs so flamboyantly describes as "an eternal, mildly accentual, duple time" with "a lack of drive" and "a binary rhythm of quiet staticism."[1] My assembly of quotations tends to overstate Sachs' point, but I believe his generalization valid for what we know of ancient Chinese music.

Simple explanations are usually the best, and apparently the Chinese took time organization in their music very much for granted.[2] As practically-minded people the Chinese had little use for speculation on topics they considered to be successfully and naturally employed in their music. In Chinese literature, the focus was clearly on macro-time and its calendric significance; the structure of music was viewed as a harmonious reflection of the successive seasonal aspects of cyclical time. Musical time was to be relished in these successive aspects as a resonance to the cosmic scheme of "works and days" that was prescribed by the ancient classical texts. Micro-time seems not to have been taken seriously, or at least not seen as a problem that required speculation or solution, and hence the absence of descriptive or prescriptive literature dealing with the complex of rhythm/beat/measure/tempo/structure.

I can suggest two further reasons for the relatively simple nature of Chinese rhythm: (1) as Sachs points out, drum cultures have tended to develop an array of interesting and intricate rhythmic patterns; and ancient China was definitely not a drum culture.[3] Her stone chimes, bells, and cymbals served more as symbolic and ritual punctuation and signal than as percussion *per se*. Time-keeping and percussion are separate functions, a generalization that holds true for many Asian musics -- notably, as we shall see, for India. Also (2) ritual and ceremonial styles of ancient music have generally featured a slow pace, even rhythms, and a close relationship to the accompanying text.

The only evidence for irregular rhythms in Chinese music exists in the form of metrically-free song types, certain pieces imported from India and Central Asia, and in the irregular poetic lines of texts such as those from the Han Dynasty. The imports clearly failed to take root in the main tradition, and no one has shown convincingly that irregular syllable counts are associated in music with irregular rhythmic patterns or groupings of beats. On the contrary, Picken finds a clear relationship between regular, symmetrical tunes (8 beats) and verse lines of 3, 5, or 7 syllables:

> ...in a musical culture where song is measured rather than unmeasured, heterometric verse is a necessary consequence of setting words (one-syllable-to-one-note) to a tune in which the metrical framework is filled out with notes of more than one time-value, distributed in different patterns in each musical line.[4]

In this style of text-setting we see the process of *regulation* at work, using longer durations and breath pauses to adjust the lines of text to the regular metric framework. Signs for holds or rests[5] are present in enough of the repertoire to make Picken's explanation plausible, and the customary marks that signify the ends of lines support this tendency toward even, balanced phrases. In later Chinese song the notation of the music in the form of a rectangular grid, with regular vertical columns of text, indicates that the ancient tradition is still alive.

We find little evidence for rhythmic practice in Chinese literature. Needham has supplied a few tantalizing extracts from ancient sources in his great *Science and Civilization in China*, including the following:

> As the *Shih Ching* says: "Guiding the people is very easy. That is why the sages established the pellet drum (*thao*) and the stand drum (*ku*), the instrument which starts the miming (*chhiang*) and the instrument which stops it (*chieh*)...[6]

Other similar passages from the old texts indicate that beginnings, interruptions, and endings were marked by particular bell or percussion sounds, and that other types of drums regulated the pace. As Needham comments:

> From this brief extract the impression emerges that what the ancient Chinese were seeking above all in their dance rituals was control... the control of movement by which the elements were to be influenced.[7]

Elsewhere Needham has summarized the arguments between his own interpretation of the general Chinese view of time and Granet's. Whether one accepts Granet's picture of Chinese time as discontinuous, compartmentalized, "packaged" time or agrees with Needham that both compartmentalized time and continuous time were influential in Chinese thought, it is clear that Granet's view is readily applicable to the theory and practice of musical rhythm in ancient China.[8]

The time of Chinese music, as embodied in the standard quadruple meter, is analogous to a miniature cycle of seasons; each successive beat displays its own aspect, *yin* or *yang*, strength or weakness, and is linked with the other substances and phenomena of nature by elaborate tables of correspondences. The musical elements were thus aligned with the material elements, the seasons, the points of the compass, smells, tastes, colors, animals, and other orders of the world hierarchy. The remarkable result was that each discrete moment of musical time acquired its own unique "savour", as Larre remarks.[9] Music both participates in and is a symbol of universal order.

I cannot resist one further quotation from Needham which sums up the preceding discussion: "For the ancient Chinese, time was not an abstract parameter, a succession of homogeneous moments, but was divided into concrete separate seasons and their subdivisions."[10] The time of Chinese music is not a creative or causal time -- it is a time to be *kept*.

## V. TIME ORGANIZATION IN ANCIENT GREECE AND INDIA: RHYTHM AND TĀLA

In contrast to China's simple, rigid rhythmic traditions, the time systems governing music in ancient Greek and Indian civilizations display both an intense musical vitality and intellectual sophistication. We have little evidence for their evolution from earlier tribal phases; by the time we first encounter the descriptions in ancient treatises, each system of rhythm had already become highly codified. The two major sources for the Greek subject of rhythmics are the incomplete treatise of Aristoxenus of Tarentum, who was a pupil of Aristotle and lived during the fourth century B.C., and the more complete but intellectually inferior *περὶ μουσικῆs* of Aristides Quintilianus, who wrote during the second century A.D.[11] For the Indian *tāla* system, the earliest sources are Bharata's famous treatise on the ancient Indian musical theatre, the *Nāṭyaśāstra*, with the later commentary of Abhinavagupta, and the more concise treatise of Dattila.[12] One can only guess as to their dates: most scholars concede that both works were written sometime between the first and fifth centuries A.D.; Abhinava wrote during the tenth and/or eleventh centuries.

Both traditions stemmed from the musical stage, and while the Indian treatises are more practical in their prescriptions, both Greek and Indian authors recognized the problems of performance in a medium that combined recitation, dance, song, and gesture. Both traditions featured ensemble performance, thus requiring more careful directions than music designed for a soloist. Physical gesture was a vital part of both Greek and Indian musical performance, both as a purely practical means of keeping the performers together and as a significant component of the more abstract formal patterns. Both these theatrical musics trace their origins in part to myth and liturgy and were influenced by the ceremonies, conventions, and movements of sacred chant. Although the rhythmic patterns of language served as models for certain aspects of the rhythmic systems, our principal authors were well aware of the distinction between the temporal patterns of music and poetry. Certainly each tradition included some purely instrumental music; scholars are not certain whether such music was patterned closely after the vocal/texted music or was organized on different principles.

In addition to these similarities, the Greek and Indian systems for musical time have the following common properties:

1. Each proceeds from the smaller to the larger and attempts to define the minimal time unit.

2. Each features an explicit hierarchy of structural levels.

3. In each system, through a set of conventionalized gestures, time is given energy, motion, direction, and weight -- as well as duration.

4. Each system includes a vocabulary of patterns, rhythmic "words."

5. Each is designed to be expandable from within.

6. Each reveals a concern for the *continuity* of music and promotes continuity through an assortment of coupling and linking devices.

7. Each contains what I have already referred to as "regulators": adjusting techniques that fit the smaller units neatly into larger frameworks, trimming or stretching when necessary like the ancient Procrustes and his famous beds.

8. Each recognizes that rhythm and melody are interdependent.

9. Each recognizes that the role of a component in the system is determined more by its function than by its absolute size, an essential concept in an art where time organization is almost wholly relative.

10. Each includes specific prescriptions for composers and is obviously designed for a living tradition.

11. Each attempts, with varying degrees of success, to grapple with four extremely difficult issues: tempo, silence, change, and expression through style.

12. Each links the concept and terminology of musical time with the prevailing cosmology and world outlook.

My mode of presentation for the rest of this paper will be (VI) a brief examination of the Indian *tāla* system and the Greek subject of *rhythmics* in terms of their principal topics, with some basic definitions, (VII) the etymology and semantics of some of the most important terms, and (VIII) comparative discussions of certain key features of these two temporal systems, which will highlight the major differences and serve as a set of conclusions. The reader will find herein illustrations of the twelve properties I have set forth above as well as more general material.*

## VI. TOPICS, DEFINITIONS

In Abhinava's celebrated definition of *tāla*, we learn that measure, number, regulation, and equilibrium are the goals of time organization in music. *Tāla* is

> an immutable rule-bound entity which measures [time] through a fixed number of demarcations and unites *svara* and *yati* with the instrumental *vṛtti* and is regulated thoroughly by its secondary position (to *svara*); its solitary aim is to establish *sāmya* or equipoise, the nature of which cannot be explained in words.[13]

*Tāla*, like many other Sanskrit terms, is used both in a general sense and in several special senses: the most general application of the term is to the overall rhythmic organization of the system, as measured by manual actions (clapping, waving, finger counting). The word *tāla* thus combines the abstract concept of temporal structure with the physical gestures that translate this structure into concrete musical actions, *kriyās*. *Tāla* is also used for the short patterns formed by groupings of beats. In more special usage it can mean one of the prescribed *saśabda* (sounding) beats, in which the left hand slaps downward upon the upturned palm of the right hand, or the small bronze cymbals used to make the *tāla* audible in large ensemble performance.

Implicit in Abhinava's definition is the notion that rhythm is clearly subordinate to pitch (*svara*), a concept that Greek authors stated in quite a different way:

---

*Here I must apologize to the reader for the bristling thicket of Sanskrit terms that follows. Be reassured that most of the technical content of Section VI may be skipped, if necessary, without rendering the final conclusions any less intelligible.

Aristides Quintilianus held that melody was the passive, indefinite, feminine aspect of music and that rhythm was the active, masculine principle that imposes form and structure upon the inert ῥυθμιζόμενον--the stuff that receives the rhythm.[14]

The hierarchy of *tāla* topics appears to consist of four main levels, with the topics clustered as follows, proceeding from the small to the large:

Infra-structure: beats, rests, and their synchronization

*kalā*, a silent but visible beat

*pāta*, a sounding beat

*laya*, the space between beats, in modern terms "tempo"

*yati*, the law that regulates and coordinates all aspects of the music

*pāṇi*, the law that keeps performers "in phase" with one another, telling them when to begin

Structure: phrases and sections

*pādabhāga*, a phrase, often one of a group of four

*mātrā*, another type of phrase[15]

*parivarta*, a repetition of a phrase or section

*vidārī*, a pause or cadence

*aṅga*, a short musical section of several phrases

*vastu*, another type of section, often longer than an *aṅga*

Supra-structure: complete compositions

*prakārana*, the *saptarūpas* -- the seven fixed *gītaka* forms of ancient Indian theatrical/ritual music

*avayava*, expansions or contractions of the above forms, produced by the systematic interpolation or deletion of beats

General: properties that pervade the rhythmic hierarchy at all levels

*gīti*, expression produced by various combinations of *tāla*, *laya*, *yati*, etc. -- in other words, "style" (cf. the Greek ἦθος)

*mārga*, a curious concept: pattern length with respect to some fixed standard of measurement

The only other term in Abhinava's definition that is excluded from the formal list of *tāla* topics is *vṛtti*. The term is roughly equivalent to *gīti* except that it is most often applied to instrumental music; it too can be best translated as "style". The largest level of structure is occupied by the seven *gītaka* forms, the *prakāraṇa* (literally "accomplishments"). These were fixed compositional patterns that were assembled in modular fashion from various combinations of *mātrās, vastus, aṅgas,* etc. Mukund Lath describes the process as follows:

> a single *gītaka* was...composed of a multifarious group of patterns with a distinct internal organization of sounded and unsounded beat structures, tempic or rhythmic formations, numbered repetitions of smaller or larger patterns within greater patterns, introductions of fixed irregularities and other specific features all pre-decreed...[16]

The relationship of the *gītaka* Gestalts to the shorter *tāla* patterns (grouping of beats) is not clear. Perhaps the later *tālas* are indeed abstractions of the larger fixed forms; or it might just as well be the other way. One thing is clear: early Indian musicians thought of music in terms of large and complex fixed patterns -- not as a free series of repetitions or variations on a short, simple rhythmic cycle.

By way of general introduction to the Greek system of *rhythmics*, I quote the introductory paragraph of Aristides Quintilianus:

> Rhythm is a system of time units arranged in accordance with a certain order. Its properties are *arsis* and *thesis*, noise and silence. For generally, while the tones -- because of their similarity in motion -- render the melodic texture inexpressive and the mind barren in its wandering, the divisions of the rhythm show forth the function of the melody with clarity, first by dividing it and also by stimulating the thought in an orderly manner. *Arsis* is an upward motion of a part of the body, *thesis* a downward [motion] of this same part. Rhythmics therefore is the knowledge of the [proper] employment of the aforementioned.[17]

In this definition we find the same combination of abstract time organization and physical gesture that was the basis for *tāla*. But we find also an additional element: the emphasis on mental imagery and sense perception that pervades all Greek musical speculation. And in contrast to the complex, interlocking set of *tāla* topics, the Greek categories for the subject of *rhythmics* are few in number, simple in arrangement, and designed to follow the same sequence as the categories of the parallel discipline of *harmonics*. The progression of ideas proceeds from pervading to small to large, from material to process.

Introduction: rhythm defined.

ῥυθμιζόμενον, the raw material that receives the rhythm

times and their properties, especially ἄρσις and θέσις

αἴσθησις, sense perception of rhythm

The basic units:

χρόνος πρῶτος, the unit of primary time

πούς, the rhythmic foot (simple, composite; rational, irrational)

Structure:

the coupling of feet by συζυγία and περίοδος

the rhythmic species or genera: δακτυλικός (1:1)
ἰαμβικός (2:1)
παιωνικός (3:2)

General:

κενοὶ χρόνοι, rests (literally "empty times")

ἀγωγὴ ῥυθμική, rhythmic progression, tempo

μεταβολὴ ῥυθμική, rhythmic modulation

ῥυθμοποιΐα, rhythmic composition or style

## VII. ANALYSIS OF TERMS

Many of the terms just mentioned contain important verbal clues to the cultural view of time as embedded in that culture's music. *Rhythm* is a particularly pregnant term that has aroused controversy as to its origin and proper application. I do not go as far as de Groot in claiming that rhythm "is frequently used for any kind of repetition or periodicity in the physical world, also for any kind of correspondence in aesthetic experience, and, generally, for practically anything connected with experience as long as it is not clearly defined."[18]

Classicists do not agree on a uniform derivation for ῥυθμός, tracing the word either to ῥέω "to flow" (the traditional explanation) or to ἐρυ, ῥυ "to hold". Jaeger, inclining toward the latter derivation, argues that

> [ῥυθμός] is that which imposes bonds on movement and confines the flux of things; just as it is in Archilocus...the original conception which lies beneath the Greek discovery of rhythm in music and dancing is not *flow* but *pause*, the steady limitation of movement.[19]

These two basic meanings seem to have become mingled in the fully developed semantic range of ῥυθμός: (1) measured motion, (2) proportion, symmetry, (3) arrangement, disposition, (4) state, condition, (5) form, shape, and finally (6) manner, character. In his excellent study on *Accent and Rhythm*, Sidney Allen comments:

> In its earliest uses...the term ῥυθμός means little more than "form", being commonly equated with σχῆμα, though with a characteristic specialization of use. For whereas σχῆμα generally denotes a fixed, unchanging form, ῥυθμός tends to be found in contexts referring to the pattern assumed at a given moment by a mobile changing medium. But in Plato the term undergoes an important development of meaning; it is used to designate the form of the movement itself, and in particular a regular ordering of such form...comparable with harmony as the ordered combination of musical sounds; it is a κινήσεως τάξις," "an ordering of movement," which is closely associated with the idea of measurement (μέτρον) and of number (ἀριθμός) -- whence also the Latin use of *numerus* as the equivalent of ῥυθμός.[20]

In later usage, I believe the term *rhythm* has taken on this entire cargo of meanings: measured movement, form, arrangement, character. In a not uncommon ambivalence of meaning, it is both that which *permits* and *limits* movement. And I suggest also that the phonetic similarity between ῥυθμός (rhythm) and ἀριθμός (number) is neither accidental nor without consequence, despite the difference of the radical vowel; it did not escape the attention of Aristoxenus when he attempted to distinquish between time units formed according to the proper proportions of rhythm and those formed by number alone.[21] Thus, in the Greek concept of rhythm, a value judgement of "proper" motion or order was affixed to the term at an early date.

The standard Greek word for musical time was *χρόνος*, a very general and neutral term signifying measured, regular, seasonal clock time -- as opposed to *καιρός*, a more dynamic term that plays an enormous role in Greek literature, meaning "due measure, fitness, a critical time or season, the time of advantage, the moment to be seized." I have not found *καιρός* in a musical context.

Another Greek term that reveals a characteristic cultural world outlook is *σημεῖον*, literally "sign" but, more applicable to musical contexts, also a "point" in geometry. In the theory of Greek music the *σημεῖα* are the points that mark the extremities of musical figures, a dancer's pose, and of gestures in general. The Greek authors clearly thought of single musical tones and single minimal time units as points, a highly atomistic view of such a notably fluid medium as music. Indeed, music was conceived as an analogue to geometry, and the two sister disciplines were later paired with arithmetic and astronomy in the Mediaeval *Quadrivium*, perhaps on the strength of the celebrated analysis of Nicomachus:

| | | | |
|---|---|---|---|
| Numbers: | absolute and *per se* | = | arithmetic |
| | in mutual relation | = | music |
| Quantity: | at rest | = | geometry |
| | in motion | = | astronomy[22] |

The salient point here is that all four disciplines could be represented by a nexus of lines and points, implicitly supporting the concept of atomistic time. The central paradox of musical time is contained in this idea: that the essential motion or "flow" of music takes place only over a "riverbed" of discrete points or instants.

Other Greek terms in the literature of musical speculation are not as provocative in their meanings: *σχῆμα* clearly means both "form" and "character" and refers to both static and mobile structures. *πους*, "foot", has the same range of meanings as the English word "foot", signifying a human or animal foot, a unit of length measurement, and a base for anything. *ἀγωγή* means little more than a "going", comparable to the Sanskrit *gati*, and signifies the manner of going, progression, a way of moving. It is easy to see how *ἀγωγή* might variously be interpreted as "tempo" (the rate of going), "style", or simply "progression".

Indian terms deserve equally close attention: *tāla* is generally derived from the root √*tal*, a minor root meaning to accomplish, establish, fix.[23] *Tala* means a surface, plane, the sole of the foot, or the palm of the hand, and *tāla* designates an action applied to this surface: hand-clapping (the basic musical meaning), the waving of a palm-leaf fan, the flapping of an elephant's ears. The musical application goes directly back to the radical meaning, for, as Abhinava says, "*tāla* measures and limits all [musical] actions."[24]

The most striking incursion of Indian cosmology into musical terminology occurs in a much-analyzed compound of Abhinava: *kalā-kāla-laya*, which appears in the introductory verse of his commentary to chapter 31, the *tāla* chapter, of the *Nāṭyaśāstra*. Abhinava links the three musical terms to the threefold process of creation in traditional Indian thought: *kalā* is equated with *sṛṣti*, the process of splitting and differentiating the elemental matter (*prakṛti*); *kāla* is compared to *sthiti*, the ordered distribution of these elements and their movement in time; and *laya* signifies *pralaya* or *saṁhāra*, melting and dissolution back into primal matter, and ultimately rest until the next cycle of creation begins.

The derivation of these terms is not completely understood. Although the Hindu grammarians recognized three separate roots √*kal*, their meanings are not clearly distinguished from one another. One means "to sound" and "to count", another "to push on, drive forward", and all three can mean "to count, calculate, enumerate." The picture is even more complicated with primitive Indo-European, which apparently contained no less than ten cognate roots **kel*; the following appear to be the most relevant to our study:

**kel*[4] - to have spots, be articulated

**kel*[5] - to drive, impel to quicker movement

**kel*[6] - to call, cry out, sound

*Kāla*, the most general term for time, is assigned to the third Sanskrit root √*kal* in the sense of "calculate." Its meanings include the following: a fixed or right point *or* space of time, time in general, proper time or occasion, a measure of time, a season, and also time as destiny (fate) and time as the destroyer (death). As its range of semantic development widens, *kāla* approaches the Greek *καιρός* in meaning. The common adjective *kāla*, meaning primarily "black", appears to have no discernable connection with notions of time. And I might add that I have not found two common Vedic words for time, *āyus* and *ṛtu*, in any musical contexts.

The etymology of *kalā* is questionable. Betty Heimann has pointed out that this, like most Sanskrit words for time, is primarily a spatial concept.[25] Its basic meaning is a small part of anything, especially a sixteenth part, and the range of meanings extends to a particular division of time, an atom, embryo, menstrual discharge, any fine, mechanical, or practical art, skill, ignorance, or one of the elements of the material world. *Kalā* seems to have two musical applications in Indian texts: (1) a group of actions, especially the *nihśabda* (silent) beats when combined with the *pātas*, the *saśabda* (sounding) beats; and (2) the unit of time measured by these actions. Based on these semantic clusters, it is not too far-fetched to claim that *kāla* represents creative, subjective time, whereas *kalā* stands for measured, objective time. Taken together the two terms demonstrate our ambivalent view of time as both "becoming" and "being".

*Laya* derives from the root √*lī, lināti* -- to adhere, be sticky, melt, disappear; hence *laya* is the act of sticking or clinging to, melting, or dissolution. As

Abhinava tells, its nature in music is *viśrānti* (rest), and its function is *śleṣa* (joining).[26] The traditional Indian view implanted in the term *laya* is that the measuring of musical time occurs by means of actions separated (but also joined) by rests.

The great Indian philosopher of grammar Bhartrhari, in his *Vākyapadīya*, attributes the operation of time to the two properties of "suspension" (*pratibandha*) and "permission" (*anujñā*).[27] *Pratibandha*, the principle of constraint and that which separates events in time, is equated with *laya* and *viśrānti; anujñā*, the principle that releases, corresponds to the *kriyās* (actions) represented by the musical beats. The overall process is called *kālaśakti*, the causal power of time, which is compared to the rim of a wheel, the force that allows causes to produce their effects or prevents them from so doing. In its inexorable alternation of constraint and release, time's progress advances along the larger cycle of creation, preservation, and destruction.

Another Sanskrit term that conveys clearly the notion of limitation is *yati*, from the very common root √*yam*, to hold, restrain, control, regulate. In music *yati* is the law that regulates *laya*, the flow of tempo, and in modern usage has come to mean the sequence of tempi, *i.e.* from slow to fast or *vice versa*. But the basic meaning signifies restraint, control, guidance, stopping, a musical pause, or a caesura in verse.

The key words in both Greek and Indian traditions develop these three themes -- movement, number, and limitation, often reconciling perceived conflicts through that happy ambivalence that so often accompanies the semantic development of controversial terms. The language of musical discourse has come to reflect the accepted world outlook, suggesting that music functions as a model of temporal organization -- a controllable tonal universe -- that can be set in motion, precisely measured, and appropriately restricted.

## VIII. COMPARISONS, CONCLUSIONS

In earlier sections of this paper I pointed out the similarities between the Indian and Greek systems of time organization in music; now I would like to present the important differences. The *tāla* system described in the ancient *śāstras* is unquestionably a great intellectual achievement, scarcely inferior to the contemporary body of phonetic observations and organization attributed to the grammarian Pānini. It is a sophisticated network of related and interdependent temporal concepts, built on sound principles of structure. Its extreme flexibility and adaptability to practical performance situations demonstrates the musical sensitivity of its creators.

I would not rank the Greek achievement so highly, but some of the insights in what survives of Aristoxenus are fully as penetrating as those of Bharata or Abhinava. The development of the Greek rhythmic system was restricted by their insistence on organizing time by the same scheme they used, more successfully, to organize pitch. They failed to recognize that the two major musical dimensions, though coordinate, required two sets of laws. Following the Greek example, Western theorists have for centuries sought a unifying principle by which the tonal and temporal dimensions could be organized. Unfortunately this ideal has remained elusive. Greek rhythm continued to be bound to the temporal patterns of poetry and did not become fully independent of these patterns until Philip de Vitry proposed his brilliant system of mood, time, and prolation in the fourteenth century.[28]

*Time, Gesture, and Energy*. One of man's most instinctive experiences is his physical response to the temporal organization of music, whether it be a vigorous handclapping to a rock beat or the sophisticated mental imagery evoked by an elaborate passage of Baroque counterpoint. We cannot measure the mental images, but the variations in gesture from one culture to another can be observed, and we can also observe the intensity of the gestures in terms of energy expenditure. Physical feelings and habits produced by these responsive gestures "feed back" into the musical repertoire, influencing both performance traditions and the composition of new music, and ultimately become a distinctive feature of a body of music.

The ancient Indian *tāla* system was regulated by eight *kriyās*, or "actions", four sounding and four silent beats, all apparently produced from a sitting position as in contemporary Indian performance. These include claps, finger snaps, waves of the hand, soundless finger counting, and a variety of other silent motions. These gestures emanate from a bodily stance of stability and repose, are confined to the space immediately surrounding the body, and are differentiated more by direction and sound/silence than by differing energy levels. The silent gestures focussed attention on the control of time *during* the duration of the beat, not just upon the "tick" itself. The prescribed sequence of gestures, the *tālavidhi*, made it possible to learn, remember, and recognize complicated formal patterns.

Because of the relative lightness and equality of the *tāla* gestures, accent became more a function of the environment than of the individual rhythmic pattern. I like to think of the Indian rhythmic pattern or event as a *polymorph*: a neutral sound-structure without strong intrinsic rhythmic weight or energy that can easily adapt to a variety of rhythmic environments. This perhaps helps to explain why the superimposition of patterns is such a characteristic feature of Indian music, then and today, creating a pleasantly suspenseful tension until the end of the superimposed patterns coincides once more with *sam*, the normal accent of the underlying *tāla*. As Heimann comments:

> India sees Time as a series of time-waves. We think of the Greek χρόνος, a time-concept which the Greeks have complemented with their concept of καιρός, the "fertile moment of decision". Disguise and interchange of form and function, as accepted by mythology and by all Indian thought, remove the arbitrary certainty and constancy of each single form...[29]

Both Indian and Greek mythologies abound in stories of gods, demons, or heroes with the ability to change form at will: the *kāmarūpin* is a standard character in Sanskrit literature, and one is reminded of the Greek Proteus, the son of Poseidon, whose ability to change his form symbolized the passing seasons of the year and the stages of human life.

This brings us, I think, to a major point of difference: temporal forms, in Indian thought and musical practice, are fluid, transformable, and even illusory. To the Greek mind, however, rhythmic formations displayed no such protean character but were stable, mentally comprehensible (so long as they were formed according to proper proportion), endowed with indigenous accent, and analogous to eternal, fixed patterns and shapes. In the Indian musical world of simultaneous possibilities, form gives way to function within a larger design; in Greek musical thought, form is persistent.

Metric weight in Greek rhythm was the product of *arsis* and *thesis*, the upward and downward motion of the chorus leader's foot on the *scabellum* (a kind of castanet, originally a human skull) that kept the chorus together. By transfer the same rhythmic feelings of "lift" and "descent" were communicated to the dancers, other actors, and governed the stage motions of the choristers. The energy level must have been higher than in India, since the movement involved the balance of the entire body and was produced from a position of greater instability, suggesting a more dynamic, kinetic rhythmic impulse. Thus I propose that the accents were heavier and, of course, fewer in number than the *tāla* gestures. Here there was no question of left or right, hand folded or spread out, sounding or silent motions -- merely a feeling of ascent and descent; and since each *thesis* was virtually the same, a greatly simplified alternation of stress and nonstress governed the temporal organization of the music.

When the same principle of *arsis/thesis* was applied at higher architectonic levels in the musical hierarchy (the foot, colon, phrase, period), the result was a simple duple meter with even groups of stresses. In this respect, I believe, the principles of Greek rhythm have influenced the entire temporal development of Western European music.

*Time-keeping and Percussion*. Indian musical culture, from the earliest days, has been a drum culture; drumming is virtually non-existent in accounts of ancient Greek music. Although drumming and rhythm are popularly assumed to be synonymous, in Indian rhythmic practice the time-keeping and percussive functions were and still are largely separate. Since the drummer was not required to serve as a time-keeper, the percussion part was free to develop its own language -- the *bols*, a language of drum syllables which functioned as a timbral counterpoint to the melody. This language, which depends heavily on the tonal characteristics of the different drum strokes, can almost be said to constitute a new musical dimension. Time-keeping, on the other hand, was a function of metal instruments and of hand-counting; the practice of *tāla* was more closely related to the underlying temporal structure of the music than to the percussive accompaniment of the melody. Therefore, percussion instruments have little to do with the larger organization of the rhythmic system, and their characteristic patterns are set forth in a different chapter of the *Nāṭyaśāstra*.[30]

*Continuity*. The subject of continuity was both a philosophical and practical issue for Greek and Indian authors. As Plutarch wrote,

> Indeed, continuity is required for the exercise of critical judgement, since beauty and the opposite do not arise in this or that isolated note or time or speech-sound, but in the series, as they are a blend of the smallest elements in an actual composition.[31]

Abhinava compares *tāla* to the thread that stitches a garment together,[32] and the sage Nārada describes musical continuity by the metaphors of a flash of lightning in a cloudy sky or the thread running through a necklace of pearls.[33] Indeed the image of continuity-through-reticulation is one of the most important and persistent cultural preferences in India: the language of Indian art is a language of small articulations which at higher speeds becomes a texture of psychedelic "flicker" or shimmer. The *aksara* (syllable) is the common basis for Indian language, music, dance, and theatre, and reticulated patterns are typical in architecture and the decorative arts -- from lattice window-screens to elephant painting.

The difference is, I think, that to the Greeks continuity was a property of the temporal form itself, whereas to the Indian mind continuity was a property of *mind* and must be sought out in the inner reality that connects all discrete events. A favorite symbol was the apparent circle produced by a whirling torch, representing to many Indian authors the *kālaśakti* -- the creative power of time.

*Complexity*. Turning once again to Plutarch, we find that

> ...in the conduct of rhythm, the ancients employed a complexity greater than that in use today, for they set great store on complexity in rhythm. Further, the interplay of the accompaniment was then more varied, as moderns like music for the tune, whereas the ancients were interested in the beat.[34]

Plutarch's statement has a familiar ring about it and is more popular mythology than musicology. All rhythmic systems have an enormous potential for complexity, since they deal with so many variables, but any attempt to standardize how "complexity" is defined is futile. The musical mind seems to require a certain degree of complexity but will satisfy this urge either through the elaboration of a single dimension (melody) or by constructing a sophisticated interplay between two or more simpler dimensions. An individual rhythmic line in a Mozart quartet may seem childishly simple, but it interacts with the melodic and harmonic dimensions in an exceedingly complex way. The melodic contours of an Indian singer's improvisation appear incredibly complicated to Western ears, but one's attention is free to concentrate upon this single dimension in its melodic/rhythmic synthesis. There are obvious morals here for the understanding of another culture's music.

*Part and Whole*. In the relationship of the part to the whole, I find an Indian concern for Gestalt and macro-rhythm in distinct contract to the Greek preference for micro-rhythm and the exhaustive definition of the smallest temporal elements. Aristides Quintilianus referred to the foot as "the part of rhythm by which we discern the whole.[35] In *rhythmics* the minimal time unit, *χρόνος πρῶτος*, was the basis for the entire system, and all larger rhythmic structures were reckoned in terms of the total number of primary time units they occupied. Larger time structures in Indian music were seen not as simple multiples of a basic unit but as complex, self-sufficient Gestalts. And in the *tāla* system the *guru* (long) syllable was the basis for the expansion of the smaller patterns and was thus more fundamental than the *laghu* (short) syllable.

In moving from the small pattern to the whole, we can identify three distinct formal processes that seem to be popular musical strategies: inflation, cyclical repetition, and serial addition -- in other words, the expansion, repetition, and juxtaposition of patterns. Inflation is preferred in the musical system of ancient India. Although both Indian and Greek texts provided for the systematic expansion of forms by the doubling and quadrupling of beats, this practice was widespread in Indian music and became the favorite means of achieving large-scale musical structure; in Greek music it was quite insignificant. Formal inflation in Indian music was the result of interpolating beats between the gestures of the original *tāḷavidhi*. In contrast, the Greek concept of rhythmic form is modular and depends rather on the linking of smaller patterns, a practice surprisingly inconsistent with their concept of cyclical time. I have been at some pains to avoid the term "cycle" until this moment, but καιρός has come!

*Cyclical time*. Cyclical time, as represented by the "modern" *deśi tālas*, is the dominant type of rhythmic organization today in both North- and South-Indian practice; but such was certainly not the case in the period of Bharata or even Abhinava. The temporal system that they set forth featured fixed compositional patterns of considerable length, not short and freely-repeatable cycles. The one treatise that might shed some light on this remarkable transformation, the *Bṛhaddeśi* of Matanga, lacks the *tāla* chapter that it formerly contained. One can only conclude that the older system of *mārga tālas*, which so clearly prepared the conceptual foundation for later cyclical time, evolved into the modern system between the seventh and thirteenth centuries.

The roots of later cyclical practice include the following: (1) the structural use of repetitions (*parivartas*), (2) the use of *saṁnipāta* as a beat of structural significance at the beginning or end of a pattern or at the concurrence of several accents, (3) the recognition of a few basic *tāla* patterns as a *pramāṇa*, a standard for measuring the larger structures of which they were abstractions, (4) the concept of *mārga*, a fixed "path" or extent of time within which a pattern was to be set, (5) the directions for remembering one's place in the sequence of *pādabhāgas* by counting with the fingers, the ancestor of the *jātis* in modern *tāla* counting, (6) the persistence of specific patterns of *tāla* gestures under new melodic material, and (7) the conceptual notion that rhythm proceeded in circles from a point of balance, of "zero gravity", similar to the image of Brahman in the Upanishads, likened to the cosmic spider sitting in the midst of a web of concentric threads representing the entire world order.

As the older *tāla* system evolved, it succumbed to the relentless pressure of cultural ideas, despite the authority attached to the prescriptions of the ancient *śāstras*. Musical time became more harmonious with the established Indian preference for circularity. *Cakras* (circles) are important symbols in Indian culture, and it is worth noting that their different "powers" are called *kalās*: one power or aspect of the circle passes into another in organic progression just as the seed passes into the leaf, the bud, and the fruit. According to Abhinava, *cakras* possess these attributes -- they shine, give spiritual satisfaction, cut bondage, possess the power of action, and manifest the universal energy.[36]

But cyclical time in music involves more than the primitive concept of cycles as described by Hinks:

> [for the primitive mind] it is the repetition of a fixed point in space, not the duration of an infinitely subdivisible process in time, which constitutes a temporal event. It is therefore the *completion* of the given cycle which is regarded as significant, not the *chronometry* of this process.[37]

Cyclical time in music, whether it be the long and complex later Indian *tālas* or the relatively simpler $\frac{4}{4}$ time of Handel's "Hallelujah" Chorus, requires a precise knowledge of the chronometry of the cycle in terms of metric strength and weakness and of one's present location within the cycle -- and also the location of the present cycle within the larger organizing framework. In a rhythmic cycle accent falls naturally upon the concurrence of beginning and end. But, as we have seen, neither the Greek nor the Indian rhythmic system could accurately be described as cyclical in ancient times. The proper placement of musical accent becomes, therefore, a subject for speculation.

There is no evidence for end-accent in Greek musical thought or practice, so one may assume that the strong initial accent characteristic of Western music in the last several hundred years has roots that go back well into Hellenic times. But in Indian musical thought there are numerous indications of end-accent as the norm: (1) the placement of the *saṁnipāta* beat on the final (or often an extra) beat of a pattern, (2) the traditional placement of *pluta* (thrice the value of the short syllable) at the end, (3) the technique of formal expansion by prefixing and infixing silent beats, always reserving the final sounded beat for the end, and (4) adjusting a pattern to a shorter duration by trimming off its beginning -- never its end. These devices are consistent with the typically Indian statement of a logical proposition, which to Westerners seems like reasoning backwards.

*Time and Perception*. Finally one must speak of the ultimate purpose behind each of these great temporal systems. To the Greek mind, the experience of musical rhythm was an outward manifestation of man's biological rhythms and the proper proportions of the world of forms he inhabited. For rhythm to work its effects upon man, it must be intelligible to his sense perception, the αἴσθησις, and his apprehension of rhythms required him to form mental imagery that resembled the sounds he perceived. In this way he was brought into tune with the world of eternal forms in a totally balanced, harmonious, mental and physical state. But if music was a means of apprehending the eternal forms for the Greeks, it was a means of escaping from the illusion of forms for the Indian mind. *Vaikṛta* (apparent sound) was limited by duration, but *prākṛta* (real sound) is *sphoṭa* -- indivisible, continuous, and independent of duration. The correct performance of *tāla* led not to sensory satisfaction, mental imagery, or clear perception but to *siddhi* (success) and *adṛṣṭa phala* (unseen benefit). According to Abhinava, the sole aim of *tāla* was to establish *sāmya*: ultimate equality, balance, and equilibrium -- a neutral balance between time (*tāla*) and pitch (*svara*), form and function, music and text.[38] When all worldly actions attain this perfect equilibrium of *sāmya*, the ultimate goal is near -- *mokṣa* (liberation).

NOTES

1. Curt Sachs: *Rhythm and Tempo* (New York: W. W. Norton 1953) pp. 57-61.

2. For the contents of this paragraph and other information I am especially indebted to Fritz A. Kuttner and Laurence E. R. Picken. This is also an appropriate place to express my profound gratitude to Dr. Prem Lata Sharma of Banaras Hindu University, Varanasi, and to Dr. V. Raghavan of Madras for their expert guidance and patient courtesy.

3. *Op. cit.*, p. 65.

4. L. E. R. Picken: "Secular Chinese Songs of the Twelfth Century," *Studia Musicologica Academiae Scientiarum Hungaricae*, 8 (1966), pp. 130-131.

5. The Chinese character *chu*, usually translated as "rest", signifies a dwelling or staying rather than silence; hence it is not clear whether the Chinese differentiated between extended notes and true rests. The distinction becomes quite academic, of course, in a music that features the highly transient sounds of plucked string instruments, stone chimes, and bells. Rests are, all the same, problematic in many early notations and remain one of the greatest obstacles to the study of time organization in ancient music.

6. Joseph Needham: *Science and Civilization in China*, IV, 1 (Cambridge: Cambridge University Press 1954--) p. 145.

7. *Ibid.*, p. 150.

8. *Cf.* Joseph Needham: "Time and Knowledge in China and the West," in *The Voices of Time*, ed. by J. T. Fraser (New York: George Braziller, Inc. 1966) pp. 92-135, especially 98-100, and Marcel Granet: *La Pensée Chinoise* (Paris 1934).

9. Claude Larre: "The Empirical Apperception of Time and the Conception of History in Chinese Thought," in *Cultures and Time* (Paris: The Unesco Press 1976) p. 36.

10. *Science and Civilization in China*, II, p. 288.

11. These works are supplemented, of course, by many other short treatises and fragments. For the Greek texts, see especially Rudolf Westphal: *Die Fragmente und die Lehrsätze der griechischen Rhythmiker* (Leipzig: B. G. Teubner 1861). The most comprehensive study of the rhythmic fragments of Aristoxenus is also by Westphal: *Aristoxenos von Tarent, Melik und Rhythmik des classischen Hellenentums* (Leipzig: A. Abel 1883; rpt. Hildesheim: Georg Olms 1965). For Aristides Quintilianus see his *De Musica Libri Tres*, ed. by R. P. Winnington-Ingram (Leipzig: B. G. Teubner 1963) and the excellent German translation by Rudolph Schäfke: *Von der Musik* (Berlin: M. Hesse 1937).

12. Of the numerous editions of the *Nāṭyaśāstra* [NŚ], the Baroda edition is perhaps the best: Bharatamuni: *Nāṭyaśāstra* of Bharatamuni, with the commentary *Abhinavabhāratī* by Abhinavaguptācārya, IV, ed. M. Ramakrishna Kavi and J. S. Pade (Baroda: Oriental Institute 1964). Most references are to chapter 31, the chapter on *tāla*. For Dattila see Mukund Lath: *A Study of Dattilam* [Diss.] (University of Delhi 1976) and E. Wiersma-Te Nijenhuis: *Dattilam, a Compendium of Ancient Indian Music* (Leiden: E. J. Brill 1970).

13. Lath, p. 239, translating Abhinava's commentary on the NŚ, 33, 1.

14. I, 19.

15. *Mātrā*, like many other Sanskrit musical terms, is used in a bewildering variety of contexts and meanings: in Sanskrit metrics it is the unit of time required to utter a short syllable; in ancient Indian music it was also the basic duration of the musical beat, five times as long as the metric *mātrā*.

16. *Op. cit.*, p. 247.

17. I, 13.

18. A. W. de Groot: "Phonetics in its Relation to Aesthetics," in *Manual of Phonetics*, ed. B. Malmberg (Amsterdam: 1968) p. 541.

19. W. W. Jaeger: *Paideia* (Oxford: Oxford University Press 1945), I, 125-126.

20. W. Sidney Allen: *Accent and Rhythm* (Cambridge: Cambridge University Press 1973) p. 96.

21. *Passim*.

22. Nicomachus: *Introduction to Arithmetic*, tr. M. L. D'Ooge (Ann Arbor: University of Michigan Press 1926), Bk. I, iii, 6.

23. This root, like many other seldom-used roots, may be merely a figment of the Hindu grammarians' imagination.

24. Commentary to NŚ, 31, 369.

25. Betty Heimann: *Facets of Indian Thought* (London: Allen & Unwin 1964) p. 121.

26. Commentary to NŚ, 31, 370.

27. Peri Sarveswara Sharma, tr.: *The Kālasamuddeśa of Bhartṛhari's Vākyapadīya* (Delhi: Motilal Banársidass 1972) p. 45.

28. in his *Ars Nova*, ca. 1320.

29. *Op. cit.*, p. 65.

30. Chapter 33, on the *avanaddha* ("covered") instruments.

31. Plutarch: *Moralia*, XIV, tr. Benedict Einarson and Phillip H. De Lacy (Cambridge, Mass.: Harvard University Press 1967) p. 437.

32. Commentary to NŚ, 31, 368.

33. *Nāradīyā Śikṣā*, I, 6, 11.

34. *Op. cit.*, pp. 397-399.

35. I, 14.

36. K. C. Pandey: *Abhinavagupta: an Historical and Philosophical Study* (Varanasi: the Chowkhamba Sanskrit Series Office 1963) pp. 525-527.

37. Roger Hinks: *Myth and Allegory in Ancient Art* (London: the Warburg Institute 1939) p. 43.

38. Commentary to NŚ, 31, 1.

DISCUSSION AND COMMENT

*by David Epstein*

Professor Rowell has shown elements common to Indian, Chinese and Greek musical systems and how they emanated from philosophical viewpoints, expressing thereby a cosmological or cultural view. This is brave scholarship in a time when many Western musicologists move gingerly among non-Western musics, hesitant to infer connections, much less universality.

The paper raises interesting points. It implies that musical works written within these systems were shaped, i.e. somewhat predetermined, by the systems themselves. To what extent was this the case, however, and how much did a body of works existing prior to a theory lend themselves to systematic characterization? What was the interaction, in other words, between system and individual creation?

With the description of musical systems that this paper provides, it would be valuable to understand the mechanisms that controlled time and motion in works written within these systems. Dr. Rowell suggests that gesture generates rhythmic motion, and I agree. In these musics, however, what properties embodied this motion, regulated its progress and the expenditure of its energies until ultimate resolution?

To know this we need to demarcate more precisely the role played by meter (alas, the rhythmic/metric "arguments" cannot be avoided), and whether and how rhythmic/metric conflict generated musical energy and motion. We should also examine accent more fully: Were all accents generically equivalent? (Unlikely.) Were there distinctions between structural and ornamental accents, between agogics and other articulations?

Further, did meter engender motion by the implantation and repetition of pattern? Or did motion arise organically through the counterbalancing of weight and relative degrees of stability? Another look at *thesis* and *arsis* might throw light on these questions, particularly if we could know whether all *theses* or *arses* were generically equivalent, or if by any inequivalence they created imbalance and hence a tendency toward motion. End-accented music is relevant to this point; it creates through music a sense of "becoming" rather than of "being". In so doing it also illustrates another aspect of Dr. Rowell's paper -- the way in which this music embodies philosophical ideas.

# Poiesis: Time and Artistic Discourse

F. Turner

ABSTRACT

*The paper sets itself the task of distinguishing and describing metaphorically that mode of thought which proceeds with, rather than against, the direction of time; that is, from past to future, from earlier to later, rather than vice-versa.*

*Analysis, which is the usual method of knowledge in the sciences and the humanities, explains the complex in terms of its simpler components. But the process of evolution, which Fraser has generalized and assumed to be fundamental to the nature of time, generallly proceeds from the simple to the complex. Analysis explains by deducing origins and antecedents. Evolution (and time itself) adduces consequences and fruitions.*

*Analysis deals necessarily with the past of its subject. Since past events are no longer subject to variation, their relationship to each other can conveniently be represented by analogy with spatial relationships. Hence analysis tends toward spatial metaphors. However, when the spatial analogy becomes dominant, certain systematic errors creep into our understanding: analysis cannot by itself handle novelty, synthesis, indeterminacy, self-reference, and the problem of the observer.*

*I have named that mode of thought which synthesizes and which*

> *projects itself into the future* <u>*poiesis*</u>*, from the Greek* <u>*poiein*</u>*, to make or create. Poiesis is the continuation of evolution in noetic, human, and historical terms. It can be understood as possessing the kind of truth inherent in performative or stipulative statements, which enact themselves by their utterance, as opposed to logical or empirical statements, whose truth is either tautologous or dependent upon verification.*
>
> *Poiesis can be represented by the metaphor of the blaze, that is, the mark that an explorer cuts on a tree when leaving familiar territory and entering the unknown. The blaze symbolizes the construction of a poietic symbol itself. A blaze extends the known territory by creating a space (within eyeshot of the blaze) from which return to the known cosmos is possible even though that space has not yet been entered by the explorer. This space is the play-space of art, and is essential to the decision-making whereby we construct the future. The expansion of the known world in this fashion can be generalized to include the expansion of language and the expansion of the past into the empty future.*
>
> *Versions of this metaphor can be found throughout literary art itself, which is often self-referential. The great literary themes of exploration, journey, the magic island, paradise, monsters, and homecoming correspond to the various phases of poietic expansion.*

The problem this paper sets itself is to find a way of describing that mode of thought which proceeds with, rather than against, the current of time; that is, in the direction of the coming into being of new events in the world, rather than in the direction of the discovery of the antecedent components of those new events.

The classical method of knowledge in both the sciences and the humanities since the Renaissance has been the explanation of the complex in terms of its simpler components, whether those components are material or structural. Indeed, this distinction itself, between material and structure, can no longer be held to be valid in an absolute sense: the material of which any structure is made is itself a structure of a still finer material, and so on. We have, as the continuing vigor of particle physics demonstrates, not yet discovered an irreducible physical object. Be this as it may, the direction of analysis is always from the relatively complex to the relatively simple.

The theory of evolution demonstrates that more complex organisms result from the interplay of less complex ones. In other words the simple necessarily at some point precedes the complex, whereas the complex does not necessarily precede the simple. A universe of non-living physicochemical processes is conceivable without the prior existence of life; but a universe containing life is not conceivable without the prior existence of the less complex physicochemical processes. In its general trend, then, evolution proceeds from the simple to the complex: this trend applies not only to the evolution of life but also, for instance, to the evolution of the more complex heavier elements out of the less complex lighter ones inside stars and in supernovas.

Analysis, then proceeds in the opposite direction in time from evolution. We might therefore expect it to be an accurate and appropriate way of thinking when dealing with the entropy-increasing aspects of events, but to be liable to systematic incompleteness when dealing with the entropy-decreasing aspects. Or, to put it more precisely, analysis tends to see *only* those aspects of an event that can be described in terms of the increase of entropy, and has no vocabulary to describe that local decrease of entropy which accompanies evolutionary processes, and especially the processes of living organisms.

In order for analysis to have a starting-point or subject, it must have a complex object or event upon which to perform. It is of no use if that complex entity is yet to come into existence. The process of analysis, as we have seen, proceeds from complex to simple, that is, generally, from later to earlier. Analysis, therefore, deals primarily with the past. Analysis explains by pointing out origins.

When dealing with various past events at different times there is no apparent problem in treating the separation between them as if it were fully analogous to a spatial separation. That is, we conveniently discuss numbers of events separated in time as if the priority of some of them or the subsequentness of others did not in itself confer on them any special quality or marked distinction.

One property unique to space, conceived of classically and non-relativistically (an important exception, to which I will return) is that no order of spatial sequence is *ipso facto* specially marked or irreversible. If I go from London to New York I can always go back. But if I go from 1970 to 1976, there is no return. However, in recalling past events in 1970 and 1976 I can just as easily think of them in reverse order as in the order in which they occurred. Because both events are past, their separation can be thought about analogously to a spatial separation.

On the face of it, then, the relationship between past events can usually be treated like that between points in space. The tendency of analysis, therefore, is toward spatial metaphors: of size, shape, amount, quantity; mappings, diagrams, pictures, graphs, calendars, date-charts (even, in literary criticism, the little diagrams of the structure of a poem that literature professors like to draw on blackboards!).

J. T. Fraser's description of time as a hierarchy of creative conflicts suggests another way in which analysis tends towards a spatial understanding of the world: the "earliest" temporal umwelt is atemporality, the world of pure energy that existed in the first moments of the "Big Bang."[1] "Atemporal" relations cannot be distinguished from spatial ones: there is as yet no "arrow" or preferred direction of time. As we rise evolutionarily towards the higher temporalities, time distinguishes itself more and more clearly from space. Analysis, which proceeds in the opposite direction, tends towards explanations in which time is indistinguishable from space.

At this point two objections might be made: one is that the efficacy of scientific prediction apparently contradicts the proposition that analysis tends to deal with the past; the second is that some fields of analysis have denied the distinction between time and space, notably relativity theory.

In what I have said already, in the replies I shall make to the two objections raised above, and throughout this paper, I beg the reader's indulgence of my ignorance in the special fields that I shall discuss. The examples I shall give from them should be treated more as the illustrations of an idea than as the proofs of an argument. To summarize the first objection: science, which pre-eminently uses analysis, relies heavily upon prediction as proof of its hypotheses. Successful prediction proves a proposition about the world's existing or past condition by demonstrating that *under the same circumstances* the proposed result would occur again.

However, the qualification "under the same circumstances" is crucial. Scientific prediction can only legitimately apply to relatively *closed* situations: an experiment in laboratory isolation, for instance, or an observation in the rare naturally isolated cases such as planetary motions. (It could be argued that even in such exceptional cases we are isolating them simply by choosing them over other objects as objects of study.) Any scientifically predicted result, then, takes place in a medium isolated from the rest of reality. I wish to suggest that part of that isolation consists in insulating the experimental situation from evolutionarily later contamination, such as in the obvious case of an experiment in physics or inorganic chemistry, an invasion of mold or bacteria, the inquisitiveness of the laboratory cat, the sabotage attempts of a rival, or one's own desire for an experimental outcome consistent with one's convictions. Because of continuous evolutionary change, the circumstances are never the same as when the predicted event first occurred, and scientific isolation is an attempt to recreate those ideal past circumstances. Scientific prediction can only take place in enclaves of evolutionarily past time artifically or naturally insulated from evolutionarily more recent phenomena. What is called "prediction", then, is really a form of retrodiction, which is the *forte* of analysis; true prediction is impenetrable to analysis.

But suppose we knew *all* the variables in the circumstances, in other words, could treat the whole universe as an isolated experiment? Would we not then be able to predict? Here we run into a paradox resembling the "set of all sets" problems of Russell and the incompleteness theorem of Gödel. The observer of the universe who knew all those variables would have to include himself as one of them. Grant him as complex a nervous system as we will, if that nervous system is to know not only the rest of the universe, but also itself *knowing* the rest of the universe, it must, paradoxically, need to be more complex than itself.

I hope I may be permitted a highly speculative aside at this point: it may be that in a very approximate sense we human beings do in fact possess such exhaustive knowledge, by means of our senses; that our consequent ability to predict consists in our capacity to freely act and therefore in part to condition the future; and that our highly subjective and unique sense of self-consciousness and of the passing of time is none other than the continual self-inclusion suggested by the paradox above. Perhaps, finally, the universe itself is a gigantic Laplace calculator,[2] working out predictions of the future at a calculation-speed equal to and constituting the "speed of time:" predictions which are announced by their enactment; and our human actions are an increasingly significant part of that calculation.

In any case, I hope I have shown that successful "predictions" based upon analysis are peculiarly limited by the need for isolation, and work in part by the creation of archaic circumstances which rule out the effects of later and more complex forms of lawfulness.

The second objection is one which I hope to show is not an objection at all. As I understand it, the special theory of relativity, by combining space and time within the same concept of space-time,[3] was an attempt to resolve inconsistencies that showed up in either category when they were conceived of as distinct. Relativity makes space describable in temporal terms and time describable in spatial terms. My point is that relativity theory was itself a response to the very same deficiencies hidden in the predominantly analytic and spatially-oriented mode of thought that I have described. It had taken several centuries for the scientific powers of the spatial metaphor, discovered in the Renaissance, to begin to weaken. However, the stopgap nature of Einstein's accomodation of time into the spatial worldview is accentuated by the curious debate between its proponents and those of quantum theory early in this century.[4] Essentially, in reducing time to the status of a spatial dimension, relativity theory excluded most of the evolutionarily late temporal umwelts. Relativity theory treated all time as if it were past. Hence its quarrel with those who asserted the indeterminacy of certain future events.

The fundamental problem with exclusively spatial and analytical thought is that even when it deals with the past it is liable to systematic error--error which is peculiarly difficult to diagnose. Analysis, as we have seen, is correctly applied when it moves from later events to earlier, but tends to run into difficulties when it moves from the earlier to the later, even when both sets of events are in the past of the analyst. Analysis cannot see past events as novelties. Any event helps to create the very conditions under which it may later be judged plausibly to have been inevitable given its peculiar circumstances. The reason for this is that the event that occurred, the survivor, as it were, of all the other possibilities that were not realized, is part of the only surviving evidence of those circumstances. The event biases the future toward the inevitability of its occurrence. It is the victors who write history.

The foregoing should not be taken as an attack on analysis or on the spatial view of things. Analysis, or the pastward way of thinking, is just as vital a complement to the futureward way of thinking I wish to describe, as the futureward is to the pastward. Furthermore, I have ignored certain non-analytical elements of the sciences and the humanities, such as the creation of hypotheses. However, non-analytical and futureward thought is less well understood than analytic and pastward thought, and in order to discuss it intelligibly it should be clearly distinguished from its opposite, which I am attempting to do.

The world *did* evolve. What kind of thinking, to repeat the earlier question, would go in the same direction as the evolutionary process--from simple to complex?[5] Explanation, for this mode of thought, would consist not in deducing origins and reduction to components, but rather in adducing destinations and the production of syntheses. Both methods reach a kind of truth: the former says "the rose is *really* the dung it grows in"; the latter says "the dung, at its most concrete, most realized, most characteristic, is the rose". On human motivation, for instance, the former would adhere to what one might call the walnut theory of personality: "crack the outer shell of civilized artificiality, and you discover the true nature of man, his kernel, in his naked economic interests, drives and instincts"; the latter would rather adhere to the onion theory: "If you peel away all the outer skins of a human being you are left with nothing: as a *man*, he *is* all those layers of culture, art, custom." The former says: "altruism is misplaced sex"; the latter, "sex is primitive altruism".

The word I wish to use for the futureward way of thought is *poiesis*, from the Greek POIEIN, to make or create. Properly speaking, poiesis is as much a part of science as analysis is of poetry (as Professor Sebba demonstrated in his comments); but the language of poetry and art is better adapted to describing poiesis than is the language of the predominantly analytic disciplines. Poiesis is the act of creating fictions; it prescribes rather than describes; yet despite its apparent arbitrariness, it possesses some peculiar philosophical advantages, as I shall attempt to show.

Traditionally philosophy allows two kinds of statements that are both true and not nonsense: analytic statements such as that triangles contain $180^{\circ}$ (I use the term "analytic" in its strict logical sense here, rather than in the general sense in which it is used earlier in this paper); and statements of fact, such as that it is, or is not, raining--that is, empirical statements. I wish to add, following certain ideas of Wittgenstein's and Austin's,[6] a third kind of true and legitimate statement: the statement that stipulates a game or fiction. To give an example: if in a poker game, as dealer, I stipulate that "red threes are wild", this statement cannot be refuted: it enacts itself. But it is not, like the example of the triangle, tautologous; nor is it a matter of fact, like "it is raining", for unlike "it is raining", "red threes are wild" is not falsifiable. Whether it is or is not raining is independent of whether I say it is, and therefore it would be possible for me to be making an incorrect statement about the weather. My eyes might even be deceiving me. On the other hand, there is no way that I could say "red threes are wild" and be wrong about it. No other player could check his cards and say "I've got a red three and it *isn't* wild." And the statement, moreover, is perfectly correct English. Fictions, such as those stories which begin with "once upon a time", have exactly the same kind of philosophical form as "red threes are wild". They cannot be refuted or falsified, but they are not nonsense either. Consider, now, a human society. Each individual, considered analytically, is an animal whose every action is uniquely determined by physical laws. However, they agree to pretend that, on the contrary, they are completely autonomous, free, responsible beings existing in a metaphysical and fictional medium called society, equivalent to the ground-rules of poker, undetermined by any physical necessities. The words "I do" in the marriage ritual, for instance, like "red threes are wild" stipulate a shared social fiction which becomes the truth by its statement. Suppose that the members of this society became so wrapped up in their game that it took up all their time and they forgot that it was simply a game or a pretense that they were participating in. They would in fact *become* fictions, and as such, the qualities of autonomy, freedom, responsibility, could be predicated of them without any violation of philosophical truth or scientific fact. Like actors in a play they would express, and, in a fictional way, would really feel, emotions and thoughts of which they were originally incapable. In fact, if the "play" called for them to be immortal, they would indeed be immortal. It is not a grammatical eccentricity that we write of dead authors, artists, philosophers, etc., in the present tense, for instance "Socrates argues that the soul is immortal" (rather than "Socrates *argued*..."); as far as the cultural game or play or fiction is concerned,

Socrates is still alive and still capable of giving us an argument. This cultural game is an advanced form of poiesis; and the performative statements that generate it possess a truth value of their own.

The other two kinds of true and correct statements, the logical and the factual, do not afford any such space for human freedom and responsibility. Together they exhaust the types of statement allowable to what I have called the analytic, spatial mode of thought. Poietic thought, by contrast, involves an understanding that is uniquely temporal. I wish now to organize and collate that understanding into a single set of metaphors, that we may share a coherent language when discussing the question of time.

I do not consider the idea of fiction, or to use the more precise word that appears in the title of this paper, poiesis, to apply only to certain unusual cases in the realm of culture. In fact all the various forms of evolutionary emergence,[7] from the endless self-generation of more and more exhaustive mathematical systems, through the synthesis of the heavier elements and biological speciation, to perceptual, linguistic, and psychological generativeness, are relatively simpler and more primitive forms of poiesis. The universe, considered poietically, is a single hierarchical act of self-utterance, which refines and intensifies its own language by speaking it, and which creates in the process the more complex tenses of time.

The metaphor I wish to use is that of the blaze. I have borrowed this metaphor from the Ndembu, a Bantu tribe of Central Africa. They use the same word, *chinjikijilu*, in two senses: a symbol or meaningful statement, and a blaze, a mark that a hunter or explorer cuts on a tree when entering unfamiliar territory, in order to find his way back. Let us explore the implications of this collocation of ideas.

First we must establish what is for us the "known" territory, by means of an imaginary diagram. The known territory is represented by a circle. It contains, first of all, all the sets comprehended within the set of all possible sets. Secondly, it contains the completely axiomatized system of logical connections implied by Gödel's theorem.

Thirdly, it contains the relativistic physical universe, in other words, all that can be known, or, more precisely, the domain of dimensional time, the "past" of durational time. Fourthly, it contains the existing system of the living ecology. Fifthly, the domain of correct language. Sixthly, the self as it is known (as opposed to "as it knows"). Seventhly, the repertoire of the sensorium. Eighthly, the contents of history. Ninthly, the conventionally valuable. Tenthly, the True.

Let us put outside the magic circle of the familiar world all the negations of these entities: that which cannot belong to a set, what is not logically expressible, the future, the as-yet-unevolved species of life, nonsense, the self as unknowable, that for which there is no sensory language, the historically unpredictable, the unvalued, the untrue. Wittgenstein said "the limits of my language are the limits of my world".[9] Let us generalize this statement to "our" language and "our" world: and I shall for convenience now refer to what is on the inside of my circle as "our world" and what is outside as "nothing", where "nothing" means "whereof one cannot speak".

By drawing the boundary where I have drawn it, I realize that I have ignored for the present the distinctions between the mathematical, the inorganic, organic, and noetic worlds which are so important to us. I would refer you to J. T. Fraser[10] for an admirable discussion of them; moreover, my study of the boundary is a study of the general strategy by which the lower umwelts gave rise to the higher. However, for now, I wish us to include in the pronoun "we" all knowable entities, from mathematical abstractions through elements and animals to people of all cultures and periods. Together we confront the outer darkness; those lower umwelts or temporalities are our companions, even our contents or components, as we do so.

Let us now return to our explorer or hunter, who wishes to make his way from where he *is*, inside the circle of our world, to where he is not, on the outside. Let us universalize him, so that he is not merely an explorer but also the potentially emergent in general: the logical proposition which refers to the system in which it can be expressed and which is thus headed for transcendence of the system; the physical disequilibrium that makes a new moment necessary; the individual or group that is destined to be the ancestor of a new living species; the speaker who is about to produce a new sentence; the mind on the edge of self-awareness; the sensorium about to encounter and create a new sensation; the emergent historical event; the birthing value; the unwritten poem.

Symbolizing these ideas in the figure of the explorer we find an apparently insuperable difficulty. Aristotle's logic contains two values for any statement, true or false, assertion or negation. The explorer is either in familiar territory, or he is lost; either inside or outside the circle.

What I wish to suggest is that this problem disappears if we picture the boundary of the circle expanding, and metastable at any given moment. The "blaze" metaphor expresses this quality admirably. In order to connect familiar with unfamiliar territory, in other words to make the unfamiliar familiar, to be able to find his way back, the explorer cuts a blaze precisely on the boundary of the known world. The blaze instantly creates a neutral space between the familiar and the unfamiliar, a sort of fold in the surface of the probability-plane which satisfies the definitions of both "familiar" and "unfamiliar". The region from which the blaze is visible is unfamiliar in the sense that the explorer has never seen it before, but familiar in the sense that he still knows his way back from it, and can safely venture there.

Certain implications follow from the analogy. It makes no sense, for instance, to cut a blaze inside the circle, for one still knows where one is. Nor does it make sense to cut it outside the circle, for by that time one would already be lost. The great theorems in logic are not the ones which exist within the bounds of logic, nor are they merely illogical contradictions: they are the limitation theorems which establish and transcend the boundary of logic itself. A new physical entity exists on the edge between being and not-being. Speciation is the generating of something which is not exactly a monster but not exactly a true-born chip off the old block either.

Meaning occurs at the precise junction of correctness and nonsense. Self-consciousness is the touching of self and nonself. New sensation (and indeed, in one sense, all sensation) occurs at the frontier between the sensorially expected and unexpected. The historical event is unpredictable but retrodictable. The good, the true and the beautiful affirm and deny the system that gives them value. The fiction is created as and when

> "imagination bodies forth
> The forms of things unknown, the poet's pen
> Turns them to shapes, and gives to airy nothing
> A local habitation and a name."
> (Shakespeare, *A Midsummer Night's Dream*, V.i 12)

The poet cuts his blaze at the boundary of heaven and earth.[11]

And this last idea, that of fiction, is the best metaphor for how time happens. Fiction consists (1) in the assertion of a paradox at the boundary of our world (the blaze itself); (2) the creation, thereby, of a neutral space not as yet bound by the laws that govern the world-up-to-now; (3) the addition of that neutral space, with the monsters it contains, to the existing mainland; and (4) the adjustment of the new whole to itself so as to restore the lawfulness of the whole and erase the seam between the old and the new. And these phases constitute the microstructure of every new present moment as the past expands into the future, as fast as it can, at the "speed of time." Evolution on the physical level and sanity on the mental level consist in the capacity to perform each of these phases in proper sequence, and in the actual exercise of that capacity. Freud defines sanity as the ability to love and to work,[12] which nicely defines the evolutionary capacity as well; love and work are creative acts which generate time. Without all four phases the world becomes discontinuous, voids or chaosses appear in it, or it is trapped in a cyclic or fixed present, an unresolvable doublebind, the paralysis of Hamlet, who, a "neutral to his will and matter", stands irresolute between the alternatives of "to be" and "not to be". Fiction is the only answer to his dilemma. I wish I had time here to list, detail, and explain the pathologies of incomplete fictions, the lesions of time; but that must be saved for another occasion.

One implication of the model of time I propose here is that when time is genuinely poietic or creative, the present moment is not a point or dividing-line with no temporal thickness; rather, it is a region, a specious present, which contains a field of undetermined possibilities and within which a pure teleology, governed only by the will of the individual, can operate. And now we have an explanation for the curious phenomenon that is obvious to all of us but inexplicable in analytical terms: freedom. Freedom can be predicated of that neutral space opened up by the blaze; appropriately enough it exists as such only at the time, and if we look back on it from a later stage, when the neutral space has become a legitimate part of the known world, it disappears. Incidentally, such a model makes possible a forensic morality which would preserve both the conservative impulse to put the responsibility for a crime on the individual, and the liberal impulse to blame society and history for the crime. If freedom is a fiction, but no less real for that, then punishment, whose rationale is admittedly a fiction also, becomes philosophically necessary and justifiable. Punishment is a fiction which creates freedom.

It is not entirely necessary that the blaze or landmark be at the edge of the known world. If it is sufficiently conspicuous, it can continue indefinitely to generate a neutral space at the borders of the world. Great fictions, like the *Odyssey*, have lost little of their effectiveness in generating new presents for our culture.

I would like to conclude this paper with a group of citations from major works of literary art, which will demonstrate that all poets, in the broad sense of the word "poet", are implicit adherents of the kind of theory of art that I have described here.

Perhaps the most fundamental of all poetic metaphors is the journey. Whether the journey is epic, as in the *Odyssey*, or picaresque, as in Cervantes' *Don Quixote*, or mystical as in Dante's *Divine Comedy*, or allegorical, as in Spenser's *Faerie Queen* , or satirical, as in Swift's *Gulliver's Travels*, or psychological, as in Coleridge's *The Ancient Mariner* , or surreal, as in *Le Bateau Ivre* of Rimbaud, or all of them, in

Melville's *Moby Dick*, this core symbol expresses the essentially exploring, interloping nature of the artist as he feels his way outwards beyond the known world (often symbolized by the land) into the unknown (often the ocean). "We were the first", says the Ancient Mariner in Coleridge's poem, "that ever burst Into that silent sea".[13] We watch the new ocean "silent, upon a peak in Darien". (Keats: "On First Looking into Chapman's Homer.") Sometimes the unknown that the adventurer penetrates is conceived as a labyrinth or maze: that is, not an external mystery but an internal one. The nighttown sequence of Joyce's *Ulysses*, Spenser's labyrinth of Error, the "caverns measureless to man" in Coleridge's *Kubla Khan*, and the heart of darkness, the snake-like river that Marlowe navigates in Conrad's story to find the mad lost artist, half-beast, half-man, at its center--all these spring to mind. Sometimes the voyager discovers a magic island: Ogygia, Aiaia,[14] Dante's Purgatory, Utopia (which means in Greek, "noplace"), Prospero's island in Shakespeare's *Tempest*, Lilliput;--or he is menaced by monsters of the deep: whales in *Beowulf*, the White Whale in *Moby Dick*. The island is the poetic subject, the monsters are the half-formed and terrible conceptions that tempt and threaten the poet; the poet is redeemed by blessing them in *The Ancient Mariner*, goes to hunt them in *Moby Dick*, is distracted from his swimming-race by them in *Beowulf*, and is nearly engulfed by them in the Scylla and Charybdis episode of the *Odyssey*. A monster is a perceptual category which includes the perceptually uncategorizable: it is a new kind of perception in the process of birth.

Related to the island-symbol is the poetic Paradise: the world of the deathless in the Epic of Gilgamesh, the garden-world of Calypso,[15] Milton's "delicious paradise" of Eden, shaped, we find, like a breast and crowned by a fountain;[16] Coleridge's Xanadu,[17] Shakespeare's fairyland in *A Midsummer Night's Dream*. Paradise is the new poietic world that is opened up beyond the border of this one by the poet's act of explanation or imagination: an enclave surrounded by a rampart of tall trees, or a "silver sea" which "serves it in the office of a moat", or "with walls and towers engirded round". Thoreau's *Walden*, whose pond is "no intermitting spring" is an American Transcendentalist parallel.

The idea of the limit, or boundary, or edge is itself a central poetic symbol. The poet reaches across that edge into the other world--whether of the dead or of eternal life--and brings something back. In Lockwood's dream in Emily Brontë's *Wuthering Heights* he finds his hand seized by the ghost-hand of a little dead girl when he reaches out through a broken window into the dark (Melville in *Moby Dick* recalls a similar ghostly grasp of the hand, and the Ancient Mariner holds his victim with his "skinny hand"). Hamlet speaks of the undiscovered country from whose "bourn No traveller returns'--the word bourne, or boundary, is taken up again in *Antony and Cleopatra:*

Cleo: I'll set a bourn how far to be belov'd.

Ant: Then must thou needs find out new heaven, new earth.[18]

Shakespeare wonderfully describes the "bourn" between heaven and earth, that the poet crosses, in *A Midsummer Night's Dream:*

"The poet's eye, in a fine frenzy rolling
Doth glance from heaven to earth, from earth to heaven".

For Captain Ahab, though, the boundary or wall between us and the mystery behind the world is a "pasteboard mask", and the human project is to "strike through". Kurtz, in *Heart of Darkness*, who has gone where no man should go, "had kicked himself loose of the earth. He had kicked the very earth to pieces". To cross that limit is to be accursed, followed by the furies like Sartre's Orestes,[19] or troubled by a ghastly urge to prophetic speech, like the Ancient Mariner. There are "more things in heaven and earth than are dreamt of in your philosophy", says Hamlet, but to find them out one must venture

"...to the dreadful summit of the cliff,
That beetles o'er his base into the sea"

and encounter monsters that can

"...deprive your sovereignty of reason
And draw you into madness." (see note 20)

Still the ghost calls, and the poet, who has a fine temperament for his fate, must follow. But the journey outward is not enough; the poet must return, must stake out the new territory in words. "Report me and my cause aright to the unsatisfied"; "pray you, in your letters...Speak of me as I am, nothing extenuate".[21] Odysseus must return to tell his tale. The Mariner has "strange powers of speech". "I only" says Ishmael, quoting the servant of Job, "am escaped to tell thee".[22] Despite the dangers of the journey, we need, in Thoreau's words, "to see our limits transcended"; we must, in Orestes' words, "blaze our trail".

The pattern of metaphors I have sketched here could be much further elaborated. It is my considered belief that some version of it is fundamental to every major work of literature--for literary art is itself the expansion of the linguistic universe. It is, perhaps, in these metaphors that we can begin to talk about that fictive, stipulative, productive and synthetic way of thought which I have here contrasted with the analytic mode and which I have given the name Poiesis. Poiesis is the way in which we deal with the future, and with relationships which proceed in the direction of evolution, from earlier to later. And it is peculiarly adapted to those aspects of the world in which time is more important than space.

NOTES

1. See J. T. Fraser: *Time As Conflict: a Scientific and Humanistic Study* (Basel: Birkhäuser Verlag and Brookfield, Vt.: Renouf U.S.A., 1978).

2. See Pierre Simon, Marquis de Laplace: *A Philosophical Essay on Probabilities* New York, 1952), pp. 73-106.

3. A classical Newtonian graph of motion contains a time axis which cannot be distinguished mathematically from a space axis. That is, if the axes were not labeled *s* and *t*, we should have no way of telling whether the graph described the acceleration and deceleration of a moving body, or merely a curve in more than one dimension of space. The Minkowski diagram in relativity theory, on the other hand, does distinguish mathematically between the time axis and the space axes; but the distinction is a simple one, and it would still be possible to imagine a point of view for which the time dimension were simply a rather twisted space dimension, as, for instance, in the theory of geodesics. Relativity still describes time as a *dimension:* this is the problem.

4. See Werner Heisenberg: *Physics and Philosophy* (London, 1959).

5. I wish to distinguish the point of view I am taking here from that of Henri Bergson, as expressed, for instance, in *Creative Evolution*(London, 1964), pp. 329-331, and *Time and Free Will* (New York, 1960), pp. 163, 236. Bergson's intuitive contemplation of *la durée* does indeed resemble in some respects what I have called futureward thinking; but the difference is this. Bergson regards human language as essentially analytical, as imposing an essentially discontinuous and spatial conception of time. The point I wish to make is that the artistic use of language, or poiesis, is perfectly capable of dealing with, and in a sense *generating*, time in its non-dimensional and entropy decreasing aspects. In this connection the analogy between the syntactical

structure of language and the chemical structure of DNA, and between linguistic and biological evolution, becomes suggestive. Language may be evolution by other means.

The difference between Bergson's view of language and the one espoused by myself and such Anglo-Saxon philosophers as Whitehead (whose book *Science and the Modern World* is clearly an influence on this paper), may bc related to the differences between the French and English languages. A good general discussion of such differences may be found in George Steiner's *After Babel* (London, 1975). In a conversation I had with Mr. Steiner after a series of lectures he had given on the differences between Racine and Shakespeare, this point became clear.

6. Ludwig Wittgenstein: *Tractatus Logico-Philosophicus* (London, 1955). J. L. Austin: *Philosophical Papers* (Oxford, 1970), pp. 233-252.

7. I use the term 'emergence' in Fraser's sense.

8. See V. W. Turner: *Revelation and Divination in Ndembu Ritual* (Cornell, 1975), pp. 212-213.

9. Op.cit., 5-6.

10. Op. cit., 436-40.

11. We might add to this list the paradigm-changing hypothesis, a 'blaze' itself, as described in Thomas Kuhn's *Structure of Scientific Revolutions* (Chicago, 1973), pp. 52-76.

12. E.g. in *Civilization and its Discontents* (New York, 1961), pp. 26-29.

13. 1. 105.

14. *The Odyssey*, books V,X.

15. *The Odyssey*, book V.

16. *Paradise Lost*, IV. 223-235.

17. In 'Kubla Khan'.

18. I.i.16.

19. In *The Flies*.

20. *Hamlet*, I.iv.70.

21. *Othello*, V.ii.339.

22. In *Moby Dick*.

# VIII. CHRISTIANITY, HINDUISM, MITHRAISM

## Time, Space and Freewill: The Leibniz-Clarke Correspondence

D. Corish

*ABSTRACT*

*The Newtonian theory, as expressed by Clarke, of absolute time and space, and the opposing Leibnizian theory of relational time and space, are both advocated in the context of the question of divine freewill. For Clarke and Newton the Freedom of God entails the choice of creating the world here or there, at an earlier time or a later - so that space and time are conceived of as constituting a pre-existing matrix, independent of the world, into which, at this or that temporal or spatial position, the world is placed. The choice of such temporal or spatial positions is entirely free, there being nothing to recommend one position over another. For Leibniz, on the other hand, such a choice, if it were possible, would be arbitrary, inexplicable, and contrary to the rational structure which the scientist expects the universe to exhibit. For Leibniz then there is no such arbitrary divine choice, and consequently, time and space are not a pre-existing matrix offering such a choice. They are not a framework into which the world is placed but a framework which arises only as a result of the creation of the world; they are relations between created things. Clarke objects that it is not clear how time and space as relations between things afford the mathematical magnitudes which the scientific view requires. Leibniz's reply seems weak, as it does not show exactly how relations between things can exhibit quantity. The subsequent history of physics however has seemed to bear out the Leibnizian rather than the Newtonian view. Hence we must ask whether in fact*

> *it is the Leibnizian view, that time and space are relations between things, which has triumphed, or something much more like the Newtonian view: that time and space inherently, and not merely derivatively, exhibit a quantitative nature.*

The *Leibniz-Clarke Correspondence* is usually read, by historians and philosophers of science at any rate, for the exchange contained in it on the absolutist and relationist theories of time and space. The larger question of divine freewill, into which the question of time and space is incorporated, simply as an example, is commonly ignored. And this is a pity. For though one may study the theories of time and space without reference to divine freewill, nevertheless the larger context does serve to throw an interesting light on those theories themselves, and does tend to make clear, I think, better than the subsequent history of the theories in question can do, some of the real problems on both sides. Furthermore, the discussion of freewill itself in the *Leibniz-Clarke Correspondence* is one of the most lively and articulate debates on that issue to be found anywhere. The fact that what was at stake was divine rather than human freewill simply made the issues clearer - for both writers could of course assume that they were dealing with the freewill of an omniscient, infallible mind, so that the question became a pure one, so to speak, of the analysis of the concept of freewill, and inessential but obfuscating questions of human conditions, and especially of human weakness and ignorance, could be ignored. Similarly, the questions concerning time and space which are raised in this context become questions of what properties time and space must have, essentially, and not simply how they appear to humans.[1]

What I see to be gained from an examination of this discussion in its historical context, straddling as it does natural theology, metaphysics, physics, and even the philosophy of mathematics, is an appreciation of the arguments on both sides of the question. The historian of philosophy does not always have to take a stand and argue for one side against the other. He may be permitted a pleasure which is all too often denied the serious and partisan philosopher: the delight in a good argument for its own sake. Indeed it may well be that the most useful function of the historian of philosophy, his most useful service to philosophy itself, is realized in precisely the exercise of that delight; for by its means he is prompted to give the most sympathetic and strongest account of the systems he describes. At any rate, perverse or not, such a delight in a good argument is possible on both sides of the Leibniz-Clarke controversy, both as regards the freewill question itself and as regards its exemplification in temporal and spatial terms.[2]

The over-riding consideration of both correspondents, the consideration indeed in terms of which the controversy becomes possible at all, is the intelligibility of the world. For both the correspondents the world must be intelligible for a rational science, either philosophy or physics, to be possible - and in this view of course they continue the main traditions of both Greek and mediaeval thought. But there was in traditional thought, as there is in the Leibniz-Clarke controversy, a difference of opinion as to how intelligibility relates to choice, and we are going to have to consider that a little, because it has an effect on the doctrines of time and space that will be chosen to exemplify choice.

Leibniz and Clarke may be said to take quite classical, and classically opposed, positions on the issue of choice - and their positions on it illuminate the issue considerably. Leibniz takes a basically Socratic-Platonic view that every choice must be explicable in terms of the best reasons available to the chooser, so that a choice by a fully knowing mind of anything other than the best alternative would be quite inexplicable, and therefore impossible. Clarke, on the other hand, takes a broadly Aristotelian view.

Aristotle had claimed that Scorates's doctrine that a knowing agent tends naturally to follow the known better course (so that the worse can be followed only through ignorance) ignores the notorious fact that men sometimes know the better course but follow the worse. On the basis of this assumed fact then, Aristotle constructs his own doctrine of choice, in terms of which a knower might pay no attention to, might deliberately turn his attention away from, a better course, and attend to a worse for whatever good might be seen in it, and thus follow the worse course.[3]

Aristotle, in trying to reconcile this view with the Socratic-Platonic one of ill-doing and ignorance, does not hold to it as strongly as his own theory would give him leave to do, but the view does come into the literature, and becomes for one school the only possible doctrine of free choice - in this version: that the recognizer of alternatives is as such not bound to any of them. In the thirteenth century Aquinas espouses this view,[4] and this is basically the view we find in Samuel Clarke.

The battle-lines then are drawn. For Leibniz it is inconceivable that God should not have chosen the best possible course in creating the world. There could be no reason why the best course was not chosen - which is why of course for Leibniz this has to be the best of all possible worlds. And if some course other than the best had been chosen, the world would be unintelligible, science and philosophy impossible. For Clarke, on the other hand, to say that God is bound to one course of creation rather than another is to deny the freedom of the divinity and make him an automaton. There is a reason why the world is the way it is; but that reason is simply the will of God, who chose with absolute freedom between many equally possible alternatives - so that this is not necessarily the best of all possible worlds. The intelligibility of the world must allow an intelligible account of the freedom of possessors of intellectual knowledge, and of God most of all. The controversy then unfolds as follows.

Leibniz asserts in his second letter that the mathematical principles of Newton's system, to which Clarke, a student and friend of Newton's, adheres, are not sufficient for combating materialism; that their foundations are merely the principles of contradiction and identity; but that "to proceed from mathematics to natural philosophy" another principle is needed. This is "the principle of a sufficient reason, viz. that nothing happens without a reason why it should be so, rather than otherwise" (L, II, 1, pp. 15-16).

It is in reply to this contention that Clarke introduces the subject of divine freewill and its exemplification in terms of absolute space. He agrees that there must be a sufficient reason why anything is, and why it is so rather than otherwise, but contends that that sufficient reason is "oft-times no other than the mere will of God." As an example, he says that there can be no other reason why one system or particle of matter should be in one place rather than in another, since mere position has no effect on matter, "all place being absolutely indifferent to all matter." There is then nothing to motivate the will of God to place such matter in one position rather than another, and that will is entirely free in this respect. If it were not, but, like a balance, had to be inclined one way by a predominating weight on that side, "this would tend to take away all power of choosing, and to introduce fatality" (C, II, 1, pp. 20-21). If God's reason, or anything else, necessitates him to act, then God is not free.

It is to this allegation that Leibniz must address himself. He says that Clarke grants the principle of sufficient reason "only in words, and in reality denies it." The evidence that Clarke does not see the full strength of the principle of sufficient reason is to be found, Leibniz asserts, in Clarke's use of the example of space, as though space were "a real absolute being." For Leibniz can show, in accordance with the principle of sufficient reason, that space is not as Clarke and Newton conceive it - or time either; for both time and space are only relations of order in which bodies can be placed.

Suppose we were to ask why God did not create everything a year sooner than he did. If he could have, then there could be no reason why he should choose the one time over the other, because it really would be a matter of indifference which time should be preferred, and there never then could be a sufficient reason why one time should be preferred over the other. But then, Leibniz urges, this consideration itself shows (since God cannot, according to the principle of sufficient reason, have made such an impossible choice) that time is not some absolute real being in itself, independent of things existing in time. It is merely a certain order - namely, the intuitively recognized temporal order - of those things themselves. Time then is simply the order of the things which we say are in time. God could have had no such impossible choice as deciding, for no reason at all, between two different times at which the world might be created, since there are no two different times until the world is created. The different times are merely different positions of things arranged relatively to each other in what we recongize to be a temporal order. And similar conditions hold with regard to space - so that space too is merely the intuitively recognized spatial order of things (L, III, 5-6, pp. 26-27).

For Clarke, as for Newton also, time and space form a four-dimensional matrix, independent of the physical world and infinite in extent, the one temporal dimension being independent of the three spatial. The points of this matrix, which are the instants of time and the points of space, have each an individual identity distinct from that of every other point. They have, or indeed are, different Cartesian coordinates, except that any given origin is not arbitrary but is a point of space or time with its own absolute identity and its own absolute distance from each other point. In short, the Newtonian space-time matrix is absolute not only in the sense of not being relative to the existence of the physical world but also in the sense that each spatial or temporal position, and consequently each spatial or temporal distance, is fixed once and for all. Into this pre-existing, infinite matrix God the creator introduces the physical world. As a consequence, the spatial and temporal positions within that physical world are pre-existing, immaterial positions which happen to be occupied by various pieces of matter. We may not indeed, as Newton himself confesses in the *Principia*, be able to pinpoint a single one of those absolute positions, and may have to be content to measure with our rulers and clocks the merely relative distances between material things - but the theoretical framework of Newtonian mechanics, like that of Euclidean geometry, appeals to the "absolute, true, and mathematical," the ideal mathematical magnitudes, and not simply to the relative and merely approximately accurate measurements of rulers and clocks.

A consequence of this Newtonian absolutist view of time and space is that God must be conceived to position the physical world in the pre-existing matrix at a certain time and place in it. If one conceived of the matrix as a box, one could say that

God places the world in this part and not that part of the box, or that he places one part of the world in this part of the box, another in that. Consequently, it makes perfect sense on the Newtonian view for Clarke to say that God could have placed various parts of the world here rather than there, and that he could have created it at this rather than that time. The times and places are already there and only have to be occupied. There is no reason, Clarke will say, why one point rather than another should be occupied, since all points are equally occupiable, all equally indifferent to occupation - no reason, that is, except the mere will of God the disposer.

Now Leibniz sees in all this a violation of the principle of sufficient reason. For Leibniz time and space are not a pre-existing matrix which contains the world; they are rather a consequent matrix, which the world constitutes and contains. For time and space are merely the intuitively recognized temporal and spatial arrangement of things in the physical world; nothing more. As arrangements of things time and space do not exist until the things in arrangement do. The things existing then constitute by their order relative to each other temporal and spatial arrangement. Time and space are purely relative: their positions and distances are the relative positions and distances of things from each other, and time and space themselves, as wholes, are relative to the existence of things which can assume between themselves such an order and arrangement as time and space are. So time and space do not exist until the universe is created, and instead of containing it, it contains them. The universe itself, as a whole, cannot then for Leibniz be somewhere and at some time, as it is for Newton and Clarke, for, on the contrary, all wheres and all times are totally within the universe, being established by relations of order within it.

God therefore, for Leibniz, can have no such impossible choice as that of placing the world in time and space, since time and space, being relations between things in the world, cannot exist unless the world does. "Instants and also points of space considered without the things, are nothing at all; and...they consist only in the successive order of things" (L, III, 6, pp. 26-27). But if, *per impossibile*, time and space constituted a pre-existing matrix, as Clarke supposes, then Clarke would be right in saying that God could have no reason for choosing one position over another for occupation by bits of matter, since the positions as such would, as Clarke says, be absolutely indifferent to what occupied them. But the conclusion to be drawn from this, says Leibniz, is not that God would simply decide, without any reason other than freewill itself, at which indifferent positions to place the material elements, but that God would not decide, and precisely because of the lack of such a reason. To think in terms of a pre-existing space-time matrix which then imposes arbitrary, reasonless, decisions upon God is to misunderstand the principle of sufficient reason:

> It is plainly maintaining, that God wills something, without any sufficient reason for his will: against the axiom, or the general rule of whatever happens [the principle of sufficient reason, which Leibniz takes Clarke to grant, at least "in words"]. This is falling back into loose indifference, which I have confuted at large,...and contrary to the wisdom of God, as if he could operate without acting by reason (L.III, 7, p. 27).

God then can act no more than Buridan's ass can where two alternatives are perfectly equal, so that there is no reason for preferring one over the other. But such an equality itself, as far as Leibniz is concerned, violates the principle of sufficient reason. For if the principle of sufficient reason is "the axiom, or the general rule of whatever happens," then when something has happened there must have been a sufficient reason why it has happened, and such a sufficient reason cannot have been found in a situation in which there were two equally possible but mutually exclusive alternatives. Hence, when something has happened there was no such situation. The principle of sufficient reason rules it out. The Newtonian system, which allows such situations, is thus itself in violation of the principle of sufficient reason. Only Leibniz's theory, which makes time and space relations between things, is in accord with that principle, since it avoids saying that the creator must have to make impossible decisions between equally possible positions.

Clarke has various replies to this, of various degrees of adequacy. One reply, which is clearly inadequate, is that "if time were nothing but the order of succession of created things; it would follow, that if God had created the world millions of ages sooner than he did, yet it would not have been created at all the sooner" (C, III, 4, p. 32). It is plain here that Clarke understands Leibniz only so far as to say that an earlier creation would not be earlier, which is of course a contradiction. Clarke does not understand Leibniz's contention that time itself does not exist - that is to say that there *is* no earlier - unless the created world exists. For Clarke it makes sense to say that the world does not exist before God creates it, and that this 'before' is temporal. He simply cannot see the possibility of a beginning of time, and so misunderstands Leibniz on this point.

Another, and much more serious, objection which Clarke has to Leibniz's view is the contention that "space and time are quantities; which situation and order are not" (C, III, 4, p. 32). We shall come back to this - but first let us deal with the question of divine choice as Clarke sees it bearing on the question of time and space.

For Clarke there is no violation of the principle of sufficient reason in the contention that there is a pre-existing space-time matrix into which, at whatever indifferent positions, God introduces the world. There are absolutely equal choices to be made; God can, if he so chooses, create the world earlier or later, or place any parts of it in this or that position in the spatial matrix. The sole sufficient reason for any such temporal or spatial positioning is the mere will of God himself, since the temporal or spatial positions provide no ground for the preference of themselves over any others. Leibniz, as we have seen, contends that under such circumstances God could make no choice at all, since he could have no sufficient reason for making one - and we must suppose him to be guided by reason. Clarke replies that such a view:

> Leads to universal necessity and fate, by supposing that motives have the same relation to the will of an intelligent agent, as weights have to a balance; so that of two things absolutely indifferent, an intelligent agent can no more choose either, than a balance can move itself when the weights on both sides are equal (C, IV, 1 and 2, p. 45).

He argues that an intelligent power is not merely a patient, as a balance is, but an agent, able to move itself "sometimes upon the view of strong motives, sometimes upon weak ones, and sometimes where things are absolutely indifferent." The intelligent being then may be indifferent to its own motivation, and the sufficient reason for its choice may simply be its own will.

Leibniz in his last letter accepts the image of the balance: - "It is true, that reasons in the mind of a wise being, and motives in any mind whatsoever, do that which answers to the effect produced by weights in a balance" (L, V, 3, p. 55). But, he contends, this is merely a matter of moral necessity - we might better perhaps call it a matter of the necessity of explanation - and not of logical necessity. By moral necessity, and in accordance with the principle of sufficient reason, "a wise being chooses the best, and every mind follows the strongest inclination," just as a balance tips to the greater weight (L, V, 4, p. 56). He explains that things are logically necessary only where their negations are contradictions (for example, it is logically necessary that the sum of the internal angles of a Euclidean triangle be equal to two right angles), whereas in the case of contingent existences, such as that of the physical universe, their negation implies not a contradiction but only a different state of affairs from the existing one. Nevertheless, for Leibniz the existing state of affairs is the best possible one, because God the creator foresaw all possibilities, and could have no reason for not choosing the best. This is the best of all possible worlds, and the moral necessity with which the creator chose it and all its details is the necessity of an omniscient, omnipotent mind which is guided by reason and always acts according to its own infallible view of what is best. Other arrangements than the actual one are perfectly possible, in the sense that their negations are not contradictions; but the actual situation, being one among such possibles, is also necessary, in the sense that it represents the best that can be effected by an omnipotent, omniscient creator. So other situations than the actual could in fact never have occurred actually, because they were not for the best, though they were possibilities. This, says Leibniz:

> Does not derogate from liberty. For when a wise being, and especially God, who has supreme wisdom, chooses what is best, he is not the less free upon that account: on the contrary, it is the most perfect liberty, not to be hindered from acting in the best manner. And when any other chooses according to the most apparent and the most strongly inclining, he imitates therein the liberty of a truly wise being, in proportion to his disposition. Without this, the choice would be a blind chance (L, V, 7, pp. 56-57).

It is this "blind chance," this arbitrariness - enemy, obviously, of all rational explanation, - that Leibniz sees lurking behind the Newtonian system of absolute time and space, a system which would impose on God the irrational choice of preferring one indifferent position over another. Irrational, indeed impossible, because there could be no sufficient reason, no preponderating good, to tip the balance of God's will to one alternative rather than another. Such a choice could only be one of "blind chance."

To this Clarke not unnaturally replies that Leibniz in requiring always a preponderating motive does make God into an operator who works with mere mechanical necessity - no matter that the necessitating agents are reasons rather than physical weights. This, Clarke thinks, is to misunderstand the notion of agency, "the power of self-motion or action: which in all animate agents is spontaneity; and, in moral agents, is what we properly call liberty" (C, V, 1-20, p. 97). The balance cannot act out of its own spontaneity, whereas a mind, and especially God's mind, can. To think that "for want of a sufficient weight" God could not act where two opposite alternatives exactly balanced each other "is making God not an active, but a passive, being: which is, not to be a God, or governor, at all" (C, V, 1-20, p. 98). What then Leibniz denounces as "blind chance" Clarke advocates as the spontaneity essential to the agency of a free being. And the Newtonian time and space, with their indifference of positions to the material occupying them allow God just such a suitable spontaneity of choice.

The necessity which Leibniz claims is merely the "moral" necessity of God's choosing the best course is, Clarke contends, absolute necessity. For what is at stake is "some other reason sufficient, which is the real cause of the action, by operating upon the agent, and making him to be, not indeed an agent, but a mere patient"

(C, V, 1-20, p. 99). God's reason for choosing the best necessitates him to choose the best and leaves him no choice, which is to say no liberty, no freewill. And indeed it does make sense to ask whether Leibniz's principle of sufficient reason does not in the last analysis become conflated with the principle of contradiction. For if God must choose the best course, and so cannot have a choice if two equal alternatives should present themselves, and if the actual situation must in consequence be the best of all possibilities, is it not in fact contradictory to assert the possibility of other situations, which can never be actual because they are not the best? God, because he must act for the best, cannot in fact choose any other course. Any other course then is an impossible one. To assert the possibility then of any course other than the actual one (the actuality of which proclaims it was the only one choosable by God) is to assert a contradiction.

Granted: man may not be able to see the formal reason why some state of affairs other than the actual should not be. But that is merely a question of human ignorance. We may be sure, if the principle of sufficient reason holds in the strong version of Leibniz rather than in the weak version of Clarke, that there is a reason why a non-existing state of affairs cannot be, even though we cannot see that reason. The principle of sufficient reason becomes merely a version, suited to human ignorance, of the principle of contradiction. The whole realm of being becomes a realm of absolute necessity. And what disappears in particular is the freewill of God, who no longer has any real choice, whether of temporal and spatial positions or of anything else.

We have now come to this pass: if Leibniz is right, then time and space are merely relations between things in the world, the world seems to be susceptible of scientific explanation, but freewill, even divine freewill, disappears in the interests of such explanation; if Clarke is right, time and space are an absolute, physically independent, matrix, the divine freewill is upheld for choices concerning that matrix, but it appears that the possibility of scientific explanation ceases, since mere will, mere arbitrary choice, now becomes a sufficient reason for some states of affairs - and mere arbitrary choice is itself obviously not susceptible of scientific explanation. It may have been some such considerations which prompted Kant later on to declare that we can prove as an "antimony" both that there is freedom in the world and that there is not. And it may also have been some such considerations which moved Kant, who ultimately supported the Newtonian views, and asserted freedom, to declare that freedom could not be subject to human objective explanation, which is necessitarian.

Let us return now to the opposed space-time structures which are respectively consonant with such opposed views of divine freewill: for Clarke the Newtonian space-time matrix, and for Leibniz the relational space and time of the created world. I have said that Leibniz appears to have a scientifically explainable world, even at the cost of divine freewill, but there is still one outstanding criticism of Clarke's that Leibniz's theory of time and space must satisfy. That is the criticism that "space and time are quantities, which situation and order are not." Leibniz does not in fact answer this in his next, his fourth, letter, and Clarke reproaches him with this in his reply (C, IV, 14, 16, and 17, p. 49). So in his fifth and last letter Leibniz takes up the point: -

> As for the objection that space and time are quantities, or rather things endowed with quantity; and that situation and order are not so: I answer, that order also has its quantity; there is in it, that which goes before, and that which follows; there is distance or interval. Relative things have their quantity, as well as absolute ones. For instance, ratios or proportions in mathematics, have their quantity, and are measured by logarithms; and yet they are relations. And therefore though time and space consist in relations, yet they have their quantity (L, V, 54, p. 75).

To this Clarke replies that:

> Going before, and following, constitutes situation or order: but the distance, interval, or quantity of time or space, wherein one thing follows another, is entirely a distinct thing from the situation or order, and does not constitute any quantity of situation or order: the situation or order may be the same, when the quantity of time or space intervening is very different (C, V, 54, p. 105).

For example, A may come three days or three hours or three seconds before B, in which cases though the order is precisely the same - A is earlier than B - nevertheless the distances are entirely different. Clarke goes on to say: first, if certain sorts of relations were quantities, it would not follow that the relation of order was; secondly, proportions are not in fact quantities but the proportions of quantities (for example, the proportion of six to one as compared with the proportion of three to one "is not a double quantity of proportion, but the proportion of a double quantity"); thirdly, "space and time are not of the nature of proportions at all, but of the nature of absolute quantities to which proportions belong." For the same quantity (say, a day) can bear different proportions to other quantities (say, half a day on the one hand and one hour on the other), and yet remain the same quantity. "Time therefore, (and space likewise by the same argument) is not of the nature of a proportion, but of an absolute and unvaried quantity, to which different proportions belong" (C, V, 54, p. 107).

It has to be admitted, I think, that Leibniz's contention that time and space viewed as relations can nevertheless exhibit quantity is very weak, whereas Clarke's reply is by comparison very strong. It is not surprising that Leibniz's view fell out of favour with succeeding scientists - and especially not surprising when we remember also that Leibniz also argued on the basis of the principle of sufficient reason against the possibility of a vacuum. As Max Jammer puts it: "With the gradual acceptance of the Newtonian system, and as the rival Cartesian theories fell out of grace, Newton's concept of absolute space [and time, we might add] became a fundamental prerequisite of physical investigation."[5]

But in fact, as Jammer points out, during the eighteenth century the great French physicists Lagrange, Laplace, and Poisson, lost interest in the problem of the absolute matrix, and tended to accept the idea "as a working hypothesis without worrying about its theoretical justification."[6] And in England in the nineteenth century "the great success of Newtonian physics led to the paradoxical situation of the adherence to the concepts of absolute time and absolute space, on the one hand, and their absence from practical physics, on the other."[7] Then in 1888 Ludwig Lange proposed eliminating "the concept of absolute space from the conceptual foundation of physics," in favour of an "inertial system," which is "a co-ordinate system [of mass points] in respect to which Newton's law of inertia holds."[8] Finally, as it became apparent that it was impossible to detect absolute space in any sense, we come to the abandonment of Lorentz's attempt to identify the motionless ether with absolute space and Einstein's establishment of relativity theory:

> Physics, and not only mechanics, was ready to abandon the concept of absolute space altogether. Poincaré's words "Whoever speaks of absolute space uses a word devoid of meaning," became an accepted truth.[9]

And of course with the notion of absolute space went that of absolute time.

I produce, or rather reproduce, this drastically encapsulated history of the fate of Newtonian theory only by way of commentary on Clarke's criticism of Leibniz's contention that time and space are relations, and yet "have their quantity." It surely appears as if Leibniz's view won out in the long run, though his defense of it is weak and Clarke's criticism of it strong. But is it in fact correct to say that Leibniz's view won out?

I think not. We must remember that Leibniz considers time and space to be relations between created things, so that both distance and dimensionless positions, instants and points, must be constituted in terms of those relations. Time, he suggests, is not "any thing distinct from things existing in time." And "instants, consider'd without the things, are nothing at all; and...they consist only in the successive order of things" (L, III, 6, p. 27). Now how does one derive instants from "things existing in time" - that is, how does one derive the concept of dimensionless position from the concept of "the successive order of things"? It is noteworthy that the modern mathematical theory of the continuum does not attempt to do so.[10]

It envisages "elements" in a preceding-succeeding relation (which may be read as 'earlier-later' for time, 'left-right' or 'up-down', *etc.*, for space, and 'less-greater' for number), and it is quite clear that the "elements," which may be considered to be infinite in number and densely packed (between any two there is a third) are point-like - that is, they are indivisible positions in the relationship of preceding or succeeding to other such "elements."[11] In other words, these "elements" are not derived from anything; they are simply assumed - and as such, assumed indivisible positions, they are far closer to Newton's instants and points than to Leibniz's.

It is also worth pointing out that Leibniz does not here mention the monads, which are his "true Atoms of nature, and, in fact, the Elements of things."[12] Leibniz's accounts of time and space, and of their relation to the monads, are scattered, and not always entirely consistent with each other, but we may certainly agree with Herbert Wildon Carr that for Leibniz "space is the order of coexistence, time the order of succession, in the monad's perceptions."[13] Each monad is conceived of as a simple, indivisible, substance, having a succession of "perceptions," which are mirrorings of other monads and each of their perceptions, the whole arranged by God in a pre-established harmony, so that no substance, no monad, need be considered to act directly on any other - for Leibniz thought that only God could act on other substances - and yet each monad could be considered as reacting to the states of other substances, through this pre-established harmony of mirroring. The net result is the ordinary world of our experience, in which it *seems* that things act on one another - and scientific accounts are perfectly possible in terms of this seeming. Time and space are also parts of this well-founded seeming, and so have genuine scientific status. As Leibniz says of the spatial, and, by implication, the temporal, relation: "it must be a mere ideal thing, the consideration of which is nevertheless useful" (L, V, 47, p. 71).

But there is nothing in all this to show how instants can be derived from the temporal relation, whether that relation be one on the level of monads or, more generally, as in the correspondence with Clarke, one between "things existing in time." And instants are for Leibniz equally as well founded scientifically as time itself: - "Whatever exists of time and of duration, [being successive] perishes continually.... Nothing of time does ever exist, but instants" (L, V, 49, p. 72). Time, we might say, is continually unravelling from the future to the past, and all we are ever left with is the present, which is a mere instant, rather than an interval, between the past and the future. Leibniz's relational theory of time requires that 'the instant' be defined in terms of the temporal relation which holds between "things existing in time," for "instants, consider'd without the things, are nothing at all." Then, since the instants must be considered ontologically more fundamental than intervals - "nothing of time does ever exist, but instants" - we should expect that 'temporal interval' should be defined by reference to instants. In view of the parallelism between time and space in Leibniz generally, one should expect somewhat similar considerations to apply to space. Leibniz might not say nothing ever exists of space but points, since space does not appear to have the same evanescent quality that time has, but one should expect a definition of 'point' and 'spatial interval' in terms of the relation of spatial order. As far as I can see, no such definitions, in the case of either time or space, are forthcoming.

Furthermore, the instants and spatial points of modern physical theory are not defined in terms of fundamental temporal and spatial relations between "things" existing in such relations. Instead, those positions are assumed. They are taken over from the mathematics of the continuum, in which they are assumed as "elements," and not defined in terms of the relations between "things." The mathematics of the continuum, as might be expected of an ideal system, is far more Newtonian absolutist than Leibnizian relationist. It is true that the Newtonian matrix of absolutely *fixed* positions disappears in modern physics in favour of the moveable positions of the inertial system. But these moveable positions are ideal mathematical entities, just as the instants and points of the fixed Newtonian matrix were, and the distances with respect to inertial systems are ideal mathematical quantities, just as the distances in Newton's fixed system were. The only thing that has changed is that the fixity of the Newtonian matrix has disappeared. In the respect of being precisely *not* relative to physical things, of being precisely ideal mathematical entities, the temporal and spatial positions and distances of modern theoretical physics are still absolute entities.

Of course it would be wrong to say that the spatial points of an inertial system are absolute points if 'absolute' means 'fixed and immoveable'. There are no absolute positions in that sense in modern physics - for all positions are coordinate or relative to other positions. But all positions had coordinate relations to each other also in the Newtonian matrix - it was certainly not a lack of such relations that made them absolute. What made them absolute was (a) their non-relatedness (except for being occupied) to physical things which occupied them, and to which they were "indifferent," having their own mathematical relations with each other, and (b) their fixity. The fixity has disappeared but the other kind of absoluteness, the possession of non-physical, purely mathematical, properties has remained. Theoretical physics still proceeds in terms of absolute mathematical magnitudes, to which the physical, measurable, world is supposed merely to "approximate." There is no hint that the instants and points of modern physics are anything else but ideal mathematical entities - there is no hint certainly that such mathematical ideals are derivable from, definable in terms of, temporal and spatial relations between things, as Leibniz's theory demands. Relativity theory is not in any sense Leibnizian, and Leibniz's theory of time and space did not win out over Newton's absolutist theory. For that to have happened, instants and points would have had to be defined in terms of temporal and spatial relations between things, and not simply assumed, as they have been, from the pure mathematics of the continuum.

We can bring all this into sharp focus by putting a single retrospective question to Leibniz on the one hand and Clarke on the other. It is this: How would the system advocated by each allow for the possibility of such purely ideal disciplines as Euclidean geometry or theoretical dynamics, which adds the concepts of force and time to those of geometry? The answer for Clarke is plain enough. The absolute matrix of space and time allows Euclidean geometry because purely mathematical points and distances are assumed in that system from the beginning. Similarly it allows dynamics, since mass points and instants are also assumed. The answer for Leibniz though turns into a problem. Geometry and dynamics can be allowed only when spatial points and instants of time can be defined in terms of temporal and spatial relations between things, such relations and such things being taken to be more fundamental than instants and points.

This is not the path that modern science has so far followed. Science has been content to assume from mathematics and to assert with a great deal of practical success if not theoretical clarity that the physical world approximates to the mathematical. For the notion of approximation, though perfectly clear in mathematics itself - that is to say, we can explain exactly what we mean by standards of approximation - loses its clarity when we turn to ask what it means to say that the physical approximates to the mathematical. Obviously no purely mathematical notion of approximation will do here.[14] We are left in a very real sense with the old Platonic problem: What is the relation of the physical world to the ideal? In a sense the notion of approximation is to the modern Platonic scientist what the notion of participation was to Plato himself: a way of relating the physical to the ideal, where all the laws reside - which way, when it is examined, proves not to be clear. And so the Platonic problem persists for any science that accepts its ontology of instants and points from pure mathematics.

Leibniz perhaps saw the way out, but was unable to furnish any details of the journey.

All this leads to an interesting conclusion. Leibniz with regard to the question of freewill was a Platonist. For in the interests of total explanation he had to assert the law of sufficient reason, which ultimately allows no choice but the best - that is, it allows no choice, no freewill. But Leibniz with regard to the mathematical entities of time and space was no Platonist.[15] For he would derive those mathematical ideals from the physical, from temporal and spatial relations between things in the world - which derivation is of course an anti-Platonic move. Leibniz's attempt at explanation fails because he does not show how such mathematical ideals can be derived from such relations.

Clarke, on the other hand, is an Aristotelian, not a Platonist, on the question of freewill. For he allows the possibility of real, choosable alternatives, even though, as Leibniz warns him, this seems to allow an element of inexplicability into the world. On the question of the positions and distances of time and space though Clarke, like Newton, is a Platonist - seeing these entities as absolute and mathematical, thus allowing the necessary explanations of pure science to illuminate the imperfect physical world.

Modern science has followed Newton on this, and not Leibniz, taking its fundamental ontology of time and space from the pure mathematics of the continuum. The result is that, for all its success, the Platonic problem persists for modern science: What is the relation of the physical world to the ideal world of mathematics? This is a problem that perhaps could be solved if a way would be found to follow Leibniz's suggestion that such entities as instants, points, and intervals should be defined in terms of temporal and spatial relations taken as fundamental.[16]

NOTES

1. In so far as this paper deals with Leibniz on time it can be taken as complementary to the paper of Waldemar Voisé's, "On Historical Time in the Works of Leibniz," in *The Study of Time II*.

2. In this paper all references to the correspondence will be made in terms of *The Leibniz-Clarke Correspondence*, ed. H. G. Alexander (Manchester: The Manchester University Press, 1956) by identification of the letter number, the paragraph number, and the page of the book. Thus 'L, V, 16, p. 59' will refer to Leibniz's fifth letter, paragraph 16, page 59. Such references will be bracketed and incorporated into the text of the paper.

3. *Nichomachean Ethics*. vii. 2-3. $1145^b21$-$1147^b20$.

4. See, for example, *Summa Contra Gentiles*, II, 48.

5. Max Jammer, *Concepts of Space*, 2d ed. (Cambridge, Massachusetts: Harvard University Press, 1969), p. 127.

6. Jammer, p. 139.

7. Jammer, p. 140.

8. Jammer, pp. 140-141.

9. Jammer, pp. 141-144.

10. Some modern philosophers have attempted to do somthing of the kind, notably Alfred North Whitehead. He attempts to define such concepts as 'instant' and 'point' in terms of extensive temporal or spatial "regions." A point is an "abstractive set" of such extensions, extending over one another (that is, getting smaller and smaller) to infinity. This "method of extensive abstraction" has been variously attacked, largely on the ground that in order to construct the abstractive set it already depends upon the point-like in some way, and so turns out to be circular. Adolf Grünbaum has argued also that the method will not identify the point-like uniquely - that is, will not distinguish between two arbitrarily close point-like positions. For a brief account of the various criticisms see Paul F. Schmidt, *Perception and Cosmology in Whitehead's Philosophy* (New Brunswick, New Jersey: Rutgers University Press, 1967), pp. 71-73. In addition the following may be said. The method of extensive abstraction seems to depend upon the concept of the mathematical limit; indeed the point can be considered as a "limit approached by a geometrical representation of the extensive features of an abstractive set" (Nathaniel Lawrence, "Whitehead's Method of Extensive Abstraction," *Philosophy of Science* 19 (1950), p. 148). This being so, the method depends upon the point-like "elements" of the mathematical theory of the continuum, in which case again circularity may arise - or at least a Newtonian rather than Leibnizian account of time and space ultimately prevail, as I go on to argue.

11. For an account of the basic theory of the continuum see Edward V. Huntington, *The Continuum* and Other Types of Serial Order, 2d ed. (Cambridge, Massachusetts: Harvard University Press, 1917).

12. Leibniz, *Basic Writings*, tr. Montgomery (La Salle, Illinois: The Open Court Publishing Company, 1962), "The Monadology," 3, p. 251.

13. Herbert Wildon Carr, *Leibniz* (London: Constable and Company, Ltd., 1929), p. 153.

14. This criticism again applies to some interpretations of Whitehead's method of extensive abstraction. Victor Lowe has said: "Approximation is the only way in which we can handle space and time.....[ The point] is the idea of an undefined superlative not exemplified in experience.... The definition and realization of the ideal, the superlative, can be achieved only by an unending series of comparatives. This is the lesson of extensive abstraction." (Victor Lowe, *Understanding Whitehead* (Baltimore: The Johns Hopkins Press, 1962), pp. 68-69). The trouble is that, mathematically speaking, approximation is always to some definite value, which is thus presupposed rather than established by the method of approximations. There is simply no well-defined sense to the notion that the physical approximates to the mathematical, thus enabling us to find and identify the mathematical through the physical.

15. We must take 'Platonist' here in a rather wide sense of the term, suitable to the seventeenth century. There is a dispute (See Guthrie, *History of Greek Philosophy*, Vol. IV) about whether "the mathematicals" are for Plato forms themselves or intermediates between forms and sensibles.

16. For the outline of one such attempt see my "The Continuum," *The Review of Metaphysics*, 1969.

DISCUSSION AND COMMENTS
*by R. S. Brumbaugh*

I am sure we are all in Mr. Cornish's debt for this interesting and original study of historical controversy which is a landmark case in the systematic problems of relating theology, physics, and freedom to the concept of time. The paper is particularly important because of its insistence that the controversy involves the status of Divine Freedom just as essentially as it involves the absolute or relational nature of time and space. In this total frame, as Professor Corish points out, both Leibniz and Clarke have two metaphysical standpoints and two logics, one for natural science, but another for God.

When, over-optimistically, a scientist or theologian assumes the total identity of the real world and an abstract model, what Whitehead called a fallacy of misplaced concreteness results. We see this happen in both Leibniz and Clarke. For our present Conference, the particular interest of this case study is that it is the nature of time which is taken as the key property of both physical and theological models by both disputants.

One particularly relevant detail is that both Leibniz and Clarke assume God to be an observer who is outside of the system; the observer is assumed not to be modified in any way by his observations, nor is the system supposed to be changed by His making them. I wonder, after our earlier discussion of uncertainty and measurement, whether this notion - which clearly fails for a human observer who interacts with the observed world - does not also fail in the extrapolated case of a Divine one. In this wonder, I am joined by a group of process philosophers, whose work I find exciting.

Looking back, at our Conference and at the history of similar discussions before it, it strikes one as surprising that Truth, daughter of slow Time, takes such a long time to come out of hiding from the bottom of her well. But for all this delay in her appearance to reveal her Father's nature, there is no reason to cancel plans to greet her.

What finally lures Truth to appear at some future Conference may not be a learned paper, but a dazzling digital wrist watch; or the promise of a last look at receding galaxies through a new telescope; or a celebration at which electronic music finally captures the sound of Time itself - her Father's music that attracts his Daughter to this future festival.

# The Concept of Time in the Mithraic Mysteries

H. Ogawa

*ABSTRACT*

*There are two kinds of plastic representations of time in Mithraism. One is the legend of Mithras, which depicts the sacred history of the Mithraic world. One of the important features of the history is the succession of divine rulership from father to son and the establishment of fatherly sovereignty at last. Another is the image of the lion-headed monster which depicts the course of time and the situation of the god's activities for the salvation of human beings. This idea of time is cyclic.*

*In short, Mithraic time was complex and twofold: the successive generation and the cyclic process. Both were typically ancient. It was the combination of them in one system that was peculiar to Mithraism.*

## 1. INTRODUCTION

There are several problems of time in the study of the Mithraic mysteries.[1] Like other religions throughout the world, Mithraism had its own idea of history which can be observed in the iconography of Mithraists. Their sacred history in the legend of Mithras was divided into three specific periods. Moreover, there were several epoch-making occasions during the sojourn of Mithras -- the principal god of the mysteries -- in this world.

First I will discuss the concept of world periods. Next, I will review a second problem in Mithraic time. There is a very peculiar Mithraic image of a lion-headed monster. It stands stiffly and is decorated with many enigmatic emblems and designs. The difficulty in understanding the nature of the monster is that we do not know if this figure is really a god of time, or perhaps a god of evil and vice, that is, Ahriman. If this figure represents the time-god, then it is important for our interest in understanding time. It would be unique indeed, and astonishing, to know that such a figure could represent a time-god.

In brief, in this paper, I shall attempt to treat two particular problems: first, the idea of time as it is observed in the iconographical representation of the legend of Mithras and, second, the possible representation of the Mithraic time as a lion-headed monster.

## 2. THE LEGEND OF MITHRAS AND TIME

The central image of the Mithraic religion was no doubt the representation of Mithras as the bull-slaying god. This action was described in relief, in round sculpture, and in painting. This image was always central in the holy of the holies of the Mithraic temple. The slaying was no doubt the most significant action of the god and was considered important for the salvation of the world. However, Mithras's bull-slaying was not the only divine act which was expressed through Mithraic iconography. The birth scene of the god was often expressed in an independent image and appears also in one of the successive panels of the legend of Mithras. Moreover, other acts of the god were gathered into a series of many small panels in relief. These describe not only scenes from the birth of the god to his victorious heavenly ascent, but also picture the preceding history of the world, in which Mithras was to be born miraculously.

This kind of artistic expression of the divine legends as a consecutive narrative is in itself remarkable. Its purpose was to clarify the origin of the god's saving action. Such series of consecutive narratives in plastic art were not without parallel in ancient religious art, however. We can refer to the wall-painting of the Synagogue of Dura-Europus.[2] Some Dionysiac scenes from Pompeii and Köln or in Roman mosaics, as well as reliefs of the Danubian Rider-God,[3] belong to the same genre. But, the Mithraic narratives are most firmly established from the typological and iconographical point of view. Perhaps one of the most remarkable parallels is the set of Buddhist reliefs which depicts several scenes of the Buddha's life. These appeared first in the second century before Christ, but seem to have flourished in the second and third centuries.[4] The imperial art of the Roman and Sasanian Empires, though they were not primarily religious, also had a similar kind of narration (reliefs of Roman triumphal arches and columns and Sasanian rock-cut reliefs).[5] However, the historical relationships of these examples are at present far from certain.

Next, let us look at the Mithraic legend itself.[6] Most of it was represented in the temples of Mithras, in the Danube and Rhine region. In other areas of Mithraic diffusion it is rather sporadically known, but some important examples have come out of the temples of areas outside the Danube and Rhine region, like that of Dura-Europus in Mesopotamia.[7] This raises the question whether there was a difference between the belief of the people in the Danube and Rhine region and that of other worshipers of Mithras. The answer is most likely *no*. The examples from the latter area, although not many, show remarkably many common traits with those from the former sites. The order of each divine act, the manner of expression, and the *dramatis personae* are almost identical. Moreover, the fundamental principle of the architecture and the inner arrangement of the temple, as well as the organization of the Mithraic community, is in every case identical. Thus, it is clear that the one and the same legend was commonly understood by all Mithraists in the Roman world, and that only the plastic expression in relief possessed any local peculiarities.

In the first panel,[8] the god Saturn appears standing in his full glory; sometimes a nimbus with radiation adds effect behind his head. He holds a sceptre; this indicates that he was the ruler of the world; but in looking at the next picture, we see that something terrible has happened and it appears that he has lost his supreme authority.

Suddenly Jupiter, the successor to Saturn, just as in Greek mythology, appears armed, brandishing the thunderbolt in his hand and raining blows on a tribe of Giants. Jupiter has already been invested with the sceptre, perhaps through peaceful means, and has acquired sovereignty over the world. Saturn, it seems, has retired to a remote mountain to rest, and we can sometimes see him in a peaceful, recumbent position or as an old man looking down on important divine acts of his successors. For example, he watches calmly on the occasion of the rock-birth or bull-slaying of Mithras, and on the heavenly ascent of Mithras with Sol.

Before the moment of Mithras's rock-birth, one revewal of the ruling generation occurred which was the rule of Saturn being replaced by that of Jupiter. A kind of revolution or conflict was fought out between the two generations of Saturn and Jupiter. When Mithras was born out of the rock, the world was under the sway of Jupiter. Mithras's birth-scene was naturally very important for Mithraists. Therefore, in most cases, it was represented separately and independently, but sometimes the scene was also included in another of the legend.[9] When Mithras was born, there must have been something amiss in the world under Jupiter. At that time, the reign of Jupiter seems to have been ending in some unknown disorder. Saturn, the retired god, appears to be at least partly responsible for the birth of Mithras, the young god, who incidentally would become the saviour who wards off the maladies and disorders of Jupiter's world. A recently reported Armenian story of Mithras[10] tells that Mithras attacked his father, but afterwards the two were reconciled. It is possible that the father of Mithras was Jupiter. The sovereignty of Mithras, thus acquired, can be shown by some half-political and half-religious words in Mithraic inscriptions[11] --- *summus* (top), *omnipotens* (in full power), *augustus* (revered), *insuperabilis* (unsurmountable), *cosmocrator* (world-ruler) and *dikaios* (righteous). Some ideological Mithraists thought that Mithras usurped the name of Zeus Helios, the Hellenistic high god (Dura-Europus, Anazarbus and Rome).[12]

The next panels depict Mithras's lifetime, or rather his sojourn in this world. At first, he went hunting a mysterious bull which was sent from a heavenly house to this world by a boat and was subjugated at last by Mithras, after a rather dangerous pursuit. The killing of this bull was not just a simple hunt. It was, rather, a miracle. The bull's tail changed into ears of corn; its blood was welcomed by representatives of the creatures (the dog and snake); and its genitals provided the sacred liquid of fecundity which was received by a krater. This liquid, too, was weldomed by the worldly creatures (the lion, snake, and scorpion).

From other symbols we know that this act was aided by the sun god, Sol.[13] It was enacted at the beginning of the Zodiacal year, that is, at the spring equinox, and was interpreted as the creation by Porphyry, the neoplatonist philosopher (in the third century), as well as by his predecessor Eubulus (in the 2nd century).[14]

Then the skin of the hunted animal was used as a table-cloth, and sometimes his legs formed the supports of a side-table; both tables were used for the feast of the gods, Mithras and Sol. This feast may represent a kind of thanksgiving.[15] Mithraists seem to have imitated this feast,[16] which became the most important of the Mithraic rituals in the temple. Before both gods attended this cosmic feast, Mithras had been out hunting wild animals (deer, boars, gazelles, etc.), products of the divinely fertilized world, to supply the table for the feast. This hunting scene was significant because only through the divine act of hunting could human beings be supported every year. Therefore this hunting scene, too, is sometimes represented separately and independently in the temple.[17] After both gods had finished the feast and imparted the grace of fecundity to the believers, there occurred the last scene -- the joyful, victorious ascent into heaven on a chariot.

Bull-slaying renews the world at the time of the new year. It has been argued that Tertullian, a Christian apologist in the second and third centuries, noted the similarity of the idea of resurrection in Mithraism and Christianity. According to Turcan, however, Tertullian actually refers to the iconography of this divine act, that is, the *renewal of the world*.[18]

In short, in the legend of Mithras there were depicted three generations: at first, the reign of Saturn, who was conquered by Jupiter at one moment of divine history; then, the reign of Jupiter; and, at last, the world under Mithras.[19] This division of sacred history into three periods is not a new invention of Mithraists in the second and third centuries after Christ. There were similar theogonic stories in ancient Mesopotamia and especially among the Hurrians in Northern Syria and Anatolia in the second Millennium before Christ. The renewal of generations of the divine rulership is clearly observed in those mythologies and takes an important role in the theogonic development of the world. It is observed, too, that the crucial subject of this development is paternal authority, as is seen in the title of both the original gods of those myths, "the father of the gods." Specialists in ancient Near Eastern religions have recognized a remarkable similarity between the Hurrian legend of Kumarbi and the Phoenician myth of El-Kronus which was transmitted to us by Eusebius and his predecessors Philo of Byblos and Sanchuniathon. This similarity has been supported by another important document. Since the decipherment of cuneiform texts from Ras Shamra-Ugarit, in which political and cultural relations between Phoenicians and Hurrians were definitely substantiated, this morphological similarity of the Kronus myths has also been considered to have had historical foundation. On the other hand, there was a similar legend in Greek mythology, that is, Kronus, the treacherous father of the gods, and the coup d'état of Jupiter that overthrew him. Scholars believe that this myth came from the Near East and was related to the Phoenician myth of Kronus.

The Theogonic myths of this sort had existed everywhere from Mesopotamia to the Eastern Mediterranian before the Mithraic mysteries established themselves; perhaps first in the Eastern Mediterranean region. Actually, Mithraic founders could have adapted this type of theogony from any place mentioned above, in and after the Hellenistic period. We do not know, therefore, from where the Mithras-legend originated.

Then, the next question is why the Mithraists needed this type of sacred history. The theme was basically the establishment and loss of paternal authority. To wit:

1) The main subject of the legend in Mesopotamian, Hurrian, Phoenician, and Greek theogony was the succession of the sovereignty over the god's world from the father to the son by means of violence and trickery. There is no clear literary account of this myth by Mithraists themselves. I refer only to the above-mentioned iconography.[20]

2) Mithraism contained another type of paternalism as well as this myth of paternal authority. The highest position in the Mithraic community was that of the Father (*Pater* in Latin); the Father was skilled in ritual performances as a priest, as well as in theological problems (*studiosus*).[21] According to Porphyry, a philosophical interpreter in the third century, Mithras was called the Father of all creatures (perhaps because of his fertilizing act in the bull-killing).[22] We can take Christianity and Judaism as other contemporary examples. In both religions, paternal authority was most seriously considered in the theology. God was the father of Christ: they ruled the world successively as the kingdom of God the Father and the kingdom of Christ the Son. In the community of believers the chief Christian was Pope, while priests were fathers. There are other designations such as "patristic literature," "Abbot," "Greek fathers," or "Latin fathers" and the father of the synagogue of the Jews.[23] Those contemporary religions were eminently masculine. Neither of them had female deities; Mithraism did not have any female believers and Christianity did not allow for female clergy, apart from some prophetesses of the Montanists. Therefore, they were remarkably masculine and, as I say, paternal or fatherly. At the time the quest for righteous paternal authority and order was everywhere and made these religions popular.[24]

3) From evidence in Persia and Eastern Roman provinces it can be deduced that Mithras had sovereignty over this world, and that he passed on this power to human beings, especially to kings. For the common people, his sovereignty meant salvation from evil and misfortune. This is because he was the legitimate successor of this authority, which had been transmitted to him from Saturn through Jupiter. Inside the contemporary

religious circle, the secular king was less evaluated, as is seen in the New Testament. Here, God gives legitimate authority to the righteous,[25] not to the king.

4) The Mithraists' sense of history was quite supernatural. No doubt the name of Mithras originated in the Iranian world. But there is no single Mithraic document to prove this transmission. One Mithraic inscription mentions Babylonia,[26] and others use strange Persian technical terms such as *nama, sebesio, cautes, cautopates,* and *nabarze*. One of the grades in the hierarchy of Mithraists was called *Perses*, possibly of non-Persian origins. However, the origins seem to have been unimportant to Mithraists[27] whose sense of history was metahistorical and mythological. Time for the Mithraists was not actual time. Their concept of time was directed towards the mythical origins of paternal authority.

In short as far as we know about the idea of time from the legend of Mithras, we may summarize our study as follows:

1) Mithraists needed and accepted theogonic history from Saturn to Mithras, instead of believing in actual history;

2) This sacred history was divided into three periods and the reason for this division was to explain the succession of the reigns for the three gods, that is, the renewal of rulership;

3) This succession was realized by passing paternal authority from father to son; and

4) There is in this theogony, as I see it, no clear trace of Iranian cosmic dualism of Ahura-Mazda and Ahriman, nor of the end of the world, that is, the Last Judgment at the Cinvat bridge; it can be said it is only Hellenistic.

As for the idea of the beginning of the world, the Mithraic evidence is very scarce. A possible representation of Chaos[28] is known, but there remains no literary account of it. Since the days of F. Cumont, Mithraic eschatology has been a popular subject. There are four pieces of Mithraic evidence concerning this problem: two inscriptions from Santa Prisca[29] and Dura-Europus,[30] which seem to tell us about a great conflagration at the end of the world; one unique relief from Dieburg, Germania[31] depicting a Phaeton myth which can be interpreted in the eschatological context; and the word *sebesio* in a Mithraic inscription[32] can be a changed form of *saushyant*, the Zoroastrian saviour who will appear at the end of the world. It is therefore sure that at least some ideological Mithraists believed in the end of the world by cosmic fire. Cumont connected this sort of evidence with the eschatology of the Borysthenic oration of Dio Chrysostomus (XXXV, 39-53, ca, A.D. 100).[33] At present, the relationship between such eschatology and the legend of Mithras is not known.

## 3. THE LION-HEADED MONSTER AND TIME

Our next problem is the enigmatic lion-headed monster,[34] which appears in most cases independently in relief or in round sculpture. Sometimes it appears also as an element in other Mithraic iconographies, the legend of Mithras or the bull-slaying Mithras. And no other contemporary sects had such a lion-headed monster as one of their plastic images. Therefore, it is certain that it is Mithraic.

However, about the nature of this monster, there have evolved two theories. One posits that this god was Ahriman, the Iranian god of evil.[35] There are four Mithraic inscriptions[36] which mention this name. Three of them were dedicated by Mithraists of higher grades, or ranks, who must have been ideological. One inscription, from Ostia, says that a statue of this god was dedicated, but the statue itself is lost. The most difficult source is one inscription from York[37] in England which was recovered in broken shape and seems to be a dedication to Ahriman. If this is so, then the name of the lion-headed god must be Ahriman because this is inscribed on the pedestal of the lion-headed statue. Considering the traces of Ahriman worship within Mithraism, we can assume that it was heterodox, or a kind of aberration. The lion-headed monsters are too many to be considered a heterodoxy. In short, the inscriptions are small in number and even if the lion-headed god is Ahriman, this does not show that the Western Ahriman and the Zoroastrian Ahriman are one and the same deity. There is no clear indication that Mithraism was a kind of Zoroastrian dualism. That the Mithraic Ahriman was the Gnostic Aeon, or Hades, who brings fertility, or the Babylonian Nergal, has also been suggested. But to prove such theories we need non-Mithraic evidence.

*Painting on the wall of the arched cult-niche of the Mithraic Temple at Palazzo Barberini, Rome. Mithras, the bull-slayer is in the center. Above him there is an arch comprising the twelve signs of the Zodiac. In the center of this arch a lion-headed monster may be seen, standing on the globe. The monster's head reaches a second arch which shows the heavenly symbolism of seven altars alternating with cypresses. The meaning of the lion-headed monster, in the particular background here depicted, relates to the symbolism of Mithraic heavenly ladders for the apotheosis of souls, and thus to the overcoming of the finity of life. The figure is reproduced from CIMRM (see text), with permission of Professor Vermaseren.*

There is another type of evidence in one of Plutarch's essays, which says that Mithras is the intermediary god between Ahriman and Ahura Mazda.[38] Some scholars have thought that these three are Mithraic, and that Plutarch (ca. 50-120) was referring to Mithraic theology. But Plutarch was no Mithraist. There is no clear evidence that he knew or wrote about Mithraic theology. Furthermore, Plutarch's theology was never heard of in Mazdaism.

The second theory is that the lion-headed god represents Zervan-Akarana,[39] the supposed Mithraic time-god, that is, the Persian God of Eternal Time, who can be equated to Greek Aion.[40] Of course, in this case, too, there is no evidence that the lion-headed monster was called Zervan-Akarana in the West. The Eternal God in some Latin inscriptions is not Mithraic. It has been asserted that in Hellenistic syncretism this Iranian god was hidden under the name Chronus (Greek anthropomorphized Time), and that after all, according to Sallustius,[41] a fourth century philosopher, Chronus-Time was equated to Kronus-Saturn: Mithraic Zervan, therefore, concealed himself under Saturn. However, Mithraic Saturn was not lion-headed as is seen in the Legend of Mithras.

The lion-headed one was possibly an unknown god. Neither the known examples (about 40) nor other Mithraic monuments give its exact names. If the inscription on the York statue indicates his name, then this is quite exceptional. It is more persuasive to think that this is not the case. Otherwise, the absence of markings on 40 very conspicuous monuments cannot be adequately explained.

Why was this monster unnamed? In some Mithraic temples, statues of it seem to have been concealed intentionally. The ineffability of his name may correspond with his retirement. The name of Yahweh was ineffable for Jews because of extreme piety, reverence, and awe towards the supreme deity. But this is not similarly applicable to such a monster as the lion-headed one who was evidently not a primary god of Mithraism.

I state here the following two points concerning the problem:

First, the monster appears also in association with the legend of Mithras and the bull-killing scene.[42] This fact signifies that the lion-headed god was related to the saving act of Mithras in this world. And second, the monster's iconography has various common elements with the rock-birth scene.[43] This fact signifies that he was also related especially to the birth of Mithras' reign, that is, to the third and last generation of the world.

The main features of this monster are easily recognized and can be summarized as follows:

The monstrous lion-headed male figure, mostly in reliefs or in round sculptures, about 50 to 160cm high, stands in a stiff, Egyptianizing, hieratic posture. The whole body is facing strictly to the front. The figure wears a peculiar loin-cloth and looks like the Egyptian god Osiris or mummies, but strangely enough, there have been found only three[44] in Egypt. Two other important examples from Merida and Strassbourg[45] are exceptionally not lion-headed. Another one from Rome[46] (now in Modena) is also included in this category. Once they were considered as the result of "beautification" or "de-anthropomorphization",[47] but at present, most students think that they represent Mithras as a youth, because of common traits with them and Mithras in the rock-birth scene. To ascertain this identification, I quote the words of an inscription from Ostia, referring to "the young god who has not been ruined."[48] Furthermore, there is a unique expression of Mythras Saecularis, that is, Mithras of the era, in the inscriptions of Housesteads.[49] It commemorates the birth of the ruling god of the third generation.

Lion-headed monsters are usually encoiled by snakes. Once the snake was considered as the heavenly course of the seven planets, but the number of times of coiling is not always seven. The number is rather variable. In ancient religions snakes sometimes coil around any sacred person or object. In Mithraism such cases are seen on the rock from where Mithras was born or on the body of sitting Saturn. Sometimes, snakes are turned to kraters. Lions appear not only as the monster's head, but also on the surface of his body. They often walk independently among the scenes of the legend of Mithras and of the rock-birth. The lion-headed one and the bull-slaying Mithras are, to be sure, common with those animal symbols and other symbols such as fire altars and torches. The best argument for this is that these symbols show altogether Mithras's manifestation in the world.

As peculiar emblems of this monster, we can mention further attributes: a thunderbolt, scepters (or staffs) in his hands and four (sometimes two) wings on his back. Among rarer emblems we see a throne, globi, four seasons and a Cerberus-dog. We already know that the thunderbolt and scepters are tools representing the heavenly hegemony, and that they were used also by Saturn and Jupiter, the former rulers. Globi and throne must also be considered as tools for the same purpose, as it is in contemporary iconography of the Roman world. That Cerberus, the three-headed dog, represented three aspects of time (the past, the present, and the future), is asserted by Macrobius,[50] a fifth century philosopher and protagonist of Mithraism.[51] This interpretation points to the possibility that the monster is time itself. I would guess that the three heads of this monster dog meant for Mithraists the course of time passing through the three generations of Saturn, Jupiter, and Mithras.

The signs of the Zodiac, Sol and Luna, and the seasons around the monster may represent the universe; but it may be more persuasive, as Turcan asserted recently,[52] that they are the astrological symbolism of the duration of time as the yearly cycle of vegetation. Wings are rather enigmatic. They seem to make monsters more dynamic. According to Oriental and Hellenistic traditions, they show that the monsters are supernatural, mysterious genii.

In short, I would summarize the following points concerning the nature of the monster:

1) The need for representing the place and the time of the manifestation of Mithras,

the ruler of the world, produced this composite and complex iconography. It depicts the world of Mithras, whose epiphany as the ruling god is also described therein;

2) Mithraists must have found it difficult to represent Mithraic time, that is, the manifestation of the god in time. Describing time in one visual dimension is no doubt difficult for an artist of any school. It is often only possible by means of symbols. In the case of the monstrous figure of Mithraism, the signs of the Zodiac and the seasons, with the planetary system of seven which is depicted by Celsus,[53] were archetypal images of a yearly cycle of divine vegetation through the act of Mithras. After the establishment of Mithras's reign, time for Mithraists was cyclic, a cyclic process; and,

3) Thus, the monster shows the time, the space, and the powers which manifest themselves in the era of Mithras' reign.

There is some additional evidence which will support this conclusion and show the relationship between the lion-headed one and other Mithraic icons. From Pettau, Serdica and Rome[54] there are peculiar bull-slaying scenes which are accompanied by the legend of Mithras or the signs of the Zodiac as usual. At the most crucial place of each there appears the representation of the lion-headed one. However, it does not seem to occupy any contextual place in the consecutive narratives or in the consecutive arrangement of the celestial signs. Its placing seems to be beyond the context of the surrounding pictures and symbols. So to speak, it transcends them. This fact signifies that the symbolical meaning of the whole iconography of the monster is also transcendental, far above those divine acts. I argue that the monster shows the aspects of time and space that were invested to explain the epiphany of Mithras. The monster was Mithraic time rather than a time-god: the last establishment of the true order (paternal authority) and Mithras's archetypal activity of salvation, which must be imitated periodically in the temple by human beings.

## 4. CONCLUSION

The Mithraic concept of time was remarkably complex. In iconographical terms, it was composed of various Greek and Oriental symbols which were related to time. It reflected two ancient concepts of time. One was the idea of generations of heavenly hegemony which can be considered to be the descent of paternal authority from father to son. This is one of the typical ancient ideas of rulership. Another concept was that of the yearly repetition of fecundity. The god gave the exemplary act as the archetype, while the believers celebrated it ritualistically in the temple, with feasts and hymns. This, too, is nothing but one of the typical ancient ideas of the procreation of nature.

Philosophically, this stands in accord with the Platonic idea of time -- the eternal cycle of going and returning between heaven and earth. When we compare the Mithraic concept of time with that of Christianity, we find that they are different. Although they are contemporary in diffusion, in Mithraism there seems to have been no idea of the creation from nothing as the beginning point of time, or of the resurrection and the Last Judgment as the ending, or of sin and redemption. Time for the Christians is unique and irrevocable, leading to the irreversible end. Mithraists did not recognize this concept. Philosophers thought that Mithras was the creator, but this creation seems to have occurred at the half-way point in the world by means of the Mithras's miracle. Actually it was nothing but the yearly fecundation of the world. Finally, I must not neglect the existence of an Irano-Hellenistic philosophical interpretation of time among some learned circles of Mithraists. Beyond each of the three generations of the world the cyclic times passes, while each world has its own limited duration of time. Some theoretically minded Mithraists may have been fond of this theory of two kinds of time to explain their theogonic view. And it might also have influenced the formation of the iconography of Mithraism. The Mithraic concept of time was basically founded upon the combination of those two ideas, which represent the two typical ancient attitudes towards time -- succession and cycle. It seems that this concept corresponds to the basic structure of the Mithraic idea of salvation.

NOTES

1. The late professor S. G. Brandon treated this problem in his article, "The Deification of Time," *Study of Time I* (J. T. Fraser et al. eds), 1972, pp. 370-382.

2. See recent work on this subject: J. Gutmann ed., *The Dura-Europos Synagogue* (Chambersburg, Penn.: American Academy of Religion, 1973).

3. See recent works on these subjects: A. Linfert, *Römische Wandmalerei der Nordwestlichen Provinzen* (Köln: Römisch-Germanisches Museum der Stadt Köln, 1975); D. Tudor, *Corpus Monumentorum Religionis Equitum Danuvinorum* I (Leiden: Brill, 1969).

4. See recent work on this subject: O. Takata, *The Origin of the Buddha Image* (in Japanese and with an English résumé, Tokyo, Iwanami, 1967).

5. About this problem and other Oriental and Greek predecessors, see C. H. Kraeling et al., "Narration in Ancient Art, A Symposium." *American Journal of Archaeology* 61, 1957, pp. 43-91.

6. The best work on the art of Mithraic cult reliefs is: E. Will, *Le relief cultuel gréco-romain, Contribution de l'art de l'empire romain* (Paris: E. de Boccard, 1955), pp. 356-455.

7. M. J. Vermaseren, *Corpus Inscriptionum et Monumentorum Religionis Mithriacae* (CIMRM) I-II (The Hague: Martinus Nijhoff, 1956-60) 42. There are two other examples from Rome (CIMRM 390; 724). A marble medallion from Caesarea Maritima contains three scenes of the legend of Mithras: *Hadashôth Arkeologiôth* (in Hebrew) 47, 1973, p. 3; American Schools of Oriental Research, *Newsletter* 1973, No. 3, Nov., p. 3; L. M. Hopfe and G. Lease, "The Caesarea Mithraeum," A Preliminary Announcement, *Biblical Archaeologist* 38-1, 1975, pp. 2-10, esp. p. 6; cf. R. J. Bull,

*Israel Exploration Journal* 23, 1973, pp. 261-262.

8. Concerning the chronological order as well as the iconographical arrangement of the panels (or columns), there is no definite proof at present. The main line, however, can be traced to the story of Greek mythology and other Mithraic evidence.

9. See below p.193 about iconographical common elements of the rock-birth scene and the lion-headed monster's manifestation.

10. I. Gershevitch, *Mithraic Studies* II, J. Hinnels ed. (Manchester: Manchester U.P., 1975), p. 355.

11. CIMRM 18; 376; 395A; 463,1;941; 1913; 1941; 1969.

12. Ibid., 70; 27bis; 463.

13. The relationship between Sol and Mithras, who is also Sol Invictus, is enigmatic. Cf. M. J. Vermaseren, *Mithras de geheimzinnige god* (Amsterdam: Elsevier, 1959), pp. 75f. When Mithras killed the bull, he was told some unknown words by a crow who came to the scene from Sol, who was also coming down from heaven. The message thus conveyed was perhaps Sol's promise that the world miraculously fertilized by Mithras would be sustained and protected by the heat sent by Sol. Afterwards each saw the other and made a contract in a ritualistic attitude. This is one of the most popular scenes of the legend of Mithras.

14. R. Turcan, *Mithras platonicus, Recherches sur l'hellénisation philosophique de Mithra* (Leiden: Brill, 1975), pp. 24; 77-83.

15. See a recent work about this subject: J. P. Kane, "The Mithraic Cult Meal in its Greek and Roman Environment." *Mithraic Studies* II, op. cit., pp. 313-351.

16. There are three kinds of Mithraic evidence of the Mithraist's thanksgiving feast: bones of animals and birds from several Mithraea (although in some cases they are foundation deposits or ritualistic burials), two purchase-lists of foods and other materials from Dura-Europus (CIMRM 64f.; cf. J. T. Milik, *Dédicaces faites par des dieux (Palmyre, Hatra, Tyr) et des thiases sémitiques à l'époque romaine* (Paris: Geuthner, 1972), pp. 200f.) and finally a relief of the believers' feast from Konijka (CIMRM 491).

17. CIMRM 52; 1247; 1289.

18. Turcan, op. cit., p. 57.

19. This third era was considered the rehabilitation of Saturn's reign, because it was always conducted under the benevolent watch of Saturn (aurea aetas). But we do not know the relationship between Saturn and the bull, the heavenly house, and the river.

20. In the temple of Mithras at Santa Prisca in Rome, moreover, there was found some important evidence of the iconography of the Giants. Cf. M. J. Vermaseren and C. C. van Essen. *The Excavations in the Mithraeum of the Church of Santa Prisca in Rome* (Brill: Leiden, 1965), p. 343. Since the days of Cumont the Giants have been interpreted according to the dualistic ethics of Mazdaism: they work for the benefit of Ahriman: thus the gigantomachy represents the victory of the Good against the Evil. Cf. Cumont, *The Mysteries of Mithra* (N.Y.: Dover Publications, 1956), pp. 112f.; 127; Vermaseren, *Mithras*, op. cit., pp. 89f. However, there is no gigantomachy in the Mazdaistic tradition. On the other hand, this myth is attested from the Bel temple in Palmyra. It is said it came from the Mesopotamian myth of Tiamat. Cf. Comte du Mesnil du Buisson, *Les tessères et les monnais de Palmyre* (Paris: E. de Boccard, 1962), pp. 190-195. From the Danube and Rhine region of the Roman Empire, carved stone obelisks are known, which are called *Jupiter-gigantensäulen*. These examples show that the problem is not the victory

of Good against Evil, but the establishment of the new sovereignty through ritualistic combat.

21. CIMRM 708.

22. Cf. Turcan, op. cit., p. 24.

23. Cabrol-Leclercq, Dictionaire d'archéologie chrétienne et de liturgie (Librarie Letouzey et Ané), Paris, XIII, pp. 2424f., s. v. pater: cf. Inscriptiones Graecae XIV, 945 (Portus near Rome: patròs tôn Hebréôn).

24. About the religious side of the father-son problem, see R. N. Bellah, *Beyond Belief, Essays on Religion in a Post-Traditional World* (N.Y.: Harper & Row, 1970), pp. 77-99 ("Father and son in Christianity and Confucianism").

25. A Mithraic father was called *nomimos* (legitimate) in CIMRM 76; 79.

26. CIMRM 522.

27. Since the days of Cumont, it has been said that one of the causes of the popularity of the Oriental religions in the Roman Empire was the respect for the Eastern tradition. On the part of Mithraists, however, this sentiment does not seem to have been felt strongly. Cf. F. Cumont, *Oriental Religions in the Roman Empire* (N.Y.: Dover Publications, 1911), pp. 20-45 ("Why the Oriental Religions Spread").

28. CIMRM 1292,4a (A head in flowerlike irregular circle from Osterburken).

29. Vermaseren and van Essen, op. cit., pp. 224-231 *(per quos thuradamos per quos consumimur ipsi)*.

30. CIMRM 68bis *(pyrōtòn āsthma tò kaì màgois ē níptron hossíōn)*.

31. Ibid. 1246.

32. Ibid. 416

33. F. Cumont, "La fin du monde selon des mages occidentaux." *Revue de l'histoire des religions* CIII, 1931, pp. 29-96; J. Bidez et Cumont, *Les mages hellénisés* II, (Paris: Les Belles Lettres, 1973), pp. 142-153.

34. About the lion-headed monster, most recent studies are mentioned in H. Lavagne, "Pour une problématique nouvelle des recherches de la religion de Mithra," *Mélanges de l'école française de Rome* 87-2, 1975, pp. 1135-1136.

35. F. Legge, "The Lion-Headed God of the Mithraic Mysteries," *Proceedings of the Society for Biblical Archaeology* XXXIV, 1912, pp. 125ff.; XXXVII, 1915, pp. 154ff.; F. Legge, *Forerunners and Rivals of Christianity* (N.Y.: Peter Smith, 1950) II, p. 252; A. B. Cook, *Zeus* II, ii (Oxford: Oxford U.P., 1925, p. 1053; J. Duchesne-Guillemin, "Aion et le léontocéphale, Mithra et Ahriman," *La nouvelle Clio* 10-12, 1958-62, pp. 91-98; Ibid., "Ahriman et le dieu suprême dans les mystères de Mithra," *Numen* II, 3, 1955, pp. 190-195.

36. CIMRM 222 (from Ostia); 369 (from Rome); 1773 and 1775 (from Pannonia).

37. Ibid. 834.

38. Plut., *De Iside et Osiride*, 45-47 (Bidez et Cumont, op. cit. II, pp. 70-79).

39. R. Dussaud, "Anciens bronzes de Louristan et cultes iraniens," *Syria* XXVI, 1949, pp. 196ff.; R. Dussaud, "Le dieu mithriaque léontocéphale," *Syria* XXVII, 1950, pp. 253-260; Leroy Campbell, *Mithraic Iconography and Ideology* (Leiden: Brill, 1968), esp. p. 348-353; R. Ghirshman, Parthes et sassanides, L'univers des formes

(Paris: Gallimard, 1962), p. 8 et fig. 11; R. Pettazzoni, "La figura mostruosa del tempo nella religione mitriaca." *Antiquité classique* XVIII, 1949, pp. 265-277 (Translated in: *Essays on the History of Religion* (leiden: Brill, 1954), 182ff.); Vermaseren, *Mithras*, op. cit., pp. 95-104; H. Sasse, *Real-encyclopaedie für Antike und Christentum,* s. v. *Aion*.

40. There are very advanced studies of the Hellenistic and Roman theology of Aion. They were done mostly by German scholars (F. Boll, R. Eisler, H. Junker, E. Norden, R. Reitzenstein, L. Troje, M. Zepf, O. Weinreich and others). Sometimes they referred to the Mithraic Aion, but it is still uncertain that the idea of Aion could be used for interpreting the Mithraic monster. In this respect several Mithraic students have been less critical. They have also been uncritical concerning the equation of Persian Zervan, Aion and the monster. They have also uncritically connected Aion with Time. Available Mithraic evidence concerning these problems is quite scarce. These authors, mentioned above, have followed Cumont's classical theory. Recently Vermaseren has emphasized the importance of the worship of Hellenistic Kronus. (Cf. "A Magical Time God," *Mithraic Studies* II, op. cit., pp. 446-456).

41. *De Diis et Mundo* IV, 2.

42. Cf. CIMRM 390 (from Rome); 1510 (from Pettau); 1935, 12 (from Apulum); 2320,1 (from Serdica).

43. The most important are the signs of the Zodiac.

44. CIMRM 94; 102f.

45. Ibid. 777; 1326.

46. Ibid. 695.

47. Cumont, op. cit., p. 223, fig. 49, while Dussaud (*Le dieu mithriaque*, op. cit., p. 255) says that the human-headed ones are earlier.

48. CIMRM 315 (*dei iubenis inconrupti Solis invicti Mithrae*).

49. Ibid. 863.

50. *Saturnalia* I, 20, 13f. Cf. Pettazzoni, *Essays*, op. cit., pp. 164-70.

51. Cf. Vermaseren, *Mithras*, op. cit., p. 155.

52. Turcan, op. cit., pp. 55f.; 85f.; 88.

53. Ibid., pp. 44-61; 132.

54. See the examples mentioned in the note 42.

DISCUSSION AND COMMENT
*By M. L. v. Franz*

Professor Ogawa has presented a complete, yet cautious evaluation of the Aion-figure, I can only amplify a few of its details.

Though it is linguistically inacceptable, it is a fact, that for the Greeks Kronos-Saturn and Chronos-Time were identical.[1] They or rather he, represents the single creative power of the universe, a kind of world-soul. He was from early times on also identified with Oceanos, the primeval water, a serpent surrounding the earth and also the universe as the path of the sun. For Pindar the word *aion* meant the life-fluid in man, his *daimon* and compelling destiny: the same liquid controlled all the changes in the world. The Chronos-serpent, as a stream, circles the universe and constantly engenders himself anew. Thus he is a cosmic belt around the universe. In the individual, *aion* was the marrow of the spine,[3] also his life-times or allotted portion of time.[4] Already in older Orphism Chronos-Aion was linked with the idea of Ananke-Necessity.[5] In a 3rd century text, Zosimus calls him "the round element of two natures, which reaches up to the seventh sphere of Kronos, but as regards to the mysteries, I shall not reveal his real name."[6]

I wish to quote a few prayers in which this pantheistic Godhead, Aion, is invoked.

"Come to me from the four regions (winds) all-ruling God, who breathes life into man, Lord of all that is beautiful on earth...Who has an unutterable name, which is feared by all demons...Heaven is thy head, the ether is they body, the earth thy feet, wound around thee is Oceanos...o Agathodaimon...who is Aion, who nourishes the Aion (world) and rules over the Aions (centuries) -- one immortal God alone, who engenders everything".[7] In the Mithras liturgy the god Mithras (who is Helios) is invoked at the Doors of the Beyond: "O Lord, who with his spirit binds the fiery keys of the fourfold belt...fire-walker, creator of light, fire-breather, with fiery courage...Aion, Lord of Light, ruler of Light...open the door for me".[8] And in a "Secret Stele" we read: 'I greet thee, thou, that fills the whole structure of the air, Spirit, that stretches from Heaven to Earth and to the confines of the Abyss...Spirit that also penetrates myself and leaves me again...thou the servant of the rays of the sun and enlightener of the world...o great circular mysterious form of the universe, heavenly Spirit, ethereal Spirit, earthy fiery, windy, light-dark Spirit that shines like a star, moist fiery cold Spirit...o Lord of Lords...God of Aions, thou art great, Lord, God, Ruler of everything."[9]

This Aion-figure was probably a gatekeeper in the Mithras mysteries representing the watery-fiery world-soul, and was also identical with the central gods of the mysteries, that appear at a later stage of initiation.[10] The lionhead of Aion probably symbolized the fiery, hot, pneumatic aspect of this god, the summer solstice and midday-position of the sun. Its snake representation symbolized the cold, feminine, earthy, watery aspect. He contained all opposites.[11] That the syncretistic religious text identified this cosmic figure with Time is all that concerns us here. Obviously Aion was primarily an image of symbol of something which we might circumscribe today as psycho-physical energy. It is a more sophisticated, polysynthetic symbol of what the Dacota Indians call *wakanda*, the Algonkins *manitou*, the Yaos *mulungu* and the Melanesians *mana* etc.[12]

In Western civilization this original concept of "power" evolved further to Heraclitus' Logos-fire, and over many further intermediary forms into our modern physical concept of energy. But on the archaic level this *mana* was a psychic power inseparable from objects and more archaic than any animistic personifications or images of the Divine. Whilst the "objective" aspect of the world-energy has been developed into the mathematical concept of physical energy, its "subjective", psychic component reappears in the Freudian idea of libido and, in the Jungian idea of psychic energy. All these concepts are regarded by Jung as derivatives of an archetypal image of energy, dormant in the collective unconscious.

Thus we must assume that Time itself was not what it seems to be today, a communal mode of thought, but was experienced as identical with the inwardly and outwardly perceived stream of coinciding events, carried along by an all-pervading psycho-physical energy.

REFERENCES

1. Cf. R. B. Onians, *The Origins of European Thought* (Cambridge, England: Cambridge University Press, 1954), p. 249 ff.

2. Ibid, p. 251.

3. Ibid. p. 316.

4. Ibid. p. 406,cf. also note I on p. 451.

5. Ibid. p. 251. This is the source of our idea of causality.

6. M. Berthelot, Collection des Anciens Alchimistes Grecs, (Paris 1887-1888) Vol. I, p. 228.

7. K. Preisendanz, Papyri Graecae Magicae, Stuttgart, Teubner 1973, Vol. II p. 74/75 and p. 125 (Authors translation).

8. Ibid. Vol. I. p. 93.

9. Ibid. Vol. I. p. 111, cf. also p. 93.

10. F. Cumont, They Mysteries of Mithra (N.Y.: Dover Publications, 1956), p. 107 ff.

11. The Fragment of Aristoxenos (Hippolytos, Elenchos ed. P. Wendland p. 7 and ibid. p. 8) Where Aion is called good and evil, male and female.

12. C. G. Jung, The Structure and Dynamics of the Psyche. Coll. Works, Vol. 7. p. 67 ff.

# Time and Sacrifice—the Sacrifice of Time and the Ritual of Modernity*

R. Panikkar

*ABSTRACT***

*In most traditions, liturgical time does not tally with ordinary, everyday time. The latter is governed by the horizontal succession of daily occurrences. The former would like us to enter into contact with a privileged moment, which appears to be discontinuous when seen from the perspective of linear-chronological time. Liturgical time follows a vertical and/or a circular time-pattern; it is qualitative, ambivalent and polydirectional (e.g. it moves 'backward' as well as 'forward').*

*Theologies of every kind have tried to explain liturgical time by means of various hypotheses, most of which rely on the* objectivity *of the event, fact, revelation, experience or any other chronogenetic moment. The modern sciences of religions, on the contrary, have generally tried to explain liturgical time by referring to the* subjectivity *of the believer.*

*Using the paradigms of sacrificial time in the hindu and christian traditions, I try to show that these hypotheses - the objective and the subjective - derive from the philosophical assumptions which underlie traditional theologies and the classical history of religions*

*A somewhat unusual system of capitalization, partly explained in the text, has been retained at the request of the Author. *Eds*.

**I understand the abstract literally, i.e., that which remains once all that the article says has been abstracted. As for the summary, see the Introduction.

*respectively. This paper suggests a possible synthesis by presenting the traditional category of sacrifice as still valid for modernity (although adequately transformed).*

*Further, this study maintains that we should overcome the subjec-object dichotomy at the epistemic level and the natural-supernatural dualism on the ontological plane when dealing with ultimate human problems. The nature of time is not an a* priori *in our minds or - if we extrapolate - in the phenomena themselves, nor is it an a* posteriori, *i.e. detectable only as a given external fact. Time is at the crossing point between consciousness and matter.*

*Finally, I hope to provide a pertinent example for our contemporary situation of a cross-cultural study which tries to relate two different traditional religions and the present-day degree of awareness. My expectation here is one of cultural fecundation, trying to find a field sufficiently wide and deep to allow a cross-fertilization between tradition and modernity.*

## INTRODUCTION

A fundamental reflection on time, if it does not beg the question from the very beginning by assuming that we already know what time is, has to take into account what Man has understood time to be.[1] Because neither Man nor time are objectifiable entities, Man's self-understanding belongs to what Man is, and similarly Man's opinions on time cannot be excluded from a fundamental research on the nature of time. In other words, we have to draw from the global human experience if we want to say something about that universal deity - speaking with the Vedas - that we call by the name of time.[2]

The immediate purpose of this paper is threefold: first, to show the intimate connection between the human experience of time and the equally human practice of sacrifice. Here my remarks will be based mainly on the hindu and christian traditions, although they will point to contemporary Man.

Second, to alleviate the temporal discomfort of Modern Man -- who longs to overcome time but does not know how to do it -- by a hermeneutics of sacrifice as a mediation between tradition and modernity.

Sacrifice is here understood as the basic human ritual and my thesis will be that sacrifice is a set of actions by which Man tries to overcome time, i.e. either escape, deny or integrate it. My second thesis is that this also applies to contemporary Man.

By time I understand the human consciousness of the sequences of events through which Man deduces the durational structures of himself and the World.

My working hypothesis goes tentatively like this: Man is a temporal being, a being immersed in time, made of time, and yet constantly dissatisfied with his temporal existence. He tries by every means possible to overcome the temporal character of his being. Cultures have traditionally done this by proclaiming "above time a brimful vessel"[3] and by exhorting Man to reach the supra-temporal;[4] in other words, by postulating a separate reality in which "there shall be time no longer."[5] By contrast, modern Man has broken the jar of eternity and found it empty.[6] Nevertheless, he has not been cured of his nostalgia for it nor been able to subdue his temporal unease.[7] Belief in the transtemporal may be a disease, but Man has so far found no remedy for it. A hermeneutics of sacrifice may help us to understand the continuity between tradition and modernity, and thus help us to discover the proper ritual for coping with the ever-recurrent problem of Man's discomfort with his own temporality.

One could ask at the very outset: but why does one want to overcome time? What exactly does that mean?

It seems to be a universal human fact that Man is the animal that wants to jump over his milieu. Like a fish striving to come out of the water or a bird flying outside the air or a beast going beyond the earth, Man seems to want to leap above space and, specifically, beyond time. And even if this is deemed to be an impossible and alienating dream, it has to be explained to the human animal that he should be fully satisfied to live in his element. I have cited the three main elements: water, air, earth. Perhaps that fourth element, fire, is the constituent of Man - and Agni, an "envoy among the Gods,"[8] "navel of the earth,"[9] "king of the waters,"[10] although "the waters are his mothers,"[11] "sustains the sky,"[12] "maintains the earth,"[13] and "has linked the two worlds with the light of heaven."[14]

It is not a trifle to be Man: a time-ridden being, thirsty and hungry - to shed his temporal skin.

## I - TIME SACRIFICED

### 1. A human invariant: the tension between the eternal and the temporal

Among the many theories on the nature of religion and the origin of sacrifice we find a human invariant - although, of course, any given expression of it has to be couched in a concrete language, thus reflecting only one particular philosophical view. But this inherent limitation of language should not prevent us from tackling a universal problem.

This human invariant can be identified as the constitutive tension in human consciousness between being and becoming, the one and the many, identity and difference, the divine and the human, change and continuity or, also, between time and eternity, understanding the latter as either time-less or time-filled.

Parenthetically, I would note here my conviction that handling this constitutive tension in dialectical terms expresses both the strength and the weakness of western culture, and that other traditions approach the problem differently.[15] Only a complementary approach can help us to overcome the increasingly dangerous cultural neo-colonialism of our times. *Sed satis* for my purpose here.

This human invariant has its source in the fact that the awakening of human consciousness carries with it an awareness of Man's limitations which entails, at the same time, an almost irresistible desire to peer over at the 'other shore'.

We could reduce these limitations to three: of knowledge (power), of space (communication) and of time (fullness). Man does not know everything, he cannot go everywhere, and he cannot encompass the complete temporal span of his own existence. The awareness of Man's limited knowledge of things and his limitation in space are ultimately not as discomforting as the awareness of his temporal limitation. We can easily understand and accept that we cannot know everything and reach everywhere: we realize that we are neither all-powerful nor the entire universe. But the awareness of the time limitation implies not only the impossibility of gathering together the past and the future into the lived present, but also the shocking discovery of a normally inexperienceable limit *a quo*, birth; and another, still more intriguing and equally inexperienceable limit *ad quem*, death. This temporal limitation touches the very core of Man and is not so much a consciousness of (a tolerable) finitude, as one of (an irritating) imperfection. That is to say, we experience the limitation as something painful, humiliating, as something that should or need not be, as an obstacle to be transcended, as a punishment to be suffered, or as an inherent human condition we must learn to accept. Birth and death are two limiting situations which become challenge situations the moment we think about them. In short, we experience this limitation as a problem which demands either its solution or its dismissal as a problem. The fact that we cannot even possess ourselves, as it were, that we cannot encompass fully our own existence, that our ego has to trust on feeble memory to gather some fragments of its own past, and is reduced to mere speculation in order to ascertain even a few hints about its own future, remains a standing insult and a constant threat to Man's self identity. How can I be sure of my own present ego if last year's now seems so different and that to come so unpredictable? My real ego cannot be only today's ego, and yet this seems to be practically all that is left to me. The most astonishing thing, however, remains the fact that we are conscious of this split so that, in a sense, in our present there is a certain presence of our past and our future. Human consciousness seems to be peculiarly transtemporal.[16] In a certain way, if I want to be my-self, I must somehow gather up all three times and, most probably, transcend time altogether.[17] In sum, conquering time - i.e. mastering my temporal dispersion - seems to be the fundamental condition for being my-self. But how to achieve it?

## 2. Ways of handling the tension

I am assuming here that there is a tension felt between the temporal present and at least the totality of our temporal existence, and that there is a human urge to cope with this tension. I say 'at least' because a traditional statement of this tension speaks not only of gathering past, present and future, but of transcending time altogether. It speaks of time and eternity.[18] Here we may also recall the tremendous rise of historical consciousness in the modern West. History tries to ease the tension between past and present and also between present and future, performing the same function in both cases, namely that of linking time with eternity or at least bringing together the different fragments of time.[19] There seem to be several ways of solving this fundamental human unease (*dubkham*). We can classify these ways as A) attempts to overcome the tension, or B) efforts to put up with it.

A) The first alternative offers two ways out: either a) denying the very basis of the tension so that it does not have to be surmounted, or b) trying to transform the conditions of this tension so that it can be conquered.

The first way out, a) is represented by the typical buddhist solution of denying altogether the existence of the patient; if everything is impermanent and each moment new, emerging from utter nothingness, as it were, the cause of the trouble is eliminated. This is the *anātmavāda* preached by the Buddha, the teaching of the non-existence of the ego, soul, *ātman* and, in general, of any kind of (permanent) substance. To be sure, the buddhist denial of the tension is not a mere intellectual discovery: it is rather a personal conquest, an experiential truth that one *realizes* and thus in a way produces. To dis-cover that *saṁsāra* is *nirvāṇa* implies that one has actually *converted saṁsāra* into *nirvāṇa* - and this buddhist conversion is not just an academic amusement. The tension is not transformed but positively denied.

The second way out, b), transforming the condition of the tension, offers a double possibility: i) either being is ultimately identified with consciousness and then we have a fundamentally gnoseological transformation, or ii) not, and then, we have a predominantly ontological one.

The first case, i), is exemplified by the typical vedāntic system, which affirms that this is a question of enlarging, expanding, piercing through the ego until consciousness of the *ātman* emerges, which then realizes its identity with *brahman*, the divine principle, without beginning or end, the immortal, the timeless. The *gnostic* discovery of our true or real nature also belongs here.

In the second case, ii), we have the majority of the religious traditions of the World, which believe in the possibility of a real transformation of Man so as to overcome the tension between the temporal and the eternal, this latter standing for any authentic victory over merely temporal existence. As to the ways of this transformation, they are as numerous as the many different religious traditions themselves.

B), the second classification of the original alternative ways of dealing with the problem of Man's temporality, dismisses as an alienating and cheap consolation any attempt to escape from the constitutive limitation of the human being. Instead, this alternative accepts our ineradicably temporal human condition. This acceptance can be seen either a) as noble and beautiful, so that the humanist is the real hero,[20] or b) as a realistic acknowledgement of the human condition so that the only coherent and true human attitude is that of despair and absurdity.[21] We could call the former attitude a) *heroic humanism* and the latter b) *radical nihilism*.

The following scheme expresses what has been mentioned so far:

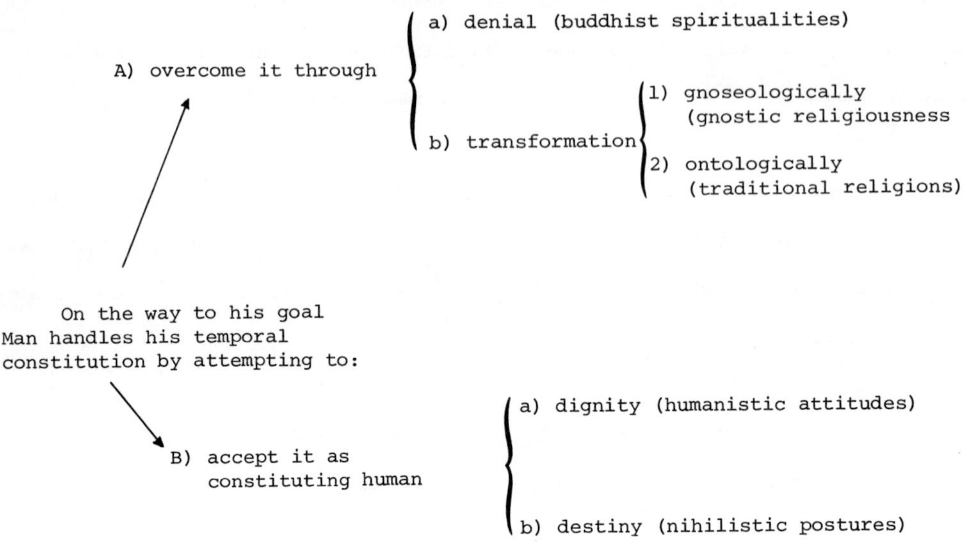


3. Sacrifice as a universal means of handling tension

The foregoing scheme is neat and clear, but it is too exclusively theoretical: historically, in point of fact, the major human traditions are hardly logically consistent. Life is more powerful than logic, and logical constructs are strictly valid only for logical entities, although, indeed, they may be helpful at the level of description.

No extreme position is stable. As the chinese saying has it, nobody can stand for very long on his toes. A rigidly coherent position seems to ignore both human weakness, which prevents a posture of constant heroism, and human wisdom, which has surmised that truth is not so esoteric and inaccessible that simple people cannot attain it. And in fact, most of the extreme positions have in one way or another reverted to a kind of middle path.[22]

Radical buddhism has been forced to speak about the ineffable; orthodox vedānta has been obliged to distinguish two planes of existence; various techniques of salvation have had to relax their rules and commandments; extreme humanisms have had to accept many models (and even non-models) of being human; formerly radical nihilism has recognized that Man is capable of growth and is thus open to transcendence, which may then become an object of hope.

This implies that all those disparate attitudes have something in common, namely a set of rules, devices and means - even if they are only convictions or intuitions - by which the meaning or end of life is reached. In other words, there seems to be a consensus that the limitation of the ego exists only for the time being, i.e. for being in time - even if this is all that there is. Such a recognition opens up the way toward the healing of this scar of temporality.

Coming specifically to our problem, even the most radical views seem to accept the fact that something must be *done* in order to possess authentic humanity and reach the full meaning of human life.

This meaning may be emptiness or a better future, or eternity, justice, revolution - but in any case the human condition demands an act or a series of actions by which it grows, develops or changes into another stage. In other words, *ritual* is needed to confer upon Man the possibility of disentangling himself from the trappings of the provisional.

Let me explain why the word *ritual* is being used here. The inconvenience of a language which tries to make sense for a plurality of world-views is that sometimes one is forced to remain vague and almost structuralistically abstract. The advantage, however, is that sometimes one may get at the very core of things. The case in point here is the recovery of the profound meaning of ritual, so often overshadowed by ceremonies and paraphernalia, not only in ritualistic practices but also in the philosophical and theological universes.

Ritual is that act by which Man tries to reach, obtain, express, or do what is otherwise inaccessible by any other means. To worship the moon can be a ritual as long as there is no other way of communicating with her on a particular level. To say - obviously with faith - a prayer, while taking a medicine, is a ritual as long as one does not believe in the total efficacy of biochemicals. To honor the king is a ritual as long as the people believe that the ruler has power that they cannot control. An embrace of peace can be a ritual when it expresses more than what I can say and do, and a meal becomes a sacramental rite when it not only feeds the body or nurtures the mind, but also instills grace into the commensals; a particular kind of dress becomes liturgical when it symbolizes what otherwise is not visible or directly graspable - to offer some examples instead of elaborating a theory. It is on this common ground, with all the ambivalence it possesses, that the nature and function of sacrifice is situated. This is what we shall have to explore.

### a) *A small phenomenology of sacrifice*

A small phenomenology of sacrifice would yield the following features:

1. Man is unstable in his human situation. He wants something more and even something else.

2. In his first attempt to get this *more* and *else,* he stretches his hand out in space in order to obtain the desired fruit, and waits in time in order to reach the expected maturity.

3. Soon he realizes that there are coveted things beyond the reach of his hand and that temporal flow alone does not bring the expected results. Something else has to be done: the machine reaches farther than the hand and internal effort is required to obtain the glory and strength he desires. No wonder that an aura of sacredness surrounded the first material tools and the first spiritual exercises.

4. These two efforts cannot be made alone. Man requires the help and collaboration of others invested with higher power: the hero, the elder, the ancestors and the God. They have a power that ordinary Man has not. Entreaty and supplication, immitation and emulation appear on the scene. The ritual appears.

5. Man comes of age when he makes the first unexpected and somewhat non-logical discovery that the human fullness he longs for cannot be obtained by a mere prolongation of the means at his disposal. Machines and techniques do not help. A rupture of planes has to take place; Man has to jump outside his given situation, he has to be initiated. He has to perform an act or a series of acts that will make this jump possible, and so reach the higher value, state, condition, etc. This is the place of the sacrifice: the act by which Man *transcends* his factual human situation and reaches what he wants - health, riches, a prosperous family, heaven, wisdom, joy, divinity....

In other words, the action by means of which Men believe they will fulfill those desires which they cannot achieve alone, is the very core of the sacrifice. It is that ritual which breaks the planes in order to reach transcendence.

6. This act always takes the form of a rupture: something is destroyed, cut, burned, offered - precisely sacrificed - in order to reach the transcendent.

I have already indicated the pure phenomenological way of understanding transcendence: that which is beyond the actual reach of a given situation, whether it exists by itself or not. It may very well be that the transcendent has an existence of itself or that there is an initiative coming from it. In fact, an analysis of many religions shows that often it is not Man who takes the initiative or even wants the sacrifice. Often Man escapes, hides himself and avoids contact with the transcendent, and it seems as if it is the latter which compels Man to such religious acts. Even in these cases, what phenomenology detects is the human feeling of a divine initiative and the human response, positive or negative, to the call of transcendence.

7. A philosophical phenomenology, further, can discover that trait which we are trying to formulate as the basis for the thesis of this paper, namely that the sacrificer seeks to deal with the temporal situation of Man in one way or

> another, and precisely by this fact, to save, redeem, enhance, make happy, enrich...the human being.

If this means realizing that there is no soul whatever to be saved, the sacrifice will take the form of an enlightenment, which will reveal the emptiness of what we had previously held as substantial. The buddhist forms of meditation, of which the Zen practices are an acute example, tend to transcend the mental and even reflexive consciousness in order to reach the goal which is the extinction of all (that we think) there is, including 'being' and of course, the 'goal'.

If it is a question of transforming our situation, whether in the gnoseological or the ontological order, the sacrifice will take the form of a mental sacrifice, or of an ontic sacred action. The 'mental sacrifice' of the Bhagavad Gītā[23] and the Brahma Sūtra[24] as well as the living sacrifice of an 'intellectual worship', of St Paul[25] and the 'spiritual sacrifices' of St Peter[26] with their corresponding traditional interpretations[27] belong here. That the sacrifice really transforms the structures of reality we can cite the traditional understanding of it in most of the major religions.[28]

If, on the contrary, we have simply to accept our humanness as either our dignity or merely our destiny, again it will be the sacrifice that will open our eyes to our factual situation and remove the veil of ignorance and superstition: from education to revelation could be the name of this sacrifice. We refer here to an immense amount of psychological, anthropological and sociological literature, plus philosophical and theological studies trying to help the human being to work out or recover his fullness, liberation or happiness.

I do not call these acts sacrifice because of a wish to reduce to a common denominator the rich variety of human efforts to cope with Man's condition, but because all these acts are intended to perform the same type of function. We might remind ourselves here that no one has a monopoly on names. Not too long ago, for example, christians considered the word 'grace' exclusively theirs, inasmuch as grace was understood as saving grace, participation in the divine nature, and as such the unique prerogative of those redeemed by Christ, the only mediator. Now, when dialogue with other religions becomes unavoidable, christians must reconsider this position, since there is no other word to express the similar state of affairs that exists in other religions. Hence, although interpretations may differ - and such differences have their rightful place - still, no one can avoid speaking about the grace which is claimed to exist also outside christiantiy. Similarly, we shall have to speak of sacrifice outside its traditional religious context if we want to understand the phenomenon of sacrifice in all its human depth.[29]

Now I shall describe what is meant by sacrifice in the two traditions I have chosen to discuss, in order to have a basis for the subsequent considerations.

### b) *The vedic conception of sacrifice*

We may describe the quintessence of the vedic tradition by mentioning a few traits.[30] It is by the sacrifice that not only Men but also Gods acquire immortality.[31] By means of the sacrifice, Man reaches heaven,[32] freedom,[33] happiness,[34] purification of sins,[35] superiority.[36] It is the sacrifice that helps Man overcome his earthly condition.[37] By performing the sacrifice, Man reaches the navel of the World.[38] Authentic existence is reached only in and through sacrifice.[39] By the sacrificial act, Man reaches the shores of the other world,[40] and is saved from the grip of time.[41] In point of fact, the brāhmanic literature will stress that Man is capable of attaining the full span of his life,[42] for "Man's immortality is a full life-span."[43] The subsequent *jñānic* spirituality will go a step further and proclaim that through the spiritual sacrifice Man is saved from time altogether, that is, released.[44] To sacrifice is the highest action because in it Man collaborates with the World and the Gods to sustain the entire universe.[45] In a word, all these and many other utterances make sense only if we discover in sacrifice the ultimate texture of reality. Namely that act by which the universe has come into being[46] and by which it is maintained.[47]

One trait emerges from all this: sacrifice is every act by which Man partakes in the power of a supratemporal agency. He reaches beyond the immediate present into the recesses of the past, sometimes even to the beginning of time, and also into the reservoir of the future, in some cases even to the end of time. The sacrificial act may also serve to acquire this or that earthly desire, but ultimately it differs from every other action because it stretches beyond the ordinary time-span and, rescuing Man from his servitude to time, truly liberates him.

### c) *The christian conception of sacrifice*

Let us now summarize the christian-biblical tradition.[48] Central to the christian tradition is the importance of the sacrifice of Christ as the unique act, which once and for all gave new life to the World.[49] It is the sacrifice that was already prefigured in the sacrifice of Abel,[50] Melchisedech[51] and Abraham.[52] It appears as well in the sacrifices of other religions.[53] Christ is the High-Priest for all humanity.[54] In reenacting the Sacrifice of Christ in the liturgy, the christian is not duplicating his act, nor simply commemorating it, but entering into a relation with that act which was at the beginning of the World, has redeemed the cosmos and continues until the total divinization of the universe.[55] For this reason the christian sacrifice forgives sins,[56] has power of impetration and expiation,[57] and its fruits can reach not only the living but also the dead.[58] That God will ultimately be all in all[59] is not something that will come about automatically, but is the result of the action of Christ, priest, i.e. mediator (not just intermediary) of all creation.[60]

A single trait also characterizes the christian understanding of the sacrifice of Christ and of the christian, namely that sacrifice is an act which transcends time and space, an act by which past sins are forgiven and future grace is treasured, an act which connects us with the beginning of the World and has eschatological repercussions.[61] Every christian who shares in the mystery of Christ by means of the sacrifice, lifts up his life into the life of Christ himself, and by doing this, he shares in the mystery of the entire 'cosmotheandric'[62] dynamism of the universe.[63]

### d) *The sacrifice of time*

The pattern underlying these two traditions, as well as many others, appears with clarity enough: Man, the prisoner of time, overcomes his temporal limitation by participating in an act which in itself has transtemporal significance. The ritual of sacrifice *saves* Man from being drowned in his everyday 'temporicity'. Performing the sacrifice, Man becomes a contemporary of the Gods, and of the God's creative act at the beginning and end of this universe. By sharing in the sacrifice, the quotidian becomes the tempiternal, i.e. that form of existence which does not so much encompass as pierce the three dimensions of time, and yet it does not abandon them entirely in order to uncover the transtemporal core of time itself.[64] Sacrifice, then, is an act by which time is overcome; it is fundamentally the sacrifice of time. Time is sacrificed, destroyed, pierced through, and a transtemporal core uncovered. But again time exists because of the primordial sacrifice that has called the temporal reality into being. Thus one could sum up at least these two highly representative traditions saying that "time both springs from and dies through ritual".[65] It is sacrifice that makes time, and ultimately creates this temporal World, and it is also sacrifice which destroys time and enables the World to reach its tempiternal core. Let me be emphatic on this. I think that if we lose sight of this primordial experience we do not only do injustice to most of the religious traditions of mankind, but automatically convert our almost immediate ancestors into primitive superstitious and irrational people, not only cutting ourselves off from understanding them, but undermining the very ground where we stand. Temporal provincialism (only modern Man counts and has got the right opinions) is worse than spatial ghetto mentality (only christians, only Americans, only blacks...).

When the christian or the hindu believer performs the sacrifice, he may have any number of immediate intentions, which may sometimes blur its ultimate meaning. Nevertheless, it is the latter, the underlying and deeper intuition that vouches for the perseverance and intensity of sacrificial action. Through the sacrifice, believers not only acquire merits, favors and forgiveness, but also and chiefly they reach salvation, i.e., an ontological realm which would otherwise be closed to them. They come into contact with the beginning and end of time, with their ancestors, and with the eschatological situation of the universe. They collaborate in the functioning of the World, and in a certain sense they feel that not only are they not wasting their time, but on the contrary, they believe they are performing the most fruitful action for themselves, for their fellow beings and for the entire World.[66] In fact, the traditional sacrifice does not save or rescue Man from the World, but saves the World - and thus also Man. To kill time is not to waste it, but to pierce it in order to extricate the everlasting from the bondage of the perishable.

In terms of the broad horizon of traditional religions: in the sacrifice, time itself is sacrificed in order to make space for a transtemporal mode of existence. Man puts his own time, and time as a whole, on the altar of sacrifice and there immolates it, so that once time is sacrificed, Man is liberated from its grasp, i.e. he overcomes death, and the World can reveal its transtemporal status. It constitutes the dignity of Man to be able to perform this act.[67] And although he cannot do it alone, Man steers the cosmos, so to speak, to its proper transtemporal destination.

Now, the popular understanding - the mystics being the clear exception - of the non-temporal status of reality, is one of a supra-temporal if not even post-temporal reality into which the believer enters - easily forgetting that the kingdom and brahman are within.[68] The secular mentality, on the contrary, comes closer to the genuine religious insight, interpreting the non-temporal not as supra- but as transtemporal. And this leads us straight into the next step of our fundamental reflection on time.

## II - THE SACRIFICES OF TIME

### 1. The intemporal nature of the temporal act of consciousness

Before proceeding futher, let us insert an ancillary philosophical reflection.

The act of consciousness is certainly a human act. It is a process that *happens in time* and is also *dependent on the time* in which it happens; but as such it is *intemporal*.

The act of consciousness happens *in time* in the sense that all of our concomitant actions are subject to time: when I am conscious, the clock does not stop, my breathing continues, my stomach functions, the sun follows its course, etc. The conscious act happens during that time.

The act of consciousness is also intrinsically dependent *on time*, i.e. on the time in which it happens. It is not irrelevant that a conscious act happens at one time or another, because the act itself is a function of the times in which it happens. The actual consciousness of a contemporary of Yājñavalkya is different from the actual consciousness of a contemporary of Heidegger, because the temporal factor belongs to the act itself, so that its temporal coordinates condition the very nature of that consciousness. In fact, consciousness does not consist in a mere formal structure of thought, but is the integral fact of being conscious of something. Now both the 'something' of which we are conscius and the 'someone' having consciousness are subjected to time. The subject of this being conscious is the temporal and historical person, immersed in his temporal situation. Consciousness - as far as we are conscious of it - is always a person's consciousness, and this person, the conscious subject, is a temporal and even a historical being. Even when we attribute consciousness to the God and/or the Gods we make them enter into the sphere of time. Furthermore, consciousness is representation, i.e. that power which reflects something by being aware of it - and there is no way of defining consciousness outside of consciousness itself. This something is what we call reality, for reality is that which consciousness directly or indirectly represents. Now, the conscious reality of Yājñavalkya's time - and thus of Yājñavalkya - is different from that of Heidegger's time - and thus of Heidegger. This applied also in the most extreme idealistic interpretation of consciousness. Every act of consciousness - by definition - reflects reality, even if this reality were only a projection of the conscious act itself.

On the other hand, the act of consciousness itself is an *intemporal* act. Notwithstanding the two facts just mentioned, namely that as act it shares in the temporality of every human process (Man is a temporal being); and that as consciousness of reality it depends on the temporal reality itself (Reality is temporal) - it remains nevertheless that *quo* act of consciousness, it is not affected by time. When I become conscious of something, I do not become conscious of temporality. The act of consciousness - when consciousness clicks - is an intemporal moment. An act of consciousness - as such - has no precursor, and no sequel. At a second moment, I may become conscious that I was conscious of something, and then situate the first act of consciousness in space and time, but this is after the fact (of consciousness) and another act altogether. This can be seen very clearly by the constitutive impossibility of measuring any primary act of consciousness by any apparatus physical or even mental: first, we can measure only the effects (of the conscious act), and secondly the act of measuring is already another act, not only different from the original act, but even modifying it. The difference here with any other act or phenomenon is that the measuring action cannot but be of the same nature as the measured one. We can measure protons by their mass and velocity, for instance, but we have to measure the act of consciousness by another act of consciousness, in spite of all the intermediaries we may put inbetween.

But I am saying more than that the act of consciousness is temporally unmeasurable. I am saying that the representation or presentation, the appearing or manifestation of reality that constitutes a conscious act, as such, is untouched by time. A conscious act dawning upon me is like a new creation. I know on subsequent reflection that a moment before, I was not conscious of what was not yet there: I know that my existence is temporal and that what I am conscious of, namely that reality, which presents itself in the conscious act, may not be an eternal reality, but the act of consciousness itself, that act which creates, uniting and separating a subject and an object, is of an intemporal nature. There is a timeless *ecstasis* behind any true act of understanding. There may be other acts preceeding my particular act of consciousness and many others may also follow it, but there is nothing in the act proper that allows for a πρότον or a ὕστερον, a *prius* and *posterius* of temporal nature.[69] Moreover, precisely because we have not a perfectly conscious act, because we are not pure consciousness, we go on living in time. Could we become pure consciousness or see God face to face, to rephrase hindu and christian terminologies, we would jump outside temporal reality altogether - and we do it, 'momentarily', each 'time' that consciousness dawns upon us.

Saying this, I am not taking issue with Heidegger's analyses or with the buddhist theory of momentariness, the yogic practice of stopping the flow of the mind, the magical or shamanistic device of bringing the World to a standstill, the christian belief in eternity or the phenomenological idea of pure awareness. I am describing a fundamental human experience, which may be at the basis of these as well as many other worldviews. I am stressing the fundamental human experience that temporality is a fact of consciousness, but that the act of consciousness *qua* act of consciousness has little to do with temporality.[70] The act of awareness differs from the reflective act of becoming aware of one's awareness, and also differs - but is not separable - from the object of awareness. It is an act that has no space or time. We may call it instantaneous, but this instant cannot be considered a unit of time, for no amount of these 'instants' would ever constitute temporal succession. Were it not for extrinsic and indirect devices, we would not be able to discover that the act of consciousness happens in time. And in fact the so-called pure sciences often claim to be intemporal. 'Three and two are five' may formulate an intemporal statement when devoid of its extramental truth (three angels and two Gods are five 'nothing'), and regarding a formal ideal content in Man's consciousness. Newton's or Einstein's physical laws may be intemporal only as long as they do not touch the real, i.e. refer to actual physical events.[71] And even pure formalism depends on the structure of our mind and our mind does not need to be eternal.

## 2. The three ways of overcoming time

We have described Man as a being having a thirst to overcome time and also as possessing the belief in the possibility of doing so. Now, there are three human acts by which Man has traditionally tried to overpower the dominion of time, or at least to master the temporal yoke. There are three temporal ecstasies, as it were, three human victories over time. One tries to encompass the flow of time by knowing everything that *is* (past, present and future), another wishes to jump outside of time, losing all consciousness of it by falling in love (reaching the intemporal), and the third claims to transform time itself or at least to find its soul by working within time (piercing it through).

In order to be brief and to the point I am going to skip philosophical and historical analyses and use what I would like to call a phenomenological irony: *cum etiam vita universa ironiam habere videatur* the romans knew well as expressed by the spaniard Quintilianus in his *Institutio Oratoria*.[72]

a) *Jñānamārga*

The first, and most sophisticated, is the *way of gnosticism:* saving knowledge, *gnōsis, jñāna,* visio...If we really succeed in knowing authentically, this very act will make us independent of time, or put us outside it. The heap of facts that we know and the amount of knowledge that we possess are certainly not removed from the grip of time, but *pure* knowledge and intellectual intuition are just as certainly time-transcending. The sage is one who has already crossed to the other shore of the river of time.

This ideal has haunted Man since he discovered himself to be *homo sapiens*. Not only gnostics, alchemists, mystics and occultists have had the longing for saving knowledge, but sober scientists and pure philosophers have also harboured the dream of one day deciphering the mysteries of the real, not just for the fun of it, but because liberation, salvation, justice, happiness, truth are believed to be behind that knowledge. Enlightenment is a word of many meanings, but most of them apply here. For the Man who really knows, past, present and future will have yielded their hidden and menacing power; supersitition and exploitation will be done with; the kingdom of Truth will emerge. Ignorance is the archenemy and education the sociological idol. Whence, otherwise, comes the sacred aura of futuristic studies?

Once knowledge has discovered all secrets hidden by time, Man is no longer fragmented in temporal bits and pieces. And what was the privilege of an immutable God becomes the utopian model of the enlightened citizen, the perfect scientist, the true philosopher, the all-knowing sage, the *jīvanmukta*.

### b) *Bhaktimārga*

Love, *agapē, bhakti, amor* is another intemporal human experience. The genuine act of love seems to be untouched by the temporal factor. That love wants eternity is something every poet knows and sings about: it makes no sense to want to love for five minutes; this is not real love. It is something else again, of course, that love may fade away after five minutes.

If the sage is the model of the first way, the saint is the ideal of this second attempt. The saint is the genuinely happy and perfect human being; he is lord over time. The saint is above the miseries of time and the temporal is here synonymous with the transitory, fallacious and ultimately contemptible. Salvation and happiness are only to be found above the fleeting and deceptive appearances of things temporal.[73]

It is not surprising that many religions have stressed either knowledge or love as the way by which Man reaches salvation, liberation, happiness, fulfillment. However this may be, the salvific effects of both paths are linked to overcoming the flow of time and being freed from the bite of temporality, *saṁsāra*.

### c) *Karmamārga*

There is yet another way, which traditionally seems to have been the most important and prominent way to reach the end of human life toward which religions of every type, ancient and modern, claim to lead. This is the way of action: *karmamārga*, the ritual performance of certain acts by means of which the desired fulfillment is attained. Religion here is first of all *orthopraxis*.

Although the two other ways have also reinterpreted the sacrifice in their own perspectives, here, in this third way we have, strictly speaking, the place of the sacrifice, or at least, of the primordial meaning of it. And here, significantly enough, the most ancient religious traditions of mankind meet the most modern trends of secular Man. Here, work redeems Man. Admittedly, the work is sacred, not merely profane activity; but nothing prevents it from being utterly secular work. Let me note here that the sacred is opposed to the profane, not to the secular.[74] We are now ready to pick up the thread of our discourse.

## III - THE MODERN SECULAR SACRIFICE

When comparing our contemporary situation with problems of the past, we have to take into account the different horizons of intelligibility; in other words, we have to consider the different myths which underlie the cultures we are discussing. Now, the myth of an epoch or a culture is the spontaneous or unproblematic horizon over against which facts and events are situated so that Man may understand them. The myth forms the ultimate ground of intelligibility for a given culture or subculture; it is that horizon in which we believe, without believing that we believe in it, so much do we take it for granted. For instance, history is a criterion for truth; a fact is taken to be real if it can be proved to be a historical fact. This *in fact* is a rather modern western myth probably of semitic origins, not at all universal in the human experience. This is why we can easily detect the myth of others without being aware that we, too, have our own myths, just as we instinctively detect the accent other people have in speaking a particular language, but are oblivious to our own accent - unless, of course, others draw our attention to it.

To speak of sacrifice as the proper ritual for overcoming time may be easily accepted by the Historian of Religions when dealing with other people and cultures. But the question becomes much more delicate when applied to our present-day situation. And I suggest that the function and scope of the Science of Religion is not just to investigate some odd culture, but to investigate the religious dimension of Man - ourselves and our culture not excluded. This understanding of religious studies, as the study of the ultimate self-understanding of Man, shows that the underlying insights of the traditional doctrines of sacrifice are still alive and valid in contemporary secular society. Further, this perspective may help us not only to understand our modern predicament, but also to reform and transform it by placing it in a wider and deeper context. This is all the more relevant since the two traditional ways, knowledge and love, seem today to be on the wane after centuries of predominance in the religious world: *homo sapiens et homo amans* are increasingly giving way to *homo faber et homo agens*. It seems to be a modern axiom that not by knowing or loving are we going to save and justify our lives, but by making and acting.

1. The sacredness of the secular work

What has been said so far should not be understood as either saying that the ways of contemplation or wisdom (*jñānāmārga*) and that those of love and devotion (*bhaktimārga*) are obsolete or that the traditional *kārmamārga* is what modern secularized Man is performing. Rather, I am detecting a connecting link with, and a growing point from, tradition.

If "the clock, not the steam-engine, is the key-machine of the modern industrial age",[75] it is fitting that a new experience of time should dawn in the post-industrial age.[76] The power of the methods of thought is not that they just provide us a way (ὁδὸs) to the real, but that they shape and assist in the creation of the very reality they claim to help us discover.[77]

To be sure, modern secularized Man is not performing the vedic or the christian sacrifice; the understanding of action has also evolved. But in a certain sense he is performing sacrificial actions: the efforts of the good citizen to increase the welfare of society, the concern of the genuine intellectual for the well-being of his fellow beings, the sincere ideal of the scientist in working for the progress of the world, the pains the honest national or international official takes for the elimination of poverty, disease, hunger, injustice and the like, could be adduced as examples. We should not minimize the religious *pathos* behind such attitudes, even if entirely secular. The work-ethic mentality is not the privilege of anglo-saxon protestantism only. Other christians as well as muslims, communists, socialists and humanists share this belief: Man justifies his existence by his work. Not to this day has the principle enunciated by St Paul: "he who does not work should not eat"[78] been better followed. Perhaps this is a latent feature in all cultures of abrahamic origin. Work is the way in which Man believes he repays his debt to society and to the past and by which he justifies his existence, for he believes he is collaborating in building a more just and human society.[79] Work is sacred and rightly demands a kind of sacred consecration to it. The full-fledged human being is a worker.[80] Nor is this all.[81] Work seems to be the heir to the traditional sacrifice and in fact most of the laws and regulations of modern civilization spell out the rituals for duly performing this grandoise sacrifice of the working community. Work, we hear in different tones, is no longer the task of slaves but of free citizens; work ennobles, "work is worship".[82] The work of everyone allows a nation to be prosperous and rich, and citizens to reach a well-deserved "paradise of abundance", freedom and happiness. *Karmamārga* is the way to salvation; educators, doctors, lawyers, engineers and politicians are the dignified and well-honored priests of this modern religiousness. Modern banks are better kept and adorned with tapestry, pictures, flowers and places to sit than churches; the sacred hours are not the time of leisure or prayer, but the working hours.[83]

Here, with as much accuracy as in the most orthodox traditional religions, time is regulated and considered sacred. Working hours are reckoned as the most precious hours of daily activity, to the point of being meticulously calcuated to the exact minute. Other hours are less important. An employee who works overtime is naturally paid more, precisely because he sacrifices more time. To 'take up your time' or to ask for 'some of your time', without compensation, amounts to exploitation or plain robbery....By means of work the ordinary citizen becomes contemporary with the Founder's dream, myth or idea that inspires him to work.[84] He also reaches the ideal of the end of times, when the hardships endemic to work will be taken away and life will be filled with justice and joy.[85] If we produce enough 'time-saving' gadgets for everyone, they will redeem us from the effort of pain connected with work...The sacrifice, the sacrificer and the sacrificed, like in the Vedas and the New Testament, ultimately coalesce.

In sum, modern work claims to liberate Man from the strictures of time and to allow him both to rescue his life from the chains of a time-bound existence and to justify his life by allowing him to collaborate in the 'salvation' of the World. All the traditional motives of sacrifice have been preserved in the process of being transplanted into another horizon. We have here a typical example of transmythicization.

## 2. The secular sacrifice

It is quite clear by now, in the last quarter of the twentieth century, especially in the most technically developed countries, that the foregoing description sounds like a caricature. Modern work tends to make people slaves, exploitation has not decreased, free time is also downgraded into mere recovery for better future production; the very success of the fittest, of the winners in 'free' competition, turns into misery for the others; technology devours its own fathers, etc.

I am not arguing for or against anything at the moment, but trying to understand this central aspect of modernity by describing the fundamental thrust of the secular attitude and detecting its deep roots in tradition itself.

Attempting another sketchy overview of human civilization in the perspective of this paper I would suggest the following:

The ancient ages were characterized by the *theological belief* that Man's life is part of a divine adventure. The rituals express the struggle of Men and Gods all together. The first hellenistic and the vedic periods could be adduced as examples.

The middle ages are represented by the *cosmological belief* that Man's dignity consists in collaborating in the sustenance of the World. The ancient rituals and sacred mysteries are thus converted into expressions of and means for the human participation in the destiny of the universe. The Gita, the hellenic and christian mysteries here come to mind.

Modernity is shaped by the *humanistic belief* that Man's life justifies itself by being of service to the human race and working together toward the progress of society. The ancient rituals are here transformed in the ethical behavior of the community, be this nation, state, party, church, academia or any other group.

The present day situation discloses itself in the crisis of modernity and man's impotence to go back to the other two attitudes. The ancient rituals have not died and in fact many new forms of old religions emphemerally appear.

This paper tries to say that both the merely traditional concepts of sacrifice and the modern secular essays are incapable of satisfying the profound urges and authentic needs of contemporary man. And yet he cannot do without them, nor can he artificially concoct new eclectic ways. Here is the place for a mutual fecundation between the old and the new, and the hope that such an encounter if authentic, may produce a new being when 'time ripens'.[86] This is what we are exploring.

The secular attitude is not only or primarily, an attack against established religions, but the fruit of an experience of the real and hence ultimately positive character of time. Temporality is an intrinsic and essential feature of all beings and of Being itself. To be sure, not only can Being be 'said in many ways',[87] but time also has many meanings.[88]

Now, in the modern world, precisely because the uncritical enthusiasms of the first hour have subsided, there is both place and need for sacrifice as the redemption of time. In a secular world, the liberating sacrifice cannot liberate us from time which, since coextensive with being -- would amount to annihilation or at least, alienation; neither can it free us from a merely cosmological temporality and so relieve us from our earthly and human condition. Here the redemption of time does not mean the setting us free from time in order to fly into an intemporal realm; it means rather our redemption from inauthentic time, reptitious time, boring time, the dictatorship of time and especially the mirage of an all-dominating time, which exhausts every dimension of our being.

The question then becomes: how to live an authentic life, cleansed of all the excrescences of wasted and inauthentic time? How do we justify our existence? In other terms: how do we save our lives? Better, however, than a sharp and negative criticism of the ailments of modern society, easy to make and true as they are, it may be more constructive to point to the profound, underlying and mostly unconscious dynamisms crossing the very attempts of modern Man to master his human condition. The facet of time is deep and central enough to provide us with a clue to some fundamental issues.

The place and function of sacrifice is precisely here. The essence of sacrifice is not the lamb, the flower, the bread or a particular rubric, but the ritual through which Man finds salvation, specifically, overcomes the dominion of time and is rescued from its slavery.

Secular sacrifice, in accordance with the belief of secular Man, does not take us away from time, transporting us to some intemporal realm. Such an independent kingdom does not exist for him. Secular sacrifice does not save us from time; rather it saves time itself, because time needs to be redeemed, purified, sublimated - and eventually made to reveal its tempiternal core. But to accomplish this, it has to be genuine sacrifice and not a mere pantomime of it.

Mankind cannot go back to a pre-technological age; we cannot take refuge in the deserts, the monasteries or even within ourselves: the modern world is more pervasive than the glitter of the big city, the lords of the ancient *bourgs*, the pandits and priests of old institutions. *Jñanāmārga* and *bhaktimārga*, important and necessary as they are, are neither self-sufficient, nor *de facto* possible without the balancing complement of *karmamārga*, the way of action.

I am not simply justifying modernity or being callously uncritical of the sorry condition of modern society, but neither do I want merely to condemn modernity or restore tradition. Rather I am undertaking the task of discovering society's radical continuity with tradition, without falling into a *laudatoris temporis acti* attitude which would not help, apart from not being true. If we discover the common roots, we may find a possibility of regeneration without alienation.

The many attempts of secular Man to master time, for instance, show the same deep concern as the more traditional forms of religiousness. One typical example in technological society is the sacred character that speed has acquired. This is especially true of acceleration. By increasing speed, one increases power, efficiency, pleasure, etc., and so the ideal becomes to increase velocity itself: acceleration.[89] But it has not taken many centuries to discover the precarious nature of such an outlet. Speed does not touch the core of Man, however much it increases the range of his possibilities: we may read faster, have more information available, accomplish more operations which would otherwise be lengthy and complicated, be confronted with many more options, etc. But we do not necessarily enhance the quality of life or Man's real power, for either time seems unlimited (and always demands more, so that we cannot stop to enjoy what we have attained) or we ourselves seem limited (and so are unable to enjoy the possibilities open to us) - even if we assume the efficient and equitable functioning of such a technological world.

The redemption of time, which secular Man does not understand as escaping from time but as its purification, cannot be brought about by making it go faster, nor by trying to slow it down and eventually stop it altogether. Neither accelerating time, on the one hand, as the pure secularist would recommend, nor stopping it, on the other hand, as the old shaman would command, would help us to 'win our lives'. The two extremes, that of building a better technology, or 'humanizing it, as well as that of destroying it or dispensing with it altogether, are, in my opinion, not only *practically* ineffective; they are also *theoretically* wrong. Mere patchwork and efforts at reform of a mortally wounded system will not do, but to stop the entire machinery of the world would also prove utopian, even for a selected elite. Neither attitude would bring a balanced and proper solution, even if it were possible.

## 3. The sacrifice of the secular

If the most salient feature of our modern culture is its secular mentality and the core of secularity is recognizing the central and inescapable character of time, modernity's basic issue will be to discover how Man can become the master of time. Now, agreeing with the secular mentality that time is constitutive of Being and thus coextensive with it, so that there is no being - and no Being - untouched by time, one should quickly add that there is not just one and only property of Being. This is the crux of the matter. Time may be a transcendental in the sense of the aristotelian-scholastic philosophy, i.e. a property inherent in any being *qua* being, but it is not the only one. Of course, the only property incompatible with time as a transcendental would be no-time, but not the supra- or transtemporal. Time may be coextensive with Being, but Being is not exhausted by it. In other terms, is there any way for modern Man to discover something built in the very heart of time, inseparable from time and yet not to be confused with it? This is what I called *tempiternity*, which is neither an everlasting time, nor a 'post-temporal' eternity but the very soul of time as it were. Time without it is a corpse, but the soul without its body is a mere abstraction.

Now, sacrifice is that set of actions which reach the tempiternal core of reality and thus gives us, first an awareness of the transcendental value of our authentic acts, and second, the possibility of acting with the full power inherent to those acts.

- "What are you doing?" asks the master-builder of the Cologne Cathedral to a stonecutter.

- "Cutting stones", answers one;

- "earning the bread for my family", retorts a second;

- "building a cathedral!" proudly voices a third.

My contention is that this awareness is more than a merely subjective disposition. In point of fact, it is the third attitude that literally builds the cathedral. Let me make this a little more explicit.

*First* of all, a sacrifice, an act, an action needs to be performed. Human life is a project. Man cannot cease to strive for something greater than himself, at any given moment. He is unfinished and this unfulfillment impels him to act. But not every act is a sacrifice. A sacrificial act is always an act that brings fulfillment, even if partially or for the time being. This is why the sacrificial act produces a certain rupture of planes, a certain discontinuity and a leap into another order. The sacrifice does not bring about homogeneous evolution, but revolution, mutation. The classical word is salvation.[90] Herein lies its sacred character, a quality which is by no means absent from the secular mentality. Sacrifice, then, has to be an act in virtue of which Man overcomes his 'ordinary', banal existence. Modern Man has to work certainly, but not just for the sake of it or in order to have a job for his livelihood. He has to regain the consciousness that his activity is a *praxis* and not a mere *poiesis* in the aristotelian sense.

*Further,* this sacrifice cannot be the mere repetition of old although respectable rituals. It has to correspond to our present degree of consciousness. Generally speaking, traditional rituals are heteronomous: there is a supreme authority, whether it be God, Book or Tradition, which prescribes what is to be done. For those who believe that this supreme authority embodies all truth, there is no conflict.

But for those who see that Man changes and that the religious source remains immutable, a problem arises. The secular mentality reacts to this with autonomous rituals: each individual, group or nation is absolute, sovereign. Thus anything that fosters one's growth or fulfills one's needs is permissible. Perhaps the only exception is the pragmatic rule of thumb whereby I limit my freedom where it impinges on the freedom of others, since if I irritate my neighbor unnecessarily and he is powerful enough to eliminate me, he will do it. This untenable position has led to modern forms of authoritarianism, be they of the state, money, intelligence, etc. Mere reactions become reactionary and will not do.

This consideration leads us already to the *third* feature of the sacrifice. We have said that it has to be an act, i.e. action including involvement, commitment, praxis, work. We have said further that it has to be adequate for our present times. We add now that it has to be the reenactment of something primordial, fundamentally human, basic, traditional - to use different words with different connotations. It has to have a link with the past and have its roots in the human soil. It can neither be absolute newness, nor an uncritical and automatic prolongation of the past. It must be a renewal.

Today, there is an increasing awareness that unlimited and unhampered growth (autonomy) nor artificial or dictatorial compulsion will solve lastingly any human problem (heteronomy). Only through an intrinsic mastery that discovers the optimum not in the maximum (population, wealth, prestige, etc.), but in the harmonious relation of the whole within an ontonomic order can we hope for just solutions.[91]

The ontonomic order recognizes the constitutive interdependence of every sphere of being. Hence, compulsion and enforcement are as deleterious as unbridled anarchy, even if they are exercised in the name of freedom. This realization would then elicit the discovery of the tempiternal core of reality not as something separable from time or still to come in a contradictory after-time, but in the very midst of time. It would also enable us to discover all those values which, being independent of space and time, allow a person to be realized even under externally difficult or socially painful conditions. The many forms of these sacrificial acts by means of which the human being acquires sovereignty over, that is freedom from the conditionings of life, are the rituals of the *sacred sacrifice of secular Man*.

Combining the three points just mentioned, suffice it to say that secular sacrifice is not a new kind of ritualistic act, but a spirit or a degree of consciousness present in Man's liturgical actions. First of all, it will manifest itself in viewing the traditional religions in a new light and enabling us to discover their underlying intention. Second, it will find new means of expression, which obviously cannot be pre-planned, much less postulated. Third, it will situate us in the face of the unexpected and put our lives at stake - perhaps for death, hopefully for resurrection.

Santa Barbara, California
April, 1977

*Special Abbreviations*

AB ...................... Aitareya Brāhmana

AV ...................... Atharva Veda or Authorised Version (of the Bible)

/B ...................... Bhāṣya (Commentary)

BG ...................... Bhagavad Gītā

Bj ...................... Bible of Jerusalem

BS ...................... Brahma Sūtra

BU ...................... Bṛhadāraṇyaka Upaniṣad

CU ...................... Chāndogya Upaniṣad

JB ...................... Jaiminīya Brāhmaṇa

KathU ...................... Kaṭha Upaniṣad

MaitU ...................... Maitrī Upaniṣad

MandU ...................... Māṇḍūkya Upaniṣad

MundU ...................... Muṇḍaka Upaniṣad

NEB ...................... New English Bible

OT ...................... Old Testament

RSV ...................... Revised Standard Version (of the Bible)

RV ...................... Ṛg Veda or Revised Version (of the Bible)

SB ...................... Śatapatha Brāhmaṇa

TB ...................... Taitirīya Brāhmaṇa

TMB ...................... Taṇḍya Mahā Brāhmaṇa

YS ...................... Yoga Sūtra

## NOTES AND REFERENCES

1. I shall write 'Man' throughout this article to express not the male, but the androgynous human being, and use the morphologically masculine pronoun with an ambivalent meaning.

2. Having dedicated much of my academic activity to elucidating how we can understand other people's beliefs, I shall skip here altogether a thematic reflection on the formidable problem of the proper method for cross-cultural studies.

3. AV XIX, 53, 3. Cf., my commentary in "Time and History in the Tradition of India: Kāla and Karma" translated in *Cultures and Time*, Paris (Payot-UNESCO), 1976, pp. 63-68 from the original French "Temps et histoire dans la tradition de l'Inde", *Les cultures et le temps*, Paris (Payot-UNESCO), 1975, p. 75 sq.

4. Cf. e.g. Luc XII, 20, sq.

5. Rev X, 6 (RV translation).

6. Even if modern exegesis is right, the shift of emphasis and even meaning of the quote just given is typical. The AV also says, "There should be time no longer", and this reflects the classical mentality of the "quia tempus non erit amplius" of the Vulgate translating literally the ambivalence of the original ὅτι χρόμος ομκέτι ἔσται as cosmological time or anthropoligical (waiting) time. Modern versions, obviously translate χρόμος by delay (RSV), "There shall be no more delay.", "Plus de delai!" (BJ).

7. Cf D. Thomas saying, "aeternitas non est aliud quam ipse Deus" (eternity is nothing but God himself), *Sum. Theol.*, I, q. 10, a. 2, ad 3.

8. Cf. RV III, 2, 8

9. Cf. RV I, 59, 2

10. Cf. RV X, 45, 5

11. Cf. RV III, 2, 9

12. Cf. RV III, 5, 10

13. Cf. RV I, 67, 5

14. Cf. RV I, 69, 1

15. It may be noted in passing that I have not worded these polarities to be mutually exclusive, as being-nonbeing, one-nonone, identical-non-identical, etc.

16. Cf. Spinoza's "sentimus experimusque nos aeternos esse." *Ethic.* Schol. 23, V; or the famous Augustinian dictum: "inquietum est cor nostrum donec requiescat in te" *Conf.* I, 1, n. 1.

17. Cf. St. Augustine's "ut ergo tu sis, transcende tempus." *In Ioan.*, tract. 38, n. 10, or YS I, 26 saying that for *Iśvara,* a model for the perfect Man, "there is no limitation by time."

18. Interestingly enough, in sanskrit we have practically no positive word for eternity, i.e., only negations of temporality (except perhaps *nitya* of disputed etymology: *ni-tya* = in-ness, or *ni-ja* = innate). Cf. the common expressions: *nitya-anitya* (constant, eternal, and inconstant, temporal), *kalākala,* temporal-nontemporal, and the adverb *nityakālam,* always, at all times or rather constantly temporal. In Hebrew we have *ʿōlam* and *neṣah* for 'eternity'. The first comes from the root *'-l-m,* to hide (hidden time?). The root of the

second means to shine, brightness. There is also a third word, '*ad* (related to '*et*, time). Greek, on the other hand, seems to have only the temporal and secular word αἰών for 'eternity', the meaning of which is saeculum, world. Cf. J. R. Wilch, *Time and Event*, Leiden (Brill), 1969, which sums up the state of the question in the semitic tradition, including J. Bau, *Biblical Words for Time*, London (SCM), 1962

19. From Cicero's history as "magistra vitae" to A. Toynbee's prophetical function of history there is a continuous line in western tradition. Cf. for the latter his posthumous book, *Mankind and Mother Earth*, New York (Oxford University Press),1976

20. A. Camus could be adduced here as a modern example.

21. Cf. E. M. Cioran, *The Trouble with Being Born*, New York (Viking), 1976, and E. Jabès, *The Book of Questions*, Middletown, Conn. (Wesleyan University Press), 1976, to cite just two French authors recently translated into English - and J. P. Sartre, of course.

22. The function of philosophies and theologies of all kinds has been not only that of unfolding the consequences of an initial and creative intuition, but also that of adapting the theoretical system to the factual development of the tradition. Not only scriptures or the foundational charisma is a *locus theologicus*, but also the life of the people.

23. Cf. BG IV, 33; IX, 22, etc.

24. Cf. BS III, 4; III, 6, etc.

25. Cf. Rom XII, 1.

26. Cf. I Petr II, 5.

27. Cf. Sáṅkara BS/B I, 1, 11; I, 4, 14; BU/B III, 3, 1: III, 9, 20; and the Philokalia, to quote only two important sources.

28. Cf. e.g. V. Warnach, "Vom Wesen des kultischen Opfers", in B. Neunheuser, *Opfer Christi und Opfer der Kirche*, Düsseldorf (Patmos) 1960, pp. 29-74

29. "Emic" and "etic" considerations could be placed here, if so desired. The terms are taken from phon*emics* which deals with the sounds of one particular language, and phon*etics* which attempts to find rules for all languages.

30. Cf. R. Panikkar, *The Vedic Experience*, Berkeley and Los Angeles (University of California Press) 1977, for further texts and the context of this succinct paragraph.

31. Cf. SB II, 2, 2, 8-14, and also IV, 6, 9, 12 as well as JB I, 2. The participation in the *aśvamedha* sacrifice results in a victory over death in all the worlds (SB XIII, 3, 5, 1; TB III, 9, 15, 1).

32. Cf. SB VIII, 6, 1, 10, etc.

33. Cf. SB XI, 1, 8, 5; CU II, 24, 12 (*svārājyāya...*) etc.

34. Cf. JB II, 140 (*śri*): TMB XXII, 4, 2 (*ṛddhi*); TB III, 1, 4, 10 (sacrificer become lucky, *bhagī*).

35. Cf. SB. II, 3, 1, 6 with reference to the *agnihotra* sacrifice. Cf. also SB XII, 8, 1, 16; XII, 3, 1, 1.

36. Cf. SB XIII, 6, 1, 1 with reference to the *puruṣamedha*. Cf. also SB IV, 5, 3, 2.

37. "Each day the sacrifice is offered, each day the sacrifice is accomplished, each day it links afresh the offerer to heavenly existence, each day the sacrificer penetrates the heavens." SB IX, 4, 4, 15.

38. Cf. RV I, 164, 35.

39. Cf. SB III, 6, 2, 26.

40. Cf. TB III, 9, 2, 1; *agnihotra* is a ship leading to heaven: SB II, 3, 3, 15, etc. Or TB III, 1, 5, 11 for the sacrifice as offering the right foundation, the firm ground *pratiṣthā*.

41. Cf. "When one worships time as if it were *brahmā*, it escapes", MaitU VI, 14, although we cannot enter into its proper context here.

42. Cf. SB II, 2, 2, 14 (*sarvam āyvus*).

43. TMB XXII, 12, 2

44. This is one of the main messages of the Upaniṣads.

45. Cf. BG III, 10-16; 20, etc.

46. Cf. RV X, 90; AB VII, 8, 2; SB I, 8, 1, 1-10, etc.

47. This is also the function of *dharma*, and *dharma* is intimately connected with sacrifice.

48. Cf. R. Panikkar, "La misa como 'consecratio temporis': la tempiternidad", in *Sanctum Sacrificium, Proceedings of the V Congreso Eucarístico de Zaragoza*, Zaragoza, 1960, pp. 75-93 for a more detailed discussion of the christian background.

49. Cf. Heb VII, 26 sq.; IX, 25 sq; etc.

50. Heb XI, 4 and also I Jo III, 12; Jud 11. For the OT cf. Gen IV, 1-25.

51. Cf. Heb V, 6-10; VII, 1 sq. For the OT cf. Gen XIV, 18 and Ps. CX, 4.

52. Cf. Heb VI, 13, sq., etc. For the OT cf. Gen XXII, 1-18.

53. Cf. B. Neunheuser (ed.), *op. cit.* especially V. Warnach *art. cit.*

54. Cf. Heb IV, 14, sq.

55. Cf. the traditional Roman Catholic doctrine of the sacrifice of the Man, for instance, as proclaimed in the Council of Trento in 1662. Cf. Denzinger-Schönmetzer (ed.) *Enchiridion symbolorum definitionum et declarationum de rebus fidei et moribus* (editio XXXIV), Barcinone, (Herder), 1967, Nrs. 1738-1759

56. To give the Denzinger references will spare us further elaboration. Cf. Denz. 1740.

57. Cf. Denz. 1753

58. Cf. Denz. 1743

59. Cf. I Cor XV, 28.

60. Cf. O. Casel, *Das christliche Opfermysterium*, Graz (Styria), 1968, as a single example of a christian theology of sacrifice. Who Christ is, remains here an open question.

61. Cf. another text of the already quoted Council of Trento: "Is igitur Deus et Dominus noster, etsi semel seipsum in ara crucis, morte intercedente, Deo Patri oblaturus erat, ut aeternum illis [ illic] redemptionem operaretur!... ut dilectae sponsae suae Ecclesiae visibile (sicut hominum natura exigit)

relinqueret sacrificium, quo cruentum illud semel in cruce peragendum repraesentaretur eiusque memoria in finem usque saeculi permaneret, atque illius salutaris virtus in remissionem eorum, quae a nobis quotidie committuntur, peccatorum applicaretur:..." Denz 1740.

62. By *cosmotheandric* or 'theanthropocosmic' intuition I understand that vision of reality which sees the divine, the human, and the cosmic as the three ultimate factors present in whatever there is. Cf. my contribution to the 2nd International Symposium on Belief, "La visione cosmoteandrica: il senso religioso emergente del terzo millennio", *Vecchi e nuovi dei*, ed. by R. Caporale, Torino, (Valentino), 1976, pp. 521-544.

63. This summary, of course, does not do justice to the entire theory of the sacrifice, which according to the same christian tradition is essential to any religion. "Remotisque sacrificiis nulla nec esse nec cogitari religio potest." Denz. S3339.

64. Cf. the notion of 'illo tempore', especially as discussed by M. Eliade in his *The sacred and the Profane*, New York (Harcourt, Brace & World, Inc.) 1957, 1959; *Cosmos and History*, New York (Harper) 1959; *From Primitive to Zen*, New York (Harper) 1967; etc. As for the term and notion of *tempiternity* Cf. R. Panikkar note 48 and "El presente tempiterno" in *Teología y mundo contemporáneo*, ed. A. Vargas-Machuca, Madrid (Cristiandad), 1975, pp. 133-175.

65. R. Panikkar, *Le mystère du culte*, p. 47, Cf. also Chapter III, "Le culte et le temps", (pp. 43-52).

66. Cf. the conception of the *Gītā:* if all actions are performed as sacrifice (cf. III, 9; IV, 23), time becomes fulfilled and thus redeemed; it is no longer alienation, but fullness.

67. *Reverend* is one who can perform *the* sacrifice in the christian tradition, like *pūjya*, with the same meaning as title of address, is the priviledge of the sacrificing castes in the hindu one.

68. Cf. Luc XVII, 21; Act XVII, 27-28 and BU III, 7; KathU V, 9; VI, 17; MandU II, 1, 9; MandU 6; MaitU VI, 1; etc.

69. Cf. Arist. Phys. IV, 11 (219 b 1).

70. "Los fenómenos espirituales o mentales no duran; los anímicos ocupan tiempo. El entender que 2 + 2 = 4 se realiza en un instante", as José Ortega y Gasset wrote in 1924. See: *Obras Completas*, Madrid (Revista de Occidente) 1966, vol. II, p. 461.

71. Cf. R. Panikkar, chapter "La unidad fisicomatemática de tiempo", *Ontonomía de la Ciencia*, Madrid (Gredos) 1961, pp. 309-551, for the distinction between physical and physico-mathematical time.

72. Is it also an irony that he was probably the first rhetorician being paid by the state?

73. Cf. the many buddhist parables and the "terrena despicere" and "i bi fixa sunt corda ubi vera sunt gaudia" of the christian latin liturgy.

74. Cf. R. Panikkar, *Worship and Secular Man*, London (Darton, Longman and Todd, Ltd.) and New York (Orbis Books) 1973, pp. 9-13, and chapter 2: "Secularization", (pp. 28-55).

75. L. Mumford, *Technics and Civilization*, New York (Harcourt, Brace & World, Inc.) 1934 - Harbinger Books edition 1963, p. 14.

76. "The bells of the clock tower almost defined urban existence. Time-keeping passed into time-serving and time-accounting and time-rationing. As this took place, Eternity ceased gradually to serve as the measure and focus of human action". *ibid.*

77. "The application of quantitative method of thought to the study of nature had its first manifestation in the regular measurement of time;"... *ibid.*, p. 12

78. Cf. II Thes III, 10.

79. Cf. the many 'theologies of work', so popular some decades ago to counteract the marxist pathos: 'To work is to collaborate in the creative act of God'. Cf. the pioneer article by M. D. Chenu, "Pour une théologie du travail", *Esprit* (Jan. 1952). *Theology of Work,* the English translation of his French book, is of 1965.

80. Cf. The entire liturgy, and the theological justification of it, of the first of May as the feast of St Joseph the Laborer in the Roman Catholic church instituted by Pius XII in 1955. Cf. also the idea and ideal of the *consecratio mundi* since the so-called Catholic Action and secular spiritualities in the same church.

81. Cf. the first article of the Constitution of the Spanish Republic of 1931: España es una República democrática de *trabajadores* de toda clase" (my underlying). Not citizen but worker is the title of the 'people'.

82. A common slogan in modern India, as well as "cleanliness is (next to) godliness."

83. Shops and offices used to open at 10 o'clock in the morning in a tropical country like India, because the best hours of the morning were supposed to be consecrated to prayer, study and leisure. Modern India is slowly "catching up"

and modern businesses make an effort at being more "rational" by beginning the "work" at "better" times.

84. The communist ideology is a typical instance, and many of the Bicentennial speeches of 1976 in the USA show another example.

85. Cf. K. Marx and F. Engels *The Communist Manifesto* in any of its many editions and translations of the London (Burghard) edition of 1848.

86. It is significant that the two indo-european roots related to time, **dí* (to part, cut, distribute) and **ten* (to extend, stretch, dilate, expand) both are related to words signifying sacrifice. Cf. J. Pokorny, *Indogermanisches etymologiches Wörterbuch*, Bern, München (Francke) 1959, *sub vocibus*.

87. Cf. Arist., *Metaph*. IV, 2 (297) (1003 a33).

88. Cf. as a pertinent example *The Voices of Time*, ed., J. T. Fraser, New York (Braziller) 1966; also J. T. Fraser *Of Time, Passion and Knowledge*, New York (Braziller) 1975.

89. R. Panikkar "Technique et temps: la technochronie" in *Technica e casistics*, ed. E. Castelli, Padua (CEDAM) 1964, pp. 195-229.

90. Would I be allowed to offer this explanation for the startling phrase that the kingdom of God suffers violence? (Matth. XI, 1, 12) It is not the automatic happy ending of a rosy discipleship, but the new life after an act of total renunciation.

91. For an elaborated discussion on the metaphysical foundation for an ontonomic order, Cf. R. Panikkar "Le concept d'ontonomie", *Actes du XIè Congrès International de Philosophie Bruxelles 20-26 August 1953*, Louvain (Nauwelaerts) 1953, Vol. III, pp. 182-188.

DISCUSSION AND COMMENTS
*by Lewis Rowell*

Professor Panikkar is uniquely qualified to present a comparative study of these two widely differing religious traditions and, at the same time, suggest a possible synthesis that may hold wider relevance for modern man. The present paper contains a wealth of insights and informative references that invites one to restate the main themes. Panikkar has described, in pleasantly unorthodox terms, a very special Now - the eternal, "privileged moment" that allows man to put himself in tune with the beginning and end of time by the performance of a sacrificial action. Man is thus enabled to vanquish time, *i.e.* to transcend his present limitations, his thresholds of consciousness.

The dimensions of ritual time are set forth in a provocative manner: it is described as vertical or circular, a pattern of time awareness that is qualitative, ambivalent, and polydirectional. Space limitations preclude even a rudimentary analysis of this challenging statement, other than to point out that Panikkar's ritual time, by means of this simultaneous alignment of past and future, comes close to what many of us understand as the time of myth. And in his delightful section on the secular sacrifices of modern man (III.1) the author describes with humor how we continue to fulfill mythical patterns in bank, factory, and supermarket.

It is worth noting that Panikkar does not find the sacred and the secular mutually exclusive - an assertion that more orthodox theologians might find hard to swallow; his sacrifice is a sacred action by secular, not "profane," man. He rejects both "turning on" and "tuning out" in favor of the way of sacrifice, the *karmamārga*. Paraphrasing his conclusion in Pauline terms: for those who seek to transcend their own limitations, there abideth these three - knowing, loving, and doing; but the greatest of these is *doing*.

One can question (with due allowance for a personal use of terminology) one or two other assertions of this paper: (1) that a real synthesis of different cultural traditions is possible for those of us who have been conditioned by a homogeneous society, and (2) that the knowledge of one's limitations in time is invariably an "irritating imperfection" and an insult to man's self-identity. Might such knowledge even be a comfort at times?

Readers will do well to relate Panikkar's thesis to Fraser's theory of *Time as Conflict* (as set forth in the latter's work by that title. Both recognize the same existential tension inherent in our perception of time as being and becoming. Perhaps the sacrificial action that reconciles these contradictions marks an ascent to a new integrative level of awareness. And further, the "new experience of time" that Panikkar refers to in section III.1 can be identified with Fraser's concept of *sociotemporality* (*cf.* his paper on "The Individual and Society" elsewhere in this volume).

The author's extremely broad definition of sacrifice - "overcoming transtemporal limitation by participating in an act which in itself has transtemporal significance" - invites one to extend the definition to such activities as building a cathedral (as Panikkar has suggested), writing a book, conceiving a child, or (as a questionner suggested) even the act of play. By at least one of these standards the activities of this Society form such a collective "sacrifice." I would hope that, for us and other seekers, the *jñānamārga* is also the *karmamārga*.